College
Zoology

SEVENTH EDITION

College Zoology

ROBERT W. HEGNER
Ph.D., Sc.D.
LATE PROFESSOR OF PROTOZOOLOGY IN
THE SCHOOL OF HYGIENE AND PUBLIC HEALTH
OF JOHNS HOPKINS UNIVERSITY

KARL A. STILES
M.S., Ph.D.
PROFESSOR AND HEAD, DEPARTMENT OF
ZOOLOGY, MICHIGAN STATE UNIVERSITY

THE MACMILLAN COMPANY
NEW YORK

Preface

THE excellent reception and wide use accorded the sixth edition of *College Zoology* were very encouraging. The marked improvements in the seventh edition should increase its usefulness as a textbook for beginning students in college zoology. The entire book has been reillustrated and revised; some parts have been rewritten, others added, and still others reorganized to make it a comprehensive, stimulating, and up-to-date work of zoological science.

A serious effort has been made to achieve a good balance between structure, function, and principles. The early chapters deal broadly with such subjects as classification, protoplasm, cellular structure and function, and the fundamental aspects of metabolism. Thus, these chapters provide an introduction to principles that apply throughout the Animal Kingdom. However, the basic plan of the book has not been altered materially, for it is believed that most teachers of general zoology prefer the approach in which animals are considered from the simple to the complex, including man. There are many advantages to this plan of instruction: (1) it aids in teaching the scientific method, which involves the deduction of general principles from many facts; (2) students find it psychologically more satisfying to proceed from the simple to the complex, and they better retain the idea of the division of labor in living things when it is presented to them in this order; (3) a background in the study of the invertebrates helps one to understand the vertebrates; (4) although students may have a superficial acquaintance with the frog, they actually know little about its biology, so there is serious doubt concerning the validity of the argument that the frog should be studied first because of the student's familiarity with it; (5) the great complexity of the frog makes its study difficult; therefore, for psychological reasons as well as for logical ones, it should not be studied first; and (6) the simple-to-complex approach best introduces the student to the principle of organic evolution.

Despite all the reasons given for the sequence of material in this book, some excellent teachers of zoology prefer the method in which the frog and most of the basic principles are studied before considering representative types in phylogenetic order. Doubtless different paths may be used to reach the same goal. If this approach is preferred, the order of chapters should be: 1, 23, 2, 8, 31, 32, 33, 34, 35, 36, 37; then these should be followed by the phylogenetic studies starting with Chapter 3. This text is designed to be so flexible that the arrangement of the chapters can be altered in any way to suit the teaching philosophy of the instructor.

Most teachers of zoology agree that the students who take the introductory course in college zoology may be divided into three groups: (1) those who will major in this field; (2) those who wish to do further work to prepare themselves for teaching in high schools, or for the medical sciences; and (3) those for whom this is a terminal course as a part of their general education. A conscious attempt has been made to develop a textbook that will satisfactorily serve all three groups.

The introductory course in zoology should give the student a knowledge of animals that will add greatly to his interest in life; it should present the various subjects in such a way that he can apply the principles of zoology to man so as to obtain a better understanding of man's place in nature; and it should furnish a good idea of the many more or less direct relations between man and the other animals. In *College Zoology* a definite effort has been made to meet these requirements. Reference is made in various chapters to human anatomy and physiology, especially in Chapters 31 to 34. At the end of most chapters, the direct relations of the animals under consideration to man are presented.

The discussion of the animal phyla has purposely been made more comprehensive than is customary to enable each instructor to make a choice of representatives of the groups; he can select those that best implement his own educational philosophy. Admittedly, it would be difficult for the average student to master the material for all forms treated.

All chapters have been revised to clarify the presentation and improve the readability. A few of the more conspicuous new features are as follows: hundreds of superior drawings by one artist possess a style designed for clarity, to attract the student's attention, stimulate his imagination, and impress his memory. The labels have been printed, and the margins are in a straight line. Also many new photographs have been added, including electron micrographs and a color photograph of a tidepool community. Wherever possible, the drawings were based on actual dissection, and the photographs are those of living animals. Decorative headpieces for the 38 chapters suggest the themes of the respective chapters and also contribute something of instructional value. This edition with over 1400 illustrations, grouped in 467 figures, tries to tell the story of zoology by means of the graphic arts. Many legends for the illustrations were rewritten and are more descriptive than in the previous editions.

The chapters on the invertebrate phyla do not merely form a survey of these groups, but they illustrate the progression of levels of organization through evolution. This edition contains more material of human interest and emphasizes the socially significant application of zoology.

A photograph and line drawing with full discussion of the newly discovered deep-sea mollusk, *Neopilina*, is included. This is considered to be a more incredible discovery than *Latimeria*, the living coelacanth. The explanation of osmosis is in keeping with present-day thinking. The newest concepts on animal behavior have been included. Recent advances in organic evolution have been incorporated. Consideration is also given to some of the problems of human flight into outer space.

There is much more emphasis on the ecology of communities and populations, natural history, parasitology, and the scientific method. The physiologic content has been increased, and there is much more emphasis on biological principles. New material has been added on experimental embryology. There is somewhat more emphasis on economic zoology. New sections have been added on the enzymes, vitamins, hormones, gene action and genetic effect of fallout, and many other subjects. A constant effort has been made to achieve better integration of subject matter throughout the text.

The problem of revising classification is always one of the most difficult encountered, for the specialists themselves are not in agreement. In the matter of classification of animals, an author cannot be all things to all people. Even a beginning zoology student should learn that there is no such thing as a definitive classification of animals. However, the classification of each major group in this text was checked by an authority.

All phylogenetic trees (dendograms) have been redrawn to bring them into harmony with the newest concepts of animal phylogeny. The number of species in the various groups is based mostly on information obtained by correspondence with authorities. If the numbers seem large, it is because taxonomists are continually making studies that result in an increase in the numbers of new species described.

The references at the ends of the chapters give the student a ready entrance to the literature; these have been greatly increased in number.

The glossary has been made much more comprehensive than those usually found in introductory texts, because vocabulary studies provide evidence that words are of great importance in the learning process. We keep an object in mind by means of a word or symbol; in fact, languages have developed from such simple beginnings. A single word recalls an experience, as well as a complex of ideas associated with it. Therefore, a glossary enables the student to learn the present meaning of the scientific term as well as its origin. By the inclusion of syllabification and accent marks, the student is helped in the pronunciation of these terms as well.

A very complete index is also provided so that the reader can easily find the information he wishes.

In an effort to achieve the highest degree of authenticity in a subject as broad as general zoology, a specialist in a given field can best exercise the critical judgment necessary for the evaluation of facts in a particular field. Such help was sought and received in great measure, as the acknowledgments below testify.

ACKNOWLEDGMENTS

The excellent spirit of cooperation shown by the writer's colleagues was a heart-warming experience. The friendly and generous help of many eminent specialists proves that they are interested in improving the teaching of general zoology. Their contribution guarantees a higher degree of authenticity than would otherwise have been possible. In a very real sense this book has been a team effort.

Above all I am appreciative of the many hours of conscientious effort spent by my wife, Nettie R. Stiles, in the exacting work of editing, proofreading, and indexing. Mrs. Olivia Jensen Ingersoll has not only contributed her outstanding talent as an artist in the preparation of all the drawings, but as a zoologist she has shown a consistent interest in her work which has made for clarity in the illustrations.

Helpful suggestions and critical comments were made by the following persons whose names are synonymous with scholarship: Hans Ris, Franz Schrader (Chapter 2), C.E. Packard (4 and 6), L.S. West (7), M.W. de Laubenfels (9), Libbie H. Hyman, J.F. Mueller (10), Libbie H. Hyman (11 and 12), G.R. LaRue (13), R.W. Pennak (14), Olga Hartman, A.W. Bell (15), T.W. Porter, A.L. Goodrich, Thomas Park (16), H.L. King, R.L. Fisher, T.W. Porter, J.B. Gerberich (18), B.J. Kaston (19), W.J. Clench, R.D. Turner, E.P. Cheatum (20), Libbie H. Hyman (21), T.H. Bullock (22), J.C. Braddock (23), V.C. Applegate, R.C. Ball, C.W. Creaser (24), L.P. Schultz, L.M. Ashley, R.A. Fennell (25), L.P. Schultz, P.I. Tack (26), C.M. Bogert, M.M. Hensley (27 and 28), L.M. Ashley (28), G.J. Wallace, A. Wetmore, M.D. Pirnie (29), H.E. Anthony, R.H. Manville, R.H. Baker (30), C.F. Cairy (31), C.F. Cairy, E. Hackel (32), C.F. Cairy (33), R.L. Watterson, J.R. Shaver (34), H.O. Goodman, E. Hackel (35), J.R. Shaver, J.E. Smith (36), J.C. Braddock, A.N. Bragg, R.H. Baker (37), and A.N. Bragg (Glossary).

In addition, the following teachers gave assistance in the preparation of the book: J.C. Braddock and W.J. Clench.

I am deeply indebted to the many instructors who filled out questionnaires and to the graduate assistants who made valuable suggestions based on their classroom experience with this textbook.

Edwin Ingersoll and other members of the Department of Zoology of Miami University, Oxford, Ohio, gave cooperation and help to the artist, Olivia Jensen Ingersoll.

Other persons who assisted in various ways were Bernadette McCarthy Henderson and Norman and Patricia Harris.

The radiograph of a rattlesnake on page 418 is reproduced by courtesy of the Air Forces Institute of Pathology.

Finally, much credit should go to the many critical students who refuse to accept everything they read on the printed page as gospel.

Because the author has been the final judge of all that is presented in this book, he alone is responsible for errors or misinterpretations of fact. Suggestions for improvement are not only welcome but greatly appreciated.

KARL A. STILES

East Lansing, Michigan

Contents

College
Zoology

CHAPTER 1

Introduction

ZOOLOGY is the science that deals with animals. It is an old, old science, almost as old as man himself. According to current estimates, man has been living on this planet for about a million years, and the science of zoology began with his curiosity about life.

Murals on the walls of rock shelters picture the life of people who lived in the Sahara Desert between 8000 and 3000 B.C. Like many prehistoric people, these early artists showed an interest in animal life by portraying the various birds and mammals that were so closely associated with their survival.

Animals play a vital role in the survival of man today: they feed, clothe, and provide him with a means of transportation. History, poetry, music, and literature are enriched with references to our animal life. Holmes philosophized about "The Chambered Nautilus," Saint-Saëns composed "A Grand Zoological Fantasy," and Frost wrote a poem entitled "The Need of Being Versed in Country Things."

Our science had its beginning in the earliest times because man had a curiosity about animal life and made an effort to place living things in groups based on their similarities. Through the centuries we have continued to study the many forms of animals, until today more than a million have been described and named.

And probably most zoologists would agree with the statement made by St. Augustine more than 1400 years ago, when he said: "Man wonders over the restless sea, the flowing water, the sight of the sky, and forgets that of all wonders, man himself is the most wonderful." Man is truly a remarkable machine, highly complex, and still not too well understood as a biologic organism.

Regardless of your role in the world's affairs, your life is not only enriched by a knowledge of living things, but this information will help you in understanding some of the most challenging problems of our times, such as population growth, disease, the effects of radiation on life, and man's survival in outer space.

To provide a background for the study of animal life, a brief consideration is given to each of the following topics:

1. The name and distinguishing characteristics of each large group of animals.
2. The features common to all animals, with emphasis on the unity of **animal life** as shown by the universal presence of the living substance, **protoplasm.**
3. Conditions under which animals live, **habitats.**
4. The value and method of classifying animals, **classification.**
5. The scope of zoology.
6. The **scientific method** and how it aids in formulating scientific principles.
7. The influence of zoology on **intellectual progress,** and its **practical value.**

VARIETY AND UNITY OF ANIMAL LIFE

Variety of animal life

Everyone is familiar with many of our common animals and knows something about where and how they live; but few people realize how many different kinds of animals there are and how greatly they vary in size, shape, structure, and habits. It is easy to observe the larger types such as cats, birds, frogs, and even some of the smaller ones such as earthworms and flies, but a considerable part of the animal kingdom consists of forms so minute that they can be seen only with the aid of the microscope. Then there are forms that live in the soil, in the ocean, or in other places where we do not ordinarily see them.

No one knows exactly how many different kinds of animals there are now in existence, but we do know that more than one million have been described by zoologists. Fortunately for us, although they differ from each

other sufficiently to be recognized as distinct kinds (**species**), they possess characteristics in common and can be arranged in groups. The principal groups are called **phyla** (singular, **phylum**). Zoologists are not in agreement with respect to the number of phyla into which the animal kingdom should be divided, but usually 11 are studied in some detail in a beginning zoology course. Representatives of some of the phyla are shown in Fig. 430. Besides these, there are a few groups of animals of more or less uncertain relationships such as the Rotifera and Bryozoa.

For each phylum, in the brief outline presented here, the approximate number of known living species is given. Figure 1 shows that the Arthropoda comprise about three-fourths of all the species of animals. We shall find later (Chap. 16, Fig. 130) that about 97 per cent of the Arthropoda are insects. Among the other phyla, the Mollusca (snails, clams, etc.), Chordata (fish, birds, mammals, etc.), and Protozoa (one-celled animals) are the most numerous. The numbers given are estimates by specialists, but no

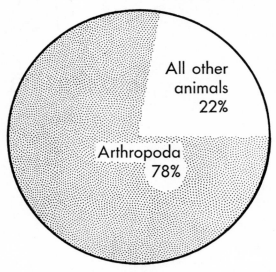

FIGURE 1. There are approximately 1,116,300 known living species in the entire animal kingdom. Of these, 875,000 or approximately 78 per cent are arthropods, leaving 241,300 species to account for the other animals.

one knows exactly how many species have been described in any phylum.

Synopsis of the phyla

Our survey of the animal kingdom will treat only the 11 most important phyla out of the 20 or more which compose it. These 11 phyla include about 98 per cent of all species of animals. The estimates of numbers of living species are from authorities, but new forms are being named all the time, so all figures must be regarded as tentative.

1. *Phylum Protozoa*

These animals (30,000 species) are mostly microscopic in size, and each consists of a single cell or of simple colonies of cells. They live in fresh water, in the sea, in the soil, and in other moist places, and as parasites on or within the bodies of other animals. Some of them, such as the malarial organisms and the dysentery amoeba, are important in our study because they produce disease in man.

2. *Phylum Porifera*

The sponges or pore bearers (5000 species) live only in water—most of them in salt water. The body wall is perforated with many pores and is usually supported by a skeleton of spicules of calcium carbonate, silica, or spongin. The commercial bath sponge consists of spongin.

3. *Phylum Coelenterata*

Most of the coelenterates (10,000 species) also live in salt water. They are the hydroids, polyps, jellyfishes, sea anemones, and corals. A common fresh-water type is the hydra. Coelenterates are radially symmetrical, possess single gastrovascular cavities, and are provided with peculiar stinging capsules called nematocysts.

4. *Phylum Ctenophora*

The ctenophores (100 species) are mostly free-swimming marine animals that resemble the coelenterate jellyfishes and are commonly called sea walnuts or comb jellies. They are biradially symmetrical.

5. *Phylum Platyhelminthes*

These are wormlike, unsegmented, bilaterally symmetrical animals (10,000 species) known as flatworms. Certain tapeworms and flukes are serious parasites of man and lower animals. Other flatworms live on land, in the sea, and a few live in fresh water, including planaria, the type usually studied in general zoology.

6. *Phylum Nemathelminthes—Nematodes*

The threadworms or roundworms (12,000 species) are likewise unsegmented and bilaterally symmetrical. They possess both a mouth and an anus. Many of them are free-living, that is, they live in salt water, fresh water, or in the soil; but others are parasites in plants and animals, such as the hookworm, roundworm, and trichinella of man.

7. *Phylum Annelida*

The body of an annelid consists of a row of little rings or segments; hence the members of this phylum (13,500 species) are known as segmented worms. The earthworm and leech are common representatives. Salt water, fresh water, and the soil serve as habitats.

8. *Phylum Arthropoda*

The joint-footed animals belong to this phylum (875,000 species); they are about three times as numerous in species as all other animals. The principal groups of arthropods are the crustaceans, including the lobsters, crayfishes, crabs, and barnacles; the centipedes and millipedes with their many pairs of legs; the insects, such as butterflies, bees, beetles, bugs; and the arachnoids, represented by spiders, scorpions, mites, and ticks.

9. *Phylum Mollusca*

Snails, slugs, clams, and oysters are common mollusks; others are known as squids, nautili, cuttlefish, and octopi; the phylum includes at least 90,000 species. An organ characteristic of most of them is a muscular foot that usually serves as an organ of locomotion. An enclosing envelope, the mantle, is also present. The soft body of many mollusks, such as the oyster and snail, is protected by a shell of calcium carbonate which is secreted by the mantle.

10. *Phylum Echinodermata*

A characteristic of most members of this group (5000 species) is a spiny skin. It includes the starfishes, brittle stars, sea urchins, sea cucumbers, and sea lilies. All are marine in habit and radially symmetrical; a skeleton of calcium carbonate is often present. Locomotion is usually accomplished by means of tube feet.

11. *Phylum Chordata*

Except for a few primitive species, the chordates (65,700 species) are vertebrates; that is, their axial support is made up of small bones or vertebrae and is known as the vertebral column, or backbone. Vertebrates are the most highly developed of all animals. They may be divided into 7 classes as follows: (1) the cyclostomes or lamprey eels and hagfishes, (2) the cartilaginous fishes, or sharks and rays, (3) the common bony fishes, (4) the amphibians or frogs, toads, and salamanders, (5) the reptiles or alligators, lizards, snakes, and turtles, (6) the birds, and (7) the mammals or four-footed animals. The birds and mammals differ from the others in that they are warm-blooded; that is, their body temperature is constant and about 100° F, regardless of the temperature of the surrounding medium; whereas reptiles, amphibians, fish, and other animals are called "cold-blooded" because their body temperature varies with that of their environment. Actually, cold-blooded is a poor name to apply to these animals, for in summer the blood of a grasshopper may be warmer than that of a man. These so-called cold-blooded forms are really animals without a temperature-controlling mechanism.

The headpiece at the beginning of this chapter helps us to realize how varied animal life is, but only a study which we are going to make of each of the 11 phyla just described can furnish a true idea of the remarkable diversities exhibited by the hundreds of thousands of different kinds of animals.

Unity of animal life

There is a tremendous variety of animal life among the more than one million different species, yet all these exhibit some features in common. Some common characteristics will be mentioned here, but they cannot be appreciated fully until they are studied later in more detail. Many of these characteristics are similar to those of plants and to those of nonliving matter, but when taken together they furnish a means of distinguishing animals from all other things.

Composition

The essential substance of which all plants and animals are composed is known as protoplasm. Nonliving things do not contain protoplasm.

Structure

The protoplasm in plants and animals is divided into units called cells; nonliving things are not divided into cells.

Form

Animals are so constant in form that they can usually be distinguished from one another by this characteristic alone. Plants are less constant in form, but more so than most nonliving things.

Movement

Animals can move their parts, and most of them are capable of locomotion. Plants, with few exceptions, are incapable of locomotion, and the same is true of nonliving things.

Irritability

Animals are irritable and respond quickly to changes in their surroundings, such as changes in temperature and in light. Plants respond less quickly, and nonliving things do not respond at all.

Metabolism

Animals and plants are "machines" that run themselves. This is due to the processes of metabolism whereby protoplasm is broken down to furnish energy and is built up again out of food. Animals require other animals and plants for food, whereas plants are able to manufacture their own food from nonliving materials. The ability to transform environmental material into its own specifically organized and active substance is one thing that distinguishes living from nonliving matter.

Growth

Animals and plants grow as a result of the building up of protoplasm within the cells. Nonliving things may increase in size, but the new material is added to the outside.

Reproduction

Animals reproduce others of their kind. In general, nonliving bodies cannot reproduce their kind.

The unity of animal life is thus clearly evident in composition, structure, form, movement, irritability, metabolism, growth, and reproduction.

ANIMAL HABITATS

Most areas on the surface of the earth are inhabited by animals. We are familiar with many species that live on land; with fresh-water inhabitants, such as fish and frogs; and with salt-water types, such as seals, whales, and sharks. Parasites that live on or within the bodies of other animals are less well known. The four major habitats of animals that are briefly described here are salt water, fresh water, land, and other organisms. A more detailed account of animal habitats is presented in a later chapter on Ecology and Zoogeography.

Salt-water animals

About 72 per cent of the earth's surface is covered by the sea; this salt water serves as a home for vast numbers of different kinds of aquatic animals. As a rule salt-water animals cannot live in fresh water or on land. Furthermore, they do not roam over the ocean at will, but are restricted to definite habitats. For example, a large number of animals are found only on the **beaches;** some live on sand beaches and others on mud beaches; some are attached to rocks and others live among seaweeds. The **open ocean** is thickly populated with animals; many are able to swim about, but others float near the surface and are carried from place to place by waves and currents. As a rule each species seeks a certain depth and does not move up or down beyond a more or less narrow range.

Plants and animals that live in the sea usually sink to the bottom when they die. On this account the **sea bottom** is a favorable habitat for scavengers, and a distinct group of animals lives in this debris. Each of these sea habitats—the beaches, open ocean, and sea bottom—may be subdivided into several **minor habitats,** which indicates how restricted animals really are in the character of their environment. The study of the relation of living things to their environment is called **ecology.** The marine animals alone may be divided into about 50 groups, according to the nature of the environments in which they live.

Fresh-water animals

Fresh-water animals live in lakes, ponds, pools, rivers, streams, swamps, and bogs. Some prefer flowing water, and others prefer standing water. They may swim about freely, float on the surface, or crawl on the bottom, and among the water plants. Each species occurs in a definite type of minor habitat. Such factors as the swiftness of the stream, the character of the vegetation, the depth of the water, and the nature of the bottom determine what species of animals are present.

Terrestrial animals

We are more familiar with animals that live on land than with aquatic species. Those on land are called **terrestrial** animals. Many live on the surface; others burrow beneath the surface, thus becoming **subterrestrial;** many make their homes in trees (**arboreal** species) and in other plants; and a few, known as **aerial** animals, spend a large part of their time in the air. The surface-dwelling animals may prefer either wet or dry ground, humus, sand, or rocks. Subterrestrial animals are profoundly influenced by the character of the soil in which they live. Plant-dwelling animals may live in evergreen (coniferous) or in deciduous trees, on the bark or in the wood, in dead wood or in living wood, on the fruit or among the leaves. Aerial animals may fly or simply glide through the air, or may be carried about passively by some balloonlike contrivance.

Parasitic animals

A parasite is an organism that lives the whole or part of its life on or within another organism of a different species, from which it obtains its food. Parasites occur among both plants and animals. Many animals that live in water are parasitized by other animals that creep over them or are attached to their surfaces. Most parasites of terrestrial animals live within the bodies of their victims; they are inhabitants of the digestive tract, the blood, and the muscle. Almost every large group in the animal kingdom contains parasites, but the parasites are mostly protozoans, flatworms, roundworms, annelids, insects, mites, and ticks.

Adaptations of animals to their environment

A study of the relation of animals to their environment reveals many ways in which they are adapted to the particular habitat in which they flourish. These adaptations involve all organs and all physiologic processes that make up the activities of the animal. Different animals are adapted to similar conditions in different ways. Thus aquatic insects and fish are able to move and breathe under water, but the methods by which these activities are accomplished are very different. A review of the structure and behavior of any animal will show how wonderfully it is adapted to life in its particular environment. Each species of animal, however, is not adapted to a certain habitat to the exclusion of other species—many species of animals and plants may live in one habitat. Animals, when associated together, form what are known as **animal communities.** An attempt has been made by students of ecology to classify these communities. It is a comparatively simple matter to determine what species of animals occupy a certain habitat, but it is more difficult to work out the actual physiologic relations between the animal and the various factors in its environment—only a beginning has been made in this direction.

Maintenance of the individual

We have already noted that each species of animal is limited to some particular type of habitat. The problems involved in merely existing in these habitats are many and varied. In the first place, each animal must protect itself from competitors, enemies, and harmful physical agents. It must find proper food and then capture and ingest it. Physiologic processes within the body must bring about digestion, transportation, and assimilation of this nutritive material. Other processes within the body must lead to liberation of energy for the animal's various activities. Oxygen must be taken in and carbon dioxide expelled. Secretions for digestive and other purposes must be elaborated, and poisonous excretions discarded. Only the fittest among each species survive in the desperate struggle for existence.

Maintenance of the race

The ability of an animal to maintain itself in its habitat is not enough; it would soon die out if others of its kind were not reproduced. As a matter of fact, the powers of reproduction of animals are enormous; any species would soon overrun the world if all offspring were to grow to maturity and reproduce their kind. The struggle for existence, due largely to limits in space and food supply, is responsible for the destruction of most of the young that are brought into the world each year. The number of each species of animal is thus kept more or less constant from year to year. Occasionally a species becomes extinct, such as the passenger pigeon (Fig. 334), or unusually abundant, as the lemming, but ordinarily a state approaching equilibrium exists in nature with respect to the number and character of the animals present in any locality.

SCIENTIFIC CLASSIFICATION OF ANIMALS

When a large number of dissimilar objects are collected, it is natural to place them in groups according to the presence or absence of certain characteristics. This is called **classification.** The science of classification is known as **taxonomy.** Animals may be classified in several ways.

Artificial classification

This groups animals according to some superficial resemblance in structure, color, habitat, etc. For example, certain animals are called aquatic because they live in the water; others are called terrestrial, because they live on land; some are called carnivo-

rous because they eat flesh; others are called herbivorous because they live on vegetable food; and still others are called omnivorous because they devour both animal and vegetable matter. This is called **artificial classification,** and it is often convenient to use.

Natural classification

For all scientific work, **natural classification** is employed. This is based on similarity in structure, physiology, embryology, and other factors. Natural classification is based on the principle of evolution and is an effort to show true genetic relationships of animals. A number of large divisions of the animal kingdom known as **phyla** are recognized by zoologists. Each **phylum** is made up of one or more **classes,** each class of one or more **orders,** each order of **families,** each family of **genera,** and each **genus** of **species.**

A phylum is a wide group of animals having some characteristics in common. A class is a somewhat narrower group, composed of individuals which have not only the structures peculiar to the phylum, but additional common structural characteristics. An order is a still smaller group in which the individuals have the same phylum and class characteristics, and, in addition, some common characteristics peculiar to the order. Likewise, the family, genus, and species represent smaller and smaller groups of individuals which possess the characteristics of the larger groups, but, in addition, each has its own identifying characteristics.

The timber wolf, for example, belongs to the species *lupus* of the genus *Canis.* This genus and others, such as the genus *Vulpes,* which contains the red fox, constitute the family Canidae. The Canidae are included with the bears (family Ursidae), the seals (family Phocidae), and a number of other groups of flesh-eating animals in the order Carnivora. Nineteen related orders, of which the Carnivora form one, are placed in the class Mammalia. Mammals possess hair and mammary glands; these characteristics distinguish them from the six other classes that make up the subphylum Vertebrata or animals possessing vertebral columns. The subphylum Vertebrata, together with three other subphyla usually called primitive chordates, are grouped together in the phylum Chordata, which contains animals possessing at some time in their existence an internal rodlike support known as the **notochord** (Fig. 207, p. 324).

Classification of a species

The scientific name of any animal consists of the terms used to designate the genus and species; the first letter of the genus name is a capital, but the first letter of the species name is always a small letter. The genus and species names are commonly followed by the name of the zoologist who wrote the first valid description of that particular species. The scientific name of the timber wolf is therefore written *Canis lupus* Linnaeus.

The complete classification of the timber wolf may be shown in outline in the following manner:

Animal Kingdom (consists of all known animals)
  Phylum Chordata (animals possessing notochords)
    Subphylum Vertebrata (chordates with vertebral columns)
      Class Mammalia (vertebrates with mammary glands)
        Order Carnivora (mammals that eat flesh)
          Family Canidae (carnivores that walk on their toes)
            Genus *Canis* (Canidae with round pupils in their eyes)
              Species *lupus* (*lupus* means wolf) Fig. 368

The classification of man, which is the same as that of the wolf up to the order, is as follows:

Phylum Chordata
  Subphylum Vertebrata
    Class Mammalia

      Order Primates (possess four limbs, each with five digits which usually end in nails, not claws)
        Family Hominidae (As compared with apes, the brain is larger; the face more vertical; lower jaw less protruding; and the teeth more evenly sized. The hair is long on the head, but scant on the rest of the body. The legs are longer than the arms; the thumbs are well developed; and the big toe is not opposed to the other digits.)
          Genus *Homo* (man)
            Species *sapiens* (means reasoning). Thus it will be seen that the scientific name of man is *Homo sapiens* Linnaeus.

Latin or Latinized names are used for genera and species. The genus name is a noun, and the species name is usually an adjective. Intermediate terms such as suborder, subfamily, subgenus, and subspecies are also in use. The typical grizzly bear, for example, is named *Ursus horribilis*, but large specimens with long ears occur in central California that belong to the subspecies *Ursus horribilis californicus*.

What is a species?

The exact meaning of the term species is rather difficult to explain. A species consists of a group of animals that mate with one another and that resemble one another more than they do individuals in other groups of animals. All members of a species possess certain characteristics in common, but differ from one another in various respects. For example, all wolves of the species *Canis lupus* (timber wolves) are large, with a body about 55 inches long, a tail about 10 inches long, and a weight of about 100 pounds. Their color is gray, varying to blackish on the back and tawny on the belly. Timber wolves vary among themselves: in the density of their color (some are lighter than others), in the length of the body and tail, in weight, and in other characteristics; but they breed with one another and are more like each other than they are like other wolves. The prairie wolf or coyote (*Canis latrans*), in contrast, is smaller and more slender, with a body about 49 inches long, a tail about 16 inches long, and a weight of only about 25 pounds. Its color is tawny, clouded with black, and its tail is tipped with black. Timber wolves and prairie wolves, as their common names indicate, live in different types of habitats.

The following is a good definition of a species: A species may be defined as consisting of groups of interbreeding natural populations, which may differ markedly among themselves, yet resemble each other more closely than the members of any other groups, and which are reproductively isolated from other such groups.

Origin of modern classification

Many attempts to classify animals were made before the present system was perfected. The Greek scientist Aristotle (384–322 B.C., p. 652) attempted to classify animals according to their similarities in structure and succeeded so well that practically no improvements were made until the time of Linnaeus (1707–1778, p. 654). This Swedish scientist, instead of giving animals common names which might be used for different species in different localities, established a universal system of classification; this is the binomial nomenclature still in use, and gave for each species a concise description in Latin. He succeeded in listing 4378 different species of animals and plants. His greatest work entitled *Systema Naturae* was published in 1735. It passed through 12 editions, and the tenth (1758) has been agreed upon as the basis for zoological nomenclature. The work of Linnaeus stimulated other naturalists to discover and name new species of animals. At first this was the only end in view, but at the present time taxonomists are interested mainly in the evolution of animals in general, and especially in the groups which they are studying.

Rules of nomenclature

In 1901 the International Congress of Zoology organized an International Commission on Zoological Nomenclature, which has served since that time. The Commission has prepared a set of International Rules of Zoological Nomenclature; these rules apply to family, subfamily, generic, subgeneric, specific, and subspecific names. They cover the formation, derivation, and correct spelling of zoological names, the author's name, the law of priority and its application, and the rejection of names. According to these rules, zoological and botanical names are independent; and the same genus and species name may be applied to both an animal and a plant, although this is not recommended. Scientific names must be Latin or Latinized. Family names are formed by adding **idae** to the stem of the name of the type genus. Generic names should consist of a single word, written with a capital initial letter, and italicized. The names of species are adjectives, agreeing grammatically with the generic name, or substantives in the nominative, in apposition with the generic name, or substantives in the genitive; they should be italicized. The author of a scientific name is the first person to publish the name with a definition or description of the organism. If a new genus is proposed, it is necessary to publish a description of it, to designate a type species of the genus to describe it, and to tell the collection in which it has been placed. The list of International Rules of Zoological Nomenclature was published in a text titled *Procedure in Taxonomy*, 1956, by Schenk and McMasters.

Derivation of terms

Every subject has its own vocabulary which must be learned by the student. New terms have more meaning and are easier to remember if their derivation is known. For this reason, the derivations of many of the common scientific terms used in zoology are given in this book; some are in the text proper, but more appear in the Glossary. Most of our scientific terms came from Greek (Gr.) and Latin (L.) words.

SCOPE OF ZOOLOGY

Fields of the zoological sciences

Zoology (Gr. *zoion*, animal; *logos*, discourse) is the science of animals, whereas botany is the science of plants. The combined study of animals and plants forms the science known as **biology.** The facts about animals alone and the methods of studying them have become so numerous that one man in his lifetime can master and become an authority on only one, or at most, a few phases of the subject. It has, therefore, been found necessary and convenient to divide zoology into a number of sciences. Some of the principal subdivisions of zoology are indicated in Fig. 2).

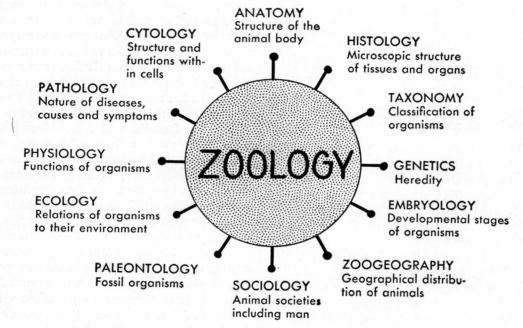

FIGURE 2. Some of the main subdivisions of zoology with concise definitions.

Many other zoological fields are recognized other than those in Fig. 2. These are often devoted to a study of a group of animals of special interest or importance. For example, **parasitology** is the study of parasitic organisms; **protozoology,** of Protozoa; **entomology,** of insects; **malacology,** of mollusks; **ichthyology,** of fish; **herpetology,** of reptiles and amphibians; **ornithology,** of birds; **mammalogy,** of mammals; **medical zoology** of animals that affect the health of man, etc.

Certain zoological sciences are involved in the study of each of the animal types described in this book. These include particularly those dealing with gross structure (anatomy), microscopic structure (histology), cellular structure (cytology), development of the individual (embryology), function (physiology), behavior (psychology), classification (taxonomy), and origin (phylogeny). Certain zoological sciences of a more general nature are considered in separate chapters; these are nutrition, coordination and behavior, the relations of animals to their environment (ecology), the geographic distribution of animals (zoogeography), heredity (genetics), reproduction and development, the origin and history of animal life (organic evolution), and the history of zoology.

Science and its methods

One of the objectives of a course in zoology is to gain an understanding of the scientific method. The method of science involves primarily (1) being aware that a problem exists, (2) formulating a supposition (hypothesis) on the basis of a relatively small amount of information, (3) testing the correctness of the hypothesis by securing more facts by direct observation or experimentation, (4) arranging the facts observed in some orderly manner to determine relationships, and (5) drawing valid conclusions. It is by this logical procedure that most of our zoological principles have been developed.

The scientific method involves skillful handling of the material being studied, careful observations, controlled experiments if possible, close attention to detail, clear thinking in drawing conclusions, and the modification of conclusions when further facts make this necessary. This is the method of discovery.

Attitudes are also very important in solving problems by the scientific method. They include (1) intellectual honesty, that is, freeing oneself of prejudice and admitting an error when facts indicate that there is one, (2) openmindedness about a subject, (3) cautiousness in reaching conclusions, (4) a willingness to repeat experiments (the facts obtained by one experimenter must be verified by others as well as himself, so that conclusions are confirmed), and (5) vigilance for the occurrence of possible flaws in hypotheses, theories, evidences, and conclusions.

Anyone can make discoveries in zoology with very little training, and few human experiences can furnish such a thrill as that of making an original discovery.

Principles of zoology

Zoological principles are scientific theories, facts, and laws of wide application. It is possible to make a list of zoological principles and to discuss them with the aid of photographs or laboratory material, but the best method of learning them is to study animals and deduce principles after a sufficient amount of original data has been accumulated. This book has been prepared with this aim in view. After each chapter has been studied and the appropriate laboratory studies have been completed, a careful review should be made of the knowledge thus obtained, and a list of zoological principles prepared. For example, Chapter 3 is devoted to the class Sarcodina of the phylum Protozoa, and the amoeba is employed as a typical species. After studying this species and possibly other Sarcodina in the laboratory and reading the account in this book, one of the principles which will be evident is that every member of the class Sarcodina consists of a single cell. From this principle we may derive the subordinate principle that among the Sarcodina a single cell carries on all of the physiologic processes necessary for maintaining the individual and the race. When all classes of the Protozoa have been studied in the chapters that follow, principles that are applicable to the entire phylum may be deduced. Later in the course, principles that apply to several phyla and finally to the entire animal kingdom may be formulated.

Evolution; Reproduction

Zoology and human progress

The study of animals has been of great intellectual and practical value to man. It has enabled him to recognize the unity of all living things and to determine his place in nature. Zoological knowledge has made it possible for man to adjust himself more successfully to his environment. It has freed him from many superstitions (Fig. 3) and fears by explaining, one by one, the mysteries that had held him in bondage for many centuries. Studies of living things have revealed the ever changing nature of the world of life and have furnished a simple explanation, namely, organic evolution, that has revolutionized modern thought. A stu-

FIGURE 3. West Africa medicine man and assistants. One of his superstitious treatments is to take the fin of a fish, the tail of a rat, the head of a snake, and the foot of a fowl; tie them together in a bundle; place the bundle beneath the nose of a patient and ask him to inhale deeply; his headache is supposed to disappear.

dent of zoology (1) learns about himself through the study of animals; (2) learns the scientific method, which will effectively assist him throughout his entire life no matter in what field his labors fall; and (3) gains an esthetic appreciation of nature that can be acquired in no other way.

Value of zoology

The practical value of zoology can hardly be overestimated. Zoology and botany form the basis of medicine, dentistry, veterinary medicine, medical technology, nursing, optometry, medical dietetics, museum work, zoological teaching, zoological research, agriculture, and conservation. Biological studies are responsible for our pure water, pure food, balanced diet, and protection against animal parasites and disease agents. Recently acquired knowledge of heredity has revolutionized plant and animal breeding and has had some effect on that of human beings. What were once considered to be inexhaustible resources in this country have for some years been in need of conservation. Only with the aid of a broad knowledge of biology can our conservation program be carried out successfully.

A state approaching equilibrium exists on the earth with respect to the association of plants and animals. In this world of living organisms, a terrific struggle for space and food is continually going on, and the situation that results is extremely complex. Part of this struggle involves human beings. Man is associated with other animals in many ways; some are of value to him, others are of no particular use, and a few are decidedly harmful.

Use of animals for scientific research

Lower animals are largely used for scientific research, and much that is learned in this way can be translated more or less directly into human terms. Thus a large part of what we know about heredity has been learned from the study of fruit flies, and most of the work on vitamins has been done with rats. Experiments on animals have given us much of our knowledge of physiologic processes and have enabled us to develop effective methods of surgery. Drugs are first tested on animals before being used for human treatment, and many new drugs have been discovered as a result of animal experimentation. Millions of diabetics are alive today because of the experimental work which sacrificed the lives of only about 30 dogs. The lower animals also benefit from the research on them. Without animal experimentation there might be no protection against rabies, smallpox, diphtheria, typhoid and undulant fevers, and many other diseases which plague the animal world. The value of lower animals in scientific work generally cannot be overemphasized.

Food and animal products

Animals are very useful to man because of their value as food. Almost every phylum or class of the larger animals contains at least a few species that reach our tables. These include especially the shellfish, lobsters, crabs, shrimps, fish, turtles, frogs, birds, and mammals. We depend largely, of course, on domesticated birds and mammals for our supply of meat. Animal products are hardly less important; among these are sponges, corals, pearls and pearl buttons, honey, beeswax, silk, tortoise shell, feathers, fur, and leather.

Harmful animals

Destructive animals fall principally into two types, predaceous animals and parasites. We need not fear direct attacks of predatory animals, but many useful wild and domestic animals are killed by them. Parasites not only destroy or make unhealthy large numbers of useful wild and domestic animals, but also attack man, and every year bring sickness or death to millions of human beings. These parasites are mostly protozoans, flatworms, roundworms, and insects. The insects, mites, and ticks not only attack man

directly, but many also carry disease germs from nonhuman animals to man, from man to man, or from animal to animal. A few animals, including certain insects, spiders, scorpions, fishes, and snakes, are poisonous to man. More details regarding the relations of the various types of animals to man are presented in the chapters which follow.

SELECTED COLLATERAL READINGS

The books listed here and in other chapters comprise a few selected works and are intended only as suggestions to the beginning student. Many of the texts cited have extensive bibliographies which give a ready entrance into the zoological literature. The following works include taxonomic reviews of the animal kingdom:

Calman, W.T. *The Classification of Animals: An Introduction to Zoological Taxonomy.* Methuen, London, 1949.

Hyman, L.H. *The Invertebrates: Protozoa Through Ctenophora.* McGraw-Hill, New York, 1940.

Manville, R.H. "The Principles of Taxonomy." *Turtox News,* 30: No. 1 and No. 2, 1952.

Mayr, E., Linsley, E.G., and Usinger, R.L. *Methods and Principles of Systematic Zoology.* McGraw-Hill, New York, 1953.

Schenk, E.T., and McMasters, J.H. *Procedure in Taxonomy.* Stanford Univ. Press, Stanford, 1956.

Simpson, G.G. *The Principles of Classification and a Classification of Mammals.* Bull. Am. Mus. Nat. Hist., Vol. 85, New York, 1945.

CHAPTER 2

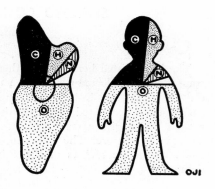

Protoplasm and Cellular Organization

What is life?

This is a question the biologists have been trying to answer for centuries. As a matter of fact, biology may be defined as the science of life. A fly buzzing about on a window pane is certainly alive, but after it is swatted successfully, it is just as certainly dead; life has departed from it. The most obvious change that has taken place in the fly is the loss of its ability to move and to take in food. It has lost the power to respond in any way to stimuli; for example, we can poke it with a pencil without observing any reaction. Evidently the visible activities of the fly have ceased. As we shall see later, the cessation of visible activities is due to the cessation of activities within the substance of the body. This living substance is known as **protoplasm**. As long as protoplasm is able to carry on its activities, it is alive; when these activities cease, it is no longer alive. Therefore, life may be studied in terms of the activities of protoplasm.

Most of our present knowledge of biology is attributable to a century of work on the chemistry and structure of protoplasm. In fact, if we want to know what makes the heart beat, a cell divide, or any other normal function of the body, we seek explanations in terms of the protoplasm that is in all living cells. Since disease and aging result from changes in the normal activities of protoplasm, understanding of normal protoplasm is one of the best approaches to understanding disease, for diseases are, in the final analysis, problems of protoplasm.

Physical organization of protoplasm

The structure of protoplasm cannot be seen with the naked eye, hence we can learn about it only with the aid of a microscope. The amoeba, to be studied later, affords an excellent opportunity to make actual observations on naked living protoplasm. A few bodies can be seen in living protoplasm, but most of the structures are practically colorless. This makes it necessary to treat it with dyes which stain certain parts. Many different dyes have been employed and numerous methods have been devised for the study of protoplasm. While most of these result in the death of the protoplasm, the structure is probably not changed very much.

When examined with a microscope, pro-toplasm usually looks like a grayish jelly in which may be embedded granules and globules of various sizes and shapes. It differs under various conditions; usually it is about the consistency of glycerin, somewhat viscous but capable of flowing. Protoplasm may exist as a **sol** that streams easily, or as a more solid **gel**; under certain conditions it may change from a sol to a gel, or a gel to a sol, and back again; this is the unique property of a colloid.

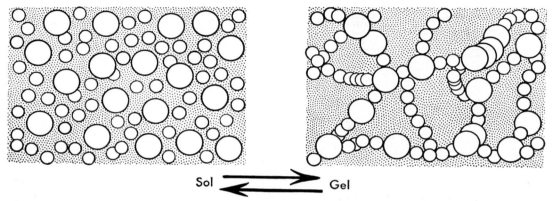

Sol ⇄ Gel

FIGURE 4. Colloidal states. Ultramicroscopic structure of a sol and a gel (diagrammatic). *Left*, a sol state. The colloidal particles are represented as circles of different diameters and the water particles (molecules) as dots. Such a solution has the physical properties of a liquid. *Right*, a gel state. The colloidal particles adhere together to form a continuous network. Such a substance has the physical properties of a semisolid substance (jellylike), which tends to be elastic. The arrows show that the sol and gel states are reversible under appropriate conditions.

Many minute granules can be seen in protoplasm with the aid of a microscope. When the protoplasm is in a liquid or sol state, the granules may be observed moving about. This is known as **Brownian movement,** having been discovered by an English botanist, Robert Brown, in 1827. This type of movement is due to invisible particles striking against larger granules. It also occurs in water and other liquids and is not necessarily a sign of life.

Certain knowledge of the fine structure of protoplasm has been contributed by the physical chemists. They tell us that protoplasm is a **colloid** and all life is associated with the colloid state. Many of the properties of protoplasm depend on the fact that it is a **colloid,** a mixture in which comparatively large but still invisible particles are suspended in a liquid medium, that is, they do not settle out. The particles are estimated to range in size from 0.0001 to 0.000001 mm. in diameter. Colloid suspensions often have a sticky, gluelike consistency; this accounts for the name, which comes from a Greek word that means glue. Changes in protoplasm from a sol to the gel condition and back again may be explained on the basis of the distribution of the colloid particles. If the particles are more or less evenly distributed in a liquid medium, as in Fig. 4, the mixture flows easily and is in the sol state, but if the particles are arranged so as to form a meshwork, with the liquid medium enclosed by the meshes, the mixture does not flow but is in a solid or semisolid gel condition. Colloidal suspensions and the sol and gel conditions are not confined to protoplasm; for example, jello forms a colloidal suspension in water—when warm it is in a fluid sol condition, but when cool it changes to a solid or semisolid gel condition. As in protoplasm, either condition may be changed back into the other. Some other colloidal substances are mayonnaise, cream, butter, glue, and soap.

Consideration of all the known details of the fine structure of protoplasm goes beyond the scope of this book. However, the electron microscope reveals that it is far, far more complex than the studies made with the light microscope led us to suspect. Life now appears to result from the complex interrelations of the microscopic and ultramicroscopic components of protoplasm.

Chemical composition of protoplasm

When protoplasm is studied chemically, it is found to be built up of the same elements that occur in nonliving materials. The 20 elements listed below appear to be essential to protoplasm:

FIGURE 5. Electron microscope. It uses a beam of electrons and magnetic fields, which take the place of light and lenses. Magnifications of over 100,000 times (diameters) may be obtained. This microscope is useful in studying the smallest living things such as viruses and the submicroscopic structures of cells. (Photo courtesy of George Jennings, Michigan Department of Health.)

ESSENTIAL ELEMENTS	SYMBOLS	PER CENT IN PROTOPLASM
Oxygen	(O)	63.00
Carbon	(C)	20.00
Hydrogen	(H)	10.00
Nitrogen	(N)	2.50
Calcium	(Ca)	2.50
Phosphorus	(P)	1.14
Potassium	(K)	0.11
Sulfur	(S)	0.14
Chlorine	(Cl)	0.10
Fluorine	(F)	0.10
Sodium	(Na)	0.10
Magnesium	(Mg)	0.07
Iron	(Fe)	0.01
Copper	(Cu)	Trace
Cobalt	(Co)	Trace
Zinc	(Zn)	Trace
Silicon	(Si)	Trace
Manganese	(Mn)	Trace
Iodine	(I)	Trace
Nickel	(Ni)	Trace

These elements, with the exception of oxygen, are generally combined to form compounds. **Compounds** can be divided into inorganic and organic. **Organic compounds** occur in nature only in living plants and animals, or in their products and remains. **Inorganic compounds** are principally water and salts, and organic compounds are principally proteins, fats, and carbohydrates. The percentages of these different compounds in protoplasm are on the average as follows:

COMPOUNDS	PER CENT
Water	80.0
Proteins	12.0
Nucleic acid	2.0
Fats	3.0
Carbohydrates	1.0
Steroids	0.5
Inorganic salts	1.0
Other substances	0.5

Compounds are made up of one or more **molecules** of the same kind; for example, water, sugar, and carbon dioxide are compounds. Molecules are so small that one computation shows that there are about 1,000,000 molecules in a single bacterium. A molecule is the smallest particle of a substance that possesses the chemical nature of that substance. For example, a molecule of water can be subdivided, but it ceases to be water when it is broken down into the 2 elements, hydrogen and oxygen, of which it is composed. Elements, such as hydrogen and oxygen, are known as atoms. More than 100 different elements or kinds of atoms are known. Many of these atoms can combine in various ways to form molecules; for example, 2 atoms of hydrogen, combined with 1 atom of oxygen, produce 1 molecule of water; 1 atom of carbon and 2 atoms of oxygen combine to form 1 molecule of carbon dioxide. Evidently there are vastly greater numbers of different kinds of molecules than of different kinds of atoms. Likewise, molecules of different kinds may be mixed together in various combinations so as to produce many more different kinds of substances than there are different kinds of molecules. Atoms and molecules are ordinarily indicated by means of symbols which provide a sort of chemical shorthand. Thus hydrogen is indicated by the letter H, and oxygen by the letter O. The **molecular formula** of water is written as H_2O, since each molecule of water is made up of 2 atoms of hydrogen and 1 of oxygen. Carbon is indicated by the letter C, and the molecular form of carbon dioxide is CO_2. The combinations of atoms, or molecules, are usually written in the form of chemical equations, such as the following:

$$\underset{2H_2}{\overset{\text{Hydrogen}}{}} + \underset{O_2}{\overset{\text{Oxygen}}{}} \rightarrow \underset{2H_2O}{\overset{\text{Water}}{}}$$

$$\underset{C_6H_{12}O_6}{\overset{\text{Sugar}}{}} + \underset{6O_2}{\overset{\text{Oxygen}}{}} \rightarrow \underset{6CO_2}{\overset{\text{Carbon Dioxide}}{}} + \underset{6H_2O}{\overset{\text{Water}}{}}$$

This reaction is reversible, as indicated by the following equation:

$$6CO_2 + 6H_2O \rightarrow C_6H_{12}O_6 + 6O_2$$

Reversible reactions are indicated by two arrows as follows:

$$C_6H_{12}O_6 + 6O_2 \rightleftarrows 6CO_2 + 6H_2O$$

Water is the most common compound in protoplasm, making up from about 60 to 96 per cent of it. Water is ingested in greater amounts than all other substances combined, and it is the chief excretion. It is the vehicle of the principal foods and excretion products, for most of these are dissolved as they enter or leave the body. Actually, there is hardly a physiologic process in which water is not of fundamental importance.

Inorganic salts are essential for life processes. They are present in solution in the protoplasm and in body fluids. In body fluids they are very similar in concentration to the salts in sea water. Although small in amount, they are important since certain salts in certain proportions are necessary for normal life activities. For example, if the calcium content of the blood is lowered sufficiently, convulsions and death ensue; and if sodium, calcium, and potassium are not properly balanced, the muscles of the heart do not function normally. The presence of certain salts is quite obvious to us, since calcium phosphate and calcium carbonate make up about 65 per cent of bone.

The three principal classes of organic compounds in protoplasm are known as **carbohydrates, fats,** and **proteins.** Carbohydrates and fats are composed entirely of **carbon, hydrogen,** and **oxygen;** protein has in addition **nitrogen, sulphur,** and **phosphorus.** Common carbohydrates are starch and sugar. The word **carbohydrate** is derived from the Latin term *carbo,* meaning coal, and the Greek term *hydor,* meaning water. Coal is a form of carbon. Carbohydrates are compounds of carbon, hydrogen, and oxygen in which the ratio of hydrogen and oxygen atoms is the same as that in water, that is, 2 of hydrogen to 1 of oxygen (H_2O). Carbohydrates are stored in the body in a form called **glycogen,** especially in the liver and the muscle cells. They are particularly valuable as fuel for the body, but are also used in the structure of protoplasm. One of the simple carbohydrates, a sugar called **glucose,** seems to be of particular importance, probably as a fuel. If there is too little glucose present, nerves and muscles become more irritable, and death may follow convulsions, just as when the calcium content of the blood becomes too low. If the sugar content of the blood is too high, a disease known as diabetes results; this condition can be corrected by injection of the hormone insulin.

Fats differ from carbohydrates in the structure of their molecules. Less oxygen is present in proportion to the carbon and hydrogen. This is evident when the formulas of a carbohydrate and a fat are contrasted.

Carbohydrate	Fat
$C_6H_{12}O_6$	$C_{51}H_{98}O_6$

Fats, like carbohydrates, serve principally as fuel, and much fat is stored in the body where it can be used when needed. When deposited just beneath the skin, it insulates the body, since it is a poor conductor of heat.

Proteins are the primary constituents of protoplasm. Their molecules are much larger than those of fats and carbohydrates; a common protein (hemoglobin) in our red blood corpuscles, for example, has the approximate formula $C_{3032}H_{4816}O_{872}N_{780}S_8Fe_4$, which means that each molecule is built up of 6 different kinds of atoms, totaling about 10,000. Since protoplasm is composed largely of proteins, we need plenty of protein in our food; and since different parts of the body, such as the liver and muscles, contain different kinds of proteins, we require food containing various types of proteins. Common animal proteins are present in meat, fish, milk, and eggs, and common plant proteins in peas, beans, and peanuts.

Proteins play the leading role in the chemical composition of protoplasm; fats and carbohydrates serve principally as fuels. Fats and carbohydrates cannot be converted into proteins in the body, but proteins can be converted into carbohydrates, carbohydrates into fats, and fats into carbohydrates.

Metabolism and growth

The term **metabolism** is used to include all chemical changes that take place in the protoplasm. **Growth** in any living thing involves a complex series of changes. The chemical compounds which make up the bodies of animals are extremely unstable; they are constantly breaking down into simpler substances or becoming more complex by the addition of new materials. There is no time during the life of any individual, even after growth ceases, when elaborate chemical reactions are not taking place. **Metabolism** is the term used to include this great complex of incessant chemical changes. Those processes which use energy to build up compounds are said to be **anabolic;** those by which substances are broken down, thereby releasing energy, are termed **catabolic.**

Animals are primarily catabolic organisms. They cannot make organic compounds from simple inorganic substances; in this respect they differ from plants, which manufacture sugar (glucose) from carbon dioxide and water, in the presence of light energy and chlorophyl. The green plants obtain carbon dioxide (CO_2) from the air, water (H_2O) from the soil, and energy from light. Chlorophyl, an additional substance, which is responsible for the green color of plants is also necessary. We do not know how chlorophyl is able to convert the light energy into chemical energy, nor how this chemical energy is used to synthesize glucose from carbon dioxide and water.

Because this synthesis is dependent on light, it is called photosynthesis. The photosynthetic equation is written as follows:

$$CO_2 + H_2O + \text{Light} \xrightarrow[+ \text{Chlorophyl}]{} \text{Glucose} + \text{Oxygen}$$

We know that the above equation is no more than a statement of input and output. Chemical studies involving the use of "labeled" carbon dioxide reveal that there are probably dozens of intermediate chemical processes.

Since animals must have organic food, plant products are necessary either directly or in the form of protoplasm built up by other animals out of plant food. Before animal growth is possible, food must be converted into living substance.

Digestion is the process by which food materials are broken down into simpler substances so they can be absorbed. This is a nutritive process, and, while not a part of metabolism as defined above, it is necessary if metabolism is to continue. Material cannot be absorbed unless it is in a liquid condition. Water may be absorbed without change. Many mineral salts are easily absorbed, the process depending on their concentration. Carbohydrates must be broken down into simple sugars, such as glucose, before their absorption is possible. This is accomplished with the help of complex substances produced by the protoplasm, which are known as **enzymes.*** Fats must be broken down by enzymes into **glycerin** and **fatty acids** before they can be absorbed. Proteins are likewise acted upon by enzymes, eventually becoming **amino acids**, which

---

* The importance of enzymes in life processes cannot be overemphasized. The modern biochemist is inclined to believe that living things are chiefly a matter of enzymatic reactions. It has been estimated that there are 3000 to 5000 different enzymes in a cell.

---

are absorbable. In very small animals, digested food does not need to be transported very far in order to become distributed throughout the body, but in larger animals some sort of circulatory system is necessary for this purpose.

Assimilation, an important part of anabolism, is the process of converting absorbed material into protoplasm. During this process comparatively simple materials are built up into more complex compounds with the aid of enzymes produced by the protoplasm; that is, the protoplasm manufactures enzymes which convert digested and absorbed materials into more protoplasm. The result is replacement of the protoplasm that is broken down; and after this has been replaced, growth takes place.

Energy is defined as the ability to do work, to produce a change in matter; it may take the form of motion, heat, light, or electricity. Energy is derived ultimately from sunlight and is stored in the molecules of food as chemical energy. Chemical reactions inside the body occur, changing the chemical energy to heat, motion, or some other kind of energy. Under experimentally controlled conditions, the amount of energy entering and leaving any given system may be determined and compared. It is always found that energy is neither created nor destroyed, but only changed from one form to another. This generalization is known as the **Law of the Conservation of Energy.** This law applies to living as well as nonliving systems.

Energy is contained in the organic molecules in protoplasm and in stored substances in the body and is liberated when these molecules are broken down by oxidation. A simple example of the oxidative process is as follows:

$$\underset{\substack{\text{Sugar} \\ C_6H_{12}O_6}}{} + \underset{\substack{\text{Oxygen} \\ 6O_2}}{} \rightarrow \underset{\substack{\text{Carbon} \\ \text{dioxide} \\ 6CO_2}}{} + \underset{\substack{\text{Water} \\ 6H_2O}}{} + \text{Energy}$$

According to this equation, oxygen splits the sugar molecule into carbon dioxide and water, thereby liberating energy. **Oxidation** is a breaking down of protoplasm and therefore a catabolic process.

This gaseous metabolism of the protoplasm, including absorption of oxygen, and elimination of carbon dioxide, is known as **cellular respiration.** In small aquatic animals, oxygen is obtained from the surrounding water, and carbon dioxide is given off into the same water. In many larger animals, a respiratory system is necessary to take in oxygen and to expel carbon dioxide. The transportation of both these gases is one of the functions of the circulatory system.

Carbon dioxide is a waste product of metabolism, an **excretion.** Other waste products due to catabolic processes are water, inorganic salts, and nitrogenous salts such as urea. These may be cast out directly into the surrounding water by small aquatic animals, or they may be carried by a circulatory system to an excretory system, the function of which is to extract waste products and expel them from the body.

Some of the energy liberated by oxidation may be used in the production of substances known as **secretions** that are of use to the animal. Certain types of protoplasm may be specialized for this purpose and concentrated in **glands.** Glands secrete sweat, digestive juices, milk, poison, the shells of eggs, and many other substances with which we are familiar. They also secrete, into the blood, substances that have a remarkable influence on our growth and behavior; these are called **hormones** and will be considered later. Biological processes involve not only continual energy transformations but varying energy levels.

Irritability or excitability

One of the fundamental properties of protoplasm is its **irritability.** This property is responsible for the reactions of an animal to changes in surrounding conditions. The change that brings about the reaction is known as a **stimulus,** and the reaction as a **response.** Most stimuli are external changes

in the environment, but certain stimuli such as hunger seem to arise from within. Some of the common types of stimuli are mechanical (for example, contact), chemical, thermal (changes in temperature), and photic (for example, changes in intensity or color of light). The stimulus may be and often is extremely small as compared with the magnitude of the response. The response may depend on the nature of the protoplasm stimulated; for example, it may appear as a movement if muscle is excited, or as a secretion if gland cells receive the stimulus. The transmission of the excitation from one part of the protoplasm to another is called **conduction.** Conduction is a general attribute of protoplasm, but the protoplasm of nerves is specialized for this purpose.

CELLULAR ORGANIZATION

Division of the protoplasm into cells

In one phylum of animals, the Protozoa, the protoplasm is continuous, but in all other animals the body is divided into units called cells, which contain the protoplasm. We owe the term **cell** to an Englishman named Robert Hooke, who, in 1665, described as "little boxes or cells" those spaces surrounded by walls which he observed in cork and pith with his new microscope. Since the essential substance in cells is the protoplasm and not the wall, the term was an unfortunate choice. The protoplasm of cells is of two principal kinds: (1) **cytoplasm** and (2) **nucleus.** A cell may be defined as a small mass of protoplasm consisting of cytoplasm and a nucleus, which are enclosed by membranes.

Size, shape, and number of cells

Cells vary in **size;** some are extremely small, for example, blood parasites are as small as $\frac{1}{25,000}$ of an inch, whereas others, like the egg of a bird, are very large. The large size of some egg cells is due chiefly to the accumulation of an enormous quantity of reserve food material, and not to the protoplasm they contain. Cells differ in **shape** (Fig. 43, p. 85); they may be columnar, flat, spherical, stellate, or long and thin. There are trillions of cells in a complex animal; there are about 9.2 billion in the gray matter of the human brain alone. On the other hand, certain animals (proto-zoans) may consist of a single cell. The size of an animal usually depends not upon the size of the cells but upon the number.

Structure of cells

The nucleus and certain other bodies can sometimes be seen in living cells when viewed under the higher powers of a compound microscope, but special preparation is necessary to make visible most of the

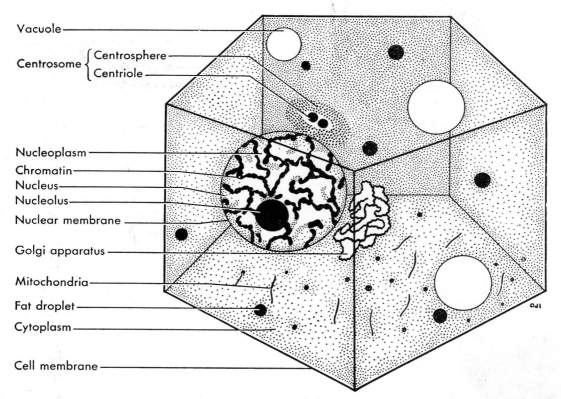

Vacuole

Centrosome { Centrosphere
             { Centriole

Nucleoplasm
Chromatin
Nucleus
Nucleolus
Nuclear membrane

Golgi apparatus

Mitochondria

Fat droplet

Cytoplasm

Cell membrane

FIGURE 6. Diagram of a generalized animal cell, that is, one showing the structures found in various animal cells; all these parts are not necessarily present in all cells. The shape of mito-chondria may change, depending on the phase of cellular activity.

structure. This is accomplished by treating living cells with dyes or by killing and then staining them. The electron microscope has greatly increased our knowledge concerning the smallest structures of the cell (Fig. 7).

A diagram of the **structure** of a stained animal cell containing most of the bodies that may be observed in cells of various types is presented in Fig. 6. The animal cell is surrounded by a thin **cell membrane.** A rigid cell wall outside of the limiting cell membrane is characteristic of plant cells, but is rare in animals. The most conspicuous body in the cell is the **nucleus.** This is

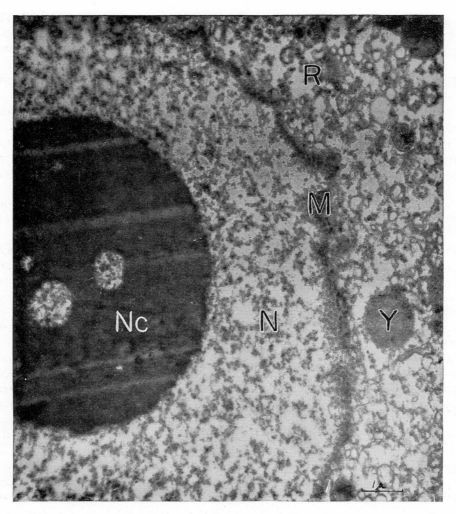

Figure 7. Electron micrograph of a cross section of a sea urchin egg, magnification 15,600 times. Note the nucleus (N) with the dark nucleolus (Nc) to the left; it has been demonstrated that the dark wavy nuclear membrane (M) has "holes" in it, covered with a thin membrane. The yolk granule (Y) barely visible under a light microscope is seen plainly, and the protoplasmic reticulum (R) is well shown. (Electron micrograph courtesy of B.A. Afzelius, reprinted by permission of *Experimental Cell Research*, 8:155, 1955, and Academic Press Inc., New York.)

bounded by a **nuclear membrane.** Within the nucleus is a colorless fluid, the **nuclear sap (nucleoplasm)**, in which there is a substance that has a strong affinity for certain dyes; this is known as **chromatin.** Some nuclei contain an intensely staining, spherical body, the **nucleolus.**

Various types of bodies may occur in the cytoplasm. Often near the nucleus is lo-

cated a specialized portion of the protoplasm, the **centrosphere,** in the center of which are one or two deeply staining bodies, the **centrioles.** The term **centrosome** includes the centrosphere together with the centrioles. Spherical vesicles of liquid of various sizes, called **vacuoles,** may or may not be present. Spherical or rod-shaped **mitochondria** contain enzymes which are involved in cellular respiration; other enzymes in the mitochondria function in chemical reactions which produce and store energy in the cell. By special staining methods the **Golgi apparatus** is sometimes made visible; its function is not definitely known. Cytoplasmic **inclusions** of various sorts that are not considered parts of the living protoplasm may also be present; these are **pigment granules, starch granules, fat globules,** and other nutritive, secretory, or excretory material.

Experiments indicate that neither the cytoplasm nor the nucleus can exist long without the other. For example, if the single cell of the protozoan is deprived of its nucleus, the remaining cytoplasm may continue to move for a few hours and may ingest food, but all its activities soon cease, and death ensues. Both nucleus and cytoplasm are necessary for normal cellular activities, due probably to the exchange of substances between them.

Passage of materials
through cell membrane

The living animal cells throughout the body are inhabitants of tissue fluid. Tissue fluid is probably of much the same composition as the sea water in which animal life is thought to have originated. All materials entering a cell must pass through the fluid surrounding each individual cell before they reach the cell membrane.

The best-known physical process which enables water and other substances to enter the cell is diffusion. **Diffusion** is defined as the movement of molecules from a region of high concentration to one of lower concentration, brought about by the inherent heat energy of the molecules. The rate of diffusion depends mainly on the size of the molecule and the temperature. Diffusion is fundamental to many biologic phenomena, and examples of it in everyday life are familiar to all of us. For example, if a tablespoonful of household ammonia is spilled on the floor, the odor will soon be noticed in all parts of the room. The molecules of ammonia have become evenly distributed throughout the entire room.

This same principle holds true if the substance is a solid, such as a small lump of sugar dropped in a jar of water. The sugar dissolves and the individual sugar molecules (solute) diffuse from their original position in the jar of water (solvent) and spread evenly throughout the liquid (Fig. 8A). The individual sugar molecules move in a straight line until they bump into another molecule; then they rebound and move in another direction.

Diffusion of a solute can be modified or prevented by the presence of a membrane. A membrane is **permeable** if it permits water and all solutes to pass through, **impermeable** if it will permit no substances to pass, and **semipermeable** (**differentially permeable**) if it will allow some but not all substances to diffuse through. This makes it clear that permeability is a property of the membrane, not the diffusing substance. The dense surface film on the outside of an animal cell, the cell membrane, is semipermeable. One of the principle functions of the cell membrane is that of regulating the passage of materials into and out of the cell. Certain liquids and dissolved substances can pass through the cell membrane and others cannot. Mineral nutrients dissolved in water pass through the cell membrane by diffusion. Water passes through the cell membrane by osmosis, a special form of diffusion.

Osmosis may be defined as diffusion of a solvent through a semipermeable membrane. In biological processes the solvent is almost universally water. Osmosis is a kind of one-directional diffusion as explained in Fig. 8B. It plays an important role in the life processes of cells, both plant and animal, because of the indispensable functions of water in a cell. Why does osmosis occur in the living animal cell? It is because the cell contains solutes such as sugars, salts, and others, which reduce the concentration of water molecules to a point lower than that of the tissue fluid in which the cell is immersed. Hence, in accordance with the principle of osmosis, the water moves from the region of higher concentration (tissue fluid) to the region of lower concentration (cell protoplasm). Cell membranes are impermeable to many substances that we eat, such as starch, because they must be digested, that is, made soluble, before they can be absorbed into the cells. For definitions of the terms **isotonic, hypertonic,** and **hypotonic** see the Glossary.

Contrary to a common misconception, exchange of foods, wastes, and respiratory gases between cells and fluids in animal bodies is not by osmosis. The chief factor in the transport of these substances is ordinary diffusion. When water molecules move either inward or outward by osmosis they do not carry other molecules along with them.

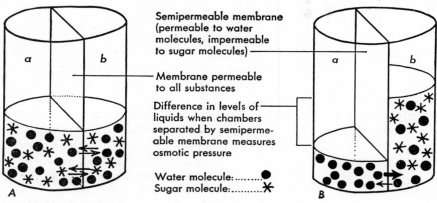

Semipermeable membrane (permeable to water molecules, impermeable to sugar molecules)

Membrane permeable to all substances

Difference in levels of liquids when chambers separated by semipermeable membrane measures osmotic pressure

Water molecule: ....●
Sugar molecule: ....✴

Water placed in chamber a, sugar solution placed in chamber b

FIGURE 8. Diagram to illustrate ordinary diffusion and osmosis. A, **ordinary diffusion.** The battery jar is divided into two chambers, a and b, by a permeable membrane which offers practically no hindrance to the diffusion of both water and sugar molecules (particles). In ordinary diffusion, any kind of molecule tends to diffuse (move) from where it is more abundant, per volume of space, to where the molecule is less abundant. Diffusion through a permeable membrane continues until every component reaches equal concentration; therefore in diagram A, the water and sugar molecules are of equal concentration on both sides of the permeable membrane. B, **osmosis.** The battery jar is divided into two chambers, a and b, by a semipermeable membrane, that is, one that is permeable to water but hinders the passage of sugar molecules. Under these conditions, water molecules will diffuse through the membrane more rapidly into chamber b than into chamber a. In accordance with the law of diffusion, the water molecules move in greater numbers from the place of higher water molecule concentration (higher water diffusion pressure) to the region of lower water molecule concentration (lower water diffusion pressure). Diffusion through a semipermeable membrane is known as osmosis. Osmosis in living things has almost always to do with the movement of water through a semipermeable membrane.

Cell division

Reproduction is a fundamental property of protoplasm, and cell division is a type of reproduction. For many years after cells were discovered, division of the nucleus, which precedes cell division, was supposed to take place by a process which we call **amitosis** to distinguish it from **mitosis.**

Amitosis means a sort of mass division of the nucleus. This type of nuclear division is rare and of little importance. As a rule, the protoplasm in a cell grows until the cell reaches a certain size; then the cell divides.

This is called mitosis. The two daughter cells proceed to grow, and they in turn divide, and so on, generation after generation. Many cells, however, notably those formed during the development of eggs, grow very little or not at all during the period between successive divisions. Why cells divide when they do is not known, but the relative quantities of nucleoplasm and cytoplasm are usually maintained in each kind of cell. It has been suggested that when the cytoplasm reaches a volume too great for the nucleus, division begins.

Interphase ("resting") cell

A cell that is not undergoing division has been called a "resting" cell. However, it is anything but a resting cell in the true sense of the word. It is carrying on all the life processes of any living cell, and a more appropriate name for it is an **interphase cell.** This period in the life of a cell is one in which no visible structural changes are taking place in the nucleus. This stage is not considered one of the phases of mitosis, although there is no sharp line of demarcation between the late telophase and interphase as shown in Fig. 9. The description of the generalized animal cell (Fig. 6) is that of a typical interphase cell.

Mitosis

Cell division involves a series of processes of considerable complexity and of great significance. The nucleus divides first and then the cytoplasm. Constant reference to Fig. 9 will make clear the following brief account of mitosis in a typical cell. Four stages are recognized.

1. *Prophase:* the mitotic figure arises and each chromosome appears to be split longitudinally (Fig. 9); actually, each chromosome has duplicated itself.
2. *Metaphase:* the duplicated chromosomes become located in the equatorial plane of the mitotic figure (Fig. 9).
3. *Anaphase:* the halves of the duplicated chromosomes separate and move as two

groups to opposite ends of the mitotic spindle (Fig. 9).
4. *Telophase:* two daughter nuclei are formed and the cell body divides (Fig. 9).

These 4 stages will now be described in more detail.

Prophase

The chromatin in the interphase nucleus (Fig. 9) may appear to be in the form of isolated granules or a network of granules. However, there is good evidence to indicate that the chromatin is actually in the form of fine threads which are much coiled. The modern view is that the so-called granules are actually a mass of very fine coils. What may appear to be chromatin granules of the interphase nucleus of some cells now can be seen as distinct threadlike structures (Fig. 9). These threads (chromonemata) are really double (Fig. 10). The chromonemata go through a process of spiralization, which is accompanied by a shortening and thickening of the chromosome. These chromosomes are characteristic in size, shape, and number, depending on the species of animal to which the dividing cell belongs. While this is happening, a halo of radiating fibers appears around the centrosphere, thus forming an **aster.** The two centrioles then separate and migrate to opposite ends of the cell, each with an aster about it (Fig. 9). Between the asters and the nuclear membrane, a number of fibers become visible in fixed material (Fig. 9). The nuclear membrane breaks down and disappears; and the fibers, extending from the asters across the nuclear space, form a **spindle.**

Metaphase

During this phase of mitosis the duplicated ("split") chromosomes become located in the **equatorial plane** of the spindle (Fig. 9). The two daughter chromosomes produced from one are identical with each other and with the chromosome from which they developed.

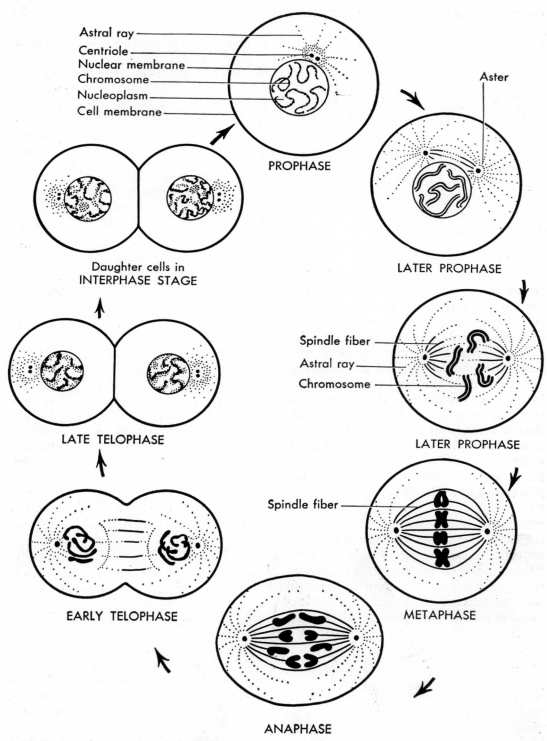

Astral ray
Centriole
Nuclear membrane
Chromosome
Nucleoplasm
Cell membrane

Aster

PROPHASE

Daughter cells in
INTERPHASE STAGE

LATER PROPHASE

Spindle fiber
Astral ray
Chromosome

LATE TELOPHASE

LATER PROPHASE

Spindle fiber

EARLY TELOPHASE

METAPHASE

ANAPHASE

FIGURE 9. Animal mitosis. Typical stages in the mitotic division of one somatic cell into two; diagrammatic. Spiralization and centromere are shown in Fig. 10.

Anaphase

The daughter halves of the duplicated chromosomes now move to opposite ends of the spindle (Fig. 9). Spindle fibers are attached to the chromosomes at definite points. The movement of the daughter chromosomes is due to the contraction of these spindle fibers.

Telophase

The daughter nuclei are now reconstructed (Fig. 9). The chromosomes return to the state in which they existed before mitosis began, a nuclear membrane appears, and the astral rays disappear. The cell body divides into two by a constriction which arises as a furrow at right angles to the spindle. This furrow becomes deeper, until finally the cytoplasm is divided into two.

The time required for nuclear and cytoplasmic division varies with the type of cell and the temperature. At a temperature of 39° C., the mesenchyme cells of a chick that were being grown in tissue culture divided as follows: prophase, 5 to 50 minutes, usually over 30 minutes; metaphase, 1 to 15 minutes, usually 2 to 10 minutes; anaphase, 1 to 5 minutes, usually 2 to 3 minutes; telophase to cytoplasmic division, 2 to 13 minutes, usually 3 to 6 minutes; telophase reconstruction of daughter nuclei, 30 to 120 minutes; total 70 to 180 minutes. Cytokinesis (cytoplasmic division) is usually quite rapid. Moving pictures of dividing cells prove that nuclear mitosis occupies most of the time, whereas division of the cytoplasm is accomplished very quickly.

Many variations occur in the structure and mitotic division of nuclei and in the division of the cytoplasm. For example, in many of the Protozoa and in certain cells of some other animals, the mitotic apparatus is built up within the nuclear membrane. Some protozoans and animals above the protozoans in the scale of life produce a type of cell that is capable of developing under certain conditions into an organism like the parent; cells of this type are called **gametes or germ cells** in contrast to the rest of the cells of the body, which are known as **somatic cells.** The description of mitosis presented here applies to the division of body (somatic) cells. Mitosis, during the development of gametes, may differ in several very important features from that of somatic cells. These differences will be described later.

Chromosomes

Every species of animal has a definite number of chromosomes that appear when the cells of its body undergo mitosis. Thus there are 4 in the nematode worm, *Parascaris equorum;* 8 in the fruit fly, *Drosophila melanogaster;* and as many as 168 in the brine shrimp, *Artemia.* An even number of chromosomes is characteristic of most animals, but some forms have an odd number. Chromosomes vary considerably in both size and shape. Typically they are rodlike, but some appear to be spherical. They may be less than $\frac{1}{1000}$ mm. or more than $\frac{1}{50}$ mm. in length. The chromosomes that appear during mitosis in the cells of an animal may differ in size and shape; when such differences are visible they are not only characteristic of all cells of that animal, but also of the species. These differences are mostly in length, the thickness usually being constant.

A chromosome is not a homogeneous mass of dark-staining material as it appears to be in many preparations, but it has a complex structure. In the interphase (Fig. 10), in some cases, it can be observed that the chromosome consists of at least two thin chromatin threads, the **chromonemata** (singular, **chromonema** *); the chromonema is the basic unit of the chromosome. The two chromonemata are often so closely applied to each other along their entire lengths that

---

* The thread or strand visible in the light microscope is called a chromonema, but the electron microscope reveals that each chromonema is subdivided into thin fibers.

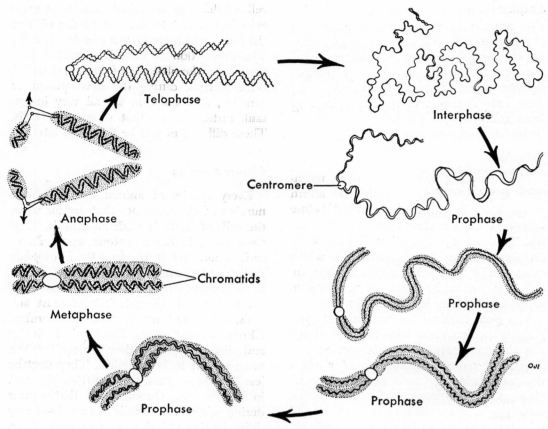

Figure 10. Structure of a chromosome during mitosis. Note spiralization (coiling) of chromonema throughout the cycle. The interphase chromosome consists of at least two chromonemata. In the early prophase chromosome, note the two distinct chromonemata and how they shorten by coiling; in the last stage of the prophase, observe that the chromonema of each half chromosome (chromatid) has been duplicated. Metaphase shows that each half chromosome is composed of two chromonemata. Anaphase shows that daughter halves of the duplicated chromosome separate and move to opposite ends of the mitotic spindle. In the telophase the chromosome forms from two daughter chromonemata. The chromosome is linearly differentiated into a variety of genes, qualitatively different from one another insofar as they affect the development of traits. The centromere has been indicated by a clear circle; this is the point of spindle-fiber attachment. (After *General Cytology* by De Robertis, Nowinski, and Saez. Second edition. Copyright 1954 by Saunders Company.)

they appear and behave as a single structure. As the prophase progresses, the chromosome thickens and shortens, probably due to the chromonemata becoming more tightly coiled, like a spring (Fig. 10).

The primary significance of mitosis is **the separation of the longitudinally duplicated chromosomes into two identical groups, constituting two daughter nuclei.** The general result is that every cell in the body contains the same number of chromosomes of the same size, shape, and quality.

Chromosomes have a persistent **individuality.** Those that appear during the prophases of mitosis are the same as those that took part in the reconstruction of the nucleus in the telophase of the preceding division. In some cases the chromosomes are distinct throughout the interphase stage of the nucleus. Observations indicate that chromosomes do not move at random during the interphase stage, but form a sort of mosaic with respect to one another in a definite order. That chromosomes retain their individuality and **genetic continuity** from generation to generation is indicated by breeding experiments.

Discovery of cells and protoplasm

As noted previously, we owe the term **cell** to Hooke, who in 1665 described the structure of cork and pith. Many other early investigators who used the compound microscope, which was then being developed, reported the presence of cells in all sorts of plants and animals. In 1674, a Dutch microscopist, Leeuwenhoek, discovered unicellular animals, the Protozoa. For many years the **cell wall** was considered the important part of the cell, but later the **protoplasm** within the wall was recognized as the essential cellular substance. A **nucleus** had been seen in cells, but was not recognized as a regular constituent until 1833, when an English botanist, Robert Brown, made this generalization and called it by that name. Two years later, in 1835, Dujardin, a French protozoologist, described the semi-fluid substance in unicellular animals and coined the term sarcode. Not until 1840 were the cell contents called protoplasm by Purkinje; and in 1846 the term was also used by the German von Mohl for the "slime" that is present in plant cells. In the meantime, the German botanist Schleiden in 1838 and the zoologist Schwann in 1839 concluded that all plants and animals are made up of simi-lar cellular units. Another German zoologist, Max Schultze, in 1861, furnished the final proof that protoplasm is the essential living substance.

Cell theory

The modern cell theory may be expressed thus: **organisms are made up of cells and cell products, or are free single cells.** Examples of the products of cells are the intercellular substances of plants and animals. The cell is not only the unit of structure but also of function. A human being begins life as a cell (the fertilized egg) which by multiplication and differentiation develops into a complex, multicellular organism. The cell principle has exerted an important influence on the development of all biology.

SELECTED COLLATERAL READINGS

DeRobertis, E.D.P., Nowinski, W.W., and Saez, F.A. *General Cytology.* Saunders, Philadelphia, 1954.

Gerard, R.W. *Unresting Cells.* Harper, New York, 1949.

Heilbrunn, L.V. *An Outline of General Physiology.* Saunders, Philadelphia, 1952.

Hughes, A. *The Mitotic Cycle.* Academic Press, New York, 1952.

Schrader, F. *Mitosis.* Columbia Univ. Press, New York, 1953.

Sharp, L.W. *Fundamentals of Cytology.* McGraw-Hill, New York, 1943.

Symposium. *Fine Structure of Cells.* Interscience Publishers, New York, 1955.

Wyckoff, W.G. *The World of the Electron Microscope.* Yale Univ. Press, New Haven, 1958.

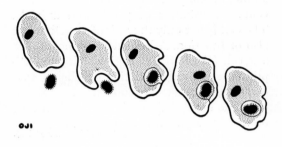

CHAPTER 3

OJI

Phylum Protozoa. One-Celled Animals

W<small>E</small> have briefly discussed protoplasm, the substance of which all living organisms are composed. It is tremendously complex both in its chemical and physical nature and is found throughout the animal kingdom.

If we think of the development of animal life in terms of increasing levels of complexity (biologic levels of organization), then the typical protozoan represents the first level because it is usually only a specialized bit of protoplasm surrounded by a membrane. A higher level consists of the simple multicellular animals, the sponges, because they are a little more complex in structure. Degrees of increasing complexity in structure and function are found among the many-celled animals, from differentiation of tissues (tissue level) to the formation of organs (organ level). Finally, there is the highest development of the organ system (organ-system level), which is found in the most complex animals, including man.

We could begin the study of animal life with one of the many-celled animals such as the earthworm, grasshopper, frog, or cat; but we shall start with the simplest animals, the protozoans, and then study the animal kingdom in approximately the order we think it appeared on the earth. This plan gives you the best opportunity to note the gradual increase in complexity of structure with varying levels of biologic organization, from protozoan to mammal.

Insofar as structure is concerned, a single-celled protozoan is comparable, in some respects, to the individual cells of the body of a many-celled animal, but the physiology of the protozoan is comparable to the whole body of the multicellular animal. The single-celled protozoan can reproduce, show irritability, metabolize, and perform the necessary biological functions of life characteristic of many-celled organisms. One of the intriguing things about protozoans is the fact that a single cell can carry on all the basic life processes.

One of the simplest protozoans is *Amoeba proteus*. Its structure, physiologic processes, behavior, and habitat, will be studied in detail later in this chapter.

CHARACTERISTICS OF THE PROTOZOA

One who examines a bit of pond scum under the microscope for the first time feels as though he were discovering a new world. The protozoans that become visible as a result of magnification do not come within our everyday experience because they are microscopic in size. If enormous numbers of them are crowded together, they may impart their color to the water in which they live, as the green species *Euglena* sometimes does to a fresh-water pond. However, few species are large enough to be seen with the naked eye when only one specimen is present.

Active protozoans are unable to live where it is dry, but they are abundant almost everywhere in water or in moist places. Freshwater ponds, lakes, and streams abound in them; billions live in the sea; the soil often teems with them to a depth of several inches where it is moist; and large numbers live on the outside or within the bodies of other animals.

Most protozoans are unicellular, that is, they consist of a single cell; but a few consist of groups of cells. If they are composed of a group of cells, the cells are not differentiated into tissues. The Protozoa are the most primitive of the large groups of animals and stand in contrast to most of the others, which are many-celled tissue animals. It seems quite remarkable that such minute organisms are capable of maintaining themselves in a world inhabited by so many larger and more complex animals.

In spite of the small size and vast numbers of species of Protozoa, it is not difficult to arrange them in classes, orders, families, genera, and species. The Protozoa are divided into 4 classes on the basis of the structure they possess for locomotion. One example from each class is described in the following chapters. The 4 classes of Protozoa are as follows:

Class 1. Sarcodina. Type: *Amoeba proteus.* Protozoa that move by means of false feet called pseudopodia.

Class 2. Mastigophora. Type: *Euglena viridis.* Protozoa that move by means of whiplike processes called flagella.

Class 3. Sporozoa. Type: *Monocystis lumbrici.* Protozoa without motile organelles, but with a spore stage in their life cycle.

Class 4. Ciliata. Type: *Paramecium caudatum.* Protozoa that move by means of cilia.

AMOEBA PROTEUS

Habitat and preparation for study

From "amoeba to man" is a common expression often seen in the popular press, suggesting that all living animals are found between these extremes, with the amoeba representing the lowest form of life and man the highest. Whether or not this expression is true is open to question, and after you have made a comprehensive study of animal life you will understand why this is said. Amoebas live in many different habitats, such as fresh water, the sea, the soil, and as parasites within other animals, including man. A common large fresh-water species, and one that is usually selected to introduce the phylum Protozoa, is *Amoeba proteus* (Gr. *amoibe*, change; *Proteus*, a sea god in classical mythology who had the power of changing his shape). The amoeba (Fig. 11) lives in fresh-water ponds and streams. It can often be found on the underside of dead lily pads and other vegetation in shallow water.

If material containing amoebas is studied under a microscope, some of the activities

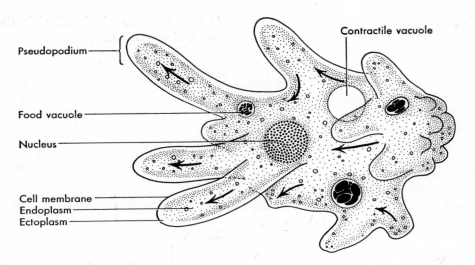

Pseudopodium

Contractile vacuole

Food vacuole

Nucleus

Cell membrane
Endoplasm
Ectoplasm

FIGURE 11. Structure of *Amoeba*. Arrows indicate direction of movement.

and a little of the structure of the animals can be observed. By changing the conditions with respect to temperature, light, etc., one can study their behavior. To obtain a satisfactory idea of the structure of the organisms, it is necessary to kill them and treat them with certain dyes which stain some of the parts, thus making them visible or more distinct than they appear in a living animal.

Structure (morphology)

Amoeba proteus (Fig. 11) is only about 1/100 inch (0.25 mm.) in length. It appears under the microscope as an irregular, grayish particle of animated jelly that is continually changing its shape by thrusting out and withdrawing little fingerlike processes. Two types of cytoplasm are recognizable in the amoeba, the central part of the body appears to consist of granular protoplasm called **endoplasm;** surrounding the endoplasm is a thin layer of clear protoplasm called **ectoplasm.** Although the ectoplasm is surrounded by only a very thin external elastic cell membrane, yet it has been observed that amoebas crawl over each other and never fuse. Within the endoplasm several

bodies may be seen that are larger than the ordinary granules. One of these, the **nucleus,** is not easy to see in the living animal, but when stained it appears to be disk-shaped and filled with chromatin granules. The nucleus is thought to play an important part in such fundamental activities of the cell as growth, manufacture and use of foodstuffs, and formation of new cells. If an amoeba is cut into two pieces, the part containing the nucleus may continue to live and reproduce, but the one without the nucleus cannot reproduce itself and soon dies.

A clear, bubblelike body can often be seen lying near the nucleus; this is known as the **contractile vacuole** (Fig. 11), because at more or less regular intervals it is carried to the surface, where it contracts and forces its fluid contents out of the body. Other vacuoles may often be seen in the endoplasm; these may be temporary and may contain food bodies in process of digestion, or they may be more or less permanent.

When an amoeba is examined with higher magnification, streaming movements may be observed in the endoplasm, indicating that this part of the protoplasm is in a liquid (sol) condition.

Physiology

An amoeba exhibits all activities necessary to maintain itself, and which are characteristic of higher animals. It moves about; captures, ingests, and digests food; egests undigested matter; absorbs and assimilates the products of digestion; secretes and excretes various substances; respires; grows; reproduces itself; and responds to changes in its environment. These facts indicate that the amoeba is physiologically a very complex organism.

Amoeboid movement

Amoebas move from place to place, capture other organisms, and ingest solid particles of food by means of fingerlike protrusions of the body known as **pseudopodia** (singular pseudopodium). These pseudopodia may arise at any point on the surface of the animal. The formation of the pseudopodium looks simple, but it has not yet been explained with certainty in spite of detailed investigations by some of our best zoologists. When a pseudopodium is formed, a blunt projection appears, which consists of ectoplasm. Granular endoplasm can be seen flowing into this. The entire amoeba moves forward in the direction of the pseudopodium. Several pseudopodia may form at the same time; usually one becomes large and effective, and the others become smaller and disappear. Actually, the amoeba moves along by thrusting out pseudopodia and then flowing into them. It has been observed to move at the rate of one inch per hour, but the rate of movement varies with the temperature, increasing up to a temperature of about 30° C., but ceasing at 33° C.

Many cells in multicellular (metazoan) animals, including man, exhibit typical amoeboid movements. For example, the white blood corpuscles in our own blood, which are known as **leukocytes**, move from place to place by means of pseudopodia and are even able to work their way through the walls of blood vessels. Leukocytes also engulf and destroy disease germs by means of their pseudopodia, a process known as **phagocytosis.**

The two principal theories that have been proposed to explain the formation of pseudopodia are based on (1) changes in surface tension, and (2) changes in the viscosity of the cytoplasm. The subject is too complex to be considered here in detail; further information can be obtained in advanced books on zoology and in scientific journals. There is still much to be learned about amoeboid movement, but when the true explanation is found it may give the key not only to the formation of pseudopodia but to the movement of flagella, cilia, and even muscular contraction.

Food

The amoeba feeds principally on minute animals and plants. Not every object encountered is ingested; a distinct selection of food particles is evident (Fig. 12). It seems rather surprising that the amoeba is able to capture such rapidly swimming creatures as the flagellate *Chilomonas* (Fig. 12A) and ciliates such as the paramecium; the former, however, is a favorite type of food. A paramecium is sometimes held and actually cut in two by the pseudopodia of the amoeba for the purpose of ingestion.

Ingestion

Food may be engulfed at any point on the surface of the body (see headpiece) of the amoeba, but it is usually taken in at what may be called the temporary anterior end, that is, the part of the body extended toward the direction of the animal's locomotion.

A food cup is usually formed in the following way (Fig. 12D): pseudopodia enclose the food particle from the sides; then thin sheets of cytoplasm cover the top and the bottom, thus entirely surrounding it. Often when the prey is active, a large food cup is

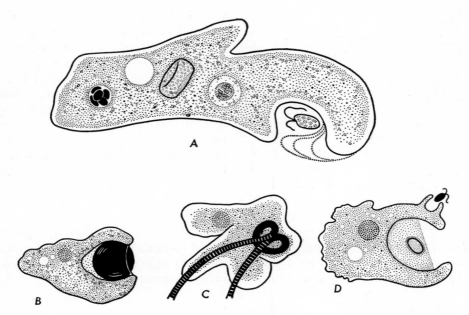

FIGURE 12. *Amoeba.* Ingestion of food. *A,* successive positions of a pseudopodium of an amoeba capturing a flagellate, *Chilomonas. B,* ingesting a cyst of a flagellate. *C,* ingesting a plant filament. *D,* a food cup for ingesting a flagellate superimposed on a food cup containing a ciliate. (*A* after Kepner and Taliaferro; *B* after Jennings; *C* after Rhumbler; *D* after Becker.)

formed and the victim is enclosed without being touched; in this manner a dozen or more flagellates may be ingested in one food cup. A small amount of water is taken in with the food, so that a vacuole is formed with walls which were formerly part of the cell membrane on the outside of the body, and contents consisting of a particle of nutritive material suspended in water.

The whole process of food taking occupies one or more minutes, depending on the character of the food and the temperature. It increases in rapidity up to 25° C., and decreases to zero at about 33° C. The amoeba is not always successful in accomplishing what it undertakes, but when it does not capture its prey at once, it seems to show a persistence usually attributed only to higher organisms (Fig. 13).

Feeding occurs only when the amoebas

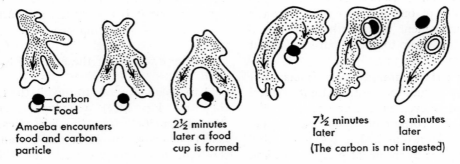

Carbon
Food

Amoeba encounters food and carbon particle

2½ minutes later a food cup is formed

7½ minutes later

8 minutes later

(The carbon is not ingested)

FIGURE 13. *Amoeba proteus* exhibiting food selection. The arrows indicate the direction of the movement of the protoplasm in the pseudopodia. (After Schaeffer.)

are attached to some solid object. At certain times any animal or plant that is not too large may be ingested, but when several species are present, selection is evident, since the small flagellate *Chilomonas* (Fig. 21) is engulfed more readily than the larger ciliate *Colpidium;* and the flagellate *Monas* is rarely taken if *Chilomonas* or *Colpidium* is available. As many as 50 to 100 chilomonads may be ingested in a single day. When amoebas are fed exclusively on chilomonads, they grow and multiply for a few days but soon die; whereas when fed exclusively on *Colpidium* they grow large, become sluggish, and multiply slowly, but do not die. The amoeba may live for 20 days or more without food, but it decreases in volume until it is only about 5 per cent of its original size.

Digestion

The **food vacuole** (food chamber) (Fig. 11) serves as a sort of temporary stomach. Digestive fluids (enzymes) are secreted into it by the surrounding cytoplasm. The contents are at first acid and then become alkaline. In man, as we shall see later, food materials encounter an acid medium in the stomach and an alkaline medium in the intestine. Chilomonads remain alive in the food vacuoles from 3 to 18 minutes and are digested in from 12 to 24 hours. Proteins, fats, sugars, and starches are broken down. The digested material diffuses out of the vacuoles into the cytoplasm, with the vacuole decreasing in size until only indigestible matter remains. This is eventually eliminated.

Egestion

Indigestible and sometimes partially digested particles are egested at any point on the surface of the amoeba, there being no special opening to the exterior for this waste matter. Usually such particles are heavier than the cytoplasm of the amoeba; and as the animal moves forward, they lag behind, finally passing out at the end away from the direction of movement; that is, the amoeba flows away, leaving the indigestible solids behind (Fig. 14).

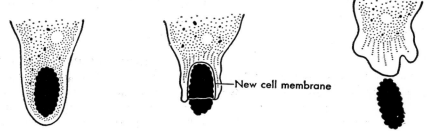

FIGURE 14.   *Amoeba verrucosa.* Part of a specimen showing three stages in the egestion of an indigestible particle; development of a new cell membrane prevents loss of endoplasm. (After Howland.)

Assimilation

The digested material absorbed into the cytoplasm is built up into protoplasm, that is, it is assimilated, and **growth** results.

Dissimilation (*catabolism*)

The energy for the work done by the amoeba comes from the breaking down of complex molecules of protoplasm by oxidation or physiologic burning. The products of this slow combustion are the energy of movement, heat, and residual matter. Ordinarily the **residual matter** consists of solids, fluids consisting mainly of water, some mineral substances, urea, and carbon dioxide. Thus it will be seen that the products of respiration are included in this residual matter.

Secretion

Very little is known about secretion in the amoeba. Undoubtedly digestive fluids are secreted into the food vacuoles. Other substances of use in the life processes of the animal may also be secreted.

Excretion

The amoeba probably gets rid of most of its excretory matter, including urea and carbon dioxide, through the general surface of the body. The **contractile vacuole** may serve in part for excretion, but its primary function is to regulate the water content of the cell body. Water enters the body with the food; it is a by-product of oxidation; and it also passes into the cell through the general surface. The contractile vacuole is formed by the fusion of minute droplets of liquid. Its "wall" is not usually permanent; it is a condensation membrane that disappears at each contraction. It forms in various parts of the body, often near the nucleus, and is carried toward the posterior end. The discharge of the contractile vacuole to the outside seems to take place through the upper surface and for that reason cannot ordinarily be seen.

Respiration

The amoeba requires oxygen for metabolism and must get rid of carbon dioxide. This interchange corresponds to the **internal respiration** of cells in higher animals. That oxygen is necessary for the life of the amoeba can be proved by replacing it with hydrogen; movements cease after 24 hours; if air is then introduced, movement begins again; if not, death ensues. Oxygen dissolved in water is taken in, and carbon dioxide passes out through the surface of the amoeba. The contractile vacuole may take part in carrying carbon dioxide to the outside.

Reproduction

Ordinarily the amoeba builds up protoplasm more rapidly than it breaks it down; and when full size is reached, it reproduces by the simple process of dividing into two amoebas. This method of reproduction is called **binary fission** (Fig. 15). The nucleus divides by **mitosis** (Fig. 15); the prophase lasts 10 minutes, the metaphase probably less than 5 minutes, the anaphase about 10 minutes, and the telophase about 8 minutes. The nuclear membrane disappears during the metaphase. The body of the amoeba, at the time of division, becomes spherical and covered with small pseudopodia; it elongates and separates into two during the telophase stage in mitosis. The time required for the entire process depends on the temperature; at 24° C. it takes about 33 minutes, and under laboratory conditions, the amoeba divides every few days.

Development in the amoeba is simply a matter of **growth**; the rate of growth is rapid just after division, and then gradually decreases until the size for division is once again reached, which takes on the average about three days. Potentially, the amoeba is "immortal," for if it reproduces by fission, there is no death from old age. If death occurs, it results only from an accident.

Behavior

The activities of the amoeba involving changes in shape, formation of pseudopodia, locomotion, capture of food, etc., constitute its behavior. These activities are due largely to changes in the animal's environment and possibly in part to internal changes such as "hunger." The environmental change is called a **stimulus**, and the animal's reaction, a **response**. The amoeba responds to a number of types of stimuli, including those due to changes in contact, light, temperature, chemicals, and electricity. Movement toward a stimulus is called a **positive reaction** and away from a stimulus, a **negative reaction**.

Contact

The amoeba when touched with a small rod will cease locomotion for a time and

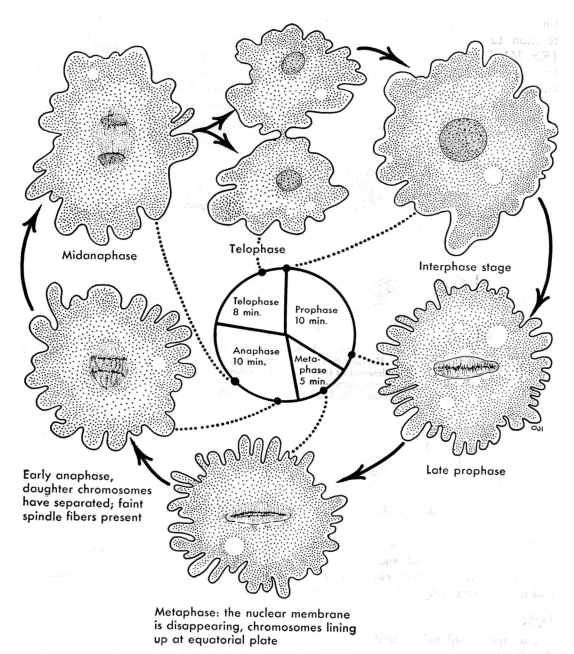

Midanaphase

Telophase

Interphase stage

Telophase
8 min.

Prophase
10 min.

Anaphase
10 min.

Meta-
phase
5 min.

Late prophase

Early anaphase,
daughter chromosomes
have separated; faint
spindle fibers present

Metaphase: the nuclear membrane
is disappearing, chromosomes lining
up at equatorial plate

FIGURE 15. The amoeba, reproducing by binary fission and showing both external appearance and the division of the nucleus by mitosis. Begin study with the interphase stage and follow the arrows. In the center of the diagram, the time in minutes for each stage is shown. Highly magnified. (After Chalkley and Daniel.)

then move away, thus exhibiting a negative reaction to contact or mechanical shock (Fig. 16). If, however, a floating specimen touches a solid object, it will react positively and move toward the object.

Chemicals

Choice of food by the amoeba is probably largely the result of reactions to chemicals; a positive reaction results in ingestion and a negative reaction in movement away from

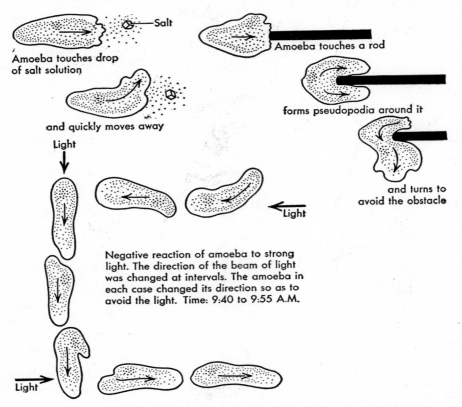

FIGURE 16. *Amoeba.* Reactions to various stimuli. Arrows show direction of movement.

the food particle. The amoeba reacts negatively to various chemicals such as table salt (sodium chloride), acetic acid, cane sugar, and methyl green (Fig. 16).

Light

The amoeba will orient itself in respect to the direction of the rays of a strong light and move away from it (Fig. 16), but it may react positively to a very weak light.

Temperature

As noted above, the rate of locomotion of the amoeba depends on the temperature of

the medium. An increase in temperature results in movements away from the stimulus, that is, in a negative response. If the temperature is decreased sufficiently, movements cease.

Conclusions

These examples of behavior of the amoeba show that it is irritable and that stimuli are conducted to all parts of its cell body. Its reactions to stimuli are of undoubted value to the individual and to the preservation of the species since the negative reactions, produced in most cases by injurious agents such as strong chemicals, heat, and mechanical impacts, carry the animal out of danger.

The data thus far obtained indicate that factors are present in the behavior of the amoeba "comparable to the habits, reflexes, and automatic activities of higher organisms" (Jennings).

OTHER SARCODINA

The amoeba was first reported by Roesel in 1755, although what species he saw is in doubt. Our type, *Amoeba proteus*, has been described as "a shapeless mass of protoplasm," but this is incorrect. Although it is continually changing its shape, it has definite characteristics such as a disk-shaped nucleus, blunt pseudopodia, and often longitudinal ridges on the surface. Many amoebas from fresh water, salt water, soil, and as parasites in other animals, have been described; some have been placed in the genus *Amoeba*, and the rest have been assigned to other genera.

Pelomyxa palustris is a large species that may reach a diameter of 2 mm.; it contains many nuclei and moves along without definite pseudopodia. Another large species, *Pelomyxa carolinensis*, which is sometimes referred to as *Chaos chaos* or giant amoeba, may be obtained from biological supply houses. This species is from 50 to 500 times the volume of *Amoeba proteus*; it may reach a length of from 2 to 5 mm. ($\frac{8}{100}$ to $\frac{20}{100}$ inch), and can be seen with the naked eye. *Pelomyxa carolinensis* usually contains from 300 to 400 nuclei, and from 3 to about 12 contractile vacuoles. Instead of dividing into 2 daughter amoebas, it generally divides into 3. Parasitic amoebas are described in a later chapter.

Several types of common fresh-water Sarcodina are protected by shells. *Arcella* (Fig. 17) secretes its shell, but *Difflugia* (Fig. 17) builds a shell of minute grains of sand. In both types, pseudopodia are thrust out through a circular opening in the shell; they serve, as in *Amoeba,* for purposes of locomotion and obtaining food. Another interesting fresh-water species is sometimes called the sun animal, *Actinophrys* (Fig. 17) because of its stiff radiating pseudopodia. This is abundant among aquatic plants. The ray-like pseudopodia are stiff because each contains an axial filament to keep it rigid.

Most of the 8000 or more Sarcodina live in the sea. The Foraminifera, of which *Globigerina* is an example, construct a perforated shell, usually of calcium carbonate, through which slender pseudopodia project (Fig. 17). Radiolaria also possess slender pseudopodia; many build elaborate skeletons of silica (Fig. 40).

CLASSIFICATION OF THE SARCODINA

(For reference purposes only)

Class Sarcodina includes mostly marine Protozoa which are free-living. They move and capture food by means of pseudopodia. A shell or skeleton may be present. Nutrition is holozoic (subsisting on other organisms) and reproduction is principally by binary fission. About 8000 species have been described. The two subclasses and four orders are described as follows:

Subclass 1. Rhizopoda (Gr. *rhiza*, root; *pous*, foot). Typically creeping forms with lobose pseudopodia, but no central filament.

Order 1. Amoebina. Amoebalike. Short, lobose pseudopodia. Some species (Gymnamoebae: Gr. *gymnos*, naked) are naked, whereas other species (Thecamoebae: Gr. *theke*, case) are covered by a simple shell with one opening. Exs. *Amoeba proteus* and *Arcella vulgaris* (Fig. 17).

Order 2. Foraminifera (L. *foramen*, opening; *fero*, bear). With simple or chambered perforated shell and from one to many branched

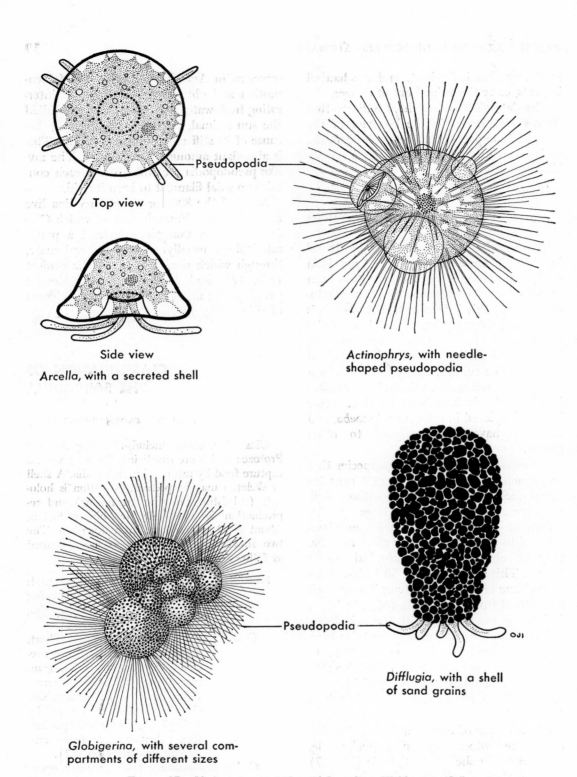

Pseudopodia

Top view

Side view

Arcella, with a secreted shell

Actinophrys, with needle-
shaped pseudopodia

Pseudopodia

Pseudopodia

Difflugia, with a shell
of sand grains

Globigerina, with several compartments of different sizes

FIGURE 17. Various representatives of Sarcodina. Highly magnified.

pseudopodia. Mostly marine. Ex. *Globigerina bulloides* (Fig. 17).

Subclass 2. Actinopoda (Gr. *aktis*, ray; *pous*, foot). Typically floating forms with radiating, unbranched pseudopodia, each with central filament.

Order 1. Heliozoa (Gr. *helios*, sun; *zoion*, animal). Pseudopodia are thin, radially arranged, and usually supported by axial threads; spherical; chiefly in fresh water. Ex. *Actinophrys sol* (Fig. 17).

Order 2. Radiolaria (L. *radiolus*, a little ray). Marine. Often spherical; pseudopodia raylike; protoplasm divided into inner and outer parts by a perforated capsule; usually a skeleton of silica or strontium sulfate. Ex. *Acanthometron elasticum* (Fig. 40).

Subclass 3. Mycetozoa (L. *mykes*, fungus; *zoion*, animal). Slime animals. Adult phase consists of a sheet of multinucleate protoplasm up to several inches in width. They are found on decaying organic matter, such as rotting leaves and wood. The mycetozoa produce resistant spores that survive dry conditions.

SELECTED COLLATERAL READINGS

Calkins, G.N. *The Biology of the Protozoa*, Lea & Febiger, Philadelphia, 1933.

Cushman, J.A. *Foraminifera, Their Classification and Economic Use.* Harvard Univ. Press, Cambridge, 1948.

Hagelstein, R. *The Mycetozoa of North America.* Published by author, Mineola, N.Y., 1944.

CHAPTER 4

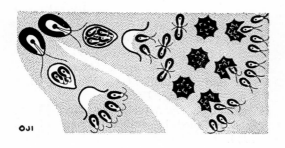

OJI

Phylum Protozoa.
Flagellates

THE flagellates are protozoa that differ from the amoeba in that they usually possess a definite shape and a front end from which arise one or more whiplike locomotor organelles called **flagella** (singular **flagellum**). The flagella are also used to capture food and to serve as sense receptors for exploring the surroundings. The flagellates are abundant in puddles, ponds, and swamps. Unfortunately, most of them are so small that they are difficult to study. The euglenas, however, are comparatively large and exhibit most of the characteristics peculiar to the class.

One of the flagellates, the Phytomonadida, includes a number of colonial species that can be arranged in a series, from a simple aggregation of cells as in *Spondylomorum* (Fig. 401, p. 562), to a very complex colony such as *Volvox* (Fig. 22). These flagellates and certain others are of particular interest since they combine the characteristics of both plants and animals and are frequently claimed by botanists. Many different species live in fresh and salt water. With diatoms, they constitute an important part of the food supply for very small aquatic animals. Many flagellates are parasitic in man, lower animals, and plants. Some parasitic forms are mentioned here, but a fuller discussion will be found in a subsequent chapter.

EUGLENA VIRIDIS

Habitat

One of the common species of the genus *Euglena*, usually *Euglena viridis*, ordinarily serves as a type of the class Mastigophora. Euglenas are common in fresh-water ponds, to which they give a greenish tinge if present in sufficient numbers. They are usually found in collections of pond weeds and thrive in the laboratory in a jar on the window sill where there is plenty of indirect sunlight. Over 150 species have been described in the genus *Euglena;* these differ from one another in size, shape, behavior, and structural details.

Morphology

Euglena viridis (Fig. 18) is 0.1 mm. or less in length, blunt at the anterior end, and pointed at the posterior end. Figure 18 presents the structural features of this species. The peripheral layer of cytoplasm is a thin elastic membrane, the **pellicle.** This pellicle has parallel, spiral thickenings that give it a striated appearance. It is rigid enough to maintain the shape of the body, but sufficiently flexible to allow euglenoid move-

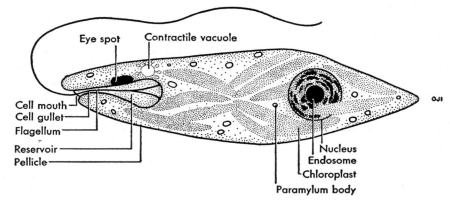

FIGURE 18. *Euglena viridis.* Diagram of a stained specimen showing structure.

ments. Near the anterior end is a funnel-shaped depression, the **cell mouth** (**cytostome**), that leads into the **cell gullet** (**cytopharynx**). The euglena does not eat solid food as these terms might imply. The cytopharynx is enlarged at the base to form a vesicle called the **reservoir,** adjacent to which is located a **contractile vacuole,** which discharges its contents into the reservoir and out through the cytopharynx.

Near the anterior end of the body is an orange-red **eye spot** which is part of a light-sensitive organelle and probably serves in orienting the euglena to light. A **flagellum,** which arises from two axial filaments within the body, extends out of the cytostome. The electron microscope shows that the flagellum consists of a core of two axial filaments surrounded by a sheath of protoplasm. Near the center of the euglena is an oval or spherical **nucleus** containing a central body, the **endosome.** The function of the endosome is controversial. Suspended in the cytoplasm are also a number of green bodies, the chromatophores, which are known as **chloroplasts.** This green color is due to the presence of **chlorophyl.** In *Euglena viridis* the chloroplasts are slender and radiate from a central point. In each chloroplast of some species of *Euglena* there is a **pyrenoid,** which is probably a center for the formation of a starchlike substance called **paramylum.** Paramylum bodies may also be free in the cytoplasm in the form of disks, rods, and links. Paramylum is produced by photosynthesis and represents reserve food material.

Physiology

Nutrition

Euglenas obtain their nutriment largely by **photosynthesis,** a process that takes place within the chloroplasts; however, it has not been proved that any species of *Euglena* can grow in light without a trace of organic material such as a peptone. In the dark the euglenas can live on organic compounds that are dissolved in water; under these conditions the chloroplasts and pyrenoids degenerate and disappear. Although the euglenas do not capture and eat other organisms, there are colorless animal-like flagellates which do eat protozoans, algae, and diatoms.

Locomotion

In swimming, the flagellum beats back and forth, moving the animal forward. A spiral path is followed, resulting in a straight course through the trackless water, provided no stimulus interferes. Although euglenas possess a definite shape, they are characterized by wormlike movements involving waves of contraction to which the term **euglenoid movement** has been applied (Fig. 20).

Reactions to light

Euglenas are easily stimulated by changes in the direction of the light. Most species swim toward an ordinary light such as that from a window; and if a culture is examined,

most of the animals will be found on the side toward the brightest light. This is of distinct advantage to the animal since light is necessary for the process of photosynthesis, just as is true in plants. However, euglenas will swim away from the direct rays of the sun; direct sunlight will kill them if they are exposed to it for a long time. If a drop of water containing euglenas is placed in the direct sunlight with one half shaded, the euglenas will avoid the shady part as well as the direct sunlight, both of which are unfavorable to them. They will remain in a small band between the two, in the light best suited for them, their optimum (Fig. 19). By shading various portions of the body of a euglena, it has been found that the region of the eye spot is especially sensitive. It should be noted that when a euglena is swimming through the water, it is this anterior end which first encounters regions of different light intensity; the animals give the avoiding reaction when they enter less favorable areas.

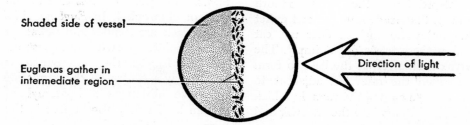

Shaded side of vessel

Euglenas gather in intermediate region

Direction of light

FIGURE 19. *Euglena.* Reaction to light. The euglenas gather in the intermediate region across the middle, where the light intensity is most favorable for them. (After Jennings.)

Reproduction

Reproduction in *Euglena* takes place by binary longitudinal fission (Fig. 20). The nucleus divides in two by mitosis; then the anterior organelles such as the reservoir are duplicated; and the animal divides longitudinally, that is, in an antero-posterior direction, splitting the cell into two equal parts. The old flagellum may be retained by one half, while a new flagellum is developed by the other. Often longitudinal division takes

place while the animals are in the encysted condition (Fig. 20). These animals are said to be **encysted** when they have become almost spherical and are surrounded by a gelatinous wall which they have secreted. In this condition, periods of drought are successfully passed, the animals becoming active again when water is encountered. Usually in laboratory cultures, cysts are present on the sides of the dish. Before encystment, the flagellum is thrown off, but a new one is produced when activity is again resumed.

One cyst usually contains two euglenas, although further multiplication by longitudinal division may produce 4, 16, or 32 young euglenas in a single cyst.

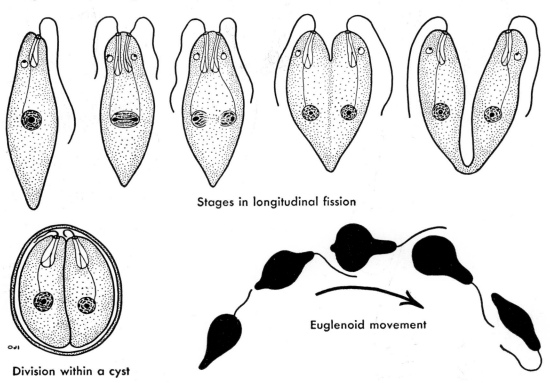

Stages in longitudinal fission

Euglenoid movement

Division within a cyst

FIGURE 20. Reproduction and euglenoid movement in *Euglena viridis*.

OTHER MASTIGOPHORA

The relations of flagellates to man are discussed in Chapter 7, where accounts will be found of species that live in drinking water, in the soil, and in the blood streams and intestines of human beings. A few other types of particular interest are as follows.

Chilomonas (Fig. 21) is a species that is very common in nature and in laboratory cultures; it constitutes a large part of the food of *Amoeba proteus*. It is about 35 microns long and has two flagella at the anterior end. It does not possess chromatophores, but absorbs nutriment through the surface of the body.

Among the flagellates that live in the sea are species of the genus *Noctiluca* (Fig. 21), which sometimes occur in such enormous numbers that, due to their orange color, the water looks like tomato soup. One quart of sea water may contain more than three million individuals. Even more striking is the appearance of the sea when one travels over it at night. *Noctiluca* is **luminescent** and glows with a bluish or greenish light when agitated. One can read the time on his watch when it is held a foot away from a glassful of these flagellates. Incidentally, this light is not accompanied by production of heat, and hence it is generated without the loss of heat energy, which is something man has not been able to do in making artificial light. Many other animals and certain plants possess a similar power of producing light without wasting energy, for example, the fireflies and their larvae, the glowworms.

Gymnodinium (Fig. 21) is a dinoflagellate

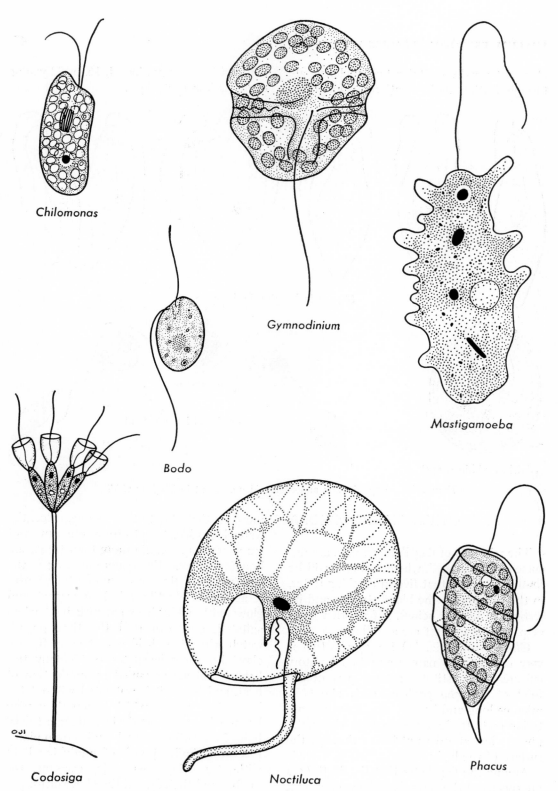

Chilomonas

Gymnodinium

Mastigamoeba

Bodo

Codosiga

Noctiluca

Phacus

Figure 21. Representatives of various orders of flagellates. All highly magnified. (*Noctiluca* after Jahn and Jahn.)

46

of which one species (*brevis*) may occur in such great numbers as to cause a periodic red tide in coastal waters. The red tide may appear anywhere in the world, in both tropical and temperate waters. The misnomer red tide is the popular name for the brownish-amber discoloration of sea water caused by this microscopic flagellate. Under certain conditions it reproduces at a fantastic rate; sixty million have been counted in a single quart.

The organism produces a toxic substance that is fatal to fish. The tiny pest also releases an airborne "poison gas" which irritates the human respiratory tract and may cause coughing, sneezing, and even shortness of breath.

During the red tide off the coast of Florida in 1952 and again in 1954 enormous numbers of fish died, and the shore was littered for miles with stinking fish. An extensive red tide results in the loss of tremendous amounts of sea food.

Another dinoflagellate, *Gonyaulax*, also causes waters to appear a rusty red at times because of its great numbers. *Gonyaulax catenella* is known to have been the cause of disastrous poisoning in man. Several kinds of shellfish along the Pacific Coast feed on them, thus making the shellfish poisonous for human consumption. In 1941, there were 346 cases of poisoning with 24 deaths. Since 1941 state laws forbid the gathering of shellfish during the season of the red waters. Experiments have shown the toxin to be about ten times as potent as strychnine, which is used for poisoning mice.

The genus *Mastigamoeba* (Fig. 21) includes species that live in fresh water or in the soil. They not only possess a flagellum, but also form pseudopodia with which they ingest food particles.

Many flagellates are very complex in structure, especially certain species that live in the intestine of termites (white ants) such as those shown in Fig. 447, p. 639. The relations between these flagellates and the termites in which they live are described in Chapter 37.

RELATIONS BETWEEN SARCODINA AND MASTIGOPHORA

Many zoologists believe that flagellates evolved from the green algae among plants and that the Sarcodina arose from a flagellate or flagellatelike organism. Many green flagellates such as *Volvox* (Fig. 22) can hardly be separated from green algae. A close relation between amoebas and flagellates is indicated by the fact that in certain species both amoeboid and flagellate stages occur in the same life cycle. Also certain types of flagellates such as *Mastigamoeba* possess both flagella and pseudopodia. Probably not all Sarcodina arose from the flagellates; some doubtless have evolved from other Sarcodina.

CLASSIFICATION OF THE MASTIGOPHORA

(For reference purposes only)

Class Mastigophora. These bear one or more flagella in the adult stage. They may be amoeboid in shape but are generally covered with a pellicle. Many of them are parasitic. Binary fission is usually longitudinal division. No sexual reproduction is known in many of the genera. Two subclasses may be recognized according to their principal method of nutrition. The members of the subclass Phytomastigina are mostly holophytic, although some are saprozoic and may be in part holozoic. Those of the subclass Zoomastigina are primarily holozoic.

Subclass 1. Phytomastigina (Gr. *phyton*, plant; *mastix*, whip). Plantlike; chromatophores usually present; often a red eye spot.

Order 1. Chrysomonadina. Small; 1 or 2 flagella; some colonial. Ex. *Uroglenopsis americana* (Fig. 39).

Order 2. Cryptomonadina. One or 2 flagella and usually 1 or 2 chromatophores. Ex. *Chilomonas paramecium* (Fig. 21).

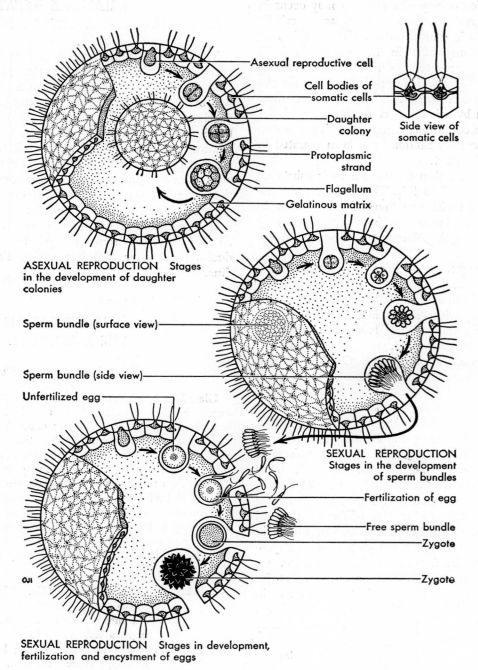

Asexual reproductive cell

Cell bodies of somatic cells

Daughter colony

Protoplasmic strand

Flagellum

Gelatinous matrix

Side view of somatic cells

ASEXUAL REPRODUCTION Stages in the development of daughter colonies

Sperm bundle (surface view)

Sperm bundle (side view)

Unfertilized egg

SEXUAL REPRODUCTION Stages in the development of sperm bundles

Fertilization of egg

Free sperm bundle

Zygote

Zygote

SEXUAL REPRODUCTION Stages in development, fertilization and encystment of eggs

FIGURE 22. *Volvox*, the largest of the colonial flagellates, is a sphere of from 500 to 40,000 cells. The whole organism barely attains the size of a pinhead. When the flagella vibrate, the organism revolves through the water. Its reproduction is described on page 562.

Order 3. **Dinoflagellina.** Two flagella, usually 1 forward and the other in a groove around the body; mostly marine. Ex. *Noctiluca scintillans* (Fig. 21).

Order 4. **Phytomonadina.** Cellulose body wall; no cytostome; many colonial. Ex. *Volvox globator* (Fig. 22).

Order 5. **Euglenoidina.** Usually 1 or 2 flagella, a cytostome and cytopharynx; often chromatophores and eye spot. Exs. *Euglena* and *Phacus* (Fig. 21).

Subclass 2. **Zoomastigina** (Gr. *zoion*, animal; *mastix*, whip). Animal-like; no chromatophores; no sexual reproduction known.

Order 1. **Rhizomastigina** or **Pantostomatida.** Colorless; amoeboid; 1 flagellum. Ex. *Mastigamoeba aspera* (Fig. 21).

Order 2. **Protomonadina.** Colorless; often amoeboid; 1 to 3 flagella. Ex. *Codosiga* (Fig. 21).

Order 3. **Polymastigina.** Mostly intestinal inhabitants; 3 to 8 flagella; some bilaterally symmetrical. Ex. *Giardia lamblia* (Fig. 37, p. 72).

Order 4. **Hypermastigina.** Intestinal inhabitants of termites (p. 638) and cockroaches; many flagella; often very complex. Ex. *Spirotrichonympha flagellata* (Fig. 447).

SELECTED COLLATERAL READINGS

Allen, W.E. "Red Water in La Jolla Bay (California) in 1945." *Trans., Am. Microscopical Soc.*, 55:149–153, 1946.

Gojdics, Mary. *The Genus Euglena.* Univ. of Wisconsin Press, Madison, 1953.

Hall, R.P. *Protozoology.* Prentice-Hall, Englewood Cliffs, N.J., 1953.

Jahn, T.L. "The Euglenoid Flagellates." *Quart. Rev. Biol.*, 21:246–274, 1946.

Pennak, R.W. *Fresh-water Invertebrates of the United States.* Ronald Press, New York, 1953.

CHAPTER 5

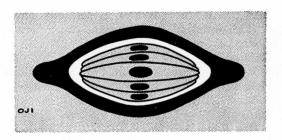

Phylum Protozoa. One-Celled Parasites

THE class Sporozoa lives on or within other animals from which it derives nutrition, and therefore these animals are classified as parasites. They are not as well known as other types of protozoans, but they may be found in animals ranging in complexity from simple invertebrates to man. The life cycles of many sporozoans involve different species of hosts. A host is any plant or animal on or within which a parasite lives and from which it obtains its nourishment. The various stages of development of the sporozoans are very interesting, and the methods by which they are transmitted from one host to another are quite remarkable. They may also cause the death of their host, including man, and are therefore very important to our welfare and economy.

The life cycle is usually complicated, involving the production of resistant stages which in some cases are called **spores**. The spore may be a spindle-shaped case containing sporozoites (Fig. 23). Spores serve as an infective stage in the life cycle. They often pass out of one host in the feces and enter another host in contaminated food or drink; or they may be sucked out of one host by a bloodsucking animal, such as an insect, and inoculated into another animal by this **intermediate host**.

MONOCYSTIS LUMBRICI—A SPOROZOAN PARASITE OF EARTHWORMS

Monocystis lumbrici illustrates many of the characteristics of the Sporozoa (Fig. 23). It is a parasite almost invariably found in the seminal vesicles of the common earthworm. The stages that are usually present are (1) the trophozoite, (2) cysts containing two individuals, or gametes and spores in various phases of development, and (3) isolated spores.

Monocystis is easily obtained for study.

A living or preserved earthworm should be pinned down and a slit made in the body wall from about the tenth to the fifteenth segment; the whitish bodies that extrude are the seminal vesicles. Parts of these should be pinched off with forceps and teased out well with dissection needles on a slide, in a drop of 0.7 per cent table salt (NaCl) solution. A cover glass should be placed on the preparation, which should then be examined under the microscope.

The life cycle of *Monocystis* is briefly outlined as follows (Fig. 23). The spores are taken into the earthworm's digestive tract where the **sporozoites** are set free. Each sporozoite penetrates a bundle of developing sperm cells in the testis of the earthworm and is then termed a **trophozoite**.

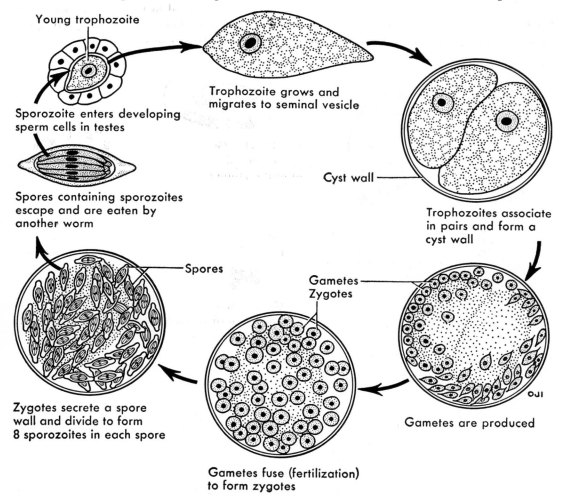

Young trophozoite

Sporozoite enters developing sperm cells in testes

Trophozoite grows and migrates to seminal vesicle

Cyst wall

Spores containing sporozoites escape and are eaten by another worm

Trophozoites associate in pairs and form a cyst wall

Spores

Gametes
Zygotes

Zygotes secrete a spore wall and divide to form 8 sporozoites in each spore

Gametes are produced

Gametes fuse (fertilization) to form zygotes

FIGURE 23. Life cycle of *Monocystis*, a sporozoan that lives in the common earthworm. All highly magnified but not drawn to scale.

Here it lives at the expense of the cells among which it lies. The sperms of the earthworm, which are deprived of nourishment by the parasite, slowly shrivel up, becoming tiny filaments on the surface of the trophozoite, making it resemble a ciliated organism. The trophozoite grows and then migrates to a seminal vesicle. Here two

trophozoites come together and are surrounded by a cyst wall. Each then divides,
producing a number of small cells called
gametes. The gametes unite in pairs to form
zygotes. It is probable that the gametes
produced by one of the trophozoites do not
fuse with each other but with gametes produced by the other trophozoite enclosed in
the same cyst. Each zygote becomes lemon-
shaped and secretes a thin hard wall about
itself. It is now known as a **spore.** The
nucleus of the spore divides successively into

2,4, and finally 8 daughter nuclei, each of
which, together with a portion of the cytoplasm, becomes a sporozoite.

OTHER SPOROZOA

Four subclasses and five orders of Sporozoa are usually recognized by zoologists.
Some of the species of great importance to
man are described in Chapter 7. Two types
that are easily obtained for study are gregarines and coccidians.

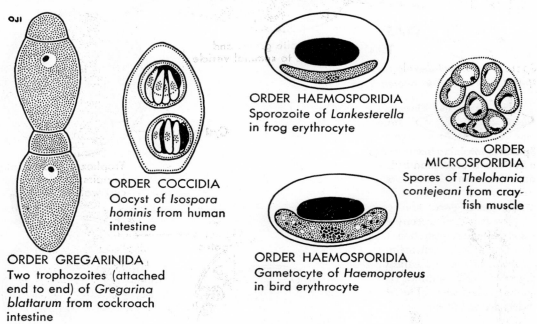

ORDER HAEMOSPORIDIA
Sporozoite of *Lankesterella*
in frog erythrocyte

ORDER
MICROSPORIDIA
Spores of *Thelohania
contejeani* from cray-
fish muscle

ORDER COCCIDIA
Oocyst of *Isospora
hominis* from human
intestine

ORDER GREGARINIDA
Two trophozoites (attached
end to end) of *Gregarina
blattarum* from cockroach
intestine

ORDER HAEMOSPORIDIA
Gametocyte of *Haemoproteus*
in bird erythrocyte

FIGURE 24. Types of sporozoa.

Gregarines may be obtained from the intestines of grasshoppers, cockroaches, and
meal worms. Spores are swallowed by these
insects from which sporozoites escape. These
penetrate the cells of the intestinal wall, and
trophozoites develop from them. The
trophozoites, after undergoing a period of
growth, break out into the intestine, where
they unite end to end (Fig. 24). The rest of
the life cycle is similar to that of *Monocystis.*
Coccidia are most easily obtained for
study from the rabbit. Oocysts may be found
in the feces of a large proportion of these

animals. They consist of a single cell when
passed, but if the material is placed in a 5
per cent aqueous solution of potassium di-
chromate to inhibit the growth of bacteria,
four spores, each containing two sporozoites,
will develop within each cyst in about three
days.

ORIGIN OF THE SPOROZOA

Parasitic protozoans, no doubt, evolved
from free-living species or from other para-

sitic species that had free-living ancestors. The origin of the Sporozoa is obscure. The different groups included in the class may have arisen from different classes. Those with amoeboid sporozoites may have evolved from amoeboid ancestors, and those with flagellated sporozoites from flagellate ancestors. Coccidia probably originated from gregarines and the blood-inhabiting Haemosporidia from the Coccidia.

CLASSIFICATION OF THE SPOROZOA

(For reference purposes only)

Class Sporozoa. These are among the most widely distributed of all animal parasites; members of almost every large group in the animal kingdom are parasitized by one or more species. They are greatly modified, due to their parasitic existence. These modifications have resulted in the absence of locomotor organelles, mouth, anal pore, and contractile vacuoles. Food is absorbed directly from the host, and respiration and excretion take place by diffusion through the cell membrane. Many organs of the host may be parasitized, especially the digestive tract, kidneys, blood, muscles, and connective tissues. The 4 subclasses and 5 orders are as follows:

Subclass 1. Telosporidia. Spores produced at end of life of trophozoite; no polar capsule nor polar filament.

Order 1. Gregarinida. Common parasites of insects; at first intracellular, but later often free in cavities. Ex. *Monocystis lumbrici* (Fig. 23).

Order 2. Coccidia. Parasites of vertebrates and invertebrates; one species in man. Ex. *Isospora hominis* (Fig. 24).

Order 3. Haemosporidia. Parasites in blood cells of vertebrates, and in bodies of invertebrates. Ex. Malaria organisms of man (Fig. 33, p. 69).

Subclass 2. Cnidosporidia (Gr. *knide*, nettle). Spores with one to four polar capsules, with a coiled polar filament.

Order 1. Myxosporidia. Principally parasites of fish. Ex. *Myxidium lieberkuhni*.

Order 2. Microsporidia. Spores extremely small; usually with one polar capsule; insects most frequently infected. Ex. *Nosema apis*, and *Thelohania contejeani*.

Subclass 3. Acnidosporidia. Simple spores without polar capsules; some parasitic in vertebrates.

Subclass 4. Haplosporidia. In lower vertebrates and invertebrates. Ex. *Haplosporidium nemertis*.

CHAPTER 6

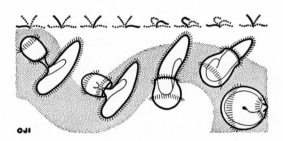

OJI

Phylum Protozoa.
Ciliates

THE ciliates are relatively large and the most complex in structure of the Protozoa. The slipperlike animal *Paramecium caudatum* is ordinarily used as a type since it is easy to obtain for study and reaches the comparatively great length of about 0.3 mm. Many other species of ciliates may be found in cultures made from pond weeds and decaying plant and animal infusions.

The ciliates (class Ciliata) are distinguished from other protozoans in possessing **cilia**, which are sometimes modified into **cirri**, during a part or all of their life cycle. In most of them the nuclear material is separated into a large macronucleus and one or more smaller micronuclei. Most ciliates are free-living in fresh or salt water. Some, however, are important parasites of man and other animals.

PARAMECIUM CAUDATUM— A FRESH-WATER CILIATE

Paramecia are common animals usually found in pond water which contains considerable decaying vegetation. This little animal was among the first living things seen with the newly invented microscope in the seventeenth century. The paramecium then became of biological interest and has continued to be investigated down through the years. Recently, it and related ciliates have been used for studies of nutrition, respiration, cancer, heredity, sex, behavior, and ecology.

The protozoans generally play a considerable role in aquatic food chains. Many species use dissolved nutrients in the water and serve as food for small many-celled animals, which in turn are eaten by larger animals.

Morphology

The 10 well-known species of paramecia differ from one another in size, shape, and structure. The following description applies principally to *Paramecium caudatum* (Fig. 25) and *Paramecium aurelia. Paramecium caudatum* ranges from about 0.15 mm. to 0.3 mm. in length, and *Paramecium aurelia* from about 0.12 mm. to 0.2 mm. Figure 25 indicates the shape of a specimen of *P. caudatum.* The anterior end is blunt and the posterior end more pointed. The greatest width is behind the center of the body.

A depression extends from the anterior end, obliquely backward, ending just posterior to the middle of the animal; this is the **oral groove.** The **cell mouth** (**cytostome**) is situated near the end of the oral groove. It opens into a short tube, the **cell gullet** (**cytopharynx**), which passes obliquely downward and posteriorly into the endoplasm. The side containing the oral groove

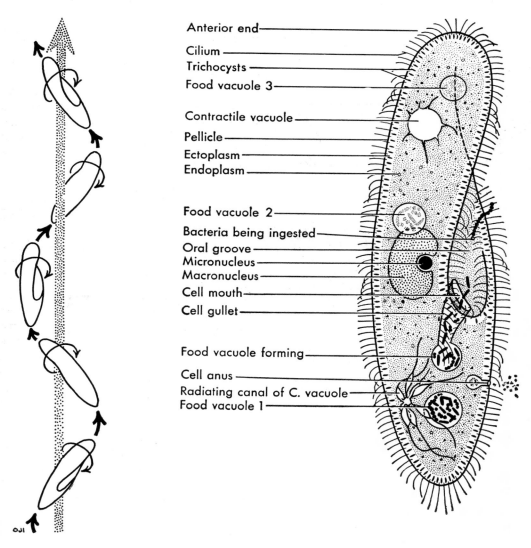

Anterior end
Cilium
Trichocysts
Food vacuole 3
Contractile vacuole
Pellicle
Ectoplasm
Endoplasm
Food vacuole 2
Bacteria being ingested
Oral groove
Micronucleus
Macronucleus
Cell mouth
Cell gullet
Food vacuole forming
Cell anus
Radiating canal of C. vacuole
Food vacuole 1

FIGURE 25. *Left*, spiral path of a free-swimming paramecium. Note that these animals rotate on their long axes at the same time that they are moving forward. *Right*, drawing designed to show the structure of *Paramecium caudatum.* Numbered food vacuoles show progress of digestion and absorption.

may be designated **oral,** and the opposite side, **aboral.** The motile organelles are fine hairlike **cilia** regularly arranged over the surface. As in the amoeba, two types of cytoplasm are visible: an outer comparatively thin clear layer, the **ectoplasm;** and an inner granular mass, the **endoplasm.** Besides these, a distinct elastic membrane, the **pellicle,** is present on the outer surface of the ectoplasm. One large **contractile vacuole** is usually situated near each end of the body, close to the aboral surface; and a

variable number of **food vacuoles** may be seen. The nuclei are two in number, a large **macronucleus** concerned with vegetative functions, and a smaller **micronucleus** that is important in reproduction; these are suspended in the endoplasm near the mouth opening. A temporary opening called the **cell anus** can be observed only when undigested particles are discharged. It is situated posterior to the oral groove, and it always reforms at the same point on the surface of the body.

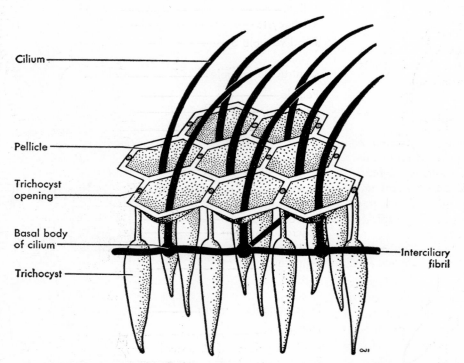

FIGURE 26. *Paramecium.* Diagram showing structure of the pellicle: the hexagonal areas are due to ridges; the cilia extend out from the center of the hexagonal areas, each being attached to a basal body; the basal bodies are located on longitudinal fibers; these fibers appear to constitute the mechanism by which the activity of the cilia is coordinated. The carrot-shaped trichocysts are attached by delicate threads to the ridges. Highly magnified. (After Lund.)

The endoplasm occupies the central part of the body. Most of the larger granules contained within it are shown by microchemical reactions to be reserve food particles; they flow from place to place, indicating that the endoplasm is of a fluid nature. The ectoplasm does not contain any of the large granules characteristic of the endoplasm, since its density prevents their entrance. In this respect the two kinds of cytoplasm resemble the ectoplasm and endoplasm of the amoeba. If a drop or two of 35 per cent alcohol is added to a drop of water containing paramecia, the pellicle will be raised in some specimens in the form of a blister. Under the higher powers of the microscope the pellicle is then seen to be made up of a great number of hexagonal areas produced by ridges on the surface (Fig. 26).

The distribution of the motile organelles, the **cilia**, corresponds to the arrangement of the striations on the pellicle, since one cilium projects from the center of each hexagonal area (Fig. 26). These hairlike structures occur on all parts of the body, those at the posterior end being slightly longer than elsewhere. Cilia are outgrowths of the cell protoplasm and arise from basal bodies. The arrangement of the cilia within the cytopharynx is rather complicated; they guide the food particles that are swept within their reach.

Physiology

Physiologic processes similar to those described for the amoeba occur in the paramecium. Paramecia defend themselves from enemies, capture and ingest food, digest it, build up protoplasm, react to stimuli, carry on processes of respiration and excretion, and reproduce.

Offense and defense

The paramecium feeds principally on bacteria and on other protozoans which as a rule are smaller than itself. No special weapons of offense appear to be necessary for the capture of food. Paramecia, however, are attacked and used for food by other protozoans and by larger animals, so they have a real need for weapons of defense; the **trichocysts** appear to answer this purpose. These carrot-shaped structures are embedded in the ectoplasm just beneath the surface as shown in Figs. 25 and 26. These bodies are oriented perpendicularly to the surface. A small amount of iodine or acetic acid, when added to a drop of water containing paramecia, causes the discharge of the trichocysts to the exterior. After the explosion, the animal is surrounded by a halo of long threads. Evidence that the trichocysts are probably weapons of defense is furnished when a paramecium encounters another species of ciliate, *Didinium*; see headpiece on first page of this chapter, which shows a paramecium attached to and being eaten by a didinium. If the seizing organ of this protozoan becomes fastened in the paramecium, a great number of trichocysts are discharged near the place of the injury. If the paramecium is a large one, it frequently succeeds in making its escape. However, it is probable that the usual function of the trichocysts is to hold the paramecium to the substratum while it is feeding on bacteria. A ciliate is at a disadvantage during feeding if it does not have anchorage because the ciliary currents used to gather food cause it to whirl around.

Nutrition

Paramecia do not possess chlorophyl and hence are unable to manufacture food by photosynthesis as euglenas do. One species, *Paramecium bursaria*, which contains minute unicellular green plants in its endoplasm, will reproduce in a solution of salts alone if it is kept in the light. This is a case of mutualism in which a mutually beneficial relationship exists between two different organisms. Paramecia do not ingest every small object that reaches the cytostome; they take in certain particles and not others. For example, if different species of bacteria are present, they may feed on one species and not on another.

Bacteria, yeasts, small protozoans, and algae are captured with the aid of the cilia in the oral groove. By the direction of their beating, they produce a sort of current that drives a steady stream of water toward the cytostome. Food particles that are swept into the cytostome are carried down into the cytopharynx; they are then driven onward by the cilia in the cytopharynx and are finally gathered together near the end into a food vacuole (Fig. 25). When this vacuole has reached a certain size, it is released into

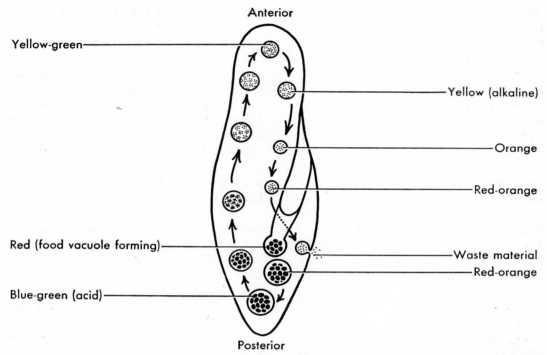

Anterior

Yellow-green

Yellow (alkaline)

Orange

Red-orange

Red (food vacuole forming)

Waste material
Red-orange

Blue-green (acid)

Posterior

FIGURE 27. *Paramecium caudatum.* Diagram illustrating cyclosis and the process of digestion. To indicate the path of the food vacuole within the paramecium, some yeast cells stained with Congo red (a red dye) should be placed near the animal. The yeast cells are taken into the body, where a food vacuole is formed. The arrows in the figure of the paramecium indicate the path of the food vacuole within the body (cyclosis). The change in color of the Congo red to blue-green indicates that the vacuole became acid soon after it was formed. As the vacuole with the yeast cells circulates through the body, it changes back to a red-orange color, indicating that the vacuole and its contents are becoming less acid. Chemical tests have proved that the vacuole with its contents actually becomes definitely alkaline even though the red-orange color would not prove this, for Congo red is an indicator of acidity only, and cannot be used to test for alkalinity. We can assume from experiments that in the digestion of food the vacuole is first acid and then alkaline.

the surrounding cytoplasm; and the formation of another vacuole is begun.

A **food vacuole** is a droplet of water with food particles suspended within it. As soon as one is separated from the cytopharynx, it is swept away by the rotary streaming movement of the endoplasm, known as **cyclosis** (Fig. 27). This carries the food vacuole around a definite course, which begins just behind the cytopharynx, passes posteriorly, then forward and aborally, and finally posteriorly to near the oral groove. In the course of this journey, digestion takes place. During the cyclosis the food is digested by enzymes

from the endoplasm, and the food vacuoles become smaller. The digested food is either stored, used for a vital activity, or is built up into protoplasm.

Regulation of water content

Two contractile vacuoles are present in *Paramecium caudatum,* occupying definite positions, one near each end of the body. They lie in the inner layer of the ectoplasm and communicate with a large portion of the body by means of a system of **radiating canals,** 6 to 11 in number (Fig. 25). These canals fill with liquid, then discharge their contents to form the vacuole, which in turn ejects the liquid to the exterior. After each discharge a new contractile vacuole is formed.

The rate of contraction varies with the activity of the animal, temperature, and the concentration of salts in the surrounding water. Since the body of the paramecium is surrounded by a semipermeable membrane, and the concentration of water molecules on the outside of the membrane is greater than that inside as a consequence of dissolved substances in the protoplasm, water is continually entering the cell. The contractile vacuoles function primarily to remove the excess water and in so doing remove excretory waste products of metabolism from the body.

Excretion

Excretion is a type of activity in which the waste products of metabolism are eliminated from protoplasm. Most of the waste products of paramecia appear to diffuse to the exterior through the pellicle, but nitrogenous substances have been detected in the contractile vacuoles, which may therefore be excretory in function.

Respiration

This process in the paramecium corresponds to the internal (cell) respiration of man. Oxygen, dissolved in the water, diffuses through the surface of the body into the protoplasm, just as oxygen is taken from the blood by our red blood corpuscles. Carbon dioxide diffuses out of the body through the surface, although the contractile vacuoles probably discharge some of the carbon dioxide as well as nitrogenous wastes.

Locomotion

The cilia are fine protoplasmic processes that cover the body of the paramecium; the effective strokes of all the cilia force the animal forward or backward. Since they beat obliquely, the animal rotates on its long axis as it swims forward (Fig. 25). The

swerving of the body away from the oral side is due to the fact that the cilia in the oral groove beat more strongly than others, but the rotation of the animal on its long axis enables it to follow a more or less straight course in forming large spirals.

The remarkable coordination of the cilia is probably made possible by a mechanism of tiny fibrils just beneath the pellicle which connect one cilium with another (Fig. 26). The fibrils concentrate at one point near the cell gullet to form a "neuromotor" center. If this center is experimentally destroyed, the cilia fail to beat in a coordinated manner; this results in the loss of coordination in movements.

Behavior

As in the amoeba and the euglena, changes in the environment serve as stimuli to which paramecia respond in various ways.

Avoiding reaction

One of the most common responses of the paramecium is known as the **avoiding reaction (negative response)** (Fig. 28). When a free-swimming paramecium encounters a harmful chemical such as strong salt, it may reverse its cilia and swim backward for a short distance; then its rotation decreases in rapidity, and it swerves toward the aboral side more strongly than under normal conditions. Its posterior end then becomes a sort of pivot upon which the animal swings in a circle. During this revolution, samples of the surrounding medium are brought into the oral groove. When a sample no longer contains the stimulus to which it reacts negatively, the cilia resume their normal beating and the animal moves forward again. If this movement once more brings it into the region of the harmful chemical, the avoiding reaction is repeated; this goes on as long as the animal receives the stimulus to which there is a negative reaction.

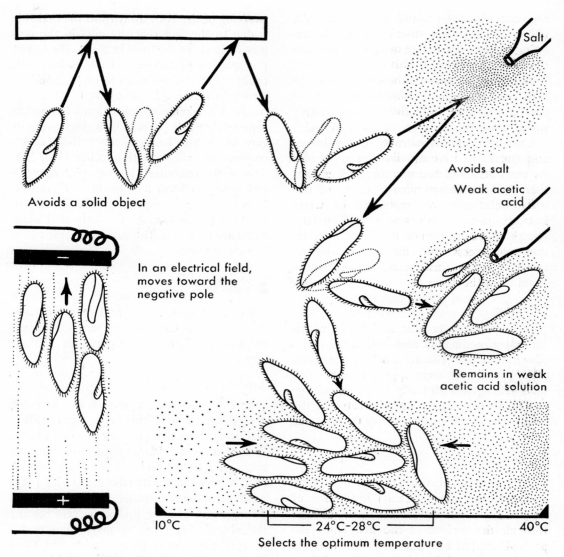

Avoids a solid object

Salt

Avoids salt

Weak acetic acid

In an electrical field, moves toward the negative pole

Remains in weak acetic acid solution

10°C   24°C-28°C   40°C

Selects the optimum temperature

FIGURE 28. Behavior of the paramecium to various conditions in its environment.

Reactions to stimuli

The paramecium not only reacts to chemicals, but to contact, to changes in temperature, to light, to electric current, and to other stimuli. If the anterior end of a paramecium, which is more sensitive than the other parts of the body, is touched with a glass rod, the avoiding reaction is given. Frequently, a paramecium when swimming slowly comes to rest with its cilia in contact with an object; this **positive response** often brings it into an environment rich in food. Paramecia do not respond in any way to ordinary visible light, but give the avoiding reaction when ultraviolet rays are thrown upon them.

The **optimum temperature** for the paramecium lies, under ordinary conditions, between 24° C. and 28° C. A number of animals placed on a slide which is heated at one end will swim about in all directions, giving the avoiding reaction where stimulated, until they become oriented and move toward the cooler end. This is the method of **trial and error**; that is, the animal tries all directions until one is discovered which allows it to escape from the region of injurious stimulation.

Chemicals of various sorts and in various concentrations have a striking effect on the paramecium. For example, sodium chloride (salt) solution when allowed to flow under a cover glass (Fig. 28) repels any specimens that encounter it. Weak acetic acid attracts the paramecium, that is, it reacts positively, and mercuric chloride kills it.

Frequently a paramecium may be stimulated in more than one way at the same time. For example, a specimen which is in contact with a solid is acted upon by temperature, chemicals, heat, and other stimuli. The **physiologic condition** of a paramecium determines the character of its response. This physiologic state is a dynamic condition, changing continually with the processes of metabolism going on within the living substance of the animal.

Reproduction

The paramecium usually multiplies by simple binary fission. This process is interrupted occasionally by a temporary union (conjugation) of two individuals and a subsequent mutual nuclear fertilization.

Binary fission

In binary fission the animal divides transversely (Fig. 29). It is an asexual process in which one fully grown individual divides into two daughters without leaving a parental corpse. First the micronucleus undergoes mitosis and its substance is equally divided between the two daughter micronuclei; these separate and finally come to lie one near each end of the body. The macronucleus elongates and then divides transversely by amitosis. The cytopharynx produces a bud which develops into another cytopharnyx. A new contractile vacuole arises near the anterior end of the body, another just back of the middle line. While these events are taking place, a constriction appears near the middle of the longitudinal diameter of the body; this cleavage furrow becomes deeper and deeper until only a slender thread of protoplasm holds the two halves of the body together. This connection is finally severed and the two daughter paramecia are freed from each other. The entire process occupies about two hours. The time, however, varies considerably, depending upon the temperature of the water, the quality and quantity of food, and other factors. The daughter paramecia increase rapidly in size, and at the end of 24 hours divide again if the temperature remains at 15° to 17° C.; if the temperature is raised to 17° to 20° C., two divisions may take place in one day. A paramecium under optimum conditions may reproduce at the rate of 600 or more generations per year. If all the descendants of one individual were to live and reproduce at a normal rate, they would soon equal the earth in volume. Under the usual natural conditions, they do not increase at any such fantastic rate because of lack of food, internal physiology, low temperatures, drought, or falling prey to other animals.

Conjugation

Ordinarily the paramecium multiplies by binary fission for long periods of time, but at intervals this may be interrupted by the sexual process of conjugation (Fig. 30). When two paramecia conjugate, their oral surfaces are opposed, and a protoplasmic bridge is constructed between them. During conjugation the pairs continue to swim about. As soon as this union is effected, the micronuclei pass through a series of stages in which the chromosome number is reduced to one-half; this has been likened to the maturation processes of metazoan germ cells, see page 80. These are illustrated and de-

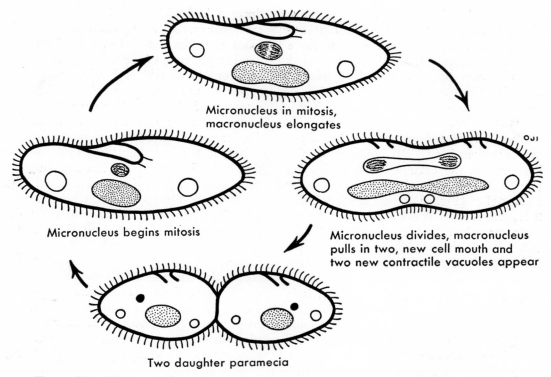

Micronucleus in mitosis, macronucleus elongates

Micronucleus begins mitosis

Micronucleus divides, macronucleus pulls in two, new cell mouth and two new contractile vacuoles appear

Two daughter paramecia

FIGURE 29. Division of *Paramecium caudatum* (binary fission). The first stage in the process of division is shown at the top of diagram.

scribed in Fig. 30. During conjugation there is an interchange of micronuclei. The migratory micronucleus (Fig. 30) is smaller than the stationary micronucleus and may be considered comparable to the nucleus of a male germ cell. Its fusion with the stationary micronucleus resembles the fusion of male and female nuclei in the eggs of higher animals at the time of fertilization. Conjugation is similar to fertilization in that there is a mixture of nuclear materials from two individuals, and some authors consider the fusion of micronuclei of conjugating individuals as true fertilization. However, after conjugation the animals continue to reproduce by asexual division in contrast to higher animals in which there is only sexual reproduction.

If the paramecia are kept in a constant medium, for example, hay infusion, they undergo a period of physiologic depression about every three months as shown by the decrease in their rate of division. Semiannual periods also occur, and recovery from these does not take place if the animals are kept under constant conditions, or conjugation is prevented; the protoplasm degenerates and becomes vacuolated, and the animals lose their energies and finally die. This suggests that conjugation is essential for continued asexual reproduction.

Experiments have been performed on one species which seem to show that in a varied environment neither conjugation nor death from old age necessarily occurs. Thus in one experiment, a culture of *Paramecium* was carried through a period of over 25 years without the intervention of conjugation, by changing the character of the medium daily. During this time there were over 25,000 generations, and there was no evidence of a decline in the vitality of the organisms as

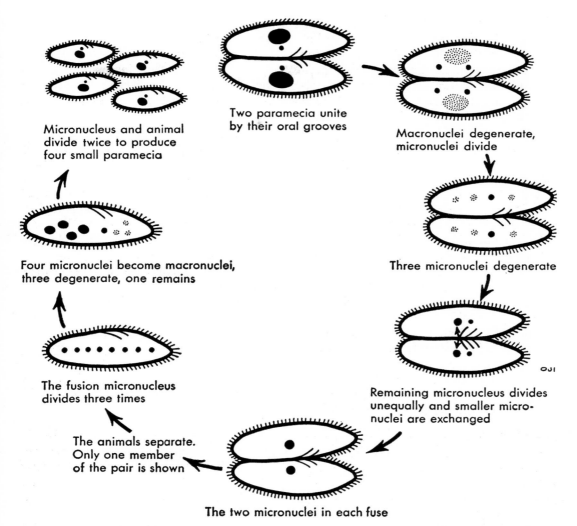

Micronucleus and animal divide twice to produce four small paramecia

Two paramecia unite by their oral grooves

Macronuclei degenerate, micronuclei divide

Four micronuclei become macronuclei, three degenerate, one remains

Three micronuclei degenerate

The fusion micronucleus divides three times

Remaining micronucleus divides unequally and smaller micronuclei are exchanged

The animals separate. Only one member of the pair is shown

The two micronuclei in each fuse

FIGURE 30. Conjugation in *Paramecium caudatum*. The first stage in conjugation is shown at the top and at the middle of the diagram. Not all stages are shown. In the interest of clarity, the macronuclei are omitted from the third stage; actually they do not disappear completely until after the conjugating animals have separated.

indicated by the rate of division. The cycle may thus be prolonged by employing a varied culture medium. However, it is now known that this paramecium does undergo a process of self-fertilization called **autogamy** at regular intervals, but some other ciliates, over a period of years, do not undergo either conjugation or autogamy. Therefore, nuclear reorganization may be essential in some ciliates but not in others.

Mating types in conjugation

At one time it was thought that there were no differences between the two paramecia which join in conjugation, but now it is known that there are mating types within each species. For example, in *Paramecium aurelia* at least two mating types ("sexes") occur, designated I and II. Members of mating type I do not conjugate with each other but will conjugate with members of mating type II; and members of mating type II do not conjugate with each other but will conjugate with members of mating type I. To determine the character of specimens of an unknown mating type, it is necessary to add them to a culture containing mating type I. If they conjugate with members of mating type I, they belong to mating type II; if they do not, they belong to mating type I.

OTHER CILIATA

Ciliata are widespread in nature. Many species live in fresh water; other species occur in the sea, in the soil, and upon or within the bodies of other animals.

Most of the ciliates are not parasites and are therefore said to be free-living. Those shown in Fig. 31 are representative of some of the more interesting free-living forms.

Tetrahymena, a small ciliate (Fig. 31) grows in a culture medium free from all other microscopic organisms and has about the same nutritional requirements as man himself. Studies show it must have a diet of vitamins, amino acids, salts, and sugar. This suggests that even a single-celled animal has physiologic processes nearly as complex as those in man. This tiny organism is playing an increasingly important role in physiologic and genetic research.

Stentor is trumpet-shaped, bluish in color, has a beaded macronucleus, and cilia spirally arranged around the "mouth"; it may be free-swimming or attached, and at the anterior end is a complicated disk of cilia. *Stylonychia* has a flattened body and groups of cilia fused to form cirri, which are used as "legs" in creeping. *Vorticella* resembles an inverted bell attached to a stalk.

Parasitic ciliates

One well-known parasitic species of ciliate lives in man (Fig. 38). Many domesticated and wild animals, both terrestrial and aquatic, are parasitized by ciliates, most of which live in the digestive tract. Species belonging to the genus *Opalina* are common in the rectum of certain frogs and toads; *Opalina* (Fig. 31) contains many nuclei of one type. One ciliate lives in the intestine of the earthworm. About 40 species of ciliates live in the first and second chambers of the stomach of cattle, and some are very complex in structure. These may be only mess mates (commensals) without either benefit or harm to cattle. Two common species of ciliates creep about on the bodies of certain aquatic animals and frequently occur on the fresh-water hydra; these are *Kerona* (Fig. 32) and *Trichodina*. Many of the Suctoria are parasitic; one (*Podophrya*) is of particular interest because it parasitizes other ciliates.

CLASSIFICATION OF THE CILIATA

(For reference purposes only)

Ciliata possess cilia at some stage in their life cycle. In most of them the nuclear material is separated into a large macronucleus and a smaller micronucleus. Most of them are free-living in fresh water or the sea, but many are parasites of other animals. They may be separated into two classes and four orders as follows:

Class 1. **Ciliata.** Cilia present throughout life; "tentacles" absent.

Order 1. **Holotricha.** Cilia typically of equal length all over the body; no adoral cilia. Ex. *Paramecium caudatum* (Fig. 25) and *Chilodonella* (Fig. 31).

Order 2. **Spirotricha.** Cilia covering entire body, an adoral zone of either large cilia or membranelles, which are wound to the left along the oral groove. Exs. *Stentor coeruleus* (Fig. 31) and *Balantidium*.

Order 3. **Hypotricha.** Dorsoventrally flattened; with cilia, cirri, and membranelles. Ex. *Stylonychia mytilus* (Fig. 31).

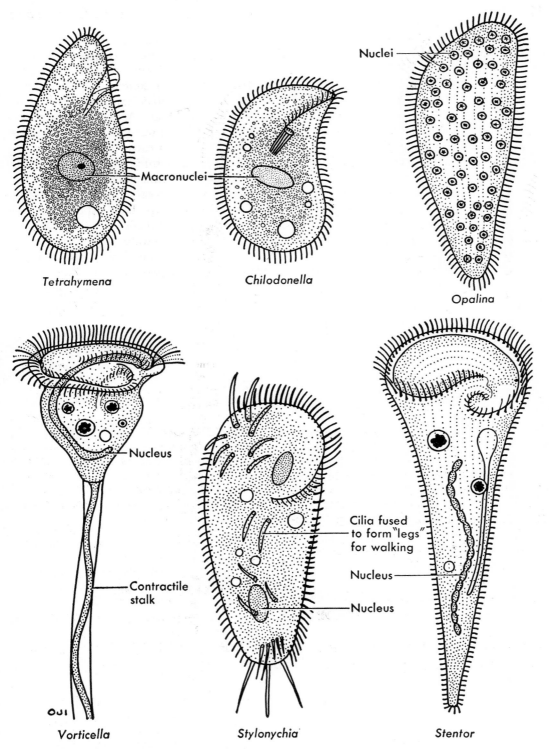

Tetrahymena

Chilodonella

Nuclei

Opalina

Macronuclei

Nucleus

Contractile stalk

Cilia fused to form "legs" for walking

Nucleus

Nucleus

Vorticella

Stylonychia

Stentor

FIGURE 31. Some representative ciliated protozoans. Highly magnified.

65

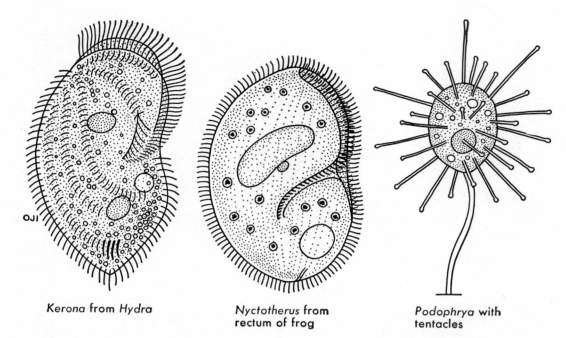

Kerona from *Hydra*   *Nyctotherus* from   *Podophrya* with
                           rectum of frog   tentacles

FIGURE 32.   Some ciliates of special interest. *Kerona*, a commensal which lives on the hydra. *Nyctotherus*, a parasite in the rectum of the frog. *Podophrya*, ciliated only in young stages, but the adult, as shown, has "tentacles." In feeding, the tubular tentacles are attached to its prey, then the suctorian sucks the cytoplasm of its victim into its own body.

Order 4. Peritricha. Body cilia generally absent; adoral spiral zone wound around the peristome. Body typically vase- or bell-shaped; mostly stalked, often colonial. Ex. *Vorticella* (Fig. 31).

Class 2. Suctoria. Cilia when young; "tentacles" in adult stage. Adults attached by stalk. Ex. *Podophrya* (Fig. 32).

SELECTED COLLATERAL READINGS

Buchsbaum, Ralph. *Animals Without Backbones.* Univ. Chicago Press, Chicago, 1948.

Carter, G.S. *A General Zoology of the Invertebrates.* Sidgwick and Jackson, London, 1951.

Grant, M.P. *Microbiology and Human Progress.* Rinehart, New York, 1953.

Hutner, S.H., and Lwoff, A. *Biochemistry and Physiology of Protozoa,* 2 vols. Academic Press, New York, 1955.

Hyman, L.H. *The Invertebrates: Protozoa Through Ctenophora.* McGraw-Hill, New York, 1940.

Jahn, T.L., and Jahn, F.F. *How to Know the Protozoa.* W.C. Brown, Dubuque, Iowa, 1949.

Kudo, R.R. *Protozoology.* Thomas, Springfield, Ill., 1946.

Wichterman, Ralph. *The Biology of Paramecium.* Blakiston, New York, 1953.

OJI

CHAPTER 7

Relations of

Protozoa

to Man

It is obvious to anyone that the larger animals, such as cattle, pigs, horses, and dogs, are important to the human economy and health, but the relation of the minute Protozoa to the well-being of man is not so evident. Nevertheless, protozoans play an important role. They exist in large numbers, but of greatest interest to us are those that live as parasites in the bodies of man and other animals; those that render water unfit to drink, fertilize the soil; and those that have built up large parts of the earth's crust with their skeletons.

PROTOZOA PARASITIC IN MAN

Approximately 15 different species of Protozoa have been found living as parasites within the human body. While the majority of these have relatively little effect upon their hosts, certain species cause some of the worst diseases in man. This is especially true in tropical areas where millions of people die each year as a result of protozoan infections. As a matter of convenience, the protozoan parasites of man may be divided into two general groups: (1) those which inhabit blood and tissue and (2) those found in the digestive tract and related cavities and passages.

Blood and tissue Protozoa

Of the blood and tissue parasites, the human malarial organism is by far the most important. Large numbers of people die from malaria each year, and the enfeebled condition of those chronically ill from the disease represents a tremendous economic loss where malaria control is neglected or haphazardly carried out.

Although malaria is probably the most devastating disease, with regard to prevalence, mortality, sickness, and economic loss, it appears to be coming under control. If malaria were finally licked, it would be due to the combined efforts of zoologists, physicians, and engineers.

There are three important kinds of human malaria. Benign tertian malaria, caused by *Plasmodium vivax*, is characterized by an attack of fever every 48 hours. Quartan malaria, caused by *Plasmodium malariae*, usually produces fever every 72 hours; while pernicious malaria, caused by *Plasmodium falciparum*, manifests an irregular temperature curve; sometimes the fever is practically continuous. *Plasmodium falciparum* is the greatest killer of man, sometimes striking in an unusual fashion, with symptoms resembling typhoid or apoplexy.

The life cycles of all three species are essentially similar and may be summarized as follows:

Malaria is transmitted through the bite of a female mosquito; the male mosquito cannot suck blood because he lacks piercing mouth parts. Animal malarias are carried by various species, but only mosquitoes of the genus *Anopheles* can transmit the parasite to man.

When the insect's mouth parts (Fig. 146, p. 247) pierce the skin, a certain amount of saliva containing anticoagulants leaves the salivary glands and passes into the wound (Fig. 33). If the mosquito is harboring malarial parasites in its glands, this gives an opportunity for some of them to pass into the human blood stream. The infective stage is called a **sporozoite**. The sporozoites do not invade the blood corpuscles directly, but penetrate certain tissue cells, where they grow, multiply, and go through at least two cycles. The persistence of the tissue-cell forms provides the reservoir from which relapses occur. Sooner or later some of the parasites are released into the blood stream, where they proceed to enter the red blood cells. Each parasitized erythrocyte contains as a rule a single *Plasmodium*. The latter assumes at first a ring shape, then an irregular form that soon fills the cell. In both stages the organism is termed a **trophozoite**. The time required for its development will depend upon the spe-

cies concerned. The mature trophozoite eventually divides into a number of daughter cells called **merozoites**, which are then released into the blood stream by rupture of the red blood cell. Each merozoite invades a new erythrocyte, where it becomes a trophozoite. Each time the cycle is repeated, a larger number of erythrocytes is involved; when these burst, chills and fever occur.

Eventually, a few merozoites, instead of becoming trophozoites, develop into **gametocytes**. These are potential gametes, but as long as they remain in the human host they undergo no further development. They are of no significance to the human host as they float harmlessly in the circulating blood; their survival depends upon their being sucked up by a mosquito of the appropriate type. Gametocytes which pass into a mosquito's stomach become active at once. There are two kinds: the **female gametocyte**, which develops into a single spherical egg or **female gamete**; and the male, which, on the other hand, undergoes exflagellation, a process by which a number of slender **male gametes** (**sperms**) grow out radially from the surface of the cell and finally float free. Union of a male gamete with an egg produces a **zygote**, which, because it has the ability to move about, is called an **ookinete**. The ookinete (fertilized egg) migrates through the stomach epithelium and takes up a position in the stomach wall. There its nucleus divides and redivides, resulting in the formation of a great number of sporozoites, which, for a time, are contained within a swelling called an **oocyst**. The stomach of an infected mosquito often bears a considerable number of these oocysts clearly visible on its exterior surface.

The oocysts finally rupture, and the sporozoites are released into the insect's body cavity. Sporozoites are motile, and many

---

FIGURE 33. *Facing page*, life cycle of *Plasmodium vivax*, one of the protozoans causing malaria in man. Diagram of a mosquito's body and a human blood vessel showing asexual stages in the blood vessel and sexual stages in the mosquito.

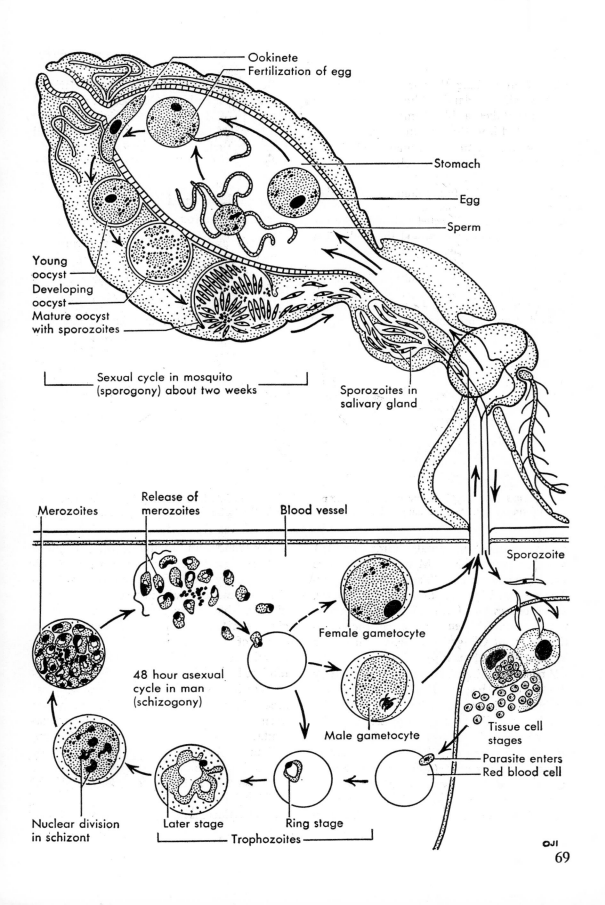

Ookinete

Fertilization of egg

Stomach

Egg

Sperm

Young oocyst

Developing oocyst

Mature oocyst with sporozoites

Sexual cycle in mosquito (sporogony) about two weeks

Sporozoites in salivary gland

Merozoites

Release of merozoites

Blood vessel

Sporozoite

Female gametocyte

48 hour asexual cycle in man (schizogony)

Male gametocyte

Tissue cell stages

Parasite enters Red blood cell

Nuclear division in schizont

Later stage

Ring stage

Trophozoites

OJI

69

succeed in making their way to the mosquito's salivary glands. The next time the mosquito takes a blood meal, sporozoites are injected into the human body.

Adequate control of human malaria involves at least three approaches:

1. Treatment of infected humans by use of appropriate antimalarial drugs.
2. Protection of uninfected individuals by use of screens, nets, gloves, and the application of solutions to the skin which are capable of repelling the mosquito.
3. Elimination of the mosquito, either by use of insecticides such as DDT, or by drainage and other engineering operations calculated to destroy its breeding places.

Because of control measures, malaria is no longer an endemic disease in the United States. In 1951 the National Malaria Society went out of existence because its goal had been attained. This was certainly a remarkable achievement in public health history.

Other blood and tissue parasites

Blood- and tissue-inhabiting forms are found among the flagellates. Two important types are (1) the **trypanosomes** and (2) the **leishmanias.**

The genus *Trypanosoma* is widespread in nature and may be found in the blood of

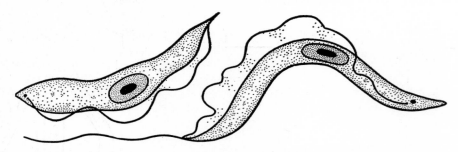

FIGURE 34. *Trypanosoma gambiense*, the parasitic flagellate of African sleeping sickness in man. Form on *left*, stage in man; and form on *right*, stage in the tsetse fly. Highly magnified.

many common mammals, birds, reptiles, fishes, and amphibians. Man is host to three well-known species: *Trypanosoma gambiense* (Fig. 34); *Trypanosoma rhodesiense*, which causes two forms of African sleeping sickness; and *Trypanosoma cruzi*, the causative agent of Chagas' disease, which occurs in Central and South America.

African sleeping sickness is transmitted by the bite of both sexes of the tsetse fly. When an infected insect takes its blood meal, the slender, flagellated **trypanosomes** pass by way of the fly's proboscis into the human host. Early stages of the disease are characterized by fever and swelling of the lymph glands in the neck. Involvement of the nervous system results progressively in drowsiness, coma, emaciation (through inability

to take food), and finally death. Treatment with naphuride, tryparsamide, or pentamidine is fairly successful, especially if the patient is reached early in the course of the disease. Recent experiments with antrycide give promise of dramatic results in the treatment of trypanosomiasis in Africa. The prevalence of sleeping sickness has greatly hindered the development of natural resources in many of Africa's richest tropical areas. In rare instances the infection has been known to be transmitted by sexual contact.

South American trypanosomiasis or Chagas' disease behaves quite differently. Only the acute stages are serious, and general involvement of the nervous system does not take place. The trypanosomes are trans-

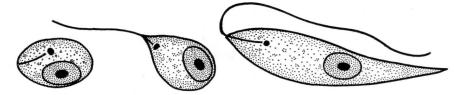

FIGURE 35. *Leishmania donovani*, the parasitic flagellate of kala-azar in Asia. Form on *left*, stage in man; forms in *middle* and to *right*, stages in the sandfly *(Phlebotomus)*. Highly magnified.

mitted by bloodsucking kissing bugs. Infection takes place by way of the bugs' feces, which the patient probably rubs into the puncture wound after the insect has ceased feeding. Besides the flagellated form which may be found in the blood stream, a spherical, nonflagellated stage is frequently encountered in the tissues. The muscular tissue of the heart is particularly susceptible, and death from cardiac failure is common. Kissing bugs feed on other animals besides man, the armadillo being a particularly important reservoir of infection.

Leishmania infections are also of more than one type. Kala-azar or dumdum fever, a disease common in India, northern Africa, and parts of South America, is caused by *Leishmania donovani* (Fig. 35). It is transmitted by the bites of small sandflies. Persons suffering from kala-azar usually show enlargement of both spleen and liver, gen-eral emaciation, and a peculiar darkening of the skin. Various antimony compounds are used in treatment. Oriental sore is caused by *Leishmania tropica*. It occurs in northern Africa, southern Asia, and southern Europe. Espundia, caused by *Leishmania brasilienis*, is limited to Central and South America. All types of leishmaniasis are carried by sandflies.

Parasites of the digestive tract

The intestinal- and cavity-inhabiting forms include representatives of all 4 classes of Protozoa. *Entamoeba* (formerly *Endamoeba*) *gingivalis* lives in the human mouth. It is sometimes found associated with pyorrhea, though it is not considered the primary cause of that condition. Kissing is the commonest mode of transmission. Over 50 per cent of the population is infected. In the intestine, and especially in the colon, a num-

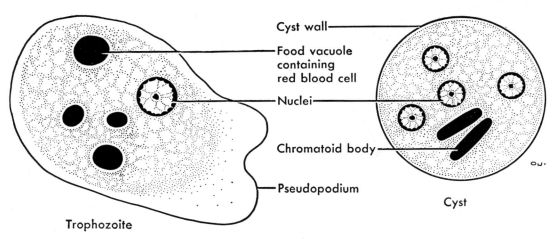

FIGURE 36. *Entamoeba* (formerly *Endamoeba*) *histolytica*, a human intestinal amoeba that causes amoebic dysentery and amoebic liver abscess. Highly magnified.

ber of related species may occur. *Entamoeba histolytica* (Fig. 36), the causative agent of amoebic dysentery, is the only serious disease-producing parasite of this group. About 10 per cent of the general population is infected, but fortunately most of them are merely carriers; that is, the entamoebas are present but do no damage, and hence no symptoms appear. Occasionally, however, entamoebas invade the intestinal wall and form abscesses, which later rupture and become persistent ulcers, resulting in diarrhea and dysentery. Occasionally they are carried to other parts of the body, such as the brain or liver, where abscess formation may cause death. Infected persons pass the cysts in their feces. These cysts gain access to new hosts by contaminated food or water, soiled

hands, or the activities of flies. Though more prevalent in the tropics, amoebiasis is fairly common in the temperate zones, and outbreaks have even been reported in arctic regions.

Several drugs have been found effective in treating amoebic dysentery, the choice of which depends on the location of the infection and the condition of the patient.

There are other intestinal amoebas of less importance such as *Entamoeba coli*, which is a harmless form often found associated with *histolytica. Dientamoeba fragilis* is characterized by the presence of two nuclei in the active state; it does not form cysts. Mild diarrhea appears to have been traced to an infection with *Dientamoeba*.

There are four flagellates which live in

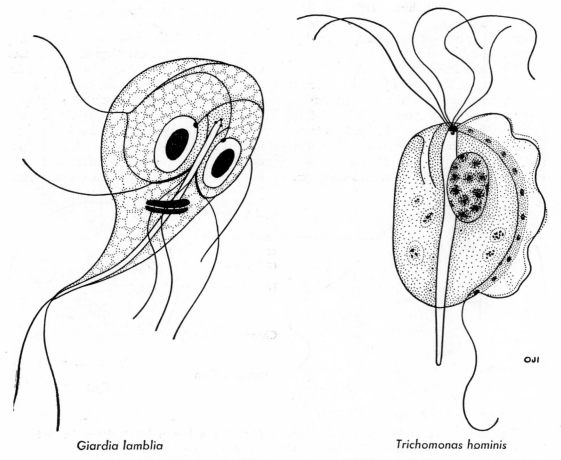

Giardia lamblia   *Trichomonas hominis*

FIGURE 37. Intestinal flagellates of man. Highly magnified.

the digestive tract: *Trichomonas tenax* lives in the tartar of the human mouth; and *Chilomastix mesnili*, *Trichomonas hominis* (Fig. 37) and *Giardia lamblia* (Fig. 37) inhabit the intestine. *Chilomastix* is a pear-shaped organism with four conspicuous flagella at its broad anterior end. Its cysts are lemon-shaped. *Trichomonas hominis* is of similar contour, but bears from three to five anterior flagella besides a longitudinal undulating membrane. There is also a central axostyle which protrudes caudally as a distinct tail. *Trichomonas* never forms cysts.

Giardia lamblia (Fig. 37) is an odd-looking protozoan with two anterior nuclei and a number of backwardly directed flagella. The cell has one flat side by which it may adhere to an epithelial cell. This species sometimes causes mechanical interference with absorption, particularly fats; and the presence of large amounts of unabsorbed fats causes diarrhea. The cyst of *Giardia* is elongate, with four nuclei grouped at one end. Atabrine is an effective drug in the treatment of giardiasis.

Trichomonas vaginalis is an inhabitant primarily of the vagina and may cause inflammation of this organ. It closely resembles *Trichomonas hominis* (Fig. 37).

The largest protozoan found in the human intestinal tract is *Balantidium coli* (Fig. 38). This large motile organism penetrates the membrane lining of the colon, where it frequently causes ulcers. It is a definite disease-producing organism and may produce symptoms resembling acute amoe-

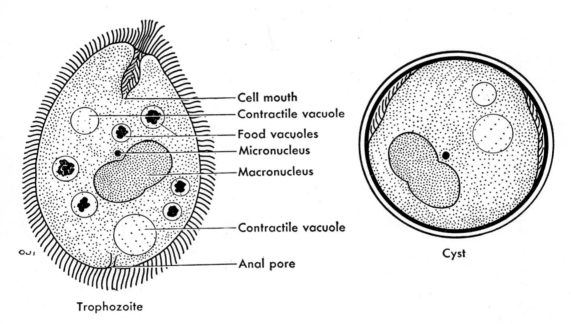

Cell mouth
Contractile vacuole
Food vacuoles
Micronucleus
Macronucleus
Contractile vacuole
Anal pore
Cyst
Trophozoite

FIGURE 38. *Balantidium coli*, a ciliate parasitic in man. Highly magnified.

bic dysentery. Infected persons pass large spherical cysts, easily identified by microscopic examination.

The Sporozoa are represented among the intestinal forms by *Isospora hominis*, a rather rare form, sometimes accused of causing a diarrheic condition.

PROTOZOA PARASITIC IN OTHER ANIMALS

Both game and domestic animals harbor a variety of protozoan parasites, which affect directly or indirectly the economic well-being of man. *Trichomonas foetus* is an important cause of abortion in cattle; while *Trichomonas gallinae* produces a fatal infection in pigeons and other birds. *Trichomonas gallinarum* inhabits the lower intestine of chickens and turkeys, and, in chronic cases, invades the liver. *Giardia* infections may cause severe diarrhea in both rabbits and dogs. Blackhead in turkeys is caused by an amoeboid flagellate, *Histomonas meleagridis*.

Balantidium coli is common in pigs and in chimpanzees, both of which probably serve as reservoirs for human infection.

Trypanosome diseases of animals are common in tropical areas. Horses, camels, cattle, pigs, dogs, and monkeys are susceptible to nagana, an African disease, caused by *Trypanosoma brucei* and transmitted by tsetse flies. Dourine or horse "syphilis" is also caused by a trypanosome, as is mal de Caderas, a South American disease of horses. *Trypanosoma evansi* is responsible for surra, a serious disease of horses, dogs, elephants, camels, and other species. *Trypanosoma lewisi* is a parasite almost universally found in rats. Bats, mice, sheep, goats, and other animals also harbor trypanosome infections.

Malaria is by no means confined to man. Several species of *Plasmodium* occur in birds; also monkeys, bats, squirrels, buffalo, and antelope become infected. At least thirteen species occur in reptiles, and two have been reported in amphibians.

Of particular interest is the malarialike disease, red-water fever of cattle, also called Texas fever; this is caused by a sporozoan, *Babesia bigemina*, which parasitizes the red blood cells. This species is transmitted by a tick, *Boophilus* (Fig. 167, p. 275). The infection passes from the mother tick into her eggs and is thus present in the larvae which emerge from them. Each new generation is therefore able to transmit the disease to new bovine hosts. This is the first case in which it was shown that an arthropod transmitted a protozoan disease agent. The discovery of this fact by Smith and Kilbourne in 1893 was an important early contribution to medical entomology.

Sporozoa are abundantly present in animal hosts. Coccidial infections of the intestine are particularly destructive to rabbits and birds; and *Nosema bombycis*, a sporozoan parasite of the silkworm caterpillar, once threatened the silk industry of the entire world. Infested caterpillars that did not succumb gave rise to moths which laid infected eggs, and thus the infection continued. Pasteur studied the problem (1865–1870) and discovered that diseased eggs may be detected by microscopic examination. Such eggs can be destroyed before hatching, and a healthy generation of caterpillars thereby assured.

Nosema apis is also a destructive parasite of honey bees. Many harmful insects are undoubtedly held somewhat in check by protozoan parasites.

PROTOZOA IN WATER SUPPLIES

Water for drinking may not only be contaminated by Protozoa of fecal origin, but it may also be unpalatable because of the multiplication of various free-living protozoans under natural conditions. This is especially likely to occur when the water is confined in a quiet open reservoir before being released for use. *Uroglenopsis* (Fig. 39) forms spherical colonies, the individuals of which are embedded in the periphery of a gelatinous matrix. *Dinobryon* (Fig. 39) is a branching flagellate, which occurs more commonly in alkaline regions. A colony of *Synura* (Fig. 39) consists of from two to fifty individuals, arranged in radial fashion.

Among several protozoans known to make water unfit for drinking, *Uroglenopsis* is possibly the worst since it imparts a fishy odor like cod-liver oil. Similar odors result from the presence of *Eudorina*, *Pandorina*, *Volvox*, and *Glenodinium*. Both *Synura* and *Pelomyxa* produce an odor like ripe cucumbers. *Bursaria* gives off an odor like a salt marsh, while a culture of *Peridinium* smells like clam shells. The fishy odor of *Dino-*

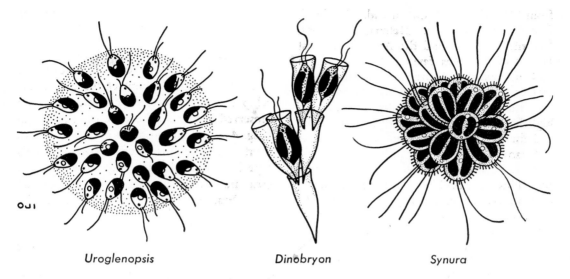

Uroglenopsis   *Dinobryon*   *Synura*

FIGURE 39. Colonial flagellates that may render water unfit to drink. Highly magnified.

bryon is more like that of rockweed. *Ceratium* produces a vile stench. *Chlamydomonas* and *Mallomonas* are less objectionable as their odors have an aromatic quality. Waters which harbor *Cryptomonas* may even smell like "candied violets."

All these odors are due to aromatic oils which are produced by the organisms during growth and liberated when they die and undergo decomposition. Treatment of the water supply with copper sulfate is standard procedure for the control of these bad-smelling protozoans.

Some species of aquatic Protozoa, on the other hand, are really beneficial to man. Kudo (1947) states that since protozoans feed extensively on bacteria, they prevent the bacteria from reaching the saturation point, that is, from becoming so numerous that they cease to multiply and thus no longer perform the important function of destroying waste materials which continually pollute the waters. Protozoa therefore help indirectly in the purification of water.

In many aquatic situations, Protozoa serve as food for small insects, crustaceans, and the like; these organisms, in turn, are fed on extensively by many species of fish. Of course, other protozoans live as parasites of fish. The Myxosporidia, especially, cause the death of large numbers of commercially important species. The relations of the Protozoa to aquatic biology are therefore many and varied.

SOIL PROTOZOA

Soil fertility is affected not only by bacterial action, but also by the protozoan fauna which may be present. It has long been held that the Protozoa probably reduce the numbers of nitrogen-fixing bacteria and thus limit the production of nitrates so essential for soil fertility. Between 200 and 300 species have been identified from soils, the small flagellates being the most common. Amoeboid types and ciliates follow in the order named. Most soil-inhabiting Protozoa are found near the surface, the greatest concentration being at a depth of about ⅜ inch, and few are found at depths of 12 to 18 inches. Very few are ever found in subsoil. Certain well-adapted species show a surprising geographical distribution. *Amoeba proteus*, for example, has been found in soils from almost every part of the world. *Trinema* is represented in soils from Spitzbergen, Greenland, England, Japan, Australia, St. Helena, Barbados, Mauritius, Africa, and the Argentine. Most species of Testacea favor soils with a high moisture content. A large amount of organic matter, combined with small soil particles, favors a rich protozoan fauna, as well as a high bacterial content. There appears to be a definite relation between the number of Protozoa and the number of bacteria present since the latter serve as food for the Protozoa. This relationship may have an important bearing on soil fertility.

PROTOZOA AND GEOLOGY

Though most protozoans leave no substantial remains after the death of the cell, at least two large groups of Sarcodina develop skeletal structures capable of being preserved as fossils. These are the Radiolaria (Fig. 40) and the Foraminifera, sometimes shortened to forams. Because species of this type have existed since very early times, a great number of distinct rock strata of the earth bear evidence of protozoan life. The

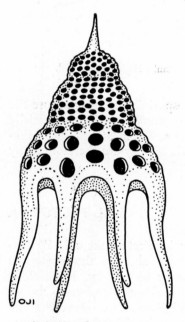

Skeleton of radiolarian

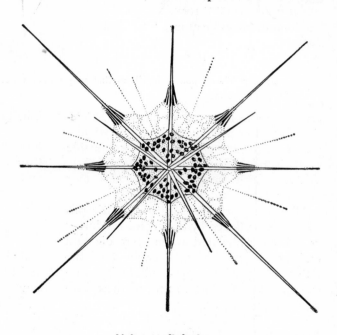

Living radiolarian

FIGURE 40.   Radiolarians are marine animals, usually with a skeleton of silicon which sinks to the ocean floor when they die, forming a layer called radiolarian ooze. *Left*, helmet-shaped skeleton of *Podocyrtis*. *Right*, *Acanthometron*. Highly magnified.

forams, especially, are of great importance to oil geologists in analyzing the results of drilling operations.

Under present conditions, as in the past, the skeletons of ocean-dwelling forms are continually sinking to the bottom to form ever growing layers of ooze. The greater portion of the bottom of the Atlantic Ocean, an area of perhaps 20 million square miles, is covered with an ooze formed of skeletons of the genus *Globigerina*. Eventual compaction of such ooze results in the production of limestone in the form of chalk. An important chalk deposit in Alabama and Mississippi, undoubtedly created in this way, is approximately 1000 feet thick in certain places. The chalk cliffs of Dover, which have played an important part in the defense of England, are deposits composed mostly of the shells of forams. The stone in the Egyptian pyramids is made up of the skeletons of very large forms of the genus *Camerina* (formerly *Nummulites*).

In various shore and deep-sea regions, ooze of radiolarian origin is equally abundant. Approximately 2,290,000 square miles in the Pacific and Indian oceans are covered by this material. Radiolarian ooze may become sedimentary rock and may be buried under other types of rock. Radiolarians, like the forams, are of great importance to geologists.

SELECTED COLLATERAL READINGS

Chandler, A.C. *Introduction to Parasitology.* Wiley, New York, 1955.

Gerberich, J.B. "An Annotated Bibliography of Papers Relating to the Control of Mosquitoes by the Use of Fish." *Am. Midland Naturalist,* **36**:87–131, 1946.

Mackie, T.T., Hunter, G.W., and Worth, C.B. *Manual of Tropical Medicine.* Saunders, Philadelphia, 1954.

Russell, P.F., West, L.S., and Manwell, R.D. *Practical Malariology.* Saunders, Philadelphia, 1946.

Warshaw, L.J. *Malaria: The Biography of a Killer.* Rinehart, New York, 1949.

CHAPTER 8

Introduction to
the Metazoa

Animals show different levels of organization, and organization increases in complexity from one level to another as they are studied from the structurally simple to the most complex. Our plan of study is to consider animals in approximately the order in which they have evolved. The patterns of organization do not suddenly appear fully formed, but are usually foreshadowed somewhere before becoming definitive. For example, a hint of tissue, but not true tissue, in the sponge, emerges as a definite tissue-level in the jellyfish.

Our studies of the Protozoa have given us insights into the **cell-level** of organization, and we will consider in increasing complexity the following additional levels of organization which exist in all the other animal phyla collectively called **Metazoa**. The **tissue-level** of organization includes a group of specialized cells similar in structure and associated together to perform some definite function; at the **organ-level**, there is cooperative specialization of groups of tissues to form an organ which performs one or more special functions; at the **organ-system-level**, there is close cooperation among several organs to perform some general function such as digestion.

This brief evolutionary history of levels of organization with gradual increasing complexity from one-celled protozoans to the most complex metazoans covers a time span of several hundred million years.

THE METAZOA AND
PROTOZOA COMPARED

The somatic cells of metazoans are not all alike as in the colonial protozoans, but differ from one another both in structure and in function. The body cells are not independent as in most of the protozoans, but are dependent upon one another. This is the

78

result of a **division of labor** among the somatic cells.

However, there is no sharp line between Metazoa and Protozoa. The colonial protozoans are composed of many cells, which, as in *Volvox* (Fig. 22), are differentiated into germ and body (somatic) cells. However, the somatic cells do not show any division of labor (specialization); this distinguishes such complex Protozoa from the Metazoa. There is a considerable number of animals intermediate between Protozoa and Metazoa, but we do not find in any of the protozoans the high degree of specialization which results in the various types of somatic tissues, such as nerves and muscles.

THE METAZOA

The differences between the Protozoa and the more complex Metazoa are so great that we will consider some of the more important metazoan characteristics before studying the various metazoan phyla.

In our metazoan study, the following subjects are of fundamental importance: (1) the origin of germ cells, (2) the methods of reproduction, (3) differentiation of somatic cells and formation of tissues, (4) the association of different tissues to form organs and of different organs to form systems, and (5) variations in the forms of animals correlated with differences in symmetry, metamerism, and the character of the appendages.

Differentiation of germ cells and somatic cells

The body of a true metazoan is always composed of germ cells (gametes) and somatic cells. The **germ cells** serve for reproductive purposes only; the **somatic cells** form a distinct body which carries on all the functions characteristic of animals, except sexual reproduction. The mature germ cells are either female or male. Female germ cells are known as **eggs** (**ova**), and male germ cells as **sperms** (**spermatozoa**). When the germ cells become mature, they may separate from the body, giving rise to a new generation, whereas the somatic cells die.

Methods of reproduction

Reproduction is one of the fundamental properties of protoplasm. Two types may be recognized: asexual and sexual. In the following paragraphs some of the common methods of reproduction are listed, but variations of each type will be encountered in the study of the metazoans. A general account is presented in Chapter 34.

Asexual reproduction

This is reproduction without sexual (germ) cells, that is, without eggs or sperms. The principal methods of asexual reproduction are fission and budding. The amoeba, paramecium, and many other protozoans reproduce by binary fission. In budding, as in the hydra (Fig. 50), there is usually an outgrowth from the parent, a bud, which separates while still small and grows into an adult.

Sexual reproduction

This type of reproduction is by means of sexual (germ) cells. Usually a female cell, the egg, fuses with a male cell, the sperm.

When eggs develop normally without being fertilized by spermatozoa, the process is known as **parthenogenesis**. For example, the eggs of plant lice (aphids, Fig. 157, p. 258) and water fleas (*Daphnia*, Fig. 110) may develop normally without fusing with spermatozoa.

Dioecious animals are either male or female; each possesses only one type of reproductive organ that gives rise to either eggs or sperms. Most species of higher animals are of this type.

Monoecious (**hermaphroditic**) animals are provided with both male and female reproductive organs, and produce both eggs and sperms; actually they are double-sexed. In some species the eggs of an individual are fertilized by sperms from the same individual; this is called **self-fertilization.** In other species the eggs of one individual are fertilized by the spermatozoa from another individual; this is called **cross-fertilization.** The earthworm is a common hermaphroditic animal.

Oviparous animals are those that lay eggs which hatch outside the body of the mother; for example, birds.

Viviparous animals usually give birth to young that develop from eggs within the body of the mother and are nourished from her blood stream; for example, mammals.

Ovoviviparous animals produce eggs that hatch within the mother's body, but are not nourished by the mother's blood stream through a placenta; for example, certain sharks and reptiles.

Origin of mature eggs and spermatozoa

Oogenesis

The primordial germ cells that give rise to eggs or ova multiply by mitosis (see pp. 24–27). As a result, many oogonia are produced. The number of oogonia that arise from each primordial germ cell may be definite as in some insects, or indefinite as in most of the metazoans. As illustrated in Fig. 404, p. 576, the **oogonia** grow in size and are then called **primary oocytes.** Instead of dividing into two cells of equal size, each oocyte undergoes an unequal division; the larger daughter cell is known as a **secondary oocyte,** and the smaller daughter cell, as the **first polar body.** The first polar body may disintegrate, or divide into two cells which eventually disintegrate. The secondary oocyte divides unequally, producing a large cell, which we recognize as a **mature egg,** and a small cell, called the **second polar body,** which disintegrates. During the divi-

sions of the primary and secondary oocytes, the number of chromosomes is reduced to one-half that in the oogonia. The significance of this will be discussed in the chapter on heredity. The end result of the divisions of the oocytes is a mature egg, and the process is referred to as **maturation (meiosis).** In many species eggs are laid before the two maturation divisions occur; eggs are considered immature until after the polar bodies are formed.

Spermatogenesis

The stages (Fig. 404) in the origin of the male sex cells, the **spermatozoa,** are very similar to those of the eggs (Fig. 404). An indefinite number of **spermatogonia** are produced by the primordial male germ cells. These increase in size and then are called **primary spermatocytes.** By the division of each primary spermatocyte, two similar **secondary spermatocytes** are produced, and not one functional and one nonfunctional cell as when the primary oocyte divides. Likewise, when the secondary spermatocytes divide, each produces two functional cells; these are called **spermatids.** The spermatids change without further division into **sperms** (**spermatozoa**). During the maturation of the male sex cells, the number of chromosomes is reduced to one-half the number in the spermatogonia.

Much scientific study has contributed to our knowledge of the sperm and its function. It is a highly specialized cell that can neither grow nor divide; it consists essentially of a condensed nucleus with means for locomotion and penetration of the egg. It plays no part in the physiology of the animal that produces it; its only function is the production of a new individual.

Fertilization

The final result of the oocyte divisions is one **mature egg,** and of the spermatocyte divisions, four sperms (Fig. 404). The mature ovum now becomes the center of the interesting process of **fertilization.** The sperm sometimes enters the egg before the polar bodies are formed, and sometimes afterward. The sperm brings into the egg a nucleus, a centrosome, and a very small amount of cytoplasm. A mitotic figure soon develops and moves toward the center of the egg. The egg nucleus also moves in this direction, and finally both the male and female nuclei are brought together in the midst of the spindle produced about the sperm nucleus. Their union forms the **zygote nucleus.** This completes the process usually known as fertilization. In this process the most important result appears to be **the union of two nuclei, one of maternal origin, the other of paternal origin.**

Chromosome reduction

It is now possible to point out the result of the reduction in the number of chromosomes which takes place during maturation. It has already been stated that every species of animal has a definite number of chromosomes in its somatic cells, two of each kind. This number remains constant, generation after generation. Now, if the mature egg contained this somatic number of chromosomes and the sperm brought into it a like number, the animal which developed from the fertilized egg would possess in its somatic cells twice as many chromosomes as its parents. However, the number is kept constant by reduction during the maturation divisions (Fig. 404), so that both egg and sperm contain only one-half the number of the somatic cells and primordial germ cells. The union of egg and sperm again establishes the normal number of chromosomes possessed by the parents.

Embryo, embryogeny, and embryology

An **embryo** is a young animal that passes its developmental stages within the egg or within the mother's uterus. **Embryogeny** is the study of the development of particular organisms. **Embryology** is that branch of biology which deals with the development of an embryo.

Cleavage

The division of the fertilized egg (**zygote**) into a number of cells (**blastomeres**) is known as **cleavage.** The chromatin material in the zygote nucleus becomes organized into chromosomes. Each chromosome duplicates itself; these daughter chromosomes are so arranged on the first cleavage spindle that each daughter nucleus receives either the original or the duplicate of each chromosome. After nuclear division, comes the division of the zygote into two blastomeres. This means that each blastomere will receive one of each chromosome of parental origin, and one of each chromosome of maternal origin. Further divisions insure a like distribution to every cell of the body. The blastomeres do not separate, as do the daughter cells produced by the binary division of the paramecium, but remain attached to one another. The resemblance of the group of blastomeres to a mulberry suggests the term morula which is sometimes used in describing the egg during the early cleavage stages.

Several types of cleavage patterns are recognizable. If the eggs contain relatively little yolk, the entire zygote divides into 2, 4, 8, etc., blastomeres. If these daughter cells are approximately equal in size, the process is known as **equal holoblastic (total) cleavage.** Such a cleavage pattern is characteristic of the eggs of starfish and amphioxus (Fig. 41). If the daughter cells are of unequal size, the process is known as **unequal holoblastic (total) cleavage;** this cleavage pattern is illustrated by the frog egg except during the first two or three cleavages (Figs. 41 and 237). If the eggs contain a considerable amount of yolk, the entire egg is not divided into cells; only restricted portions of the cytoplasm undergo cleavage. If cell division is restricted to a small cap or disk on one side of the egg (as in birds), the process is spoken of as **meroblastic** or **discoidal cleavage** (Fig. 41). If cleavage is restricted to a layer of cytoplasm around the entire egg as in insects, it is spoken of as **superficial cleavage** (Fig. 41).

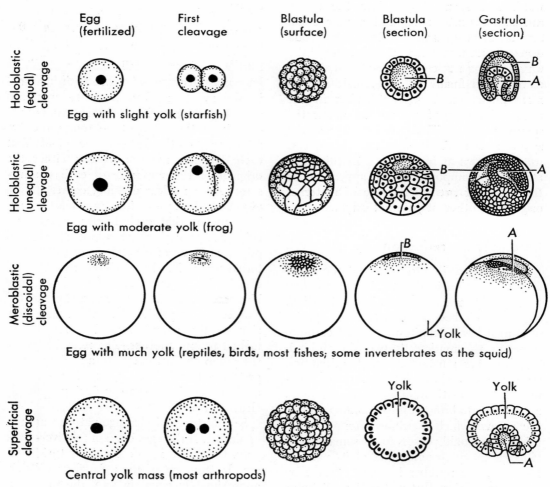

FIGURE 41. *Top three rows:* types of cleavage; blastulae, and gastrulae of vertebrates. A, archenteron (gastrocoel). B, blastocoel (segmentation cavity). *Bottom row:* cleavage; blastulae and gastrulae of arthropods.

Blastula

As cleavage advances, a cavity becomes noticeable in the center of the egg (Fig. 41), enlarging as development proceeds until the whole resembles a hollow rubber ball, the rubber being represented by a single layer of cells. At this stage the embryo is called a **blastula,** the cavity the **blastocoel** (**segmentation cavity**), and the cellular layer the blastoderm. The blastula resembles somewhat a single colony of *Volvox* (Fig. 22). The blastula wall in some cases is more than one cell thick, and the segmentation cavity may be lacking.

Gastrula

The cells on one side of the blastula begin to invaginate (infold) (Fig. 41) into the interior. The blastocoel is gradually obliterated during invagination, while a new cavity, the **gastrocoel** (**archenteron**) is established and is bounded by the invaginated cells. The gastrocoel lined by endoderm represents the future gut cavity. The developmental stage is now called a **gastrula**, and the process by which it developed from the blastula is termed **gastrulation.** In the embryogeny of many species of animals, invagination does not occur, but certain cells of the blastula divide and fill up the segmentation cavity as in the hydra (Fig. 56, p. 116).

Germ layers

The gastrula of the simple metazoan (sponges, coelenterates) consists of two germ layers, an outer **ectoderm** and an inner **endoderm.** These phyla are said to be **diploblastic.** However, in the most complex animals, a third layer, the **mesoderm,** arises as a result of gastrulation. Thus all the higher metazoans are triploblastic. The origin of the mesoderm varies in different groups, originating either as a result of multiplication of a few special blastomeres which may be recognized in the early cleavage stages, or from pouches arising from the walls of the archenteron. All the tissues and organs of the body are differentiated from these **germ** (embryonic) **layers.** The structures that develop from the germ layers are indicated in Fig. 42.

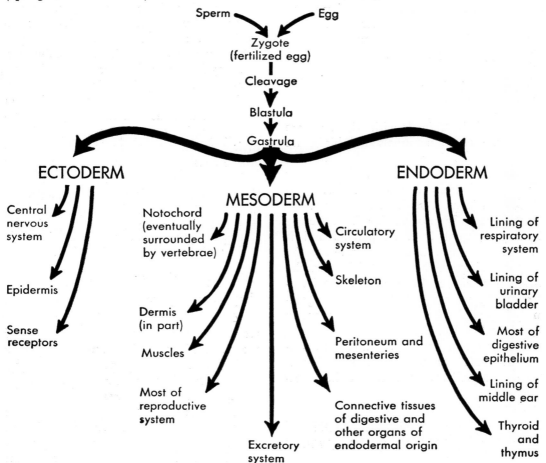

FIGURE 42. Simplified diagram of the embryonic differentiation in a vertebrate.

Coelom

The **coelom** (Fig. 92, p. 174) is a body cavity that is present in most triploblastic animals; it is, by definition, a cavity or a series of cavities completely bounded by mesoderm. The importance of the coelom, both morphologically and physiologically, will be discussed later.

Organogeny

Organogeny is concerned largely with how tissues, as structural units, are arranged to make organ systems during embryonic development. Yet it also deals with the formation of the specialized tissues which make up organs. The **characteristic tissue** making up an organ system, for example, the nervous system, is derived from ectoderm, but other tissue types from other germ layers are involved in the development of the nervous system as a whole.

Larvae and their metamorphosis

Many of the animals with which we are familiar, such as mammals and birds, are very much like their parents when they are born or hatch from the egg; but among lower vertebrates, such as the frogs and toads, and in most of the invertebrates, the animal that is born or hatches from the egg is very different from its parents and is known as a **larva**. Common larvae are the tadpoles of frogs, the grubs of beetles, the maggots of flies, and the caterpillars of butterflies. Many larvae do not develop gradually into adults, but change rather abruptly from the larval to the adult stage, a process known as **metamorphosis**. Numerous examples of larvae and their metamorphosis will be encountered in our studies of the Metazoa.

DIFFERENTIATION OF SOMATIC CELLS: TISSUES

Several types of somatic (body) cells can be distinguished in metazoans by differences in shape, structure, and function; cells of the same type are grouped together as a tissue. **A tissue is a group of similar cells so specialized that they perform a common function.** The study of tissues is called **histology.** Some of the simple metazoans possess only two kinds of somatic tissues; others are made up of a great number. The many different kinds of somatic tissues may be classified according to their structure and functions into 5 groups.

Epithelial tissue

Epithelial tissue (Fig. 43) consists of cells which cover the surfaces of the body, both without and within, such as the skin and the lining of the digestive tube. It may be protective, absorptive, secretive, or excretive in function. Epithelial tissue may be flat (**squamous**), **cuboidal**, or **columnar**, and may form a single layer or several layers (**stratified**). It may be **ciliated** or **nonciliated**. Nutritive material may pass through an epithelial tissue into the body, while excretory products may pass through it on their way out; it may contain the end organs of the sensory apparatus, and may protect delicate tissues from a harmful environment. Examples: epidermis and gastrodermis of the hydra (p. 107), lining of coelom in the frog and other animals (Fig. 213, p. 331), and lining of intestine (Fig. 43).

Connective tissues

These tissues (Fig. 43) may be encountered in almost any part of the body; they are the supporting or uniting structures of the body. Their chief functions are (1) to bind together various parts of the body and (2) to form rigid structures capable of resisting shocks and pressures of various kinds. These tissues consist largely of intercellular substances such as fibers, cartilage, and bone produced by the cells, either within or outside the cell. The fibrous connective tissues occur throughout the entire body, connecting the cells to one another and binding the tissues into organs such as muscles and nerve trunks. The tendons which unite muscles to bones consist of **connective tissue;** cartilage and bone are **supporting connec-** **tive tissues. Cartilage** is either clear (hyaline) or contains fibers (fibrous). **Bone** is a hard intercellular substance containing much calcium and phosphorus.

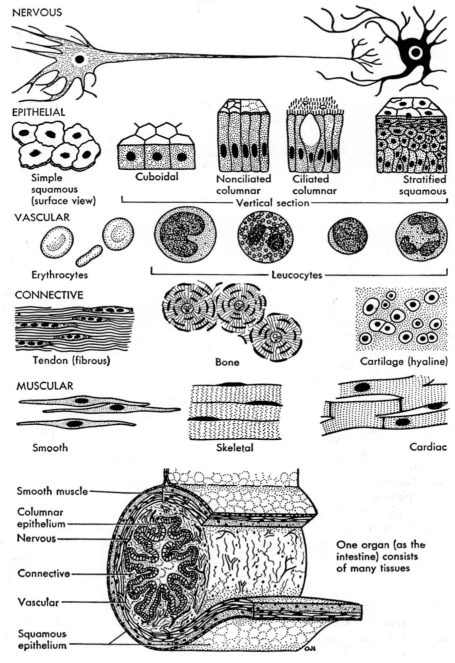

NERVOUS

EPITHELIAL

Simple squamous (surface view)

Cuboidal

Nonciliated columnar

Ciliated columnar

Stratified squamous

Vertical section

VASCULAR

Erythrocytes

Leucocytes

CONNECTIVE

Tendon (fibrous)

Bone

Cartilage (hyaline)

MUSCULAR

Smooth

Skeletal

Cardiac

Smooth muscle

Columnar epithelium

Nervous

Connective

Vascular

Squamous epithelium

One organ (as the intestine) consists of many tissues

FIGURE 43. Types of tissue.

Muscle or contractile tissue

Muscle tissue (Fig. 43) is composed of cells specialized for contraction. Muscle cells possess fibrils which are able to contract with great force. The fibrils are usually of two kinds: (1) **striated** and (2) **smooth,** without striations. The latter are found in smooth muscles of the simpler inactive animals, and in those internal organs of higher organisms not under voluntary control, such as the walls of the blood vessels and the urinary bladder; they are therefore also known as **involuntary muscles.** Striated muscles are of two types: (1) **skeletal muscles,** which are, for the most part, under control of the brain and are hence called voluntary muscles; and (2) **cardiac muscle,** which occurs in the heart and is involuntary.

Nervous tissue

Nervous tissue is composed of cells specialized for the reception of stimuli and the transmission of impulses (Fig. 43). All protoplasm is irritable, as in the amoeba, but in the metazoans certain cells are specialized for the sole purpose of performing nervous functions. This is the most highly specialized tissue in animals.

Vascular tissue

Vascular tissue (Fig. 43) is a fluid tissue which is composed of white blood cells (leukocytes), red blood corpuscles (erythrocytes), **blood platelets,** liquid **plasma,** and **lymph. Blood plasma** transports various substances to the cells of the body; **erythrocytes** carry oxygen to the tissues; and the **leukocytes** may move about somewhat like amoebas and engulf bacteria and other particles that get into the blood plasma. The **tissue fluid** is an accessory to the blood proper; it arises from the blood by diffusion through the walls of the capillaries into the tissue spaces, and it is the fluid medium in which the individual cells live. **Lymph** consists of tissue fluid and leukocytes which have entered the lymphatic vessels; these vessels return the lymph to the blood stream.

ORGANS AND SYSTEMS OF ORGANS

An organ is an aggregate of tissues arranged in a characteristic structural plan, which performs one or more special functions. For example, the human intestine (Fig. 43) is a digestive organ; it consists of a variety of tissues, including epithelial, contractile (muscles), nervous (nerves), vascular (blood), and fibrous connective. However, the lining of epithelium is of primary importance, for the digestive glands are an outgrowth of it.

Protozoa carry on physiologic processes without the presence of definite organs, but in most of the metazoans many organs are usually necessary for the performance of a single function; for example, the proper digestion and absorption of food in man require a large number of organs collectively known as the digestive system. Similarly, other sets of organs are associated for carrying on other functions. The principal systems of organs in man and in other higher animals, and their chief functions, are as follows.

Digestive system (digestion and absorption)

In the mouth, the teeth, assisted by the tongue, masticate food. Salivary glands and glandular cells of the mouth furnish saliva. The food passes through the pharynx and esophagus into the stomach where mucin and gastric juices are added to it; here it undergoes mechanical and chemical changes. Digestion continues in the small intestine, which secretes secretins and receives pancreatic fluid from the pancreas and bile from the liver. Absorption occurs in the small intestine, and both digestion and absorption continue in the large intestine. Undigested material and other wastes are eliminated by the large intestine.

Circulatory system (transportation of food, oxygen, and waste products)

Blood has many functions. It carries oxygen from the lungs to the tissues, food material to the tissues, hormones and other internal secretions to various parts of the body, and metabolic wastes to the excretory organs; it maintains a normal temperature in warm-blooded animals, and aids in maintaining an internal fluid pressure. The heart receives blood from the veins and forces it through the arteries. Arteries carry blood to the tissues, and veins carry it away from the tissues. Lymphatic ducts and lymphatic capillaries carry lymph. Tissue fluid (fluid surrounding cells) transports nourishment from the blood to the tissues, and metabolic wastes from the tissues to the blood.

Respiratory system (taking in oxygen and eliminating carbon dioxide)

Air enters the respiratory system by way of the mouth or nostrils, passing through the larynx, which contains the vocal cords; then on through the trachea, and the bronchial tubes, into the lungs, where external respiration takes place; here the blood gains about 8 per cent of oxygen and loses about 7 per cent of its carbon dioxide. Internal respiration involves passage of oxygen from the blood to the tissue fluid and thence into the tissues, and the passage of carbon dioxide from the tissues to the tissue fluid and thence to the blood.

Excretory system (elimination of waste products of metabolism)

The kidneys extract urine from the blood; urine consists largely of water and urea. Urine passes through the ureters into the bladder, which acts as a storage reservoir, and from the bladder to the outside through the urethra. The lungs, digestive tract, and skin also serve as excretory organs.

Muscular system (motion and locomotion)

Muscles receive stimuli and respond to them and are capable of contraction and recovery. Striated skeletal muscles operate the bones and produce motion. Smooth visceral muscles bring about movements of the viscera. Cardiac muscles are responsible for the beating of the heart.

Skeletal system (support, protection, attachment)

All vertebrates and many other animals have firm frameworks or skeletons that give support and protection to the bodies and may provide places for attachment of muscles.

Nervous system (sensation, conduction, and correlation)

The nervous system enables an animal to become aware of its environment, to see, hear, smell, taste, and feel. It correlates the different parts of the body, exerts control over the internal organs, and is responsible for human thought and conduct. The central nervous system consists of the brain and spinal cord. The peripheral nervous system comprises the organs of special sense and the nerves connecting the central nervous system with various parts of the body; these are the cranial, spinal, and autonomic nerves. The autonomic nerves innervate the heart, glands, and smooth muscular tissue. They are influenced by the emotions, but are not under the control of the will.

Reproductive system (reproduction)

The essential organs of reproduction are the ovaries, in which eggs develop, and the testes, in which the sperms are produced. Accessory organs include those that supply yolk and other secretions, ducts that carry the germ cells or young to the outside, and copulatory organs necessary to insure fertilization.

FORMS OF ANIMALS

Differences in the forms of animals are due principally to differences in **symmetry**, **metamerism**, and the **character of the appendages**.

Symmetry

Symmetry refers to the arrangement of parts in relation to planes and straight lines. Animals are either **symmetrical** or **asymmetrical** (Fig. 44). The symmetrical animals may be divided into three types: (1) **spherically (universally) symmetrical**, (2) **radially symmetrical**, and (3) **bilaterally symmetrical**.

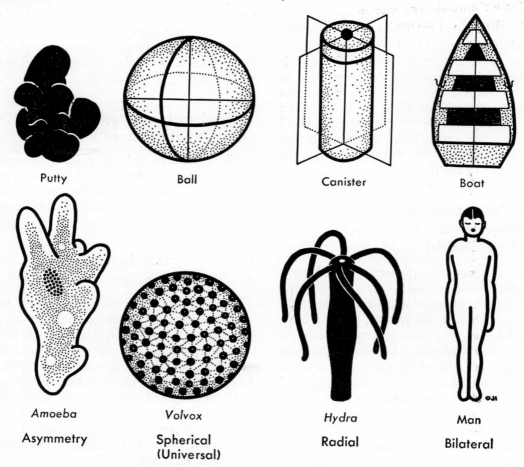

Putty   Ball   Canister   Boat

Amoeba   Volvox   Hydra   Man

Asymmetry   Spherical (Universal)   Radial   Bilateral

FIGURE 44. Types of symmetry in animals; illustrated by common objects.

In **asymmetrical** animals, the body cannot be divided by planes into similar parts; in other words, the body has no definite form or arrangement of parts. Many protozoans and most sponges are asymmetrical.

A **radially symmetrical** animal possesses a number of similar parts called **antimeres**, which radiate out from a central axis like the spokes of a wheel. It is possible to draw a number of planes through a central axis dividing the body of these animals into equal parts (Fig. 44). The hydra (Fig. 44) is an example; its tentacles are similar and radiate out from the mouth. Some simple sponges (Fig. 46), the majority of the coelenterates (Fig. 61), and most of the adult echinoderms are radially symmetrical. Radial symmetry is best suited to sessile animals, since the similarity of the antimeres enables them to obtain food or repel enemies from all sides.

The body of a **bilaterally symmetrical** animal is so constructed that the chief organs are generally arranged in pairs on either side of an axis, passing from the head (anterior end) to the tail (posterior end). There is only one plane through which the body can be divided into two similar parts. An upper or **dorsal** surface and a lower or **ventral** surface are recognizable, as well as **right** and **left** sides. In most of the bilateral animals, the anterior end is differentiated into a head, which contains a concentration of nervous tissue and which is supplied with numerous sense organs. This modification is termed **cephalization.** Bilateral symmetry is characteristic of the most successful animals living at the present time, including all vertebrates and most invertebrates.

Some animals are spherical, as, for example, certain Protozoa. Such an animal shows approximate **spherical symmetry.** It is symmetrical around the axis of a sphere like a ball. It can be divided into two similar parts by a cut in any direction through the center.

Spherical symmetry is disadvantageous, since such an animal can show only an indefinite kind of locomotion. Most spherical animals are free-floating as the radiolarians; or they progress by a rolling movement as the volvox.

It is doubtful if perfect symmetry is to be found anywhere in the animal kingdom. Animals said to show spherical symmetry usually only approach a spherical form. There are traces of bilateral symmetry in the various radially symmetrical animals. Although the human form is considered a good example of bilateral symmetry, everyone knows that the right and left sides of the human body are not identical. Nevertheless, the zoological concept of symmetry is of great importance in the study of animals; this will become evident as the different groups are studied.

Metamerism

Metameric animals have bodies composed of more or less similar parts, or they have organs arranged in a linear series along the main axis. Each part is called a **metamere, somite,** or **segment.** In many animals metamerism is not shown by the external structures, but is exhibited by the internal organs; this is true of the vertebrates, which have the vertebrae of the backbone, the ribs, and nerves metamerically arranged. The earthworm (Fig. 91) is a good illustration of both external and internal metamerism; the body consists of a great number of similar segments; and the ganglia of the nerve cord, the chambers of the body cavity, the blood vessels, and the excretory organs are segmentally arranged.

The earthworm may serve also as an example of an animal with **homonomous segmentation,** since the metameres are similar. The crayfish (Fig. 111), on the other hand, is a **heteronomous** animal, since division of labor has resulted in dissimilarity of the metameres of different regions of the body. The vertebrates, including man, are all heteronomous.

Appendages

The external appendages of animals are outgrowths of the body, which are used for locomotion, obtaining food, protection, respiration, and many other purposes. They are greatly modified for their various functions, and these modifications furnish excellent material for the study of homologous and analogous organs.

Homologous organs

These are organs that are usually fundamentally similar in structure (Fig. 433) and always the same in embryologic development, having their origin in a common ancestral type. For example, the forelimbs of the frog, the wings of birds, and the arms of man serve to distinguish their bearers from one another; nevertheless, these structures are homologous, since they are morphologically equivalent. Homologous organs may have similar functions, for example, the legs of a man and the hindlegs of a horse; or they may have different functions, for example, the arms of a man and the wings of a bird.

Analogous organs

Similar functions may make nonhomologous organs resemble each other. Such organs are said to be **analogous.** For example, the wings of butterflies and birds are analogous because they are both used for flight, but they are not homologous because they have neither the same fundamental structure nor the same embryonic origin.

THE ORGANISM AS
A WHOLE

We have been discussing cells, tissues, organs, and systems of organs as though they are independent. Nothing, however, is more certain than that these parts act together as a unit—the **organism.** The cells are not independent. In many cases actual protoplasmic bridges connect cells as in Volvox (Fig. 22) and certain epithelial tissues. Even closer union of cytoplasm and nuclei is effected in multinucleate cells, such as those of skeletal muscle; this type of cell is called a **syncytium.** Cytoplasmic connections are not necessary, however, since substances may pass from cell to cell by diffusion through their membranes, and thus one cell may have a profound influence on neighboring cells. Other relations between cells are brought about by various organs and systems, such as the nerves of the nervous system and the blood of the circulatory system.

Zoologists spend a large part of their time studying the structures and functions of the parts of animals; this is necessary for a proper understanding of the whole. The whole, however, differs from the sum of its parts; the parts cooperate to maintain the whole in its struggle to maintain itself and the race. Reproduction, embryonic and larval development, reactions to changes in external conditions, the appearance of inherited characteristics, and organic evolution itself are all manifestations of the organism as a whole.

THE ORIGIN OF
THE METAZOA

We know very little about the relationships of the major groups of animals, but it is interesting to speculate about their origin. The exact origin of the metazoans is unknown, but zoologists hold the opinion that they must have evolved from single-celled organisms; since many of the cells of the lower metazoans possess flagella, it seems probable that the flagellates were their ancestors. Certain colonial protozoans now living resemble what the metazoan ancestors may have been like. *Proterospongia* (Fig. 428, p. 605) possess two very conspicuous spongelike characteristics: (1) flagellated collar cells and (2) amoeboid wandering cells. It is not difficult to imagine *Protero-spongia* developing into a sponge. Sponges, however, do not seem to occupy a place in the main line of evolution. Another type of metazoan ancestor could have been an organism similar to a spherical protozoan colony such as *Volvox* (Fig. 22). The blastula stage (Fig. 41) is represented in the development of many metazoans. But how could the metazoans have evolved from a hollow ball of cells? Invagination may have occurred, resulting in a gastrula with two layers of cells and a cavity, the gastrocoel (Fig. 41). However, the arguments in favor of this hypothesis are not impressive. Many coelenterates (p. 106) resemble a modified gastrula such as in the adult hydra, others resemble the hollow ball filled with cells as in the embryonic stage of hydra (Fig. 56, p. 116). The metazoans may have developed from a type of larva, for example, the planula (p. 119), which is characteristic of many of the lower metazoans. The origin of the Metazoa from a two-layered primitive planula is a hypothesis which many biologists favor (Fig. 430). The subject will be discussed in some detail after more has been learned about the various groups of Metazoa.

SELECTED COLLATERAL READINGS

Baitsell, G.A. *Human Biology*. McGraw-Hill, New York, 1950.

Huettner, A.F. *Comparative Embryology of the Vertebrates*. Macmillan, New York, 1949.

Kimber, D.C., Gray, C.E., Stackpole, C.E., and Leavell, L.C. *Textbook of Anatomy and Physiology*. Macmillan, New York, 1956.

Maximow, A.A., and Bloom, W. A *Textbook of Histology*. Saunders, Philadelphia, 1957.

Stiles, Karl A. *Handbook of Histology*. Blakiston Division, McGraw-Hill, New York, 1956.

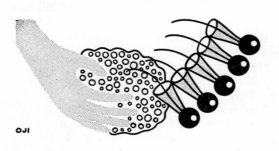

CHAPTER 9

Phylum Porifera.
Simple Multicellular
Animals

T HE phylum Porifera or pore bearers are commonly known as sponges. For centuries they were thought to be plants, but eventually their animal nature was discovered. This is not as strange as it seems, for some of the fresh-water forms are green, due to the fact that they contain many one-celled plants (algae); therefore they appear distinctly plantlike. Sponges are considered to be an ancient group of animals that belong near the bottom of the animal series but not in the direct line of evolution of the more complex animals. Even though they are not in the direct line of evolution, their study is of great interest for they show a multicellular organization that is intermediate between true protozoans and typical metazoans.

Sponges are usually attached and stationary animals in the adult stage, distribution being brought about largely by the actively swimming flagellated larvae, or by currents of water which carry the young from place to place before they become attached. The thousands of different species vary greatly in shape, size, structure, and geographic distribution. Most of the poriferans, including the bath sponges, live in the sea, but a few belonging to a single family, Spongillidae, are fresh-water inhabitants.

Sponges are more complex than Protozoa, and in them, **division of labor among somatic cells** has resulted in myocytes and other cellular specialization, but there is no grouping and coordination of specialized cells to form definite tissues. Therefore, sponges have not advanced beyond the cell-level of organization, although they are multicellular animals. Of particular interest in sponges are: (1) the lack of definite germ layers so characteristic of most metazoans, (2) the complicated systems of canals and flagellated chambers, and (3) the formation of spongin and various types of spicules.

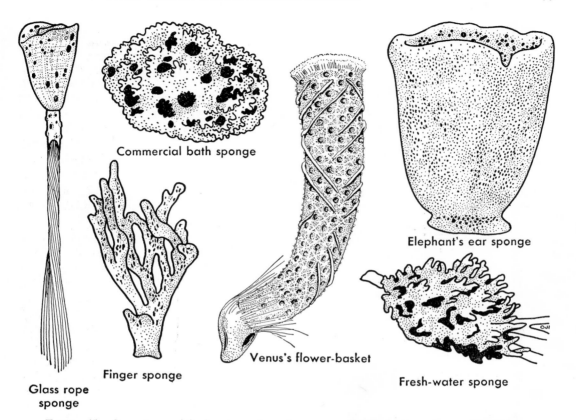

Commercial bath sponge

Elephant's ear sponge

Finger sponge

Venus's flower-basket

Fresh-water sponge

Glass rope
sponge

FIGURE 45. Some types of fresh-water and marine sponges showing various shapes. The figures are not drawn to scale.

LEUCOSOLENIA—A SIMPLE SPONGE

Leucosolenia is a simple sponge (Fig. 46), whitish or yellowish in color. It is attached to rocks at the seashore, just below low-tide mark, and consists of a number of horizontal tubes from which branches extend up into the water. These branches have an opening, the **osculum**, at the distal end, and buds and branches project from their sides. The cavity within each branch is known as the **central cavity (spongocoel)**. A large number of three-pronged (triradiate) **spicules** are embedded in the soft tissues of the body wall; these serve to strengthen the body and hold it upright.

The **body wall** (Fig. 47) is usually said to consist of two layers of cells: an outer layer composed of **dermal amoebocytes**,* and an inner layer consisting of flagellated collar cells (**choanocytes**), with mesoglea (often jelly-like material) between, in which are many **amoeboid wandering cells**. According to de Laubenfels, the term "layer of cells" must be used with reservations, for no true epithelial layers of cells exist in the sponge, such as are present in other metazoan animals. The outer and inner layers appear to be firm in sponges that are hardened in fixing solutions, but in life there is a mesoglea, sometimes nearly as liquid as water, and again almost cartilaginous in density, with cells crawling through it or clustered on its external and extensive inter-

* These cells are so termed by de Laubenfels because he reports that the cells on the external surface of the sponge are actually amoebocytes which do not occupy any one permanent position.

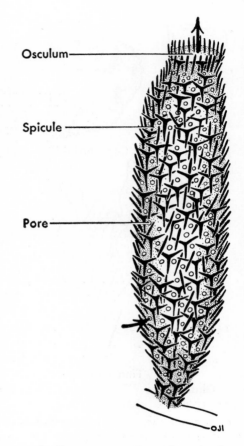

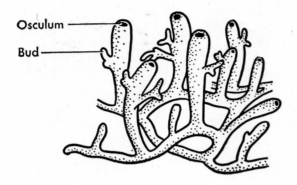

Osculum —

Bud —

Osculum—

Spicule —

Pore—

FIGURE 46. *Above,* a simple ascon type of sponge (*Leucosolenia*). A small colony. *Right,* a young sponge of the ascon type. Highly magnified. The arrows indicate the course of water into and out of the sponge.

nal surfaces. It is always much eroded with chambers and canals of various sizes connected to the exterior by pores and oscula. The mesoglea is often so fluid that a strong oscular current throws up transparent chimneys from it which are maintained erect by the forces of the current alone.

The central cavity is lined by a single layer of collar cells (Fig. 47); these choanocytes are in loose contact with one another and resemble the cells of the flagellated protozoans (Fig. 21). The flagella of these collar cells beat constantly, creating a current of water.

If a little coloring matter is placed in the water, it will be drawn into the animal through minute **incurrent pores** in the body wall and pass out through the osculum, which is therefore an **exhalent opening** and

not a mouth. Sponges are the only animals in which the large opening is limited to an outward current of water.

SCYPHA—A SYCON SPONGE

Morphology

Scypha appears to be the correct generic name of the sponge that occurs along our eastern coast which was formerly called *Grantia.** It is a comparatively simple marine type of sponge, permanently attached by one end to rocks and other solid objects. It varies in length from ½ inch to almost an inch and

* *Grantia* has been recorded three times from the Gulf of St. Lawrence and is abundant in Europe, but as yet has not been reported for the United States.

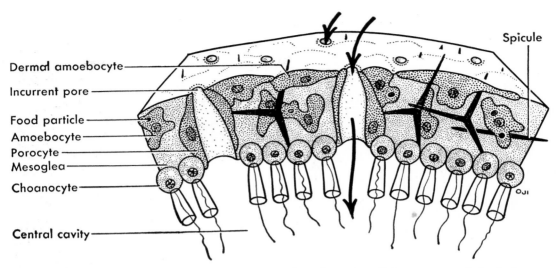

FIGURE 47. Diagrammatic cross section, designed to show the cellular structure of the body wall of a simple sponge (*Leucosolenia*). Highly magnified.

resembles in shape a slender vase that bulges slightly near the center. The osculum is surrounded by a circlet of straight spicules, and smaller spicules protrude from other parts of its body. The body wall is perforated by numerous incurrent pores.

Scypha has one large **central cavity** (spongocoel) (Fig. 48), which leads from the base of the sponge up to the osculum at the distal end. Around the central cavity, the thick body wall is built up of elongated, sack-shaped, **flagellated chambers.** Each of these is perpendicular to the central cavity, like the bristles on a bottle brush. The large exhalent opening of each chamber (apopyle) empties into the central cavity. These chambers do not fit closely together; there are narrow spaces between them. Water is drawn into these spaces and then into the chambers through many inhalent openings (prosopyles) which abundantly pierce the walls of the chambers. The flow of water through the sponge is produced by the uncorrelated but constant beating of the flagella of the collar cells (choanocytes), which more or less completely line the inside of each chamber.

In the wall of the flagellated chambers there occur (1) **inhalent openings (prosopyles),** (2) jellylike material called mesoglea (mesenchyme), (3) spicules, and (4) numerous amoeboid cells. The latter are of three types: (1) **pore cells** surround pores and may close them in a muscularlike manner; (2) **scleroblasts** manufacture **spicules,** which are mineral skeletal structures abundantly present; (3) **archeocytes** are embryonic amoebocytes with blunt pseudopodia, which can produce other types of cells, particularly reproductive cells.

The soft body wall is supported and protected by a skeleton consisting of a great number of spicules composed of carbonate of lime (Fig. 49). Four varieties of spicules are always present: (1) long straight monaxon rods guarding the osculum, (2) short straight monaxon rods surrounding the incurrent pores, (3) triradiate spicules always found embedded in the body wall, and (4) T-shaped spicules lining the central cavity. Spicules are formed within the scleroblasts. A slender organic axial thread is first built up within the cell; around this is deposited the calcareous matter; the spicule is then

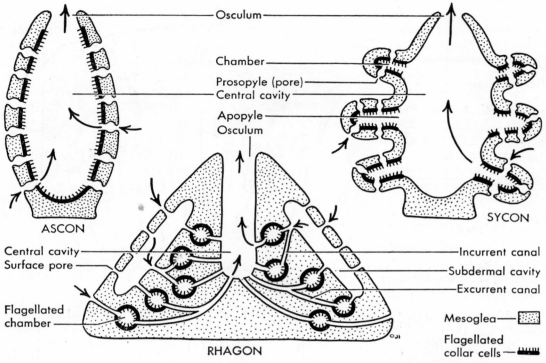

FIGURE 48. Types of canal systems of sponges; diagrammatic sections. The sycon type is derived, theoretically, by the outpushing of the wall of the ascon type of sponge into saclike chambers. Note how much each chamber of the sycon type of sponge resembles the single chamber of a simple sponge. The rhagon type, like the bath sponge, is more complex with an elaborate system of canals and flagellated chambers. The arrows indicate the course of water through the various types of sponges. (Ascon and sycon types after Minchin; rhagon type after Parker and Haswell.)

of organic matter like that composing the axial thread.

Physiology

Scypha lives on minute organisms and small particles of organic matter drawn into it by the back-and-forth beating of the flagella on the choanocytes, but little or no digestion occurs within choanocytes. The food particles are engulfed by amoebocytes where they are digested. Digestion, as in a protozoan, is **intracellular**. Distribution of the nutriment is accomplished by diffusion of digested food from cell to cell, aided by the amoeboid wandering cells.

Excretory matter is discharged through the general body surface, assisted probably by the amoeboid wandering cells, and possibly by the collar cells. **Respiration**, likewise, takes place, in the absence of special organs, by means of the cells of the body wall.

Sponges are usually considered to be very quiet and sluggish, but actually they are among the most active and energetic of all animals, working night and day to create the currents of water that bring food and oxygen into the body and carry away waste matter; they are veritable living dynamos. The amount of water that passes through the body of a sponge is tremendous; for example, an average-sized sponge draws about 45 gallons of water through its canal system in a single day.

True **nerve tissue** in sponges has not been

demonstrated and their behavior is what one would expect in the absence of nerves.* However, they are able to respond to certain stimuli; the response, as in the Protozoa, is one-celled. The pores and oscula are surrounded by contractile cells (**myocytes**) which are able to close these openings. A finger placed in an osculum may be squeezed with the force of a grip of the hand by a man. Apparently the myocytes respond to direct stimulation, since no nervous tissue is present. The entire body may contract and then expand. Reactions to stimuli are very slow since they depend upon the fundamental properties of protoplasm, that is, conductivity and contractility. Since protoplasm can only contract and not extend itself, most movement must be due to contraction of the protoplasm; and when cells elongate, it is due to the transverse contraction of protoplasm that decreases the width of the cell and causes it to become longer. But usually a return to normal by contractile cells is due to simple relaxation and a consequent return to normal shape.

Reproduction

Reproduction in *Scypha* takes place by both sexual and asexual methods. In the latter case, a **bud** arises near the point of attachment, finally breaks free, and takes up a separate existence.

The sexual reproductive cells in sponges

---

* While it is true that Tuzet and deCeccatty have reported the presence of a primitive nervous system in some sponges, this has not been confirmed at this writing by others, although several investigators in America are working on the problem. The evidence of these two investigators for interpreting the cells in question as nerve cells comes entirely from cytologic work. To the author's knowledge there is no unequivocal staining method for distinguishing nerve cells from other types of cells. As their critics have pointed out, the diffuse network of neuronlike cells demonstrated can be interpreted as connective tissue cells. Tuzet and deCeccatty are now well aware that it will be necessary to have parallel evidence from physiologic studies in order to prove the presence of nerve cells in sponges. Until such proof is available, the writer will assume that the question of nervous tissue in sponges is still an open one.

lie in the jellylike layer (the mesoglea) of the body wall. Both eggs and sperms occur in a single individual; i.e., *Scypha* is **monoecious (hermaphroditic)**. The fertilized egg segments by 3 vertical divisions into a pyramidal plate of 8 cells. A horizontal division now cuts off a small cell from the top of each of the 8, the result being a layer of 8 large cells crowned by a layer of 8 small cells. The cells now become arranged about a central cavity, producing a blastulalike sphere. The small cells multiply rapidly and develop flagella, while the large cells become granular. The small cells become partially grown over by the others, forming a structure called the **amphiblastula** (Fig. 49); this escapes from the parent as a flagellated larva. After the larva swims about for several days it becomes attached to a solid object and begins growth as a young sponge.

A peculiarity in the embryogeny of certain sponges is this: the flagellated cells of the larva do not become the outer (dermal) layer, as do the flagellated cells of certain higher animals, but they produce the layer of choanocytes; and the nonflagellated cells do not become the inner (gastral) epithelium, as do the similarly situated cells in the coelenterates, but they produce the dermal layer as well as the middle region. No sponge has anything like an ectoderm or an endoderm as do the other metazoans.

OTHER PORIFERA

Form, size, and color

Sponges may be simple, thin-walled, tubular structures like *Leucosolenia* (Fig. 46), or massive and more or less irregular in shape. Many sponges are indefinite masses of tissue encrusting the stones, shells, sticks, or plants to which they are attached; others are more regular in shape and attached to the sea bottom by means of masses of spicules. The form exhibited by the members of certain species may vary somewhat, depending on whether they develop in shallow or deep water; for example, *Microciona* in shallow water forms a thin encrustation on rocks, while in deep water the colonies become massive and reach a height of as much as 6 inches. Some are branched like trees, others are shaped like gloves, cups, or domes. The majority are irregular and without symmetry, although some are radially symmetrical. Sponges vary in size from species no larger than a pinhead to species that are as big as barrels 8 feet in diameter. Sponges are highly variable in color; some are white or gray, and others are yellow, orange, red, green, blue, purple, and velvety black.

Canal systems

If it had not been for the development of elaborate canal systems, sponges would have remained in the simple condition of *Leucosolenia* and would never have been able to become massive in size. The canal system furnishes a highway for food through the body and for transportation of excretory matter out of the body. Three types are usually recognized (Fig. 48): (1) the simplest or **ascon** type, as in *Leucosolenia*, (2) the **sycon** type, as in *Scypha*, and (3) the **rhagon** (**leucon**) type in which there are a number of small chambers lined with choanocytes.

Skeletons

The skeletons of sponges consist of carbonate of lime or silica (a mineral substance akin to glass) in the form of spicules, or of spongin in the form of fibers more or less closely united (Fig. 49). **Spongin** is a substance chemically related to human hair. It is secreted by flask-shaped cells (**spongoblasts**). Spicules are deposited in cells (**scleroblasts**, Fig. 49), and more than one

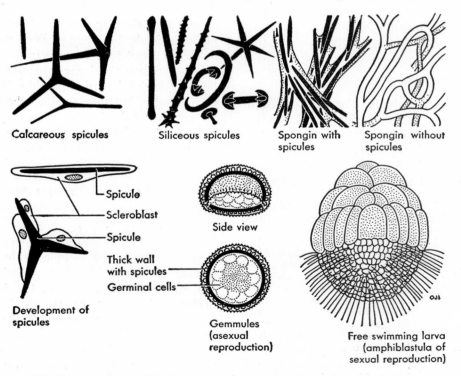

Calcareous spicules   Siliceous spicules   Spongin with spicules   Spongin without spicules

Spicule
Scleroblast
Spicule

Development of spicules

Side view

Thick wall with spicules
Germinal cells

Gemmules (asexual reproduction)

Free swimming larva (amphiblastula of sexual reproduction)

FIGURE 49. Parts of sponges. Spicules from various genera. Gemmules of a fresh-water sponge. (Amphiblastula after Parker and Haswell.)

cell may take part in the formation of a single spicule. The work required to build a sponge skeleton is almost unbelievable. The silica present in solution in sea water is about 1½ parts in 100,000; hence, to extract an ounce of skeleton, at least a ton of sea water must be drawn through the pores of the sponge and forced out again through the oscula.

Amoeboid wandering cells

The amoebocytes (Fig. 47) in the mesoglea between the cell layers in the body wall of sponges give rise to reproductive cells and to several types of somatic cells such as pigment cells, food-storage cells, scleroblasts, and spongoblasts.

Regeneration

In many sponges, if an individual is cut into pieces, each piece will grow into a normal animal, a process known as **regeneration.** Cuttings of bath sponges in Florida may increase from 2½ cubic inches to 12½ cubic inches in two months. The wool sponges of the Caribbean Sea may grow to be 2½ feet in diameter. The remarkable regenerative power of sponges is demonstrated when certain species are broken up and strained through fine bolting cloth so as to dissociate the cells; the cells will fuse on the bottom of a dish to form spongelets, which in the course of several days acquire canals, flagellated chambers, and a skeleton; and later, they will also develop reproductive bodies.

Fresh-water sponges

These all belong to the family Spongillidae. They are usually found in clear water, encrusting stones, sticks, and plants, and are often yellow, brown, or green in color. These sponges reproduce by formation of **gemmules,** and the characteristics of these gemmules are the chief means of identification. A gemmule (Fig. 49) consists of a number of cells from the middle layer of the body wall, which are gathered into a ball, and surrounded by a chitinous shell reinforced by spicules. They are formed during the summer and autumn. In the spring the gemmules develop into new sponges and are hence of value in carrying the sponge through a period of adverse conditions such as the winter season.

More than 20 species of fresh-water sponges occur in this country. *Spongilla lacustris* is the most abundant; it prefers running water.

ORIGIN AND RELATIONS OF THE SPONGES

Sponges are many-celled animals in which the somatic cells are somewhat differentiated for the performance of special functions; that is, division of labor among the somatic cells has developed. Although there is relatively little specialization of the somatic cells, the sponges represent a considerable advance over the condition existing even among such complex protozoans as *Volvox* (Fig. 22).

Despite the fact that sponges are many-celled animals and contain hints of tissues, there are no organs as in most of the higher animals, and no digestive cavity is present. It is thought that the sponges have developed from some protozoan group, probably the *Choanoflagellata.* They resemble the colonial protozoans in many ways, such as in the digestion of particles of food within cells, and in the formation of skeletal spicules by single cells. They suggest especially certain flagellates that are colonial and possess collar cells, like *Proterospongia* (Fig. 428, p. 605).

Although the sponges are well enough adapted to their environment to have lived their primitive way of life for millions of years, they do not appear to be in the direct line of development of more complex animals (Fig. 430).

RELATIONS OF PORIFERA TO MAN AND OTHER ANIMALS

Sponges are mostly beneficial to man. They supply him with the sponges of commerce, which are the spongin skeletons of certain species living chiefly near the shore of the Mediterranean Sea, the coast of Australia, the Bahama Islands, Cuba, and Florida. Only the eastern Mediterranean is superior as a sponge-producing region to that around Florida.

Sponge culture, that is, growing sponges from cuttings, is little practiced today, due to the difficulties in preventing theft of the crop. Fishing for sponges is carried on by divers either with or without a diving suit; the latter are known as skin divers. Commercial diving for sponges is dangerous because most of the shallow waters have been "fished out" and the deeper regions must be worked; these often cause the divers to suffer from a pressure disease called the bends. Sharks are another danger to the diver. There is a good market for the natural sponge, although it must compete with the cellulose and rubber substitutes.

Bath sponges in their living state resemble internally a piece of raw beef liver in both consistency and color. Externally they are black or blackish in color.

Boring sponges occur in shallow water near shores all over the world. They form irregular masses and are a bright sulfur yellow in color. Their name has reference to their habit of attaching themselves to the shells of oysters, clams, etc., and boring them so full of holes that the animals within are killed and in time the shells are entirely broken up.

Some sponges are poisonous; certain forms are as dangerous as poison ivy, when touched by man, and produce similar results. Other sponges when alive give off a strong unpleasant odor, and many contain sharp spiny spicules. Probably for these reasons as well as for purposes of concealment, certain species of crabs place sponges on their backs or on their legs. Other animals find the body of the sponge an excellent place in which to retreat for protection.

Of ornamental interest is a sponge known as Venus's-flower-basket, which builds up a beautiful skeleton of "spun glass" in the form of a cylinder about a foot long. Sponges of this type live in the sea, where they are fastened in the mud of the sea bottom by a mass of long threads at one end.

Some sponges are of economic importance in that the siliceous spicules form large flint deposits.

CLASSIFICATION OF THE PORIFERA

(For reference purposes only)

Sponges are all sessile animals in the adult stage, and asymmetrical or radially symmetrical in form. Their many cells are loosely arranged into two, more or less definite, layers, between which are amoeboid wandering cells. Neither organs nor mouth is present, the cells acting mostly independently. The soft tissues of sponges are usually held in place by skeletons of spicules or spongin. The bodies of sponges contain pores, canals, chambers, and a central cavity, through which currents of water flow. Collar cells, the choanocytes, line some of the body cavities. The 5000 or more living species of sponges are marine, except for about 150 species which comprise the fresh-water family Spongillidae (Fig. 45). Three classes and 12 orders are recognized as follows:

Class 1. Calcispongiae. Shallow-water species, comparatively simple in structure. Calcareous spicules make up the principal skeleton. Ascon, sycon, and simple rhagon types are present.

   Order 1. Asconosa. Sponges of ascon type, or ascon type at first, changing directly into rhagon. Ex. *Leucosolenia* (Fig. 46).

Order 2. Syconosa. Spongcs of sycon type, or sycon type at first, changing into rhagon. Ex. *Scypha*.

Class 2. Hyalospongiae. Mostly deep-sea species. Siliceous spicules make up the principal skeleton. The architecture is very much openwork, with structural parts often at right angles to each other. The flagellate chambers are consistently of a rhagon type, which is only slightly modified from the sycon type.

Order 1. Hexasterophora. Many spicules are starlike in shape. Ex. *Euplectella*, Venus's-flower-basket (Fig. 45).

Order 2. Amphidiscophora. No astral spicules, instead there are amphidisks. Ex. *Hyalonema*, glass rope sponge (Fig. 45).

Class 3. Demospongiae. Dominant type at present; often massive and brightly colored. The skeleton may comprise siliceous spicules, spongin fibers, both of these, or neither. The architecture is always compact, with flagellate chambers consistently of a highly developed rhagon type.

Order 1. Carnosa. Skeleton principally or entirely organic colloidal jelly. Small spicules sometimes present. Ex. *Chondrosia*.

Order 2. Choristida. Skeleton principally of spicules with 4 rays radiating from a central point. Ex. *Geodia*.

Order 3. Epipolasida. Somewhat spherical sponges, with monaxon spicules, which radiate from a central region within the sponge. Ex. *Tethya*.

Order 4. Hadromerina. Pin-shaped spic-ules. Some kinds excavate galleries into calcareous material, such as oyster shells. Ex. *Cliona*.

Order 5. Halichondrina. Double-pointed spicules, plumose or confused arrangement. Ex. *Halichondria*, the common "crumb of bread" sponge.

Order 6. Poecilosclerina. Many kinds of spicules present. Often also some spongin. Ex. *Microciona*.

Order 7. Haplosclerina. As in Halichondrina, but with reticulate, typically fibrous skeletons. Ex. *Haliclona*, the "finger" sponge (Fig. 45).

Order 8. Keratosa. No spicules; skeleton of well-developed spongin fibers. Ex. *Spongia*, the bath sponge (Fig. 45).

SELECTED COLLATERAL READINGS

de Laubenfels, M.W. *A Guide to the Sponges of Eastern North America*. Univ. of Miami Press, Florida, 1953.

Hyman, L.H. *The Invertebrates Through Ctenophora*. McGraw-Hill, New York, 1940.

MacGinitie, G.E., and MacGinitie, N. *Natural History of Marine Animals*. McGraw-Hill, New York, 1949.

Pennak, R.W. *Fresh-Water Invertebrates of the United States*. Ronald Press, New York, 1953.

Reese, A.M. *Outlines of Economic Zoology*. Blakiston, Philadelphia, 1942.

Wilson, H.V., and Penny, J.T. "The Regeneration of Sponges (Microciona) from Dissociated Cells." *J. Exp. Zool.*, **56**:73–147, 1930.

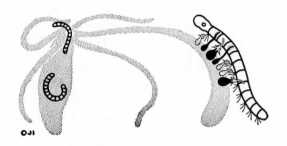

CHAPTER 10

Phylum Coelenterata (Cnidaria). Simple Tissue Animals

OJI

THE phylum Coelenterata contains a large number of interesting animals, but most of the 10,000 or more species live in salt water and are seen alive by only a small proportion of those interested in animal life. However, they exhibit the characteristics of the lower Metazoa to good advantage; and one type, the hydra, common in fresh water, affords excellent material for laboratory study. Certain types that live in the sea and that serve well as examples of the larger division of the phylum are also described briefly and illustrated; these include the colonial hydroid *Obelia*, the hydrozoan jellyfish *Gonionemus*, the scyphozoan jellyfish *Aurellia*,* the sea anemone *Metridium*, and the coral *Astrangia*. The sponges do not exhibit well-developed tissues, but the coelenterates have reached a definite **tissue-level of organization**. Another advance in their level of organization over the sponges is that the cells are more highly specialized and integrated; they are more receptive to stimuli and are capable of a great variety of responses.

The coelenterates may be used to illustrate many important biological phenomena such as budding, certain types of behavior, regeneration, grafting, colony formation, metagenesis, and polymorphism. These are all exhibited by the Hydrozoa, hence it is suggested that this class be studied more thoroughly than the Scyphozoa and Anthozoa.

Coelenterates are **radially symmetrical** animals. The principal axis extends from the mouth to the base; similar parts are arranged around this axis in a circle. The body wall consists of two layers of cells, between which is a noncellular substance, the mesoglea (Fig. 58). Within the body is a single **gastrovascular cavity** (Fig. 51). The coelenterates are provided with stinging capsules called **nematocysts** (Fig. 54).

The phylum contains three classes: (1) the Hydrozoa, including the fresh-water polyps, the small jellyfishes, the hydroid

* Usually incorrectly spelled *Aurelia*. The original and hence correct spelling is *Aurellia*.

zoophytes, and a few stony hydroids; (2) the Scyphozoa, mostly large jellyfishes; and (3) the Anthozoa, which include the sea anemones and most of the stony and horny corals.

HYDRA—A FRESH-WATER HYDROZOAN

Hydras are simple coelenterates, abundant in fresh-water ponds and streams. Nine known species occur in the United States. They are easily seen with the naked eye, are usually 2 to 20 mm. in length, and resemble a short thread frazzled at the unattached distal end. The great variation in length exhibited by hydras at different times is due to the fact that both body and tentacles are capable of remarkable expansion and contraction because of specialized contractile fibers. The coelenterates we know as hydras were named after the mythological nine-headed dragon slain by Hercules.

Hydras are of particular interest in that their adult organization corresponds roughly to the gastrula of higher animals. Thus they may be regarded as the living counterparts of some remote ancestor of the higher metazoans. They are of further interest in that they exhibit a complex organization in a so-called simple animal, but there is little division of labor. The work performed by organs in higher animals is thrown upon the tissues and individual cells in the hydra. As with most "simple" animals, anyone who studies these cells and tissues carefully comes to realize that the supposed simplicity of the hydra is largely fallacious.

Gross morphology

The body of the hydra (Fig. 50) resembles an elastic tube which may be extended to a length of 2 cm. At the distal end is a circlet of tentacles, usually 6 or 7, and as many as 10 in some species. Some hydras have extremely extensible tentacles, which

may stretch out to several times the body length; they have a stalk portion well set off from the rest of the body.

The tentacles are capable of remarkable extension, and may stretch out from small blunt projections to very thin threads 7 cm. or more in length (Fig. 50). They move independently, capturing food and bringing it to the mouth. Their number varies considerably, increasing with the size and age of the animal.

The part of the body which is usually attached to some object is known as the **foot** or **basal disk** and is referred to as the aboral (opposite the mouth) end. The foot secretes a sticky substance, and not only anchors the animal when at rest, but also serves as a locomotor organ. The foot may also secrete a gas bubble enclosed by a film of mucus. This bubble raises the animal to the surface, where it spreads out like a raft, the hydra hanging from the underside. In the common brown species *Hydra oligactis*,* the aboral region is a **stalk**, and the distal region constitutes a sort of **stomach**; these two regions together are known as the body column. A conical elevation, the **hypostome**, occupies the oral (mouth) end of the body. The hypostome is surrounded by tentacles already mentioned and has an opening at the top, the mouth. When the mouth is contracted, as during rest or digestion, it is a minute circular pore, but when swallowing objects, it and the surrounding hypostome can dilate to a relatively enormous diameter.

Frequently specimens of the hydra are found which possess **buds** in various stages of development (Fig. 50). This is a form of **asexual reproduction**, characterized by the fact that many parent cells go to make up the new individual, which is in contrast to **sexual reproduction**, in which the new individual arises from a single cell, the fertilized egg. Sexual reproduction also occurs in the hydra. Reproductive organs or gonads (Fig. 50) may be observed on specimens of the

---

* Genus *Pelmatohydra* discarded, not sufficiently distinct.

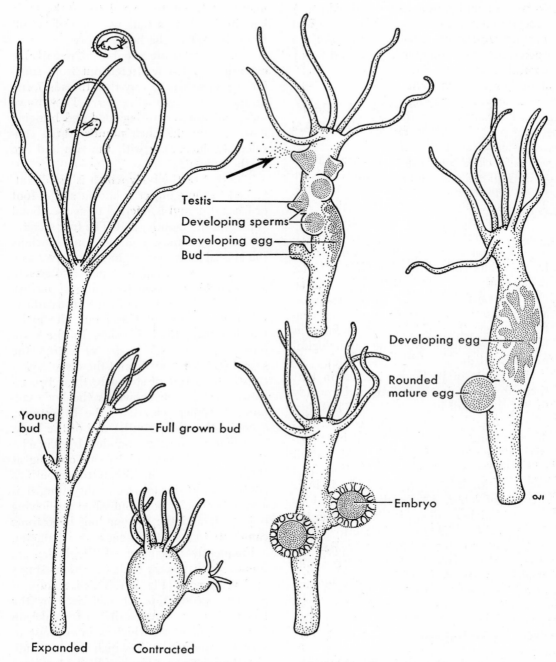

Testis

Developing sperms

Developing egg

Bud

Young
bud

Full grown bud

Developing egg

Rounded
mature egg

Embryo

Expanded   Contracted

Figure 50. Hydra. Asexual reproduction on the *left*. Sexual reproduction on the *right*. Note both sexual and asexual reproduction in *top middle* individual. Arrow points to sperms being discharged from the testes. The egg is fertilized while still attached to the parent.

hydra in the summer or autumn. The stimulus for the formation of gonads in some species appears to be a sudden change in temperature, either rising or falling. Both an **ovary** and **testes** (Fig. 50) are produced on a single individual in some species; the former is knoblike, occupying a position about one-third the length of the animal above the basal disk. The testes, usually several to many in number, are conical or rounded elevations located near the tentacles of the animal. The stalk never has gonads on it.

Histology

The body wall

The hydra consists of two cellular layers: an outer thin layer, the **epidermis**; and an inner layer, the **gastrodermis**, about twice as thick as the outer (Fig. 52). Formerly the terms ectoderm and endoderm were applied to these layers and are still retained in some textbooks, but these terms are strictly applicable to the germ layers of an embryo, and therefore cannot properly be used to designate the differentiated epithelial tissues of an adult animal. Both layers are composed primarily of **epitheliomuscular cells.** A thin space containing a jellylike material, the **mesoglea**, separates the epidermis from the gastrodermis. Although in many coelenterates the mesoglea constitutes a large part of the bulk of the body, in the hydra it is thin, especially toward the oral end of the body and in the tentacles, while in the center of the basal disk it is lacking altogether. It serves as a **basement membrane** for the epithelial cells and a place for attachment of their muscle processes. Hence in the hydra it serves as a supporting layer. Both body and tentacles are hollow, the single central space being known as the **gastrovascular cavity.**

The following outline shows the cellular elements of the several layers:

EPIDERMIS
1. Epitheliomuscular cells.
2. Sensory cells.

3. Other nerve cells.
4. Interstitial cells.
5. Cnidoblasts.
6. Germ cells (eggs and sperms).

SUPPORTING LAYER (MESOGLEA)

This layer is noncellular, but is traversed by migrating cells and crossed by intercellular bridges and nerve cell processes (fibers).

GASTRODERMIS   *digestion*
1. Epitheliomuscular or nutritive cells (variously differentiated in different regions).
2. Gland cells (several types).
3. Sparse interstitial cells, which migrate from epidermis as needed, and transform into gland cells between stalks of nutritive cells.
4. Sensory cells.
5. Other nerve cells.
6. Cnidoblasts (temporary migrants through this layer on the way to their final location).

The primary component of both epidermis and gastrodermis is the **epitheliomuscular cell,** which extends the full height of the epithelial layer and supports the other elements. Its proportions vary greatly with the expansion or contraction of the animal.

The epitheliomuscular cells of the epidermis have their polygonal outer surfaces cemented together in wavy borders to form a continuous membrane over the animal, interrupted only where stinging or sense cells come to the surface.

The epitheliomuscular cells of the gastrodermis line the entire wall of the gastrovascular cavity. The character of these cells is subject to wide variation in different regions, but since they are all concerned with either digestion or absorption of food material, they are nutritive in function, and therefore are called **nutritive cells.** The stomach cells form pseudopodia, flagella, and food vacuoles at their free ends; their bases are drawn out into extensions, and often contain contractile fibers.

On the center of the hypostome, the gastrodermal cells are either filled with small secretion granules, or they have a fine spongy texture, the two conditions alternating in

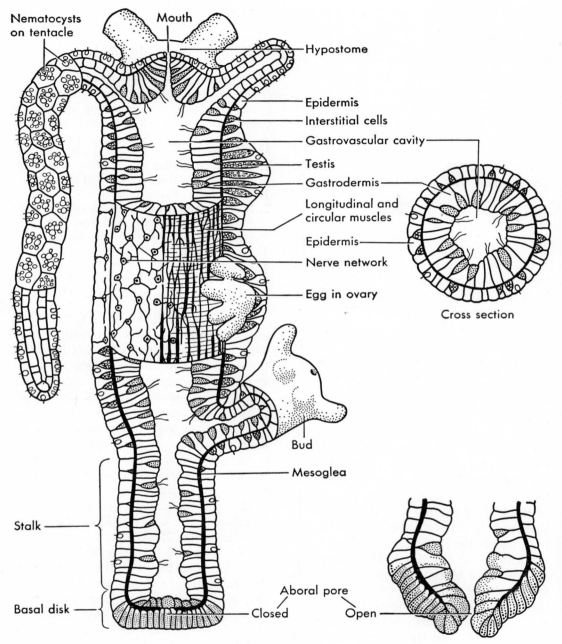

FIGURE 51. Hydra. Parts cut away and sections to show structure. (Redrawn from a drawing by Justus F. Mueller; prepared exclusively for this text.)

adjacent cells. These are the **mucous gland cells.** Their contractile fibers form the sphincter around the mouth, and they assist in swallowing food and in preparing it for digestion.

Whereas the nutritive cells rest on the mesoglea, the **gland cells** are tear-shaped and wedged in between the free ends of the nutritive cells. These gland cells occur abundantly in the stomach and in the hy-

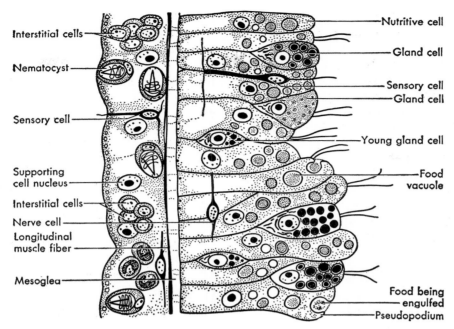

FIGURE 52.   Longitudinal section of the body wall of the hydra, highly magnified to show the structure of the epidermis, mesoglea, and gastrodermis. Note that the mesoglea is free from nerve cell bodies although nerve cell fibers pass through it. (Redrawn from a drawing by Justus F. Mueller; made expressly for this text.)

postome; sparsely in the stalk and basal disk.

The **interstitial cells** are small rounded cells with clear cytoplasm and a relatively large nucleus containing one or two nucleoli. Their cytoplasm lacks specialized structure; hence they are **undifferentiated.** Mitotic figures are frequent.

It is thought by some that the interstitial cells represent a sort of embryonic tissue carried over into the adult, that they can differentiate into any of the specialized cells of the hydra, and that hence they are the chief agents in reconstructing tissues in growth, budding, regeneration, etc. The interstitial cells also form the primordial germ cells of the gonads, and replace worn-out gland cells in the gastrodermis; but whether they have any other significance is a debated point. It has been shown conclusively that regeneration, as well as bud formation, takes place by a rearrangement of the differentiated epitheliomuscular cells of both layers, and that the interstitial cells, at least

locally, play only a subordinate part in the process. Whether cnidoblasts, germ cells, and gland cells arise from a common stem cell or from several types of interstitial cells is not known.

The muscular system

The muscular system of the hydra consists primarily of two layers of contractile fibers applied to opposite surfaces of the supporting mesoglea. The outer muscle layer is longitudinal and is formed by the contractile fibers of the epidermal cells, while the inner muscle layer is circular and is derived from the contractile fibers of the gastrodermal cells.

The circular muscle layer contracts slowly, performing movements of a peristaltic character, while the external longitudinal layer is capable of rapid response. Thus the two muscle layers of hydra already foreshadow in a dim way the visceral and skeletal muscles of higher animals.

The nervous system

In the coelenterate we find for the first time **true nerve cells** such as are found in all the higher animals. The nervous system of the hydra consists of three general types of cells which are called: (1) **conducting** and **motor nerve cells**, (2) **sensory cells**, and (3) **sensory nerve cells**. These are distributed throughout the body in such a way as to form a network in the epidermis; this can be demonstrated by a special stain in the living animal. Although often called a "nerve net," the elements of the system have not been demonstrated to be continuous. Nervous elements are present in the gastrodermis, but in such small numbers that if a gastrodermal nerve network exists, it is certainly much more diffuse than that of the epidermis. It is presumed that the two systems are interconnected by fibers passing through the mesoglea, and certain workers claim they have observed such fibers. Circumstantial evidence for their existence is afforded by the fact that in certain movements of the animal, inner and outer layers of muscles work in coordination.

Most of the conducting and motor nerve cells (Fig. 53) of the hydra have several processes; they conduct impulses in any direction, and thus differ from the neurons of

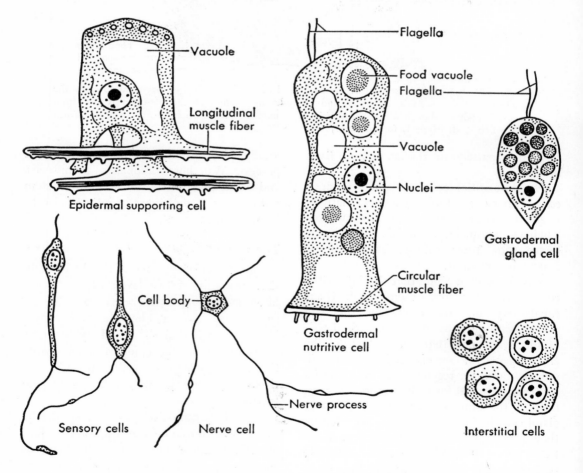

Figure 53. Principal cell types of the hydra. (Redrawn from a drawing by Justus F. Mueller; made expressly for this text.)

higher animals in that they are not polarized.

The nerve cells of the epidermis lie just external to the longitudinal muscle layer, between the bases of the supporting cells, and their processes interlace to form the so-called nerve net which extends over the entire body from the tip of the tentacles to the basal disk. Formerly it was thought that these processes were continuous from one cell to the next, but careful studies have shown that although the endings of fibers lie very close to each other, they do not join. Occasionally, however, nerve endings appear to be fused with other nerve cells, muscle processes, or bodies of epitheliomuscular cells.

Response to stimuli. The nervous system of higher animals is synaptic, that is, the nerve cells are usually separate, and the impulse must go from the endings of one nerve cell to those of another. In a synaptic system the direction of the nerve impulse is controlled and is normally conducted in one direction. In the hydra, there is probably little directional control of nervous impulses, and the resulting reactions are similar to those that would take place if there were only a protoplasmically continuous network of nervous tissue.

The greatest concentration of nerve elements occurs around the hypostome, where the fibers pass in a circular direction to form a loosely organized **nerve ring.** Another somewhat similar concentration of nerve fibers appears in the foot.

The **sensory cells** (Fig. 53) consist of slender, threadlike, specialized nerve cells, lying in both epidermis and gastrodermis, between the epitheliomuscular cells. They frequently bear a hairlike process or some other specialized structure at their tips. Basally they usually divide into two or more fibers which may connect either with the nerve plexus or with muscle fibers. The sensory cells of the gastrodermis are said to be more abundant toward the foot region. The epidermal sensory cells are found mainly on

the hypostome and inner part of the tentacles, and on the basal disk; these parts are the most sensitive to external stimuli.

The nematocysts

These **nematocysts** (stinging capsules) (Fig. 54) are present on all parts of the epidermis of the hydra except on the basal disk; they are most numerous on the tentacles. Each is formed inside an interstitial cell, which is then known as a **cnidoblast.** On the general body surface, cnidoblasts are mostly wedged in between the outer edges of the supporting cells, but on the tentacles and hypostome, cnidoblasts lie within the bodies of the epitheliomuscular cells, which are then known as **host cells.** On the tentacles the host cells are large and each contains a battery of stinging capsules, consisting of one or two large nematocysts (penetrants) surrounded by a number of smaller types.

Four kinds of nematocysts occur in the hydra as follows: (1) The largest is the **penetrant,** which, before it is discharged, is pear-shaped and occupies almost the entire cnidoblast in which it lies. Within it is a coiled tube, at the base of which are three large and a number of small spines. Three rows of minute spines spiral along the outside of the thread when discharged. (2) **Volvents** are small pear-shaped nematocysts, containing a thread, which, when discharged, coils tightly around the hairs or bristles of its prey. (3) The **oval glutinant** is large and has a long thread that bears minute spines. (4) The small **glutinant** is a straight unarmed thread. The first two types are of special help in capturing prey; the others secrete a sticky substance possibly used in locomotion as well as in food getting.

Projecting from the cnidoblast, near the outer end of the nematocyst, is a hairlike process, the **cnidocil.** Nematocysts may be exploded by adding a little acetic acid or methyl green to the water. The lid forming the apex of the cyst is thrown off, and the

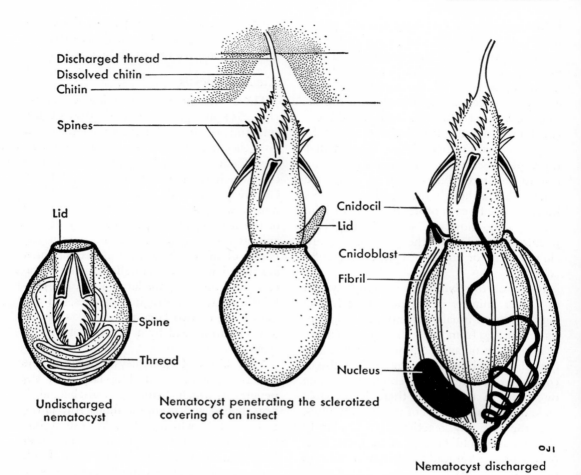

Discharged thread
Dissolved chitin
Chitin

Spines

Lid

Spine

Thread

Undischarged
nematocyst

Nematocyst penetrating the sclerotized
covering of an insect

Cnidocil
Lid
Cnidoblast
Fibril

Nucleus

Nematocyst discharged

FIGURE 54. Penetrant nematocyst of the hydra. Note cnidoblast on *right*.

tube which is coiled within is then everted. First the base of the tube with the large spines appears, and then the rest of the tube rapidly turns inside out. Penetrants are able to penetrate the tissues of other animals only when they are discharged with great speed, and before eversion is completed. Even the extremely firm sclerotized covering of insects may be punctured by these structures.

For a long time, touching the cnidocil was considered the cause of the explosion of the nematocysts, and for this reason the cnidocil is known as the trigger. One can easily prove, however, that mechanical shocks have no influence upon the nemato-

cysts. The discharge of the capsule is probably triggered by a suitable stimulus, presumbly chemical, applied to the cnidocil. However, the mechanism of setting off the explosion is still not understood, but once the process has started, the energy for eversion of the thread is provided by the progressive swelling of the shaft wall itself. It has been clearly shown that as the thread everts, it not only increases in diameter, but also markedly elongates. In the discharging nematocyst, the inverted filament comes into immediate contact with external water only at the advancing tip of the shaft. In isolated and dried nematocysts, discharge will not proceed unless the advancing tip is supplied with water, and the rate of eversion can be controlled by the rate at which moisture is supplied. Hence swelling at this point must be responsible for the progressive eversion of the thread.

Since nematocysts are discharged by direct stimuli, and not as a result of nervous control, they are independent effectors.

An animal "shot" by nematocysts is immediately paralyzed and sometimes killed by a poison that has been called **hypnotoxin,** which is injected into it through the tube.

Cnidoblasts are developed from interstitial cells (Fig. 52), which appear in nests or clusters in the epidermis of the stomach region. Before the nematocyst is completely developed, the cnidoblast in which it is formed migrates to the part of the body where it is needed. Here the cell matures, developing the cnidocil. The function of the cnidoblast is limited to the formation of the nematocyst, and possibly the cnidocil. Since the tube of the nematocyst cannot be returned to the capsule, nor can another nematocyst be developed by the cnidoblast, the cnidoblast perishes with the loss of its nematocyst, and a new cnidoblast must be formed from an interstitial cell to replace the one that has been used.

Differentiation of the body regions

The hypostome

The muscle layers of the hypostome consist of the epidermal muscle fibers which radiate from the mouth and the gastrodermal fibers which surround it. The hypostome is rich in nervous elements and is the most sensitive region of the body. Cnidoblasts and a few interstitial cells also occur here. The gastrodermal layer of the hypostome is thrown into large deep folds when the mouth is contracted, so that a cross section of the oral cone shows a star-shaped "throat," which has been mistaken for the mouth by some authors. The folds contain the mucous gland cells. The secretion of these cells is poured out over the food in swallowing and is a necessary forerunner of gastric digestion. Food introduced directly into the stomach through a pipette, or by an incision, without first coming in contact with these cells, is not digested. Hence digestion in the hydra is dependent upon an enzyme system which follows an orderly sequence of events.

The tentacles

There is a poorly developed "sphincter" formed by the gastrodermal fibers at the base of the tentacles. The tentacles can be rapidly elongated by pumping fluid from the gastrodermal cavity into them, and the "sphincter" probably influences the entrance or escape of this fluid.

Stomach-reproductive and stalk region

The epidermis of this region is about twice as thick as that of the hypostome, and harbors the great bulk of the interstitial cells. This is the region of nematocyst formation, and of testes, ovaries, and buds. The epitheliomuscular cells form the supporting cells of testis and ovary. The gastrodermis of this region is the chief digestive organ, effecting both extracellular and intracellular digestion. Correlated with this digestive activity is the presence of many enzymatic gland cells; their secretion reduces the food to a broth of fine particles. The particles are then fished out by the nutritive cells with their flagella and taken into food vacuoles, where digestion is completed. Thus digestion in the hydra reflects certain features of the process as it occurs in both sponges and protozoans on the one hand, and in the higher metazoans on the other. Although the cavity of the stomach and stalk is continuous, the hydra confines large food objects within the stomach by muscular action and does not permit them to enter the stalk.

Since the stalk is primarily a region of extension and motility, its structure is adapted to maximum elasticity. The mesoglea here reaches its greatest thickness; and both muscle layers are well developed, particularly the longitudinal.

The basal disk

The epidermis of the foot consists of columnar epitheliomuscular cells. Their outer portions are filled with refractive globules, which store the sticky mucus these cells elaborate. Their bases are provided with muscle fibers which radiate from the center of the disk.

The mesoglea is lacking over a small area at the center of the disk, and here epidermis and gastrodermis come in direct confact. This is the region of the **aboral pore**, which is opened when the hydra suddenly releases its hold on the substratum, but is completely closed during attachment. The probable function of the pore is to enable the hydra to "blast" itself loose from the sticky mucus secreted by the foot. This is accomplished by a "peeling" action of the cells at the periphery of the foot, plus a simultaneous strong expulsion of water from the gastrovascular cavity through the aboral pore.

Physiology

Food

The food of the hydra consists principally of small animals that live in the water, such as *Cyclops*, annelids, and insect larvae. Large specimens may ingest aquatic animals as big as young fish and tadpoles. Bits of meat may be ingested when offered to them in a laboratory aquarium. The hydra normally rests with its basal disk attached to some object, and its body and tentacles extended into the water. In this position it occupies a considerable amount of hunting territory. Any small animal swimming within touch of a tentacle is at once shot full of penetrants, affixed by glutinants, or grappled by volvents.

Ingestion

The tentacle which has captured the prey bends toward the mouth with its load of food. The other tentacles not only assist in this, but may use their nematocysts in quieting the victim. The mouth often begins to open before the food has reached it. The edges of the mouth gradually enclose the organism and force it into the gastrovascular cavity. The body wall contracts behind the food and forces it down. Frequently organisms many times the size of the hydra are successfully ingested.

Reactions to food

It is common to find hydras that will not react to food when it is presented to them. This is due to the fact that these animals will eat only when a certain interval of time has elapsed after their last meal. The **physiologic condition** of the hydra, therefore, determines its response to the food stimulus. The collision of an aquatic organism with the tentacle of the hydra is not sufficient to cause the food-taking reaction, since it has been found that not only a mechanical stimulus, but also a chemical stimulus must be present. A very hungry hydra will go through the food-taking movements when it is excited by a chemical stimulus alone, such as beef juice.

Digestion

Immediately after the ingestion of food, the gland cells in the gastrodermis show signs of great activity; their nuclei enlarge and become granular. This is accompanied by the formation of enzymes which are discharged into the gastrovascular cavity and begin at once the digestion of the food. The action of the digestive juices is made more effective by the churning of the food as the animal expands and contracts. The flagella extending out into the central cavity also aid in the breakdown of the food by creating currents. This method of digestion differs from that of the amoeba, paramecium, and sponge in that it is carried on outside the cell, that is, **extracellular.** However, **intracellular** digestion also takes place in the hydra; the pseudopodia thrust out by the gastrodermal cells (Fig. 52) seize and engulf particles of food; these particles are then further digested in the cells. The digested food is **absorbed** and stored by the gastrodermis.

One species of hydra, *Chlorohydra viridissima,* is green in color because of the presence of a unicellular alga, *Chlorella vulgaris,* in the gastrodermal cells. As in *Paramecium bursaria,* the plant uses some of the waste products of metabolism of the hydra, and the hydra uses some of the oxygen resulting from the process of photosynthesis in the plant. This condition is one of mutualism.

Egestion

All indigestible material is egested from the mouth. This is accomplished by a very sudden squirt which throws the debris some distance.

Respiration and excretion

Oxygen diffuses into the cells from the water in which the hydra lives, and carbon dioxide diffuses out of the cells. The metabolic waste products are excreted through the general body surfaces.

Behavior

Spontaneous movements

All the movements of the hydra are the result of the contraction of the contractile fibers and are produced by two kinds of stimuli, internal, or spontaneous, and external. Spontaneous movements may be observed when the animal is attached and undisturbed. At intervals of several minutes, the body, or tentacles, or both contract suddenly and rapidly, and then slowly expand

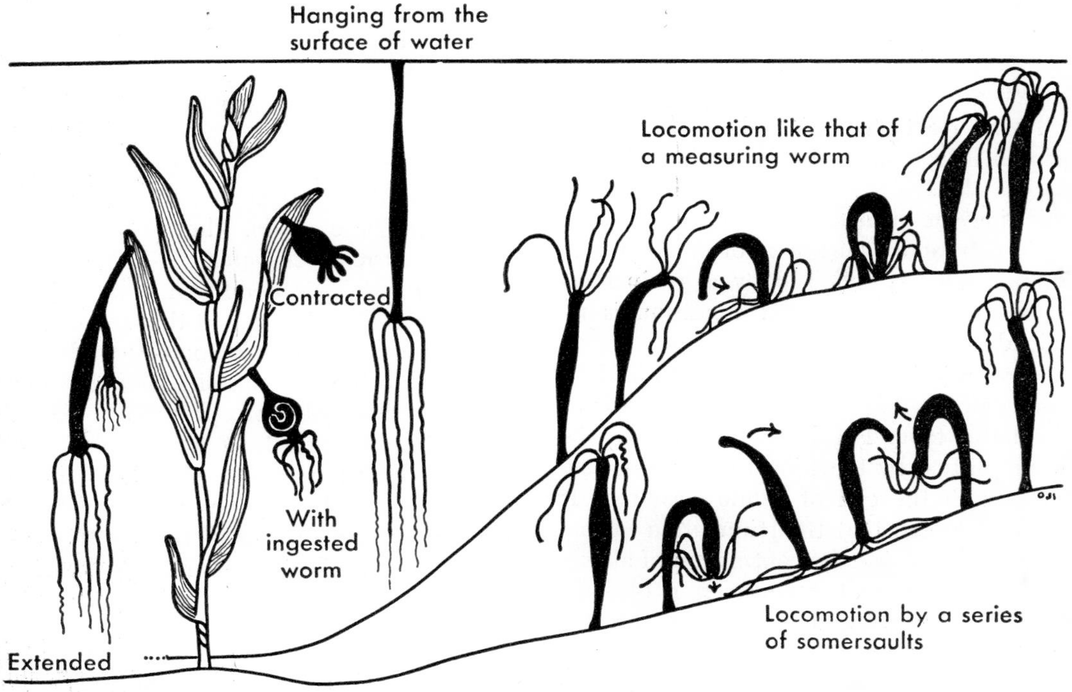

FIGURE 55. Sketches showing the hydra feeding and its methods of locomotion. Somersaulting is the most rapid method of locomotion.

in a new direction; hungry specimens are more active than well-fed individuals.

Locomotion

When going from one place to another, the hydra uses several methods. One is a gliding movement, with the basal disk slowly sliding over the object to which the animal is attached. A second method is a "measuring worm" type of movement (Fig. 55), in which the hydra bends over and attaches its tentacles to a region, slides its basal disk up close to them, and then releases the tentacles, assuming an upright position. Another method is by turning somersaults. The animal releases its basal disk and moves it completely over and attaches it to a new region. Such end-over-end movements are repeated again and again. At other times the hydra travels by a method seldom observed. It moves from place to place in an upside down position, using its tentacles as legs. To rise to the surface of water, it may form a gas bubble on its basal disk, which helps to carry it upward.

Contact

Hydra reacts to various kinds of special stimuli. Mechanical shocks, such as jarring the watch glass containing the specimen, or agitating the surface of the water, cause a rapid contraction of a part of or the whole animal. This is followed by a gradual expansion until the original condition is regained.

Mechanical stimuli may be **localized** or **nonlocalized**. The one just mentioned is of the latter type. Local stimulation may be accomplished by touching the body or tentacles with the end of a fine glass rod. It has been noted that the stimulation of one tentacle may cause the contraction of all the tentacles, or even the contraction of both tentacles and body. This shows that there must be some sort of transmission of stimuli from one tentacle to another and to the body. The structure of the nervous system would make this possible.

Light

There is no well-defined response to light, although the final result is quite decisive. If a dish containing hydras is placed so that the illumination is not equal on all sides, the animals will collect in the brightest region. However, if the light is too strong, they will congregate in a place where the light is less intense. The hydra therefore has an optimum with regard to light. The movement into or out of a certain area is accomplished by a method of trial and error. When put in a dark place, the hydra becomes restless and moves about in no definite direction; but if white light is encountered, its locomotion becomes less rapid and finally ceases altogether. The value of such a reaction is considerable, since the small animals that serve as food for it are attracted to well-lighted areas.

Other stimuli

The reactions of the hydra to changes in temperature are also indefinite, although in many cases they enable the animal to escape from a heated region. An attached hydra, when subjected to a weak, constant electric current, bends toward the anode, its body finally becoming oriented with the basal disk toward the cathode and the anterior end toward the anode. The hydra does not react to currents of water.

The **physiologic condition** of an animal determines to a large extent the kind of reactions produced not only spontaneously, but also by external stimuli. It determines whether the hydra creeps upward to the surface and toward the light, or sinks to the bottom; how it reacts to chemicals and to solid objects; whether it remains quiet in a certain position, or reverses this position and undertakes a laborious tour of exploration.

Reproduction

Reproduction takes place in the hydra both asexually and sexually; in the former case by budding, in the latter by production of fertilized eggs. Asexual and sexual reproduction may both occur at the same time in an individual.

Budding (Fig. 50)

Asexual (sexless) reproduction by a process of budding is a common occurrence in the hydra. Several buds are often found on a single animal. Superficially the bud first appears as a slight bulge in the body wall. This pushes out rapidly as a projection which soon develops a circlet of blunt tentacles about its outer end. The cavities of both stalk and tentacles are at all times directly connected with that of the parent. When full grown, the bud becomes detached and leads a separate existence; this requires about two days when conditions are favorable. Budding may occur at almost any season.

Sexual reproduction

Both ova and spermatozoa appear to develop from interstitial cells. Some species of the hydra form both sperms and eggs in one individual, but in others only one sex occurs. There may be as many as 20 or 30 testes; each is a conical outgrowth. The sexual state can be induced in some species by lowering the temperature; this accounts for the appearance in *Hydra oligactus* of sex organs in the autumn and during early winter.

Spermatogenesis. The male germ cells of the hydra are formed in little conical or rounded elevations called **testes**, which project from the surface of the body (Fig. 51). An indefinite number of interstitial cells collect locally into a mass, causing the epidermis of the animal to bulge. Each of these interstitial cells is a **primordial germ cell**; it gives rise by mitosis to a variable number of **spermatogonia**; these divide to form **primary spermatocytes**, which give rise by division to **secondary spermatocytes**; these divide, producing spermatids which transform into **spermatozoa**. The mature spermatozoa swim about in the distal end of the testis and finally escape to the exterior

through one or more small fissures in the protective covering. In most hydras definite nipples are formed on the testes, through which the sperms escape (Fig. 50). The mature spermatozoa swim about in the water searching for an egg.

Oogenesis. The egg is an interstitial cell which becomes large and spherical and possesses a large nucleus (Fig. 51). Several interstitial cells begin to enlarge to form ovocytes but one finally incorporates the others. As the ovum grows it becomes scallop-shaped, due to confinement between the columns of the supporting cells. When finally it attains full growth, it becomes spherical; but it is still surrounded by epidermal cells, which stretch enormously to cover the egg and still remain rooted to the mesoglea. (Illustrations showing a layer of epithelial cells covering the egg, but separate from the mesoglea, are incorrect; although such false interpretations in sections are easy to make.) **Maturation** now takes place. Two **polar bodies** are formed, the first being larger than the second. During maturation the number of chromosomes is reduced from the somatic number 12 to 6; this occurs at the end of the growth period. Now an opening appears in the epidermis and the egg is forced out, becoming free on all sides except where it is attached to the parent.

Fertilization. Fertilization usually occurs about as soon as the egg is extruded. Several sperms may penetrate the egg membrane, but only one enters the egg itself. The sperm brings a nucleus containing 6 chromosomes into the egg. The male and female nuclei unite, forming the **fusion nucleus.**

Embryology. The cleavage, which now begins, is total and regular. A well-defined cleavage cavity is present at the end of the third cleavage, the eight-cell stage. When the **blastula** is completed, it resembles a hollow sphere with a single layer of epithelial cells composing its wall (Fig. 56). These cells may be called the **primitive ectoderm.** By mitotic division they form endoderm cells

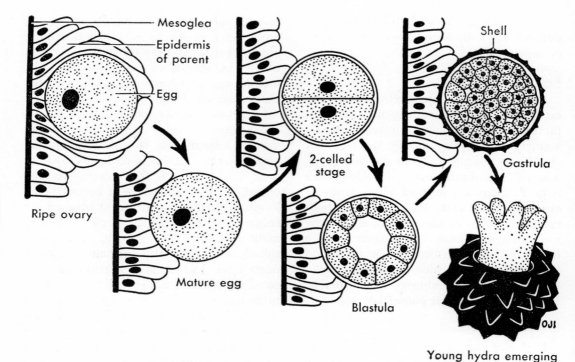

Mesoglea
Epidermis of parent
Egg
Ripe ovary
Mature egg
2-celled stage
Blastula
Shell
Gastrula
Young hydra emerging

FIGURE 56.   Stages in the development of the hydra.

which drop into the cleavage cavity, completely filling it. The early **gastrula**, therefore, is a solid sphere of cells differentiated into a single outer layer, the ectoderm, and an irregular central mass, the endoderm (Fig. 56). The ectoderm secretes two envelopes around the gastrula; the outer is a thick chitinous shell which may be covered with sharp projections; the inner is a thin gelatinous membrane. Different species of hydras can be identified by the structure of their shells.

Hatching. The embryo in this condition separates from the parent and falls to the bottom, where it remains unchanged for several weeks. Then interstitial cells make their appearance. A subsequent resting period is followed by the breaking away of the outer chitinous envelope and the elongation of the escaped embryo (larva). **Mesoglea** is now secreted between the ectoderm and endoderm cells, and these layers differentiate to form the adult epithelial tis-

sues: the epidermis and gastrodermis. A circlet of tentacles arises at one end and a mouth appears in their midst. The young hydra thus formed grows into the adult condition.

Regeneration

An account of the phenomena of regeneration is appropriate at this place, since the power of animals to restore lost parts was first discovered by Trembley in 1740 in the hydra. This investigator found that if hydras were cut into 2, 3, or 4 pieces, each part would grow into an entire animal. Other experimental results obtained by Trembley are that if a hydra is split longitudinally into 2 or 4 parts, each part becomes a perfect polyp; that when the head end is split in two, and the parts are separated slightly, a "two-headed" animal results; and that a specimen when turned inside out is able to readjust itself to these new conditions forced upon it. If a hydra remains turned inside out, the cells of the epidermis and gastrodermis migrate past each other through the mesoglea until they regain their original positions.

Regeneration may be defined as replacement of lost parts. It takes place not only in the hydra, but in many other coelenterates, and in some of the representatives of almost every phylum of the animal kingdom. The hydra, however, is one of the types that have been most widely used for experimentation. Pieces of the hydra that measure only six thousandths of an inch in diameter are capable of becoming entire animals. The tissues in some cases restore the lost parts by multiplication of their cells; in other cases, they are worked over directly into a new but smaller individual.

Grafting

Parts of one hydra may easily be grafted upon another; in this way many bizarre effects have been produced. Parts of two hydras of different species have also been united successfully.

Space will not permit a detailed account of the many interesting questions involved in the phenomena of regeneration and grafting, but enough has been given to indicate the nature of the process. The ability to regenerate lost parts is obviously of benefit to the animal. Such an animal, in many cases, will succeed in the struggle for existence under adverse conditions. Regeneration takes place continually in all animals; for example, new cells are produced in the epidermis of man to take the place of those that are no longer able to perform their proper functions. Both internal and external factors have an influence upon the rate of regeneration and upon the character of the new part. Temperature, food, light, gravity, and contact are some of the external factors. In man, various tissues are capable of regeneration; for example, the skin, muscles, nerves, blood vessels, and bones. Lost parts,

however, are not restored in man because the growing tissues do not coordinate properly. **A decrease in regenerative power seems to be correlated with the increase in complexity of animal types.** The inability of the more complex forms to replace lost parts appears to be the price of specialization.

OTHER COELENTERATA

As in the case of the hydra, coelenterates in general are diploblastic and possess nematocysts. Contractile fibers are present in a more or less concentrated condition. **Nerve cell processes (fibers)** and **sensory cells** are characteristic structures; they may be few in number and scattered, as in the hydra, or numerous and concentrated. The two principal types of coelenterates are the **polyp** and the **jellyfish** or **medusa.** These are fundamentally similar in structure, but are variously modified. Both polyps and medusae are radially symmetrical. Although the medusae may, upon superficial examination, appear to be very different from the polyps, they are constructed on the same general plan. Both have similar parts, the most noticeable difference being the enormous quantity of mesoglea present in the medusa. The **water content** of a medusa is very high; that of *Aurellia* is about 96 per cent.

Digestion in coelenterates is both extra- and intracellular; enzymes are discharged into the gastrovascular cavity for maceration of food organisms. The particles are transported to various parts of the body by currents in the gastrovascular cavity and are then taken up by the gastrodermal cells and passed over to the epidermal cells. Both **respiration** and **excretion** are performed by the general surface of the epidermis and gastrodermis. There is no endoskeleton, but the stony masses built up by the coral polyps support the soft tissues to a certain extent. The nervous tissue and sensory organs provide for perception of various kinds of stimuli and for conduction of impulses from one part of the body to another. Coelenterates are generally sensitive to light intensities, changes in temperature, mechanical stimuli, chemical stimuli, and gravity. **Reproduction** is both asexual, by budding and fission, and sexual, by means of eggs and spermatozoa.

Obelia—a colonial hydroid

Obelia (Fig. 57) lives in water up to 240 feet in depth, along our eastern coast from Long Island Sound to Labrador, on the Pacific Coast, and other parts of the world. If you can imagine a hydra budding without the buds detaching from the parent body, and then imagine these new individuals specializing for certain functions as feeding and reproduction, it will be easy to understand the development of *Obelia*. It is attached to the substratum by a rootlike mass (**hydrorhiza**), from which arise upright branches (**hydrocauli**). Hydralike feeding members (**hydranths**) and reproductive members (**gonangia**) are given off from the hydrocaulus, as shown in Fig. 57. The soft parts are protected by a cellophanelike, chitinous covering (**perisarc**), which is ringed at intervals and expands around the hydranths to form the **hydrothecae** and around the **gonangia** to form the **gonothecae**. The soft parts (**coenosarc**) are attached to the perisarc by small strands.

The hydranths resemble the hydra somewhat in structure and function, but these are specialized for feeding only. The tentacles, however, are solid and about 30 in number. The central axis (**blastostyle**) of the gonangium gives rise to buds that develop into medusae; these escape through the opening in the end of the **gonotheca**. The free-swimming medusae produce either eggs or spermatozoa. The fertilized egg (**zygote**) develops into a ciliated, free-swimming larva (**planula**) which soon becomes attached to a stone and grows into a polyp type of colony that reproduces asexually by budding.

Metagenesis

The alternation of a generation that reproduces only asexually by division or budding, with a generation which reproduces only sexually by means of eggs and sperms, as in *Obelia*, is known as **metagenesis**. The polyp and medusa stages are not equally prominent in all Hydrozoa; for example, the medusa in some species is degenerate or inconspicuous, as in *Obelia*, whereas in other species the polyp generation is only slightly developed, as in *Gonionemus*.

Gonionemus—a hydrozoan medusa

Gonionemus is a jellyfish (Fig. 58), common along the eastern coast of the United States. It measures about ½ inch in diameter, and bears around the margin from 16 to 80 or more hollow **tentacles** which bend at a sharp angle near the tip. The gonads are brown. The convex or aboral surface is the **exumbrella**; the concave or oral surface, the **subumbrella**; this is partly closed by a perforated membrane, the **velum**. Water is taken into the subumbrellar cavity and is then forced out through the central opening in the velum by the contraction of the body; this propels the animal in the opposite direction, a sort of jet propulsion. Hanging down into the subumbrellar cavity is the **manubrium** with the **mouth** at one end surrounded by 4 frilled **oral lobes**. The mouth leads to the **gastrovascular cavity** in the middle of the bell, where 4 **radial canals** extend to a **ring canal** which lies near the margin of the umbrella.

The cellular layers are similar to those in the hydra, but the mesoglea is extremely thick and gives the animal a jellylike consistency. Suspended beneath the radial canals are the sinuously folded reproductive organs or **gonads**. One individual produces either eggs or spermatozoa; therefore *Gonionemus* is dioecious. A ciliated planula develops from the fertilized egg; it is at first

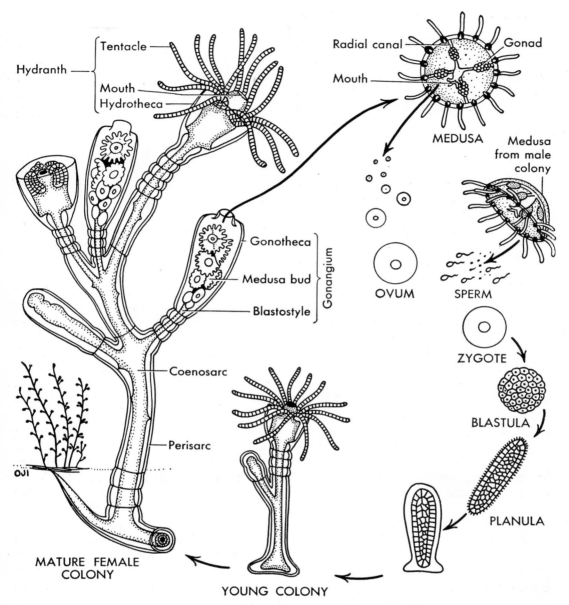

Figure 57. Life history and structure of *Obelia*, a colonial marine hydroid. The colony consists of polyps of two types, the feeding hydranths and reproductive gonangia. Both hydranths and gonangia are developed by asexual budding from stems attached to a branching rootlike tangle called the hydrorhiza. Sperms and eggs are produced by medusae which bud from gonangia of different colonies, that is, the colonies are dioecious. The embryo develops into a ciliated free-swimming planula larva; this attaches to the substratum and forms a new colony. The three kinds of individuals—the feeding polyps (hydranths), the asexual reproductive polyps, and the sexual reproductive medusae—illustrate polymorphism.

119

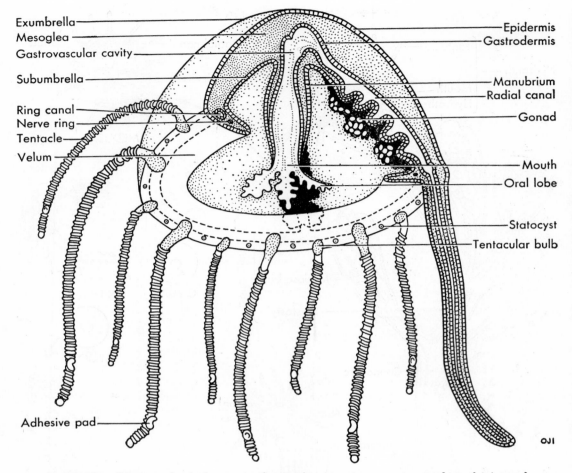

Exumbrella — Epidermis
Mesoglea — Gastrodermis
Gastrovascular cavity —
Subumbrella — Manubrium
— Radial canal
Ring canal — Gonad
Nerve ring —
Tentacle —
Velum — Mouth
— Oral lobe
— Statocyst
— Tentacular bulb
Adhesive pad —

OJI

Figure 58. Diagram of a hydrozoan medusa with part cut away so as to show the internal structure. Natural size, one inch in diameter.

free-swimming, but soon becomes fixed to some object and grows into a polyp.

Physalia—a polymorphic colonial hydrozoan

Physalia is a colony of hydrozoan polyps. A colony containing two kinds of individuals is said to be **dimorphic;** one containing more than two kinds, **polymorphic.** Some of the most remarkable cases of polymorphism occur among the Hydrozoa. *Physalia,* or the Portuguese man-of-war (Fig. 59), for example, consists of a gas-filled float (**pneumatophore**) with a sail-like crest, from which a

number of polyps hang down into the water. Some of these polyps are nutritive (**gastrozooid**), others are feelers (**dactylozooid**), and others are reproductive zooids (**gonozooid**).

The surface of the float shimmers with beautiful iridescent colors: blues, pinks, violets, and purples, and the crest may glow with vivid carmine. The different types of zooids in *Physalia* arise from a single planula larva and bud off from a section of the coenosarc just beneath the float. This strange animal occurs in the Gulf Stream from Florida northward; specimens are often cast up on the shore. It has no effective

FIGURE 59. Portuguese man-of-war. The Portuguese man-of-war floats on the surface of tropical seas. Hanging down from the float are long tentacles loaded with nematocysts. Many fish are captured by these streamerlike tentacles. The colony shown has just caught a fish; arrow points to fish. However, one species of fish of the genus *Nomeus* swims about among the tentacles of the Portuguese man-of-war with impunity. It appears to be immune to the poison of the stinging cells, possibly because it eats the tentacles of its host. These fish dart out to grasp a small food animal and hasten back amid the safety of the tentacles to devour it. The tentacles protect the fish, and particles of food not eaten by the fish are engulfed by the Portuguese man-of-war. (Courtesy of N.Y. Zoological Society.)

locomotor organs but is carried from place to place by currents in the water or by winds blowing against the pneumatophore. The stinging dactylozooids may be over 60 feet in length, with nematocysts powerful enough to inflict serious and even fatal injury on man. The dactylozooids are able to catch large fish; and by means of contraction, they draw them up to the gastrozooids; these enclose the prey in a digestive sac by spreading their lips over it.

Aurellia—a scyphozoan medusa

Most of the larger jellyfishes belong to the class Scyphozoa. They can be distinguished easily from the hydrozoan medusae by the presence of notches, usually 8, in the margin of the umbrella, and by the absence of a distinct velum. The scyphozoan jellyfishes usually range from an inch to 3 or 4 feet in diameter. The giant jellyfish, *Cyanea*, which lives in the cold water of the north Atlantic, has been found with a disk up to 7½ feet in diameter, tentacles 120 feet long, and weighing up to one ton. The Scyphozoa are usually found floating near the surface of the sea, though some of them are attached to rocks and seaweeds. There is an alternation of generations in their life history, but the asexual stage is subordinate.

Aurellia (Fig. 60) is white or bluish, with pink gonads. It differs from *Gonionemus* and other hydrozoan medusae in the absence of a velum, the characteristics of the canal system, the position of the gonads, and the arrangement and morphology of the sense organs.

The **oral arms** hang down from the square **mouth**, which opens into a short **gullet**; this leads to a rectangular central **enteron**. **Gastric pouches** extend laterally from 4 sides of the enteron. Within each gastric pouch is a gonad and a row of small **gastric filaments** bearing nematocysts. Numerous radial canals, some of which branch several times, lead from the enteron to a **ring canal** at the margin. The 8 sense organs of *Aurellia* lie between the **marginal lappets** and are known as **tentaculocysts**; these are considered to be organs of equilibrium. In addition, each tentaculocyst bears a pigment spot which is sensitive to light.

The food of *Aurellia* consists of small particles which are carried along the radial canals by currents produced by the beating of cilia with which some of the gastrodermal cells are provided and are ingested by gastrodermal cells. The physiologic processes **in**

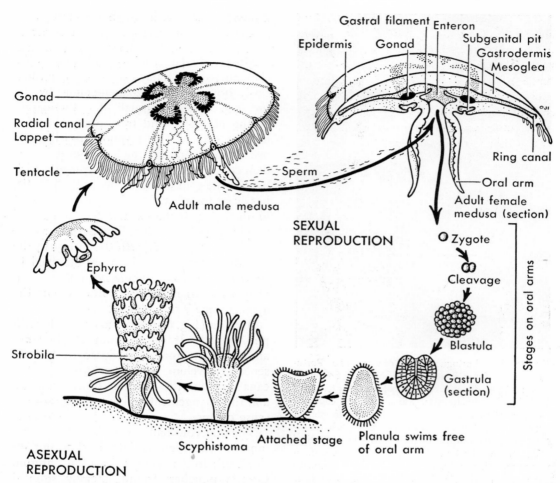

FIGURE 60. Life cycle of the jellyfish *Aurellia*. Longitudinal sections through gastrula stage. Vertical section through adult.

Aurellia are, in general, similar to those of the hydra.

The **gonads** are frill-like organs lying in the floor of the gastric pouches. The egg develops into a free-swimming **planula** which becomes attached to some object, and develops into an elongated and deeply constricted polyp, known as the **scyphistoma** stage (Fig. 60). The scyphistoma becomes divided into disks, resembling a pile of saucers; at this stage it is known as a **strobila**. Each disk develops tentacles; and, separating itself from those below, it swims away as a small medusa called an **ephyra**. The

ephyra gradually develops into an adult jellyfish.

Metridium—a sea anemone

A common representative of the class Anthozoa is the sea anemone (see colored frontispiece at beginning of text). *Metridium dianthus* (Fig. 61), is an anemone which fastens itself to the piles of wharves and to solid objects in tide pools along the north Atlantic coast. It is a cylindrical animal with a crown of hollow tentacles, arranged in a number of circlets about the slitlike mouth. The color is variable, but usually brownish or yellowish. The **skin** is soft but tough. At either side of the **gullet** (**stomodaeum**) is a ciliated groove called the **siphonoglyph**. The internal body cavity consists of 6 **radial** chambers; between these chambers are 6 pairs of thin double partitions called **primary septa** or **mesenteries**. Water passes from one chamber to another through pores (**ostia**) in these septa, and all are open below the gullet. Smaller septa project out from the body wall into the chambers, but do not reach the gullet; these are **secondary septa**. **Tertiary septa** lie between the primaries and secondaries. There is a considerable variation in the number, position, and size of the septa.

The free edges of the septa below the

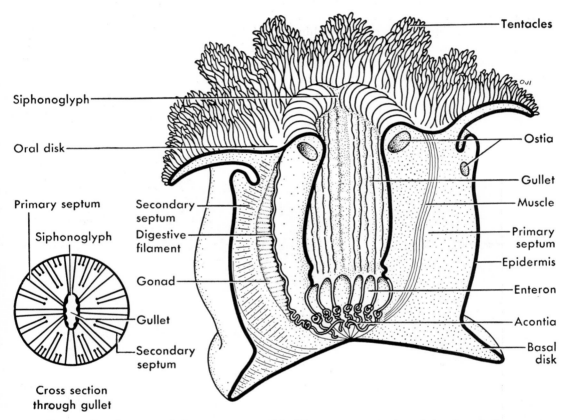

FIGURE 61. Structure of the sea anemone, *Metridium*, a representative of the class Anthozoa. *Left*, cross section through the gullet shows the arrangement of the septa. *Right*, a part of the body has been cut away to show the internal structure.

gullet in the **enteron** are expanded into thickened structures called **digestive filaments**. These bear the gland cells that secrete digestive enzymes. Near the base these filaments bear long delicate threads called **acontia**. The acontia are armed with gland cells and nematocysts. Near the edge of the septa are the gonads. The animals are dioecious. Asexual reproduction occurs by budding, by fragmentation at the edge of the basal disk, and by longitudinal fission.

Sea anemones are among the most beautiful and conspicuous inhabitants of tide pools along the seacoast. When fully expanded they form a sea garden filled with flowerlike crowns of various colors, resembling not so much the anemones after which they were named, but more closely chrysanthemums or dahlias. When greatly disturbed, these sensitive "flowers" may be drawn into a shapeless mass, and the long white acontia threads bearing stinging capsules are extended through minute pores in the body wall to drive away enemies.

In their natural habitat, sea anemones are far from flowerlike. They serve as death traps for any small animal that comes within reach of their tentacles. They may be beautiful in color but they wield their batteries of stinging capsules with deadly effect. The paralyzed prey is carried through the greedy mouth, down the gullet, and into the enteron, which is hardly more than a digestive sac. The food is digested by enzymes secreted by the cells of the digestive filaments and absorbed by the gastrodermis. Undigested wastes are ejected through the mouth. Saville-Kent's anemone, which lives on the Great Barrier Reef of Australia, is two feet across and is inhabited by small red and white fish; these swim in and out through the mouth without being injured in any way by the stinging capsules.

Astrangia—a coral polyp

Astrangia danae is a white coral polyp that inhabits the waters of our north Atlantic coast. Another species, *Astrangia insignifica*, occurs along the Pacific Coast; the polyps of this species are orange and the coral is red. A number of individuals live together in colonies attached to rocks near the shore. Each polyp looks like a small sea anemone. Each polyp secretes a calcareous

FIGURE 62. Colony of *Astrangia* which lives in the waters of the north Atlantic Coast. These corals secrete protective limestone cups into which the delicate polyps can retract. (Courtesy of George G. Lower.)

skeleton within which the animal rests. The corals on display in all museums are simply skeletons of coral polyps. Although *Astrangia* builds a cuplike skeleton less than ½ inch in height, it produces large masses of coral in the course of centuries. The physiologic processes of corals are much like those of other coelenterates.

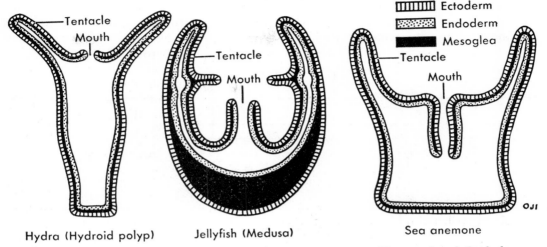

FIGURE 63. Basic plans of the three chief forms of coelenterates. The mouths of the hydra and sea anemone are held upward, but the jellyfish swims with mouth down. For purposes of comparison, however, the jellyfish is drawn with its mouth up.

ORIGIN AND RELATIONS OF THE COELENTERATA

The coelenterata probably arose from a two-layered animal (Fig. 430). We can, of course, only speculate regarding their origin and differentiation. A hypothesis based on our present knowledge is that coelenterates developed from a free-swimming ciliated form, something like the planula larvae of certain hydroids (Fig. 57). This became modified into a gastrula form with a body wall consisting of an outer ectoderm, protective and sensory in function, and an inner endoderm, digestive and absorptive in function. Between these layers a jellylike connective tissue, the mesoglea, appeared. The gastrula ancestor possessed a central cavity, the gastrocoel, a mouth, and a sense organ opposite the mouth. The muscle cells and nervous system were in a primitive stage of differentiation. Tentacles grew out from such an ancestral form, resembling somewhat a medusa. The larvae of these medusa-like ancestors may have become attached and then modified into hydroid polyps. According to the above hypothesis, the hydra is not a primitive type, but a coelenterate, well developed histologically, that has lost its medusa stage.

RELATIONS OF THE COELENTERATA TO MAN

Coelenterates are of considerable economic importance, though probably little used as food by man. However, some scyphozoan coelenterates are eaten in the Orient, and two species of Anthozoa are eaten in Italy under the name of Ogliole. Precious corals (Fig. 66), usually bright red or pink, are made into necklaces and other types of jewelry.

Coral polyps build various types of reefs, atolls, and islands. These are confined to waters at least 60° F., principally in tropical seas. The best-known coral islands are the Maldive Islands of the Indian Ocean, Wake Island, Marshall Islands, the Fiji Islands of the Pacific Ocean, and those located in the Bahama Islands region. Bermuda is a coral island and the houses are built of coral blocks mined from certain areas.

The Mariana Islands are coral islands of historic interest, for it was from an airfield on one of them (Tinian Island) that the atomic bombers took off for the bombing of Hiroshima and Nagasaki in Japan. Many of the finest landing strips on the Pacific is-

lands have been paved with coral. Coral has also been used for making roads and side-walks.

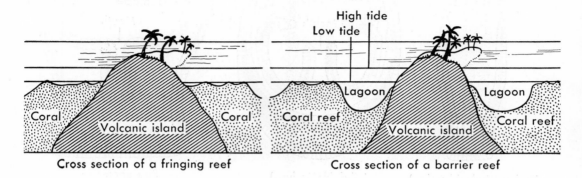

Cross section of a fringing reef   Cross section of a barrier reef

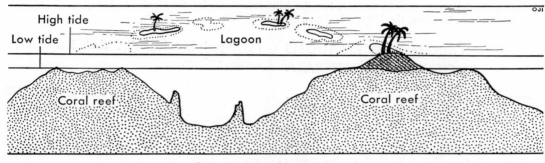

Cross section of an atoll reef

FIGURE 64. Coral reefs are grouped in three general classes: fringing, barrier, and atoll. The fringing reef lies close against the shore; the barrier reef lies off shore and is separated from the land by a lagoon; the atoll reef is a barrier reef which encloses a lagoon; it may be a continuous reef, but it is usually divided by water channels, extending through it from the ocean to the lagoon, as shown in this illustration. Vegetation grows on accumulated debris. One coral reef is known to be 690 feet in depth. (Modified from drawings by P.G. McCurdy.)

There are three types of coral reef formations: (1) fringing reef, (2) barrier reef, and (3) atoll reef (Fig. 64).

A **fringing reef** is a ridge of coral built up from the sea bottom, located so near to land that no navigable channel exists between it and the shore. Frequently, breaks occur in the reef and irregular channels and pools are created which are often inhabited by many different kinds of animals, some of them brilliantly colored.

A **barrier reef** is separated from the shore

by a wide deep channel which may afford passage for relatively large boats. These coral reefs may constitute a great danger to shipping, however. The Great Barrier Reef of Australia, which is the largest, is an enormous coral structure, 1350 miles in length, and, in places, 25 to 90 miles from the mainland of Australia. The channel is from 60 to 150 feet deep. A barrier reef may entirely surround an island.

An **atoll** is one or more islands, consisting of a belt of coral reef surrounding a central

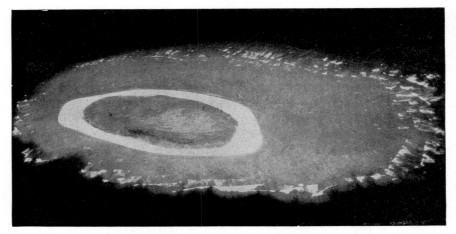

FIGURE 65. A fringing reef, Two Island, Pacific Ocean. The light streak around the island is coral, submerged in very shallow water. The gray area outside of that is also coral but in deeper water, and the black area outside of that is very deep sea water. This is one of the many islands which were used by the armed forces during World War II. (Courtesy of Major Dennis G. Cooper.)

lagoon. There are many of these in the mid-Pacific with lagoons of a few hundred yards to miles in diameter. The atoll of Bikini, of atomic and hydrogen bomb test fame, has a lagoon area of 280 square miles and a land area of only 2.87 square miles. Wake Island and Tarawa are atolls which figured prominently in World War II.

The horseshoe atoll of West Texas is well known as a prolific source of oil production. It is now buried under thousands of feet of rocks and existed as an atoll in the shallow seas which covered west Texas many millions of years ago. The horseshoe atoll is the largest limestone petroleum reservoir in North America. It is from 70 to 90 miles across and as much as 3000 feet thick. More than 5000 wells have been drilled into the reef mass and over 300,000,000 barrels of oil have been produced to date.

Barrier reefs and atolls have been built by the epidermal cells of countless numbers of small polyps, each one secreting its cup-shaped skeleton. The polyps die and new generations secrete new calcareous cups upon the old ones; only the surface of the coral mass is alive.

CLASSIFICATION OF THE COELENTERATA

(For reference purposes only)

This phylum includes polyps, jellyfishes, sea anemones, and corals. All have a body wall consisting of two layers of cells, between which is a jellylike substance, the mesoglea, which may or may not contain cells. Within the body is a single gastrovascular cavity. The epidermis is derived from ectoderm, and the gastrodermis from endoderm. They are called **acoelomates** because they do not possess a second body cavity, the coelom. All coelenterates are provided with nematocysts.

About 10,000 species of coelenterates have been described. They may be grouped into three classes and two subclasses as follows:

Class 1. **Hydrozoa.** Hydroid polyps and medusae with a velum; mesoglea noncellular; solitary or colonial; mostly marine. Exs. *Hydra, Obelia, Gonionemus,* and *Physalia* (p. 121).

Class 2. **Scyphozoa.** True medusae. No distinct velum; usually 8 notches in the margin of the umbrella; mesoglea cellular; polyp stage absent or reduced. Ex. *Aurellia.*

ORGAN PIPE CORAL *Tubipora*   SEA FAN *Gorgonia*

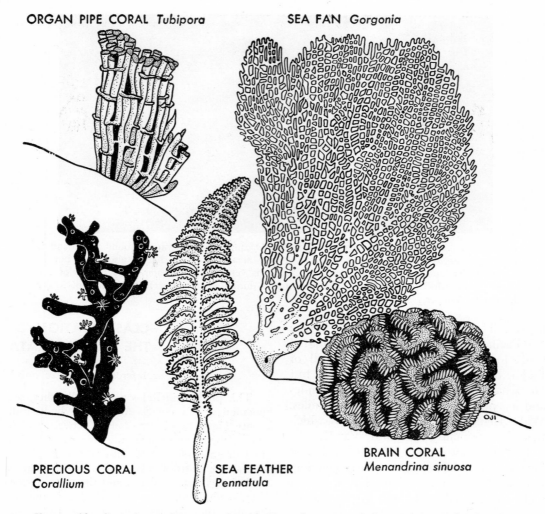

PRECIOUS CORAL   SEA FEATHER   BRAIN CORAL
Corallium   *Pennatula*   *Menandrina sinuosa*

FIGURE 66. Some interesting types of coral. Note that some of the precious coral polyps are expanded as they are when feeding.

Class 3. **Anthozoa.** Corals, sea anemones, etc. Solitary or colonial; polyps only, no medusae; distal end, an oral disk; gullet well developed; gastrovascular cavity divided by mesenteries; mesoglea cellular.

Subclass 1. **Alcyonaria.** Corals, sea pens, etc. Colonial; skeleton present; 8 pinnate tentacles; 8 mesenteries; 1 siphonoglyph, ventral. Exs. *Corallium*, precious coral (Fig. 66), *Pennatula*, a sea feather (Fig. 66).

Subclass 2. **Zoantharia.** Sea anemones, true corals, etc. Solitary or colonial; with or without skeleton; not 8 tentacles. Exs. *Metridium* (Fig. 61), *Astrangia*.

SELECTED COLLATERAL READINGS

Allee, W.C. *The Social Life of Animals.* Norton, New York, 1938.
Berrill, N.J. "The Indestructible Hydra," *Scientific American,* 197:118–125, 1957.

Carter, G.S. A *General Zoology of the Invertebrates*. Macmillan, New York, 1953.

Coker, R.E. *This Great and Wide Sea*. Univ. North Carolina Press, Chapel Hill, N.C., 1947.

Crowder, W. *Between the Tides*. Dodd, Mead, New York, 1931.

Gardiner, J.S. *Coral Reefs and Atolls*. Macmillan, London, 1931.

Hickson, S.J. "Coelenterata." *Cambridge Natural History*. Vol. 1, Macmillan, London, 1906, pp. 243–411.

Johnson, M.E., and Snook, H.J. *Seashore Animals of the Pacific Coast*. Macmillan, New York, 1935.

Mueller, J.F. "Some Observations on the Structure of *Hydra*, with Particular Reference to the Muscular System," *Trans. Am. Microscopic Soc.* 69:133–147, 1950.

Ricketts, E.F., and Calvin, Jack. *Between Pacific Tides*. Stanford Univ. Press, Stanford, 1952.

Robson, E.A. "Nematocysts of *Corynactis*: The Activity of the Filament During Discharge," *Quart. J. of Microscop. Science* 94:229–235, 1953.

Roughley, T.C. *Wonders of the Great Barrier Reef*. Scribner's, New York, 1947.

Yonge, C.M. *A Year on the Great Barrier Reef*. Putnam, New York, 1930.

CHAPTER 11

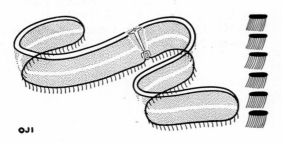

oJI

Phylum Ctenophora.

Comb Jellies

THE phylum Ctenophora (comb bearers) includes a small group of about 100 species of exclusively marine animals that resemble coelenterate jellyfishes. They are widely distributed, being especially abundant in warm seas. Ctenophores are beautifully iridescent in sunlight, and they glow like electric light bulbs at night, due to their luminescence.

Ctenophores are commonly called sea gooseberries or sea walnuts (Fig. 67) because of their shape; or **comb jellies** because of the **comblike locomotor organs** arranged in 8 rows which extend as meridians from pole to pole. They are **biradially symmetrical**, since the parts, though in general radially disposed, lie half on one side and half on the other side of a median longitudinal plane (Fig. 67). The mouth is situated at one end (**oral**), and a sense organ (**statocyst**) at the opposite or **aboral** end.

Most ctenophores possess two solid, contractile **tentacles** which emerge from blind pouches opposite each other; these are covered with **glue cells** (colloblasts), which produce a secretion of use in capturing the small animals they eat. Their food consists of fish eggs, molluscan larvae, and small pelagic invertebrates. The Bureau of Fisheries reports that large numbers of oyster larvae are killed by ctenophores.

Ctenophores are hermaphroditic. The ova and spermatozoa are formed on the walls of the digestive canals just beneath the ciliated bands. The eggs and sperms pass to the outside by way of the mouth. The fertilized eggs usually develop directly into the adult.

As in coelenterate jellyfishes, the cellular layers of ctenophores constitute a very small part of the body, most of it being composed of the transparent jellylike **mesoglea**. A thin ciliated epidermis, derived from the ectoderm, covers the exterior and lines the **pharynx** (stomodaeum); and a gastrodermis derived from the endoderm, also ciliated, lines the stomach and the gastrovascular canals associated with it.

Scattered cells and muscle fibers lie in the

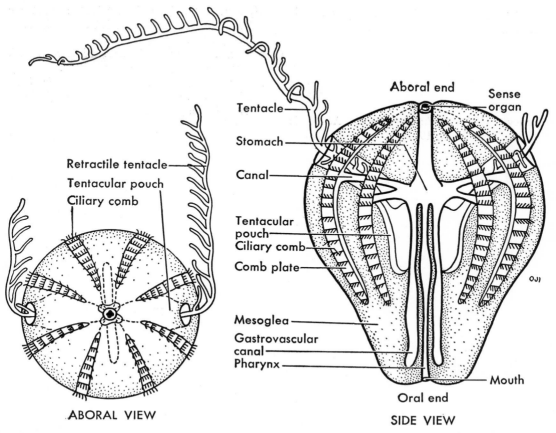

Tentacle

Stomach

Canal

Tentacular
pouch
Ciliary comb

Comb plate

Mesoglea

Gastrovascular
canal

Pharynx

Aboral end

Sense
organ

Mouth

Oral end

Retractile tentacle
Tentacular pouch
Ciliary comb

ABORAL VIEW

SIDE VIEW

FIGURE 67. The structure of a typical ctenophore. Side view of *Hormiphora*. (After Chun.)
Aboral view of *Pleurobrachia*. (From *Lankester's Treatise*.)

mesoglea; this "layer" of cells in the ctenophores resembles that in certain coelenterates but represents a higher grade of development. All the systems are of tissue
grade in construction except that there are
indications of reproductive ducts in some
forms.

Ctenophores differ from the coelenterates
in having ciliated bands, aboral sense organs,
mesenchymal muscles, more definite organization of the digestive system with anal
pores, pronounced biradial symmetry, and
no nematocysts. They probably evolved
from primitive coelenterate ancestors, but
can no longer be combined with that
phylum.

Pleurobrachia pileus is white or rose-

colored, ovoidal, about 2 cm. long, and
possesses tentacles about 15 cm. long; it occurs from Long Island to Greenland, on the
Pacific Coast, and in Europe. *Mnemiopsis
leidyi* is a transparent, luminescent species,
about 10 cm. long, that lives along our eastern sea coast. It is often parasitized by a
minute sea anemone 1.5 mm. long. Some
bizarre forms occur among the ctenophores,
for example, *Cestus veneris* (Venus's-
girdle), headpiece, page 130, may be two
inches wide and over three feet long, transparent, but showing green, blue, and violet
colors; it swims by muscular movements of
the ribbonlike body as well as by the beating
of the elongated swimming plates. It lives
in tropical seas but is sometimes carried

north along our Atlantic Coast by the Gulf Stream.

SELECTED COLLATERAL READINGS

Harvey, E.N. *Bioluminescence.* Academic Press, New York, 1952.

Hyman, L.H. *The Invertebrates: Protozoa Through Ctenophora.* McGraw-Hill, New York, 1940.

Mayer, A.G. *The Medusae of the World.* Carnegie Inst., Washington, 1910.

Mayer, A.G. *Ctenophores of the Atlantic Coast of North America, Pub. 162.* Carnegie Inst., Washington, 1912.

CHAPTER 12

Phylum Platyhelminthes. Simple Organ-System Animals

The Platyhelminthes are much flattened dorsoventrally and hence are known as flatworms. Among them are both free-living and parasitic species; the former live principally in fresh or salt water; the latter are mostly endoparasitic. The parasitic flatworms are known as flukes or trematodes, and tapeworms or cestodes. They are widely distributed among human beings and other vertebrates; they are often pathogenic, and sometimes bring about the death of the host. Free-living flatworms of North America live in springs, ponds, and streams, or in bodies of salt water.

Flatworms exhibit many advances over the coelenterates and ctenophores. They are definitely bilaterally symmetrical, a characteristic common to most of the animals above them in the scale of life. This type of symmetry is correlated with various modifications both in structure and physiology. The flatworms possess a third embryonic tissue; hence their structures are derived from ectoderm, endoderm, and **mesoderm** (Fig. 92). The mesoderm gives rise to all tissue between the epidermis and intestine, except the nervous tissue.

Like most of the animal characters, the mesoderm has been foreshadowed in the more primitive animal groups. Its early beginnings are probably represented by some of the mesenchyme cells of the coelenterates. However, mesenchyme is not generally considered true mesoderm until, as in the flatworms and other more complex animals, it is more massive and gives rise to definite structures such as muscles. The Platyhelminthes is the lowest phylum of animals built on an **organ-system level** of complexity. It is also the first phylum in which there is a distinct head with sense organs and central nervous system. The commonest free-living species of the flatworms are called planarians and for this reason a planarian has been chosen for special description.

Two entire classes of flatworms are parasites, some of which, such as the tapeworms,

133

are well known, at least by name. Parasitic species are of great interest and very important economically. Their mode of life has brought about various specializations, such as enormously increased powers of reproduction, and extremely complicated life cycles, involving in certain cases three or four different species of hosts and intermediate hosts. The relations of some species to human health and to the rearing of domesticated animals constitute a large part of what is known as economic zoology and medical zoology.

Three classes of Platyhelminthes may be recognized: these are (1) Turbellaria, (2) Trematoda, and (3) Cestoda. Most of the Turbellaria are free-living and inhabit either fresh or salt water; a few live in moist soil, and a few are parasitic. The trematodes and cestodes are all parasitic.

PLANARIAN—A FRESH-WATER FLATWORM

The commonest fresh-water planarian in the United States is *Dugesia tigrina* (Fig. 68). It lives on water plants in ponds, and along the shores of ponds, lakes, and rivers, and in small streams under stones. Its upper surface is brown or mottled and irregularly spotted with white, and its under surface is white or grayish. The body is **bilaterally symmetrical,** broad and blunt at the anterior end, and pointed at the posterior end, and may reach a length of from 15 to 18 mm.

The anterior end of the animal is quite distinctly the head. At each side of the head is a sharp projecting auricle. It contains a variety of sense cells. A pair of eyes (Fig. 68) is present on the dorsal surface near the anterior end. The **mouth** is not on the head, but near the middle of the ventral surface. It opens into a cavity which contains a muscular tube, the **pharynx** (Fig. 68), attached only at its proximal end. The pharynx consists of a complex of muscle

layers and many gland cells. By means of the muscles, the pharynx can be thrust out of the mouth some distance when feeding. On the ventral side, posterior to the pharynx is a smaller opening, the **genital pore;** this is present only in sexually mature individuals. The ventral surface of the body is covered with **cilia,** which play some part in locomotion; however, the chief method of locomotion is by almost imperceptible muscular contractions.

Planarians, like other flatworms, possess a mesoderm. The tissues of mesodermal origin, lying between the body wall and the intestine, consist of a fibrous mesh, in which are embedded fixed cells whose processes anastomose, and free cells that can move about in amoeboid manner. This mesodermal network of connective tissue is called **parenchyma** (mesenchyme). The well-developed muscular, nervous, digestive, excretory, and reproductive systems are constructed in such a way as to function without the coordination of a circulatory system, respiratory system, coelom, and anus, which are present in many more complex animals. The **digestive system** consists of a **mouth,** a **pharnyx,** and an **intestine** of three main trunks with a large number of small lateral extensions (Fig. 68).

The food of planaria consists of animals, living or dead. The pharynx is protruded into the food; and by a sucking action, microscopic particles are detached and drawn into the digestive cavity. **Digestion** occurs only within cells lining the simple intestine. There is only one opening to the digestive cavity; as in coelenterates, the undigested matter is ejected through the mouth.

FIGURE 68. *Facing page,* a planarian. Diagram on *upper left* shows the digestive and nervous systems. Diagram on *upper right* shows part of the reproductive system; and at *anterior left side,* part of the excretory system. Actually these systems exhibit bilateral symmetry, but portions of each are shown to conserve space. *Lower,* schematic diagram of pharynx. (After L.H. Hyman, *The American Biology Teacher,* 1956.)

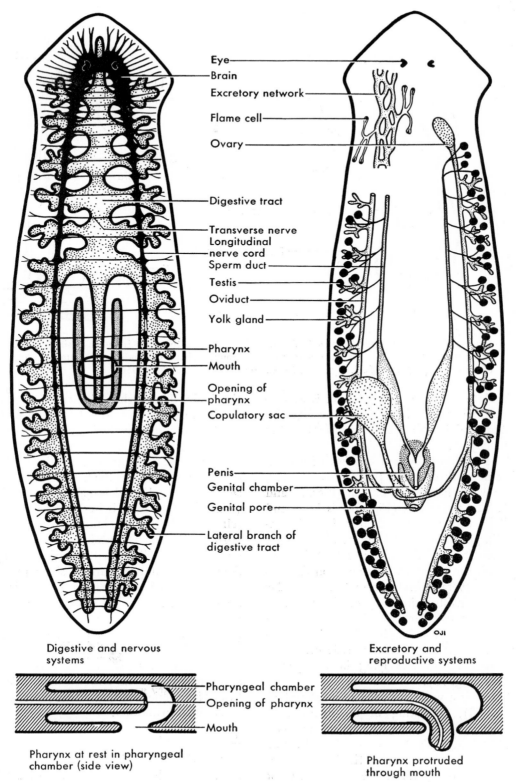

Eye
Brain
Excretory network
Flame cell
Ovary

Digestive tract

Transverse nerve
Longitudinal
nerve cord
Sperm duct
Testis
Oviduct
Yolk gland

Pharynx
Mouth

Opening of
pharynx
Copulatory sac

Penis
Genital chamber
Genital pore

Lateral branch of
digestive tract

Digestive and nervous
systems

Excretory and
reproductive systems

Pharyngeal chamber
Opening of pharynx
Mouth

Pharynx at rest in pharyngeal
chamber (side view)

Pharynx protruded
through mouth

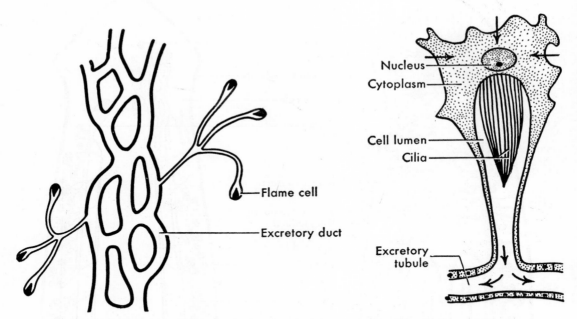

FIGURE 69. Excretory system of a fresh-water planarian. On the *right* is shown a single flame cell attached to a portion of an excretory duct. Arrows in flame cell indicate direction of flow of materials. (*Left* after L.H. Hyman, *The American Biology Teacher*, 1956.)

Circulation of the digested food is accomplished within the branches of the digestive system and in the fluid-filled spaces in the parenchyma.

The **excretory system** consists of a complex network of small tubes on each side, from which flame cells branch (Figs. 68 and 69). The **flame cell** (Fig. 69) is large and hollow, with a group of flickering cilia extending into the central cavity, which create a current and force the collected fluid through the tubules which open on the surface by several minute pores. The **muscular system** consists principally of three sets of muscles, a **circular layer** just beneath the epidermis, then a **longitudinal layer** immediately below the circular muscle cells, and **dorsoventral muscles** lying in the parenchyma (Fig. 70).

There is a well-developed **nervous system** (Fig. 68), consisting of an inverted **V**-shaped mass of tissue, the **brain,** and two ventral **longitudinal nerve cords** connected by **transverse nerves.** From the brain, nerves pass to various parts of the anterior end of the body. The highly pigmented **eyes** are sensitive to light but do not form an image.

Reproduction is by fission or by the sexual method. An animal may divide transversely; each part then becomes reorganized into a complete planarian. Each individual possesses both male and female sexual organs (Fig. 68), that is, it is hermaphroditic, but self-fertilization is not known to occur, and cross-fertilization is certainly the rule. The development is direct, without a larval stage. Some fresh-water planarians show remarkable powers of regeneration (Fig. 72). If such an individual is cut in two, the anterior end will regenerate a new tail, while the posterior part will develop a new head. A section from the middle of the body will regenerate both a head at the anterior end and a new tail at the posterior end. No difficulty is experienced in grafting pieces from one animal to another.

Axial gradients

Planarians are animals that illustrate admirably the theory of **axial gradients.** The

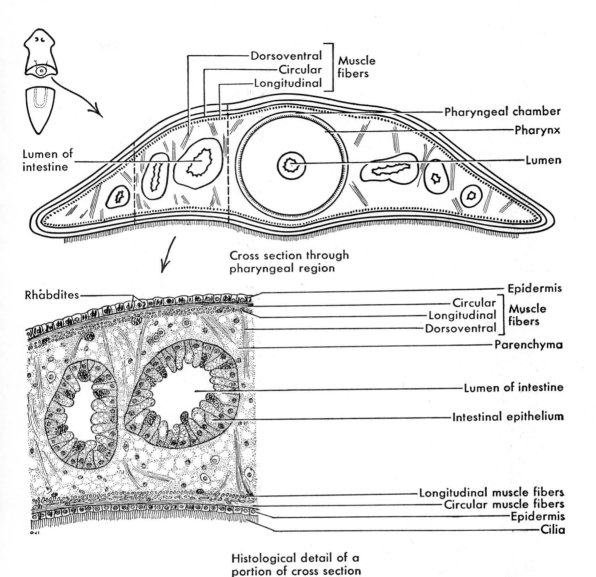

Cross section through
pharyngeal region

Histological detail of a
portion of cross section

FIGURE 70. Cross section through the pharyngeal region of a planarian. (This cross section was drawn from a histological preparation provided through the courtesy of L.H. Hyman.)

primary axis or axis of polarity is an imaginary line extending from the anterior to the posterior end of the body. In the planarian the head has a relatively high rate of metabolism and dominates the rest of the body. Experiments have shown that a gradient of metabolic activity proceeds from the anterior to the posterior end. For example, if planarians are cut into 4 pieces, the anterior piece will be found to use up more oxygen and give off more carbon dioxide than any of the others; the second piece comes next in its rate of metabolism; the third piece next; and the tail piece gives the lowest rate of all. Thus an axial gradient is demonstrated in the metabolism of the animal from the anterior to the posterior end; its significance is controversial.

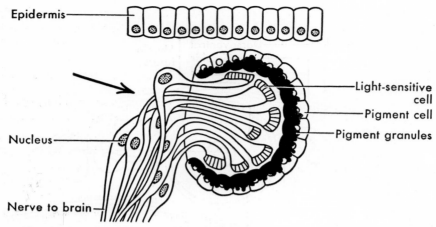

FIGURE 71. Section through eye of the planarian. The pigmented cells form a cup which insulates the light-sensitive cells within it against all light except that which enters through the open side of the cup, as shown by the arrow. Since the direction of the light determines which light-sensitive cells are stimulated, the planarian can determine the direction from which the light comes. No visual image is possible with such an organ.

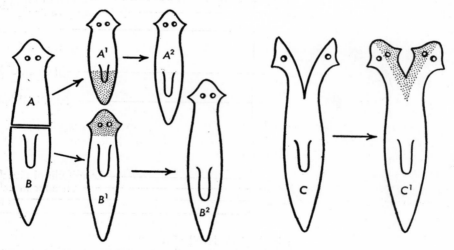

FIGURE 72. Planaria. Diagrams illustrate stages in the process of regeneration. A, B, specimen cut into two parts; the head (A) regenerates another tail (dotted) (A¹) and finally regains its normal shape (A²); B regenerates another head (B¹) and lengthens into a normal specimen (B²); C, a split head, regenerates two heads (C¹).

OTHER PLATYHELMINTHES

Flatworms differ greatly among themselves due largely to the fact that the Turbellaria are for the most part free-living, whereas the Trematoda and Cestoda are all parasitic in habit. Turbellarians probably exhibit the typical organization of the phylum, the trematodes and cestodes being modified considerably for a parasitic existence. The epidermis is ciliated in the turbellarians, but in the trematodes and cestodes there is no epidermis; they are covered with a thick **cuticle**. Sense organs are probably present in all.

In the Turbellaria and Trematoda there

is a saclike **intestine** with a single opening, which serves both as mouth and anus. In the simplest forms, the intestine is unbranched; but in others, branches occur that may penetrate to all parts of the body, thus rendering a circulatory system unnecessary. However, in certain trematode families, channels filled with fluid occupy a considerable part of the body. The fluid surging back and forth as a result of muscular contractions may in effect serve as a transport system. The Cestoda have lost the intestine and absorb nutriment through the general surface of the body. An **excretory system** occurs in almost all of the flatworms; and in some, it is very complicated. The most characteristic feature of this system is the **flame cell**. The **nervous system** consists of a network with a concentration of nervous tissue at the anterior end, the **brain**, and several **longitudinal nerve cords**. Flatworms are characterized by a **complex reproductive system**.

Fasciola hepatica—a parasitic trematode

Fasciola is known as the sheep **liver fluke**. It lives as an adult in the bile ducts of the livers of sheep, cows, pigs, and many other herbivores. Olsen has estimated that on the Gulf coast alone there is a yearly loss of 44 tons of condemned livers and 58 tons of other meat, not to mention the mortality of livestock, especially among calves, reduction in milk production, and lessened breeding. Human infections of the liver fluke are relatively rare, but this is probably due to infrequent exposure to the parasite rather than to its failure to develop in man. Water cress is one of the commonest means of human infection. In Cuba human infections are reported common, and in some years reach epidemic proportions.

The **mouth** of *Fasciola* lies in the middle of a muscular disk, the **oral sucker** (Fig. 73). The **ventral sucker** serves as an organ of attachment. Between the mouth and the ven-

tral sucker is the **genital pore** through which the eggs pass to the exterior. The **excretory pore** (Fig. 73) lies at the extreme posterior end of the body.

The **digestive system** consists of a mouth, pharynx, short esophagus, and intestine with two main branches (Fig. 73). The **excretory system** is similar to that of planarians, but only one main tube and one exterior opening are present. The **nervous system** consists of a small ganglion at the anterior end of the body which gives off a few longitudinal nerves. Sense organs are almost lacking. Complex muscle layers lie just beneath the cuticle.

The body of the liver fluke is covered with a thick, heavy, elastic cuticle. The **parenchyma** is a loose tissue lying between the body wall and the digestive tract; within it are embedded the various internal organs described above, as well as the reproductive system.

Except in the schistosomes and one other group, both male and female **reproductive organs** are present in every adult fluke (Fig. 75); they are extremely well developed, and, as in planarians, quite complex. One liver fluke may produce as many as 500,000 eggs; and, since the bile ducts in the liver of a single sheep may contain more than 200 adult flukes, there may be 100 million eggs formed in one parasitized animal. The eggs segment in the uterus of the fluke, then pass through the bile ducts of the sheep into its intestine, and finally are carried out of the sheep's body with the feces. Those eggs (Fig. 73) that encounter water produce ciliated larvae (**miracidia**) that swim about until they encounter a certain fresh-water snail, into which they burrow. Here, in about two weeks, they change into saclike **sporocysts** containing germ balls or embryos. Each germ ball within the sporocyst develops into a second kind of larva (**redia**). These usually give rise to one or more generations of **daughter rediae**, after which they produce a third kind of larva with a long tail, known as a **cercaria**. The cercariae leave the

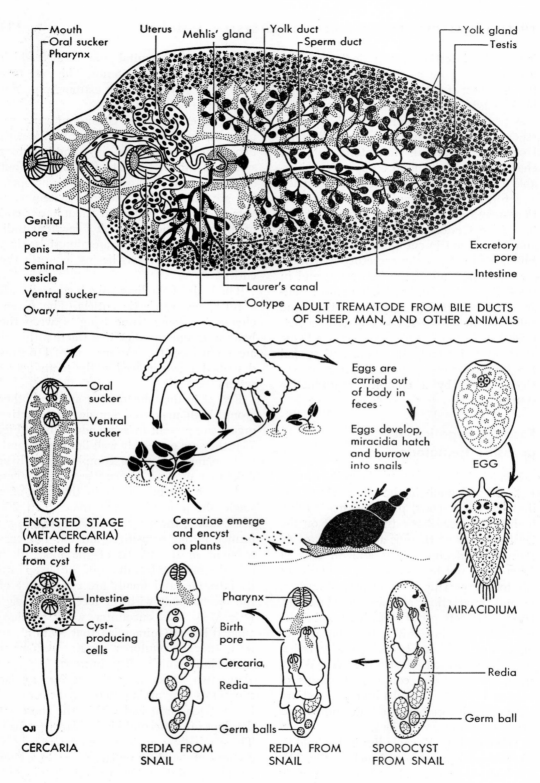

Figure 73. Life cycle and structure of the liver fluke of sheep, *Fasciola hepatica*.

140

body of the snail, swim about in the water for a short time, and then **encyst** on a leaf or blade of grass. The encysted cercaria is called a **metacercaria.** If the leaf or grass is eaten by a sheep, the metacercariae escape from their cyst wall and make their way from the sheep's digestive tract to the bile ducts, where they develop into mature flukes in about 6 weeks.

The great number of eggs produced by a single fluke is necessary because many eggs do not reach water; the majority of the larvae do not find the particular kind of snail necessary for their further development; and the metacercariae to which the successful larvae give rise have little chance of being devoured by a sheep. The generations within the snail, of course, increase greatly the number of larvae which may develop from a single egg. This complicated life history should also be looked upon as enabling the fluke to gain access to new hosts. The liver fluke is not so prevalent in the sheep of this country as in those of Europe.

Clonorchis sinensis is an important human parasite, especially in certain parts of Japan and China. An illustration (Fig. 74) is included here, since in some ways this animal is easier to study than *Fasciola hepatica,* and specimens may be obtained from biological supply houses. This species lives in the bile ducts of man, cats, dogs, and other mammals. The eggs are passed in the feces; the early larvae live in snails; the cercariae enter various species of fresh-water fish, where they become metacercariae which are infective to man; man and other animals are infected by eating uncooked, parasitized fish.

Pork tapeworm (Taenia solium)

The pork tapeworm lives as an adult in the digestive tract of man. A nearly related species, the beef tapeworm, is also a parasite of man. The pork tapeworm is long and consists of a knoblike "head," the **scolex** (Fig. 76), and a great number of similar

parts, the **proglottids,** arranged in a linear series. The animal clings to the inner wall of the intestine by means of **hooks** and **suckers** located on the scolex. No hooks, however, are present on the scolex of the beef tapeworm. Behind the scolex of the pork tapeworm is a short neck followed by a string of proglottids which gradually increase in size from the anterior to the posterior end. The worm may reach a length of 10 feet and contain 800 or 900 proglottids. Since the proglottids are budded off from the neck, those at the posterior end are the oldest.

No digestive tract is present, the digested food in the intestine of the host being absorbed through the body wall. The **nervous system** (Fig. 76) is similar to that of the planarians and the liver fluke, but not so well developed. Longitudinal **excretory canals** (Fig. 76), which have branches ending in flame cells, open at the posterior end of the worm and carry metabolic waste out of the body.

A mature proglottid is almost completely filled with **reproductive organs** (Fig. 76). The eggs develop into **6-hooked embryos** (Fig. 76) while still within the proglottid. If they are then eaten by a pig, they escape from their envelopes and bore their way through the wall of the intestine into the blood or lymph vessels to be carried eventually to the voluntary muscles, brain, or eyes, where they form **cysts.** A scolex is developed from the cyst wall (Fig. 76). The larva is known as a **bladder worm** or **cysticercus** at this stage (Fig. 76). If insufficiently cooked pork containing cysticerci is eaten by man, the bladder is thrown off, and the scolex, which develops, becomes fastened to the wall of the human intestine, and a series of proglottids is developed. Man can also serve as the intermediate host if ova are ingested or enter the stomach as a result of reverse peristalsis. Since the cysticercus may be located in the brain or eyes, infection with this parasite may be a serious matter.

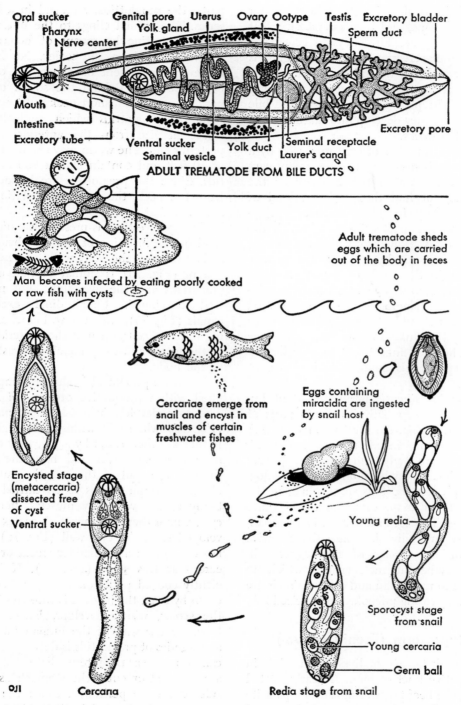

Oral sucker   Genital pore   Uterus   Ovary Ootype   Testis   Excretory bladder
Pharynx   Yolk gland   Sperm duct
Nerve center

Mouth

Intestine
Excretory tube

Ventral sucker   Yolk duct   Seminal receptacle
Seminal vesicle   Laurer's canal

Excretory pore

ADULT TREMATODE FROM BILE DUCTS

Man becomes infected by eating poorly cooked
or raw fish with cysts

Adult trematode sheds
eggs which are carried
out of the body in feces

Cercariae emerge from
snail and encyst in
muscles of certain
freshwater fishes

Eggs containing
miracidia are ingested
by snail host

Encysted stage
(metacercaria)
dissected free
of cyst
Ventral sucker

Young redia

Sporocyst stage
from snail

Young cercaria

Germ ball

Cercaria   Redia stage from snail

FIGURE 74. Life cycle and structure of the human liver fluke, *Clonorchis sinensis*.

142

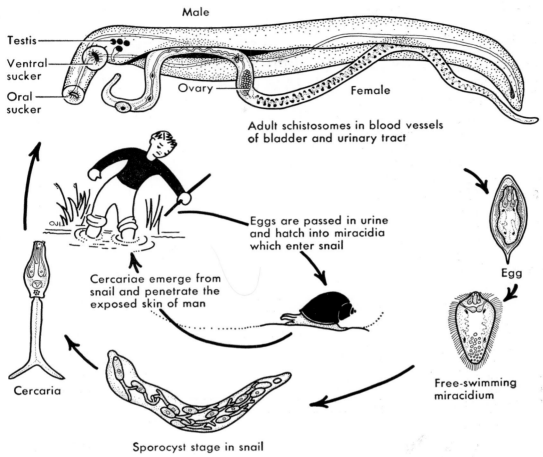

Male

Testis

Ventral
sucker

Oral
sucker

Ovary

Female

Adult schistosomes in blood vessels
of bladder and urinary tract

Eggs are passed in urine
and hatch into miracidia
which enter snail

Egg

Cercariae emerge from
snail and penetrate the
exposed skin of man

Free-swimming
miracidium

Cercaria

Sporocyst stage in snail

FIGURE 75. Life cycle of a human blood fluke *(Schistosoma haematobium)*. The large male is carrying the small female. This is an ancient human parasite, especially common in many parts of Africa and lower Egypt.

Why is the tapeworm not digested in the human intestinal juices (enzymes)? It is believed that the tapeworm is protected from the action of digestive enzymes by means of an anti-enzyme mechanism.

ORIGIN AND RELATIONS OF THE PLATYHELMINTHES

The flatworms, especially the Turbellaria, resemble the coelenterates in certain respects which indicate coelenteratelike ancestors. There is usually a single opening for ingestion of food and egestion of waste ma-

terial; a nerve net reminiscent of the coelenterates; and the parenchymal connective tissue is similar to the cellular mesoglea in higher coelenterates and ctenophores. The chief differences between the classes of flatworms appear to be due to their free-living or parasitic character.

RELATIONS OF THE PLATYHELMINTHES TO MAN

The free-living flatworms are of very little importance to man, but many of the trematodes and cestodes are dangerous parasites,

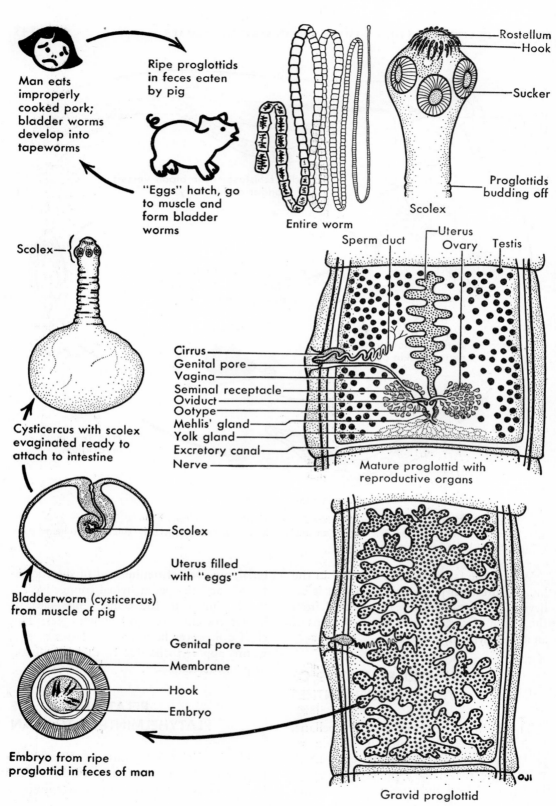

Man eats improperly cooked pork; bladder worms develop into tapeworms

Ripe proglottids in feces eaten by pig

"Eggs" hatch, go to muscle and form bladder worms

Entire worm

Rostellum
Hook
Sucker
Proglottids budding off

Scolex

Scolex

Cysticercus with scolex evaginated ready to attach to intestine

Bladderworm (cysticercus) from muscle of pig

Embryo from ripe proglottid in feces of man

Sperm duct
Uterus
Ovary
Testis

Cirrus
Genital pore
Vagina
Seminal receptacle
Oviduct
Ootype
Mehlis' gland
Yolk gland
Excretory canal
Nerve

Mature proglottid with reproductive organs

Scolex

Uterus filled with "eggs"

Genital pore
Membrane
Hook
Embryo

Gravid proglottid

FIGURE 76.   Life cycle and structure of the pork tapeworm, *Taenia*.

SOME COMMON TREMATODES OF MAN

	SCIENTIFIC NAME	DEVELOP-MENTAL STAGES	GEOGRAPHICAL DISTRIBUTION	DEFINITIVE HOSTS
INTESTINAL FLUKES	*Fasciolopsis buski*	In snails and on water-grown vegetables	China, Indo-China, Formosa, Sumatra, India	Man, pigs, in China, Formosa, Siam
	Heterophyes heterophyes	In snails and fresh-water fish	Egypt, China, Japan	Man, cat, dog, in Egypt
LIVER FLUKES	*Clonorchis sinensis* (Fig. 74)	In snails and fresh-water fish	China, Japan, Korea, French Indo-China, Philippines	Man, cat, dog, and fish-eating mammals
	Opisthorchis felineus	In snails and fresh-water fish	Europe, Siberia	Man, cat, dog
LUNG FLUKES	*Paragonimus westermani*	In snails and fresh-water crabs	Japan, China, Philippines, America	Man, tiger, dog, cat, mustelids, pig
BLOOD FLUKES	*Schistosoma haemato-bium* (Fig. 75)	In snails	Africa, Near East, Portugal, Australia	Man, monkey
	Schistosoma mansoni	In snails	Africa, West Indies, N. and S. America	Man
	Schistosoma japonicum	In snails	Japan, China, Philippines	Man, cat, dog, pig, etc.

the trematodes especially in Africa, Asia Minor, Arabia, West Indies, Brazil, and Venezuela; the cestodes throughout the world. The scientific names, location of developmental stages, geographic distribution and hosts of some of the species that live in man are presented in the accompanying tables. Hydatid cysts represent a larval stage of the tapeworm, *Echinococcus granulosus*. They occur in the liver and other organs of man, cattle, horses, sheep, etc., and may attain the size of a child's head. One abdominal cyst has been reported which contained 42 liters of fluid. Within each cyst the germinal layer may give rise to thousands of brood capsules or daughter cysts in which scolices develop. Operative measures only are effective in treatment.

Certain schistosome cercariae incapable of infecting man cause a severe swimmer's itch (dermatitis) when they penetrate the skin of bathers who have become sensitized by repeated exposures. This condition is common in the north central states, in southern Canada, as well as in some other parts of the United States, Europe, and India. Swimmer's itch can be avoided by swimming in deep water. The first symptom of swimmer's itch is a prickly sensation followed by the development of very itchy pimples, which sometimes become pustular. The itch organism can be controlled in small bodies of water by the use of copper sulfate to kill the snail in which the cercariae spend part of their life cycle. One midwest state used over 25 tons of copper sulfate in a recent summer to destroy infected snails to free the beaches from swimmer's itch.

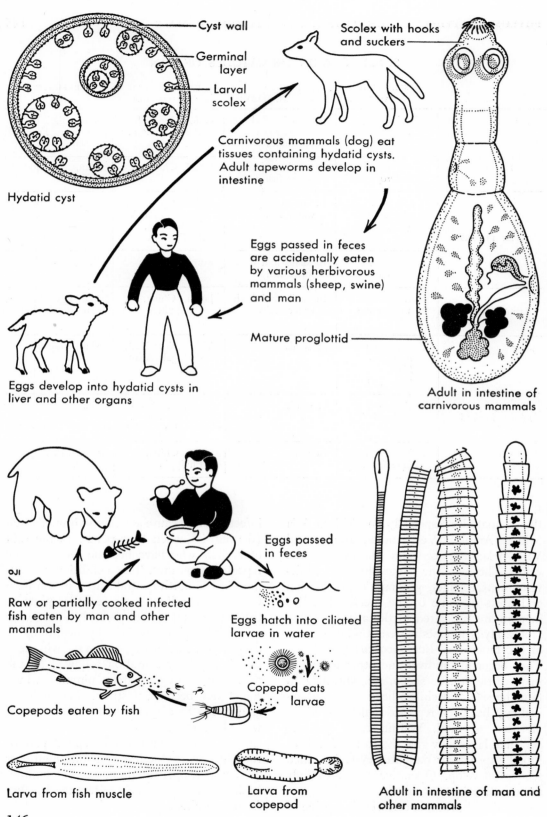

Cyst wall

Germinal layer

Larval scolex

Hydatid cyst

Scolex with hooks and suckers

Carnivorous mammals (dog) eat tissues containing hydatid cysts. Adult tapeworms develop in intestine

Eggs passed in feces are accidentally eaten by various herbivorous mammals (sheep, swine) and man

Mature proglottid

Eggs develop into hydatid cysts in liver and other organs

Adult in intestine of carnivorous mammals

Raw or partially cooked infected fish eaten by man and other mammals

Eggs passed in feces

Eggs hatch into ciliated larvae in water

Copepod eats larvae

Copepods eaten by fish

Larva from fish muscle

Larva from copepod

Adult in intestine of man and other mammals

146

SOME COMMON CESTODES OF MAN

SCIENTIFIC NAME	DEVELOPMENTAL STAGES	GEOGRAPHIC DISTRIBUTION	HOSTS
Dibothriocephalus latus (Fig. 77)	In copepods and fresh-water fish	Widespread	Man, dog, cat, bear, fox (intestine)
Echinococcus granulosus (Fig. 77)	In liver, brain, lungs, of man, pig, sheep	Widespread	Dog and other carnivores (intestine)
Taenia saginata	Muscles of cattle	World-wide	Man
Taenia solium (Fig. 76)	In muscles of pig, and man, accidentally	World-wide	Man

CLASSIFICATION OF THE PLATYHELMINTHES

(For reference purposes only)

The Platyhelminthes are animals characterized as being unsegmented, triploblastic, and bilaterally symmetrical. The body is flattened dorsoventrally. No anus (usually) or coelom is present. They have no skeletal, circulatory, or respiratory systems; but they have an excretory system with many flame cells. They have a head, sense organs, and a central nervous system which consists of a brain and two longitudinal nerve cords. Most flatworms are hermaphroditic.

The principle classes, subclasses, and orders are as follows:

Class 1. Turbellaria. Mostly free-living; epidermis at least partly covered with cilia, with rodlike rhabdites and many mucous glands. No suckers.

Order 1. Acoela. Marine; no intestine. Ex. *Polychoerus caudatus.*

Order 2. Rhabdocoela. Intestine simple, unbranched. Ex. *Stenostomum leucops.*

Order 3. Alloeocoela. Usually cylindroid; intestine straight or with short branches; mostly marine. Ex. *Prorhynchus.*

Order 4. Tricladida. Intestine of three main trunks, each with many lateral branches. Ex. *Dugesia tigrina* (Fig. 68).

Order 5. Polycladida. Marine; central digestive cavity with many irregular branches. Ex. *Stylochus ellipticus.*

Class 2. Trematoda. Parasitic; intestine present; no cilia on adult; cuticle present; suckers on ventral surface.

Order 1. Monogenea. External or semiexternal parasites; direct development with no asexual multiplication. Ex. *Benedenia (Epibdella) melleni.*

Order 2. Digenea. Internal parasites; an asexual generation in life cycle. Two or more hosts required, with alternation of hosts. Exs. *Fasciola hepatica* (Fig. 73); *Clonorchis sinensis* (Fig. 74).

Class 3. Cestoda. Endoparasites; no intestine; no cilia on adult; cuticle present; usually proglottids. Ex. *Taenia solium* (Fig. 76).

FIGURE 77. *Facing page, upper part of illustration,* life cycle of the dog tapeworm, *Echinococcus granulosus. Lower part of illustration,* life cycle of the broad tapeworm of man, *Dibothriocephalus latus* (formerly *Diphyllobothrium latum*).

SELECTED COLLATERAL READINGS

Chandler, A.C. *Introduction to Parasitology.* Wiley, New York, 1955.

Craig, C.F., and Faust, E.C. *Clinical Parasitology*. Lea & Febiger, Philadelphia, 1951.

Faust, E.C. *Animal Agents and Vectors of Human Disease*. Lea & Febiger, Philadelphia, 1955.

Hyman, L.H. *The Invertebrates: Platyhelminthes and Rhynchocoela*. McGraw-Hill, New York, 1951.

Mackie, T.T., Hunter, G.W., III, and Worth, C.B. *Manual of Tropical Medicine*. Saunders, Philadelphia, 1945.

Wardle, R.A., and McLeod, J.A. *The Zoology of Tapeworms*. Univ. of Minnesota Press, Minneapolis, 1952.

CHAPTER 13

Phylum Nemathelminthes, Phylum Nematomorpha, and Phylum Acanthocephala. Roundworms

Nematodes are one of man's worst enemies. Their activities are less spectacular than those of insects, but they are nearly as detrimental. They are universally present in the sea, in the fresh water, and in the soil. They occur also as parasites of plants and animals, including man. It is estimated that roundworms cause millions of dollars of crop damage every year. On the other hand, some of the many free-living species are known to be beneficial. Together, the parasitic and free-living roundworms form a subdivision of the animal kingdom which is of the utmost importance to man because it affects his well-being and economy.

Formerly, three different groups of roundworms were placed together in a single phylum. However, this arrangement was unsatisfactory to most zoologists, who preferred to classify them separately as the phylum Nemathelminthes, phylum Nematomorpha, and the phylum Acanthocephala. These three groups will be considered in the same chapter, even though divided into three separate phyla, for they do have some characteristics in common.

PHYLUM NEMATHELMINTHES

The Nemathelminthes are called **unsegmented roundworms** to distinguish them from the flatworms and segmented annelids. They are, typically, long slender animals, usually with a smooth glistening surface, and tapering at one or both ends. In size, they range from $\frac{1}{125}$ of an inch to 4 feet in length.

Many of them are so important economically and undergo such amazingly complex life histories that a knowledge of some of the parasitic species of animals is of great interest to everyone. For this reason, a brief description of *Ascaris* is presented, as well as an account of a number of the more important parasitic species. These include the hookworm, trichina worm, pinworm, whipworm, filaria, eye worm, and guinea worm.

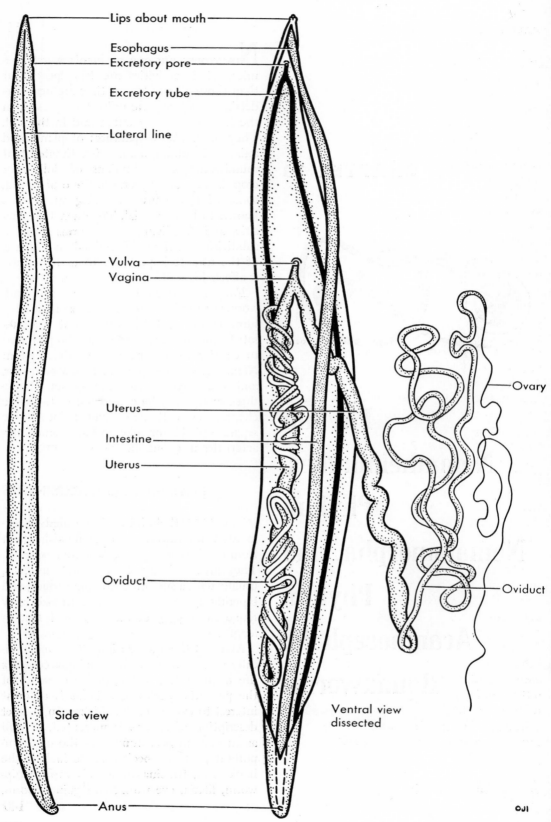

Lips about mouth

Esophagus

Excretory pore

Excretory tube

Lateral line

Vulva

Vagina

Uterus

Intestine

Uterus

Oviduct

Ovary

Oviduct

Side view

Ventral view
dissected

Anus

150

OJI

Ascaris lumbricoides—a roundworm parasitic in man

Anatomy

This is the common roundworm parasitic in the intestine of man. The sexes are separate. The female is the larger and measures up to 16 inches in length and to ¼ inch in diameter. The body has a dorsal and ventral, narrow white line, running its entire length, and a broader lateral line on either side. The tough **cuticle** is smooth and marked with fine **striations**. The mouth opening is in the anterior end and is surrounded by one **dorsal** and two **lateroventral lips**. In the male, near the posterior end, is the cloacal opening, from which extend two chitinous rods, the **penial spicules**, of use during copulation. Many ventral, preanal, and postanal papillae are also present in the male. The male is considerably smaller and more slender than the female; one of its best distinguishing characteristics is the sharply curved posterior end. In the female, the **vulva** or **genital pore** is located ventrally at about one-third the length of the body from the anterior end.

The body contains a straight **digestive tract** and other organs (Fig. 78). Between the intestine and the body wall is a body cavity, which is called a **pseudocoel**. It is not a true coelom because there is no true mesodermal epithelium covering the intestine. The digestive tract is very simple. A small **mouth cavity** opens into the **muscular esophagus**, or **pharynx**, which is from 10 to 15 mm. long. The esophagus draws fluids from the intestinal contents of the host into the long nonmuscular **intestine**, and the nutriment is absorbed through the walls. The posterior portion of the intestine is known as the **rectum** in the female, which discharges through the **anus**. But in the male the intestine and reproductive system open into a common passage way, the **cloaca**, and the opening to the outside probably should be called a cloacal opening; however, it is usually termed an anus.

The **excretory system** consists of two longitudinal tubes, one in each lateral line (Fig. 79); these open to the outside by a single **excretory pore** situated near the anterior end in the midventral body wall.

A ring of **nervous tissue** surrounds the esophagus and gives off two large nerve cords, one dorsal, the other ventral, and a number of other smaller strands and connections.

Reproduction

The male **reproductive organs** are a single, coiled, threadlike **testis**, from which a **vas deferens** leads to a wider tube, the **seminal vesicle**; this is followed by the short, muscular, **ejaculatory duct** which opens into the **cloaca**. In the female (Fig. 78) lies a Y-shaped reproductive system. Each branch of the Y consists of a coiled threadlike **ovary**, which is continuous with the **oviduct** and **uterus**. The uteri of the two branches unite into a short muscular tube, the **vagina**, which opens to the outside through the **vulva**. **Fertilization** takes place in the oviduct. The **egg** is then surrounded by a thick, rough-surfaced shell, and passes out through the vulva. The genital tubules of a female worm may contain as many as 27 million eggs in various stages of development at one time, and each mature female lays about 200,000 eggs per day.

The eggs of the ascaris are laid inside of the intestine of the host and pass out in the feces. They are very resistant; if deposited on the soil they may remain alive for many months. **Embryos** are formed, under favorable conditions, in about 14 days. Infection with the ascaris results from ingesting eggs containing embryos. The eggs are usually carried to the mouth with either food or water, or by accidental transfer of soil containing them. They do not regularly hatch in the stomach but pass on to the small intes-

---

FIGURE 78. *Facing page*, female *Ascaris*. Side view of a specimen on *left*, and a dissection on the *right* to show the internal organs.

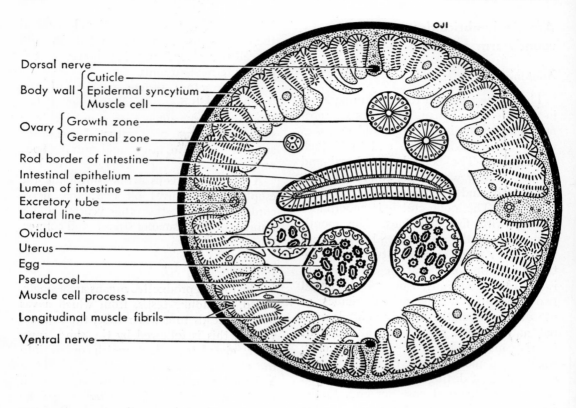

OJI

Dorsal nerve
Body wall { Cuticle
            Epidermal syncytium
            Muscle cell
Ovary { Growth zone
        Germinal zone
Rod border of intestine
Intestinal epithelium
Lumen of intestine
Excretory tube
Lateral line
Oviduct
Uterus
Egg
Pseudocoel
Muscle cell process
Longitudinal muscle fibrils
Ventral nerve

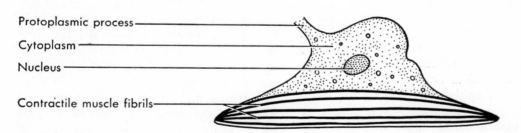

Protoplasmic process
Cytoplasm
Nucleus
Contractile muscle fibrils

FIGURE 79. Cross section of a female *Ascaris* in the *upper* figure. Details of a muscle cell in the *lower* figure.

tine, where they begin to hatch within a few hours.

The newly hatched **larvae** burrow into the wall of the small intestine and enter the veins or lymphatic vessels. If the larvae pass into the lymphatics, they are eventually carried into the blood and to the right side of the heart. They may also be carried in the blood to the liver and then to the right

side of the heart. From here they pass on to the lungs, where they pass into the air passages, after which they move through the trachea, throat, esophagus, and stomach, to the small intestine again. This journey through the host requires about 10 days. They become mature worms in the intestine in about 2½ months.

Ascaris worms found in man and pigs are

structurally indistinguishable, but they differ physiologically in that the human ascaris eggs do not usually produce mature worms in pigs and vice versa.

How does the intestinal parasite resist digestion?

This is a very interesting and perplexing question. That they resist digestion when alive is common knowledge. However the mechanism is by no means clear although much research has been done on it. There are two schools of thought: (1) that there is a passive anti-enzyme action, due to the chemical constitution of the parasite, which makes it resistant to enzyme action, and (2) that the parasite secretes chemical substances by means of which the host's digestive enzymes are neutralized or inhibited.

In the case of nematodes there is some experimental evidence for the production of enzyme-inhibiting substances. More specifically, there is recent proof of an interference with the digestion of dietary protein by intestinal juices because of the anti-enzymatic action of the ascaris. This strongly suggests that there is an anti-enzyme secreted by the ascaris, which counteracts the effect of the host's digestive enzymes. Of course, the thick cuticle covering this worm provides some protection from the host's digestive juices.

The results of investigations on the resistance of tapeworms to digestion have been inconclusive.

Free-living roundworms

The vinegar eel

The vinegar eel *Turbatrix (Anguillula) aceti* is a free-living nematode, easily obtained at any time of the year from the bottom of a cider vinegar barrel. It is visible to the naked eye when held before a bright light and exhibits characteristic nematode movements. Heating the vinegar for a minute kills and straightens vinegar eels, and clearing them in phenol, after fixing, reveals the internal organs.

The **female** worm is about 2 mm. and the **male** about 1.4 mm. in length. Most of the anatomical features of a female are shown in Fig. 80. The **eggs** are not only fertilized within the body of the female but also develop there. The thin egg membrane ruptures in the uterus and the young are born in an active condition, that is, the vinegar eel is **ovoviviparous**. One female may produce as many as 45 larvae. Males and females are equal in number; they may live for 10 months or more.

Other free-living roundworms

Free-living nematodes are mostly small, a large specimen being only one cm. in length. Many of them possess an **oral spear** with which they puncture the roots of plants, badly injuring economically valuable species, as well as others. Several hundred millions of dollars of damage result every year from these attacks. They live in almost every conceivable type of environment, such as wet sand or mud, aquatic vegetation, standing or running water, the soil, the sea, tap water, fruit juices, and moist places almost everywhere. They have been found in such varied habitats as Pike's Peak, Alpine snows, the Antarctic Ocean, and in hot springs. "If all the matter in the universe, except the nematodes, were swept away, our world would still be dimly recognizable, and if, as disembodied spirits, we could then investigate it, we should find its mountains, hills, vales, rivers, lakes, and oceans represented by a film of nematodes. The location of towns would be decipherable, since for every massing of human beings there would be a corresponding massing of certain nematodes. Trees would still stand in ghostly rows representing our streets and highways. The location of the various plants and animals would still be decipherable, and, had we sufficient knowledge, in many

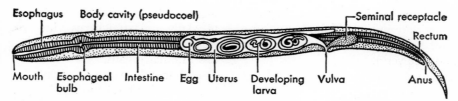

Figure 80. Internal structure of the free-living vinegar eel. Parts of digestive and reproductive systems are shown. Natural size 2 mm. in length.

cases even their species could be determined by an examination of their erstwhile nematode parasites" (Cobb).

Parasitic plant nematodes

Nematodes live in or on many different kinds of plants, causing enormous economic loss. More than 1000 different species of nematodes are known to attack plants. The damage these tiny parasites do on American farms amounts to $500,000,000 a year. The common garden roundworm *Meloidogyne* lives in roots of over 1700 species of plants. The worms lay their eggs either directly in the roots or in the nearby soil. Certain nematodes stimulate plant tissue to form knotlike galls on the roots. Others enter leaves and move about eating the contents of the cells. Some worms stay on the surface of the plant, bury their heads into the tissue, and suck out the juice. These parasites sap the plant's vigor, open the way for bacteria and fungi, and injure growing points. The only means of control of these plant parasites is by crop rotation, soil sterilization, and development of resistant varieties of plants. A lima bean has recently been developed by scientists which is nematode resistant.

Other parasitic roundworms

Among the representative roundworms that may be found in other vertebrate animals are the cecum worm of chickens, the dog ascarid, the horse roundworm, and horsehair worms.

The dog ascarid

Toxocara canis is especially prevalent in puppies which became infected through the placenta. Dogs become infected by swallowing the eggs. The larvae migrate through the body as do those of *Ascaris* in man. Dogs acquire an immunity as a result of the infection; and after three or four months, the worms are cast out and susceptibility to further infection is greatly reduced.

The cecum worm of chickens

Heterakis gallinae (Fig. 81) lays eggs, which are passed in the feces of infected birds and are swallowed by other birds; the young that hatch from these eggs in the small intestine move on into the ceca. They do not seriously injure the fowls but are of great economic importance since they carry with them a protozoan parasite, *Histomonas meleagridis*, which is the causative agent of the disease of turkeys known as blackhead.

The horse roundworm

Horse strongyle (*Strongylus vulgaris*) is world-wide in distribution but especially prevalent in warm countries. It lives in the cecum or colon, attached by the mouth to the mucosa, from which it sucks blood. Loss of blood results in anemia. The eggs of *Strongylus* are deposited in the feces, where they give rise to infective larvae. These, when ingested by a horse, migrate to the posterior mesenteric artery, where an aneurysm may be produced; they then move on to the cecum where they become encysted in the submucosa; and finally they break out

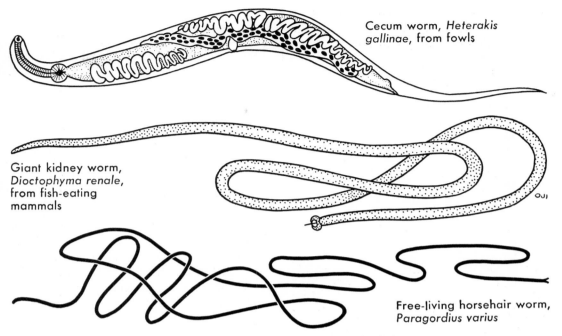

Cecum worm, *Heterakis gallinae*, from fowls

Giant kidney worm, *Dioctophyma renale*, from fish-eating mammals

Free-living horsehair worm, *Paragordius varius*

FIGURE 81.   Roundworms, parasitic and free-living.

into the lumen, attach themselves to the mucosa, and develop into adults.

PARASTIC ROUNDWORMS OF MAN

Ascaris lumbricoides

Human beings are parasitized by at least 45 species of roundworms, some of which are widespread and cause great suffering and thousands of deaths annually. *Ascaris lumbricoides* is an important human parasite. One survey in the tropics showed that in over 200 natives studied, only one did not suffer from ascariasis. When large numbers of the ascaris larvae pass through the lungs, inflammation is set up and generalized pneumonia may result. The adults may be present in the intestine in such large numbers as to produce fatal intestinal obstruction. One thousand to five thousand worms have been recorded in a patient, but even a hun-

dred worms can cause a blockage that is fatal. One of the most frequent complaints of a patient suffering from **ascariasis** is abdominal pain or discomfort. Nervous symptoms such as headache or convulsions may appear as a result of the secretion of toxic substances by the worms. Fortunately, several drugs are available which remove the worms. The amount of infection with ascarids is a measure of the sanitation present in the region. In some areas and economic strata in the United States there is still considerable worm infection. Ascariasis occurs more frequently in children than in adults because of the carelessness of children with regard to sanitary matters. Infection can be prevented by enforcing sanitary practices.

Hookworms

The hookworms, *Ancylostoma duodenale*, and *Necator americanus* (Fig. 82) are also widespread and injurious; about 95 per cent of the hookworms in the United States are of the latter species. The larvae develop in moist earth and usually find their way into the bodies of human beings by boring through the skin of the foot. They enter a lymph or blood vessel and pass to the heart; from the heart they reach the lungs, where they make their way through the air passages into the windpipe (trachea), and thence into the intestine. The adults attach themselves to the walls of the intestine and by suction they feed upon the blood and tissue juices. In the case of the dog hookworm and probably also of the human hookworm, blood is continuously being sucked into the body of the worm and expelled from the anus in the form of droplets, consisting mainly of red corpuscles. Calculations indicate that a single worm may withdraw blood from the host at the rate of 0.8 ml. in 24 hours. When the intestinal wall is punctured, a small amount of poison is poured into the wound by the worm. This poison prevents the blood from coagulating and therefore results in a considerable loss of blood, even after the worm has left the wound. The victims of the hookworm are anemic and subject to other diseases because of malnutrition. Hookworm disease is not as serious in this country as it once was, although there is still some infection in the southeastern coastal states. However, hookworm disease is very prevalent in large areas of the tropics where soil and climate favor these parasites. In fact, hookworm is considered the most important parasitic intestinal worm of man. Hookworm disease can be cured by several drugs, but tetrachloroethylene or hexylresorcinal are commonly used by physicians. The most important preventive measure is the disposing of human feces in rural districts, mines, brickyards, etc., in such a manner as to avoid pollution of the soil, thus giving the eggs of the parasites contained in the feces of infected human beings no opportunity to hatch and develop to the infective larval stage.

Trichina worms

Trichinella spiralis causes the disease of human beings, pigs, and rats which is called **trichinosis**. Estimates in 1953 placed the number of persons in the United States infested with trichinae at several million, undiagnosed cases at several hundred thousand, and animal deaths at several thousand. The parasites enter the human body when inadequately cooked meat from an infected pig or bear is eaten (Fig. 83). The larvae soon become mature in the human intestine, and each mature worm deposits from 1500 to 2500 living larvae. These larvae are either placed directly into the lymph or blood vessels by the female worms, or they burrow through the intestinal wall; they eventually encyst in muscular tissue in various parts of the body. As many as 15,000 encysted parasites have been counted in a single gram of muscle.

Pigs acquire the disease chiefly by eating restaurant meat scraps and slaughterhouse garbage; however, infected rats may be a source of infection also. The incidence of trichinosis among hogs fed with raw garbage is almost 20 times higher than the incidence among other hogs. In this country, it has not been found practical for the government to inspect pork for the trichina worm. The only protection is to avoid eating pink pork. Pink color in freshly cooked pork is evidence of inadequate cooking.

It has been stated that there is a death rate of about 5 per cent of those who actually show symptoms for trichinosis; specific treatment is lacking. ACTH hormone and cortisone provide relief from symptoms and may prevent a fatal outcome. Trichinosis seems to be a greater problem in the United States than in most countries. However, it is on the decrease because of a relatively recent law (1953), in most states, which requires the cooking of garbage before feeding it to hogs. Recent experiments have shown that a dose of 25,000 rep (rep is a unit of radiation) of gamma radiation is sufficient

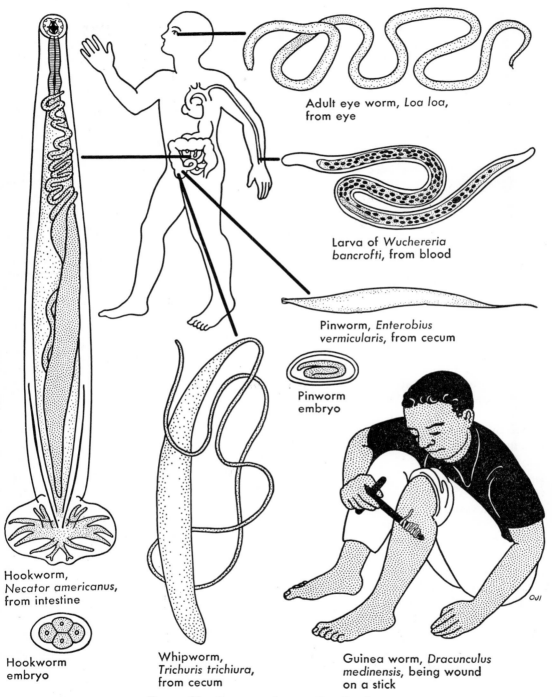

Adult eye worm, *Loa loa*, from eye

Larva of *Wuchereria bancrofti*, from blood

Pinworm, *Enterobius vermicularis*, from cecum

Pinworm embryo

Hookworm, *Necator americanus*, from intestine

Hookworm embryo

Whipworm, *Trichuris trichiura*, from cecum

Guinea worm, *Dracunculus medinensis*, being wound on a stick

FIGURE 82. Some roundworms that live in man.

157

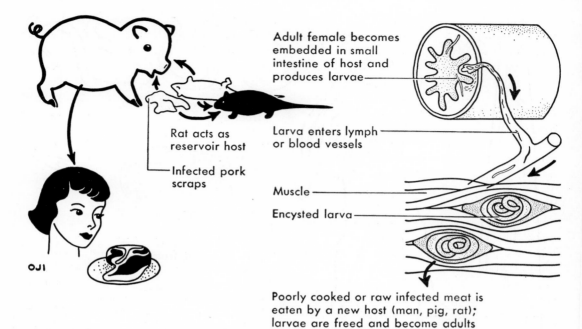

Adult female becomes
embedded in small
intestine of host and
produces larvae

Rat acts as
reservoir host

Larva enters lymph
or blood vessels

Infected pork
scraps

Muscle

Encysted larva

Poorly cooked or raw infected meat is
eaten by a new host (man, pig, rat);
larvae are freed and become adults

FIGURE 83. Life cycle of *Trichinella*.

to destroy the *Trichinella* larvae in pork and
make it safe for human consumption even
though the meat is not thoroughly cooked.
Further studies are needed to determine the
practicality of radiation in the control of
trichinosis.

Pinworms

The pinworm of man, *Enterobius vermicularis* (Fig. 82), measures from 9 to 12
mm. in length, is world-wide in distribution,
and lives in the adult stage in the upper
part of the large intestine. Pinworm infection is nearly a universal experience of mankind in infancy, since nearly all children
become infected. Most cases show no symptoms and many children get over the disease
without treatment. In some cases, however,
the infection persists, even into adulthood.
Sometimes over 5000 worms are present in
a single person. Sample surveys of white
children in the United States and Canada
revealed that 30 to 60 per cent were infected. Colored races are less susceptible.
Species of pinworms, closely related to the

one that lives in man, occur in monkeys
and apes.

Whipworms

Trichuris trichiura (Fig. 82) lives primarily
in the cecum and appendix of man. Its
body is drawn out anteriorly into a long
slender, whiplike process. There is no intermediate host. The eggs escape in the feces
and ripen outside of the body. Ripe eggs
when swallowed hatch in the intestine, and
the larvae become located in the cecum.
Heavy infections may cause abdominal discomfort, anemia, and bloody stools. It has
been estimated that there are 355.1 million
people in the world infected with whip-
worms. Sanitary disposal of human excrement breaks the life cycle and prevents the
spread of this parasite.

Filaria worms

Wuchereria bancrofti is a species of filaria
that is widely spread in tropical countries.
The larvae of this species are about $\frac{1}{100}$

inch long (Fig. 82). Mosquitoes, which are active at night, suck up these larvae with the blood of the infected person. The larvae of the worms develop in the body of a mosquito, make their way into the mouth parts, and enter the blood of the mosquito's next victim. From the blood they migrate to the lymphatics, where they become adults and obstruct the lymph passages, often causing serious disturbances. This may result in a condition called **elephantiasis** (Fig. 84). The limbs, scrotum, or other regions of the body swell up to an enormous size. Infection with this parasite is common in man, especially in the South Pacific islands, the West Indies, South America, and west and central Africa. A recent survey on St. Croix, one of the Virgin Islands, showed 16 per cent of the people suffering with filariasis. Thousands of World War II service men

FIGURE 84. Elephantiasis due to *Wuchereria bancrofti.* This woman lives on a South Pacific Island. The infection started in the left arm when she was 33 years of age, and at 38 both arms and legs were affected. This photograph was taken at the age of 43. The filaria worms block the lymph vessels, which results in the diversion of lymph into the tissues and the enormous growth of connective tissue. (Courtesy of W.A. Robinson.)

contracted filariasis in the islands of the South Pacific. These men made good recovery and none showed the severe symptoms exhibited in old chronic cases among native inhabitants. Another interesting species of filaria is the eye worm, *Loa loa,* of West Africa (Fig. 82). The adult migrates around the body through the subdermal connective tissue and sometimes across the eyeball. No severe pathological lesions are produced.

Guinea worm

Dracunculus medinensis, the guinea worm, is a common human parasite in tropical Africa, Arabia, India, South America, and the West Indies. It has been known for centuries and is probably the "fiery serpent" mentioned by Moses (Numbers 21). The adult female, which may reach a length of over three feet, is usually located in the subcutaneous tissue of the arms, legs, and shoulders. The young larvae are discharged from the worm and escape through an opening in the human skin when that part of the body is submerged in water. The larvae may be eaten by the water flea (*Cyclops*), and man becomes infected by swallowing the water fleas in drinking water. The method of extracting the worm, practiced by natives for hundreds of years, is to roll it up gradually on a stick, a few turns each day, until the entire worm has been drawn from the body (Fig. 82). Serious poisoning of the host occurs if the worm is broken.

Beneficial nematodes

Research has discovered a beneficial roundworm that attacks insects, and there is good evidence that this nematode can be used in pest control because it carries a type of bacteria that quickly kills many insects. The nematode acts as a microsyringe to introduce the bacterium into the infected insect's body cavity. This bacterium has proved deadly not only to codling moths but to at least 35 other kinds of insects, including the corn earworm, boll weevil, pink bollworm, vegetable weevil, cabbage worm, and white fringed beetle.

Origin and relations of the Nemathelminthes

The Nemathelminthes seem to occupy a rather isolated position in the animal series. In many respects they resemble the platyhelminthes; they are unsegmented and possess excretory canals but no flame cells. There is an absence of cilia. In the nematodes, we encounter, for the first time, animals with two openings in the digestive tract, a mouth and an anus. The sexes are usually separate, whereas in the Platyhelminthes hermaphroditism is the rule. The parasitic roundworms evolved from free-living roundworms.

PHYLUM NEMATOMORPHA OR HORSEHAIR WORMS

The horsehair worms

The name "horsehair" comes from a popular superstition, not yet dead, that this roundworm develops from horsehairs that fall into water. Actually their life cycle is as follows. The adults live in fresh water where the eggs are laid. The larvae that hatch from the eggs penetrate the body of some aquatic insect larva. These worms migrate to the body cavity and continue to develop until they escape as young adults or juveniles. They have been found in different stages of development in the body cavities of beetles, crickets, and grasshoppers, all of which are terrestrial, suggesting that these land forms may eat aquatic insects containing the minute roundworm larvae. Infested crickets appear to migrate to the edge of water, and, if caught by a wave, *Paragordius* emerges from their bodies within 20 to 50 seconds. What brings the

crickets to the water is problematical. However, one investigator discovered that when crickets found near the edge of a lake were placed in the water, a horsehair worm invariably escaped from the cricket's body in less than a minute, but crickets collected 100 to 300 feet from the lake did not yield worms. *Paragordius varius* is a horsehair worm common in North America (Fig. 81).

The Nematomorpha are like the Nemathelminthes because of body form, presence of cuticle, simple musculature, and absence of segmentation. However, in Nematomorpha there are important differences, such as a body cavity which is nearly filled with parenchyma, a degenerate digestive tract in adults, a single nerve cord, and a cloaca. No circulatory, respiratory, or excretory organs are present in the Nematomorpha. The physiology of this group is not well understood.

PHYLUM ACANTHOCEPHALA (SPINY-HEADED WORMS)

The spiny-headed worms

These peculiar parasitic worms (Fig. 85) belong to the phylum Acanthocephala, a name that means spiny-headed and refers to a retractile proboscis armed with rows of recurved hooks. They live in the intestine of vertebrates and are attached to the wall by a protrusible proboscis covered with recurved hooks; they vary in length from less than an inch to more than a foot. The body of most species is elongate, flattened, and capable of extension. No digestive tract is present at any stage in their life cycle, food being absorbed directly from the host's intestine. The sexes are separate, and the reproductive systems are complex. Species have been reported in the United States from fish, turtles, birds, rats, mice, pigs, squirrels, dogs, and man.

The Acanthocephala differ from the Nem-

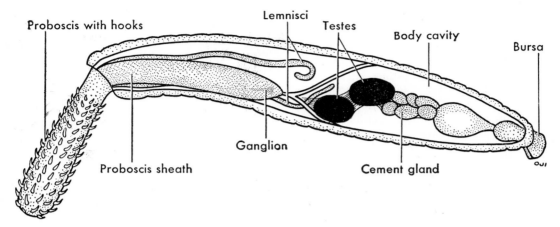

FIGURE 85. Spiny-headed worm, Acanthocephala: internal structure. These intestinal parasites are found in all classes of vertebrates. Occasionally the worms cause perforation of the gut of the host, resulting in its death.

athelminthes in the absence of a digestive tract, presence of a proboscis, circular muscles, ciliated excretory organs, and certain peculiarities in the reproductive organs.

CLASSIFICATION OF THE NEMATHELMINTHES, NEMATOMORPHA, AND ACANTHOCEPHALA

(For reference purposes only)

Phylum Nemathelminthes (Aschelminthes). These roundworms are unsegmented, three-germ-layered (triploblastic), bilaterally symmetrical animals. The body is cylindrical and elongate with tough resistant cuticle. Digestive tract is a straight tube with mouth and anus at opposite ends of the body. Body wall with longitudinal muscles only; space within body is a pseudocoel. There are no respiratory nor circulatory organs; excretory organs are simple, consisting of one, two, or none. The nerve ring around the esophagus connects with other nerves or cords. No cilia are present and the sexes are usually separate. One class and 5 orders are listed here as follows:

Class 1. Nematoda. With intestine but no proboscis. Body cavity not lined with epithelium; gonads continuous with their ducts; no cloaca in female; lateral lines present.

Order 1. Ascaroidea. Free-living or parasitic; with three prominent lips. Ex. *Ascaris lumbricoides* (Fig. 78).

Order 2. Strongyloidea. Parasitic; male with copulatory bursa supported by muscular rays; esophagus club-shaped and without posterior bulb. Ex. *Necator Americanus* (Fig. 82).

Order 3. Filarioidea. Parasitic; filiform worms without lips; esophagus without bulb, the anterior portion being muscular and the posterior glandular. Ex. *Wuchereria bancrofti* (Fig. 82).

Order 4. Dioctophymoidea. Parasitic; moderate to very long nematodes; mouth without lips, surrounded by 6, 12, or 18 papillae; esophagus elongated without bulb. Ex. *Dioctophyma renale* (Fig. 81).

Order 5. Trichuroidea or Trichinelloidea. Parasitic. Body filiform anteriorly; mouth without lips; esophageal portion of body more or less distinct; esophagus a cuticular tube embedded in a single row of cells. Ex. *Trichinella spiralis* (Fig. 83).

Phylum Nematomorpha or Gordiacea. Very long slender cylindrical worms; gonoducts in both sexes enter the intestine; lateral nerve cords absent. Parasitic as juveniles, adult free-living. Ex. *Paragordius* (Fig. 81).

Phylum Acanthocephala. Parasitic; without intestine but with spiny proboscis. Ex. *Leptorhynchoides thecatus* (Fig. 85).

SELECTED COLLATERAL READINGS

Baer, J.G. *Ecology of Animal Parasites.* Univ. of Illinois Press, Urbana, Ill., 1952.

Chandler, A.C. *Introduction to Parasitology.* Wiley, New York, 1955.

Chitwood, B.G. and others. *An Introduction to Nematology.* Monumental Pub. Co., Baltimore, 1950.

Goodey, T. *Plant Parasitic Nematodes.* Dutton, New York, 1933.

Hull, T.G., and others. *Diseases Transmitted from Animals to Man.* Thomas, Springfield, Ill., 1946.

Hyman, L.H. *The Invertebrates: Acanthocephala, Aschelminthes and Entoprocta.* McGraw-Hill, New York, 1951.

Pearse, A.S. *Introduction to Parasitology.* Thomas, Springfield, Ill., 1942.

Shipley, A.E. "Nemathelminthes." *Cambridge Natural History,* Vol. 2. Macmillan, London, 1896.

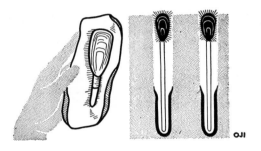

CHAPTER 14

Miscellaneous
Minor Phyla

A NUMBER of groups of animals are considered together here because their relationships to other animals and to each other are rather uncertain. This chapter is something of an invertebrate catchall; it contains several groups that in prehistoric times were large, but at present are represented by relatively few types. However, an introduction to general zoology would be incomplete without at least a look at these interesting though highly specialized groups.

PHYLUM NEMERTINA (RHYNCHOCOELA)— RIBBON WORMS

The members of the phylum are called ribbon worms because they are long and flattened dorsoventrally (Fig. 86). They range in length from less than an inch to over 90 feet. Most live in the sea, but a few inhabit fresh water and land.

The most important anatomic features of the nemertines are the presence of (1) a long retractile **proboscis**, which lies in a proboscis sheath just above the digestive tract and may be everted and used as a tactile, and a defensive organ; (2) a **blood vascular system**, usually consisting of a median dorsal and two lateral trunks; and (3) a **complete digestive tract** with both **mouth** and **anal openings**. The circulatory system is encountered here for the first time.

The nemertines resemble the free-living flatworm or Turbellaria in being bilaterally symmetrical, in having flame cells, unsegmented and contractile bodies, and in lacking a true coelom and respiratory system. However, they differ from the flatworms in that they have a complete digestive system with mouth and anus, a functional circulatory system, a less complex reproductive system, and they are usually dioecious.

Nemertines feed on other animals, both dead and alive. They live, as a rule, coiled up in burrows in mud, sand, or under stones, but some of them frequent patches of sea-

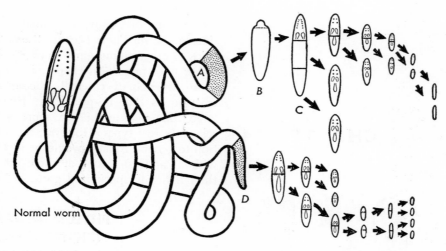

Normal worm

FIGURE 86. *Lineus:* regeneration in a ribbon worm. A, section cut from body. B, its appearance after 12 days. C, the same after 30 days, cut in 3 pieces. Successive cuttings and regenerations indicated by arrows. This worm occurs around Long Island Sound. (After Coe.)

weed. Locomotion is effected by the cilia which cover the surface of the body, by contractions of the body muscles, or by the attachment of the proboscis and a subsequent drawing forward of the body. The adults have great powers of regeneration and some reproduce in warm weather by fragmentation of the body (Fig. 86). If, for example, *Lineus socialis*, which is only 100 mm. in length, is cut into as many as 100 pieces, each piece will regenerate a minute worm within four or five weeks. These minute worms may again be cut into pieces that regenerate, and these in turn may be cut up, and so on, until miniature worms result which are less than $\frac{1}{200,000}$ the volume of the original worm.

PHYLUM ROTIFERA (ROTATORIA)

The Rotifera or Rotatoria are commonly known as wheel animals (Fig. 87). The common name refers to the beating of the cilia on the head, which suggests the rotation of wheels. These cilia aid in locomotion and draw food into the mouth. The rotifers are, generally speaking, the smallest of the Meta-

zoa. Because the rotifers possess fantastic forms and brilliant colors they usually attract the attention of amateur microscopists. Most are inhabitants of fresh water, but some are marine, and a few parasitic. The tail-like **foot** is often forked and adheres to objects by means of a secretion from the cement glands. The body is usually cylindrical and is covered by a shell-like **cuticle.**

Protozoa, other minute organisms, and debris, used as food, are swept by the cilia through the **mouth** into the **pharynx,** the lower end of which forms the very characteristic grinding organ called the **mastax.** Here **chitinlike jaws,** which are constantly at work, break up the food. The movements of these jaws easily distinguish a living rotifer from other animals. A short **esophagus** leads into the **stomach.** The food is digested in the glandular stomach, or in the stomach and intestine, depending on the species. Undigested particles pass through the **intestine** into the **cloaca** and out of the **cloacal opening** ("anus"). The excretory system consists of two long tubes with **flame cells** at intervals along their sides. These tubes open into a **bladder** which contracts at intervals, forcing the

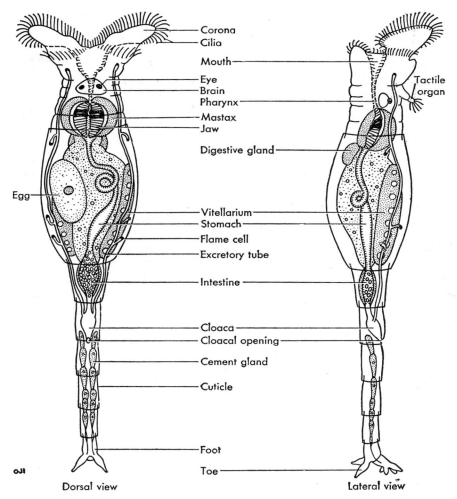

Corona
Cilia
Mouth
Eye
Brain
Pharynx
Mastax
Jaw
Tactile organ
Digestive gland
Egg
Vitellarium
Stomach
Flame cell
Excretory tube
Intestine
Cloaca
Cloacal opening
Cement gland
Cuticle
Foot
Toe
Dorsal view
Lateral view

FIGURE 87. Phylum Rotifera. General structure of a female rotifer. *Left*, dorsal view. *Right*, lateral view of the same animal.

contents into the cloaca and then out the cloacal opening. This bladder, besides being excretory in function, doubtless serves to maintain a proper water balance in the animal, just as the contractile vacuole does in the protozoans.

The sexes of rotifers are separate. The males are known in only a few species; and where found, they are usually smaller than the females, and often degenerate. Two kinds of eggs are laid: the **summer eggs**, which develop **parthenogenetically**, are thin-shelled and commonly of 2 sizes; the larger produce females and the smaller pro-

duce males. The **winter eggs**, which are fertilized, develop into females and have thick shells which protect the contents during unfavorable weather.

One peculiarity of rotifers is their power to resist desiccation. Certain species, if dried slowly, secrete gelatinous envelopes which prevent further drying; in this condition they live through seasons of drought and may be subjected to extremes of temperature without dying.

The resemblances between certain rotifers and the **trochophore larvae** of certain mollusks, annelids, and other animals to be described later is quite striking. This has led to the theory that the rotifers are animals somewhat closely related to the ancestors of the mollusks, annelids, and certain other groups. However, some of the most competent investigators believe that these resemblances of certain trochophore larvae are purely coincidental, the result of adaptive radiation and of no evolutionary significance. It appears more likely that the rotifers have originated from a primitive turbellarian.

Some common rotifers are *Epiphanes senta* (formerly called *Hydatina senta*), a species used widely for experimental purposes; *Asplanchna,* which often occurs in enormous numbers in the plankton of the Great Lakes; *Floscularia,* which lives in a transparent tube and has a beautiful corona with 5 knobbed lobes; *Melicerta* which builds for itself a tube of spherical pellets; and *Philodina* (Fig. 87), characterized by a slender rose-colored body.

The rotifers eat microscopic organisms which they convert into their own tissues. In turn the rotifers may serve as food for larger species and eventually, through fish, serve as food for man. Thus the rotifers may serve an important part in a fresh-water food chain.

PHYLUM BRYOZOA
(POLYZOA)

The Bryozoa, a name that means "moss animals," are so-called because they appear plantlike. They are mostly colonial, and resemble hydroids in form, but they are more advanced in internal structure (Fig. 88). The majority of them live in the sea, but a few inhabit fresh water. *Bugula* is a common marine genus, and *Plumatella* is the most common fresh-water genus. A colony of *Plumatella* is made up of cylindrical, more or less branched, tubes. These **tubes** protect the soft parts of the body. The anterior end of the body of *Plumatella* consists

of a rounded ridge called a **lophophore;** this bears a horseshoe-shaped double row of **tentacles.** These tentacles are from 40 to 60 in number, hollow, and ciliated. When these tentacles are spread out in the water, the cilia cause currents that sweep microscopic food organisms into the mouth. The **mouth, esophagus, stomach, cecum, intestine** and **anus** of *Plumatella* are shown in Fig. 88. Between the digestive tract and the body wall is a true **coelom** which is lined with a peritoneum. There are no **respiratory, circulatory,** or **excretory organs.** Bryozoans are hermaphroditic. The larvae of some of them resemble a **trochophore** (Fig. 107). This suggests an ancient origin from some annelid stock.

Certain fresh-water Bryozoa produce disklike buds (Fig. 88) which secrete a hard chitinous shell and are known as **statoblasts.** These survive when the animal dies in the fall or during a drought, giving rise to a new colony in the spring or when the wet season returns.

Of special interest is the fouling of pipes by certain fresh-water bryozoans. They form thick crusts inside pipes, and dead colonies sometimes break loose, become fragmented, and clog small pipes and meters.

In prehistoric times there were many more species than are living today. Since their first appearance in the Cambrian period (an early geologic period), bryozoans have made substantial contributions to layers of calcareous rock in every geologic period.

PHYLUM BRACHIOPODA
(LAMP SHELLS)

The Brachiopoda are marine animals living within a calcareous **bivalve shell** (Fig. 89). They are usually attached to some object by a muscular stalk called the **peduncle.** Because of their shell, they were long regarded as mollusks. The valves of the shell, however, are dorsal and ventral instead of lateral as in the bivalve mollusks. The name

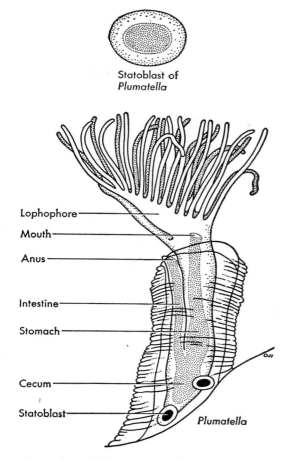

Statoblast of
Plumatella

Lophophore
Mouth
Anus
Intestine
Stomach
Cecum
Statoblast

Plumatella

Figure 88. Phylum Bryozoa. *Plumatella*, a common fresh-water bryozoan. *Below*, drawing showing the structure of a single individual (a zooid). Enlarged. *Above*, statoblast of *Plumatella*.

"lamp shell" refers to the resemblance of the shells to the oil lamps of the Romans. Within the shell is a conspicuous structure, the **lophophore**, which consists of two coiled ridges, called **arms**; these bear ciliated tentacles. Food is drawn into the **mouth** by the lophophore. A true **coelom** is present, within which lie the **stomach, digestive gland**, short blind **intestine**, and the "**heart**."

The group Brachiopoda is extremely old, dating since Cambrian time; and, although found in all seas today, brachiopods were formerly more numerous in species and of much greater variety in form than at present. Some of them, for example *Lingula*, are apparently the same today as they were in the Ordovician period, estimated at over 400 million years ago. *Lingula* (see headpiece, p. 163) is thought to be the oldest animal genus known; it is called a "living fossil" because it has not changed, on the outside at least, during long geologic periods.

PHYLUM CHAETOGNATHA (ARROW WORMS)

The Chaetognatha are marine animals which swim about near the surface of the sea (Fig. 89). The best-known genus is *Sagitta*, the arrow worm. The bilaterally symmetrical body consists of three regions, **head, trunk**, and **tail. Lateral** and **caudal fins** are present. There is a distinct **coelom**, a **digestive tract** with **mouth, intestine**, and **anus**, a well-developed **nervous system**, two **eyes**, and other **sensory organs**. There are no circulatory, respiratory, or excretory organs. The mouth has a lobe on either side provided with **bristles** which are used in capturing the minute animals and plants that serve as food. The members of the group are **hermaphroditic**. Many species are very widely distributed.

PHYLUM GASTROTRICHA

To this group belong certain microscopic animals that live in both fresh and salt water and are often abundant among algae and debris upon which they feed. They range in length from 0.06 to 1.5 mm. The gastrotrichs resemble some ciliate protozoans (Fig. 89). The body is indistinctly divided into **head, neck, trunk**, and **toes**. The **mouth**, which is at the anterior end, is surrounded by oral bristles; locomotion is accomplished by longitudinal bands of cilia on the ventral surface. On the dorsal surface there are many slender spines. The **intestine**

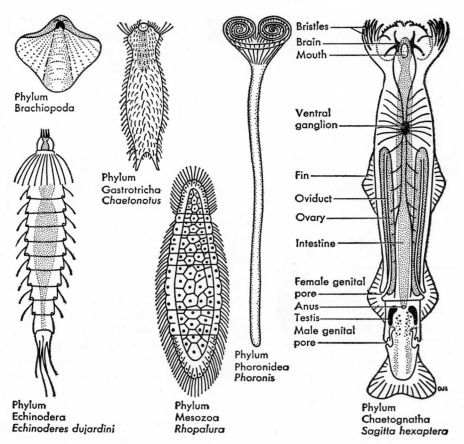

Phylum
Brachiopoda

Phylum
Gastrotricha
Chaetonotus

Bristles
Brain
Mouth

Ventral
ganglion

Fin
Oviduct
Ovary
Intestine

Female genital
pore
Anus
Testis
Male genital
pore

Phylum
Phoronidea
Phoronis

Phylum
Echinodera
Echinoderes dujardini

Phylum
Mesozoa
Rhopalura

Phylum
Chaetognatha
Sagitta hexaptera

FIGURE 89. Phylum Brachiopoda. Ventral view of the shell (one-half natural size). Phylum Mesozoa; *Rhopalura*, a parasite of the brittle star. Phylum Gastrotricha; *Chaetonotus*, a free-living species. Phylum Phoronidea; *Phoronis*, removed from its tube. Phylum Echinodera; *Echinoderes dujardini*, a marine species. Phylum Chaetognatha; *Sagitta hexaptera*, an arrow worm (6 mm. in length).

is a straight tube leading to an **anus** near the posterior end of the body. The excretory organs are a pair of coiled tubes with a **flame cell** at the inner end of each. The eggs are very large. There is no larval stage. About 200 species of Gastrotricha are known. *Chaetonotus* (Fig. 89) is a typical gastrotrich.

PHYLUM PHORONIDEA

Most of the species in this group, about 15 in all, belong to the genus *Phoronis* (Fig. 89). They are small, wormlike, marine ani-

mals of sedentary habit, that live in tubes. The larva, called an actinotrocha, is free-swimming and resembles a trochophore. The adults are **unsegmented, coelomate, and hermaphroditic.** They possess a horseshoe-shaped **lophophore,** U-shaped **digestive tract,** two **ciliated nephridia,** and a **vascular system** which contains red blood corpuscles.

PHYLUM KINORHYNCHA (ECHINODERA)

The Echinodera are very small marine worms that range from 0.18 to 1 mm. in length. They live in the mud or sand on the bottom of either deep or shallow water. The body consists of a series of 13 or 14 rings, two of which form the head, which is encircled by spines and has a short retractile proboscis. There are two excretory organs, each consisting of a flame cell connected to a flagellated ciliated duct opening dorsally on ring 9. *Echinoderes dujardini* (Fig. 89) is reddish in color; it lives in mud and less often among algae in the north Atlantic Ocean.

PHYLUM MESOZOA

These are small slender animals, with the simplest structures of any metazoan. They are parasites; and their simplicity may be partly the result of modifications due to a parasitic existence. They live in the internal spaces and tissues of squids, flatworms, starfishes, annelids, and other invertebrates. The body consists of an outer layer of cells enclosing one or more reproductive cells. The life cycle is complicated by an alternation of sexual and asexual generations. *Dicyema* lives in the nephridia of the octopus, and *Rhopalura* (Fig. 89) parasitizes the gonads of the brittle star.

The Mesozoa resemble some colonial protozoans in that they have external cilia, digestion which occurs in external cells, and special reproductive cells as in *Volvox*. The Mesozoa are unlike the typical metazoans in that their two-cell layers are not comparable with the ectoderm and endoderm of typical metazoan animals, and they have no internal digestive tract. The name Mesozoa implies that these organisms are intermediate between the Protozoa and Metazoa, which, indeed, they may actually be. Either they are intermediate between unicellular and multicellular animals or else degenerate forms. Some of the best authorities believe that their characters are chiefly primitive and not the result of parasitic degeneration.

SELECTED COLLATERAL READINGS

Bassler, R.S. "The Bryozoa, or Moss Animals." *Smithsonian Inst. Ann. Rept.*, 1920.

Hyman, L.H. *The Invertebrates: Acanthocephala, Aschelminthes, and Entoprocta.* McGraw-Hill, New York, 1951.

Johnson, M.E., and Snook, H.J. *Seashore Animals of the Pacific Coast.* Macmillan, New York, 1927.

MacGinitie, G.E., and MacGinitie, N. *Natural History of Marine Animals.* McGraw-Hill, New York, 1949.

Michael, E.L. "Classification and Vertical Distribution of the Chaetognatha of the San Diego Region." *Univ. Calif. Pub. Zool.*, 1911.

Ward, H.B., and Whipple, G.C. *Freshwater Biology.* Wiley, New York, 1918. (New edition in press.)

CHAPTER 15

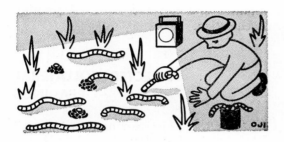

Phylum Annelida.
Segmented Worms

ANNELIDS (Fig. 90) are usually called segmented worms in order to distinguish them from flatworms and roundworms, which are not segmented. The body consists of a linear series of similar parts, which are known as segments, somites, or metameres. These are usually visible externally as rings; the rings of an earthworm's body and the vertebrae of man's backbone are evidences of segmentation.

Most annelids are marine, but many live in fresh water, in the soil, or in other moist places. Earthworms, sandworms, and leeches are common examples. Most everyone is familiar with the common earthworm for it is distributed all over the earth except in regions where the soil is nearly pure sand and in mountain regions where the soil is scanty and poor. For the most part earthworms are nocturnal. During the day they are usually hidden in their burrows, but at night they come out to feed. Apart from its being not difficult to obtain, the earthworm provides an opportunity for studying annelid characteristics under advantageous conditions.

Metamerism, both external and internal, is very conspicuous; the coelom is large and obvious; several systems of organs, such as the circulatory and nervous systems, are well developed; and the details of behavior, regeneration, and embryonic development are well known. Several other annelids are very briefly described; included in these are the sandworm, *Neanthes virens*,* which is representative of the class Polychaeta, and the leech, *Hirudo medicinalis*, of the class Hirudinea.

---

* There seems to be a rather common misconception that *Neanthes* is the generic name for a group of annelids formerly called *Nereis*. Both genera *Neanthes* and *Nereis* are old, well established, with many species attributed to each. Zoologists have sometimes identified specimens as *Nereis* when more critical determination would have shown that *Neanthes* was correct. Figure 99 was drawn from an actual specimen which came from a container labeled *Nereis*, but it was positively identified by Olga Hartman as *Neanthes*.

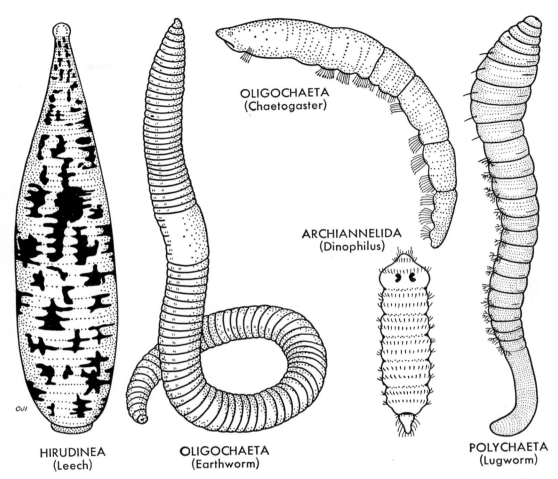

OLIGOCHAETA
(Chaetogaster)

ARCHIANNELIDA
(Dinophilus)

HIRUDINEA
(Leech)

OLIGOCHAETA
(Earthworm)

POLYCHAETA
(Lugworm)

FIGURE 90. Representatives of 4 classes of segmented worms. They are varied in form and widely distributed. The figures are not drawn to scale.

LUMBRICUS TERRESTRIS— AN EARTHWORM

The common earthworm, *Lumbricus terrestris*, serves well to illustrate the principal characteristics of the annelids. Figure 91 shows many of the structural features of a segmented worm.

Earthworms are soft and naked, and hence must live in moist earth; for this reason also they venture out of their burrows chiefly on damp nights. They are never "rained down" but are "rained up" out of their burrows when these are flooded. The burrows usually extend about two feet underground. Earth-worms can force their way through soft earth, but must eat their way through harder soil. The earth which has been eaten passes through the digestive tract and is deposited on the surface as castings.

External anatomy

The body of *Lumbricus* is cylindrical and varies in length from about 6 inches to 1 foot. The ventral surface is slightly flattened, and the dorsal surface is darker colored than the ventral surface. The **segments** (**somites**), of which there are over 100, are easily determined externally because of the

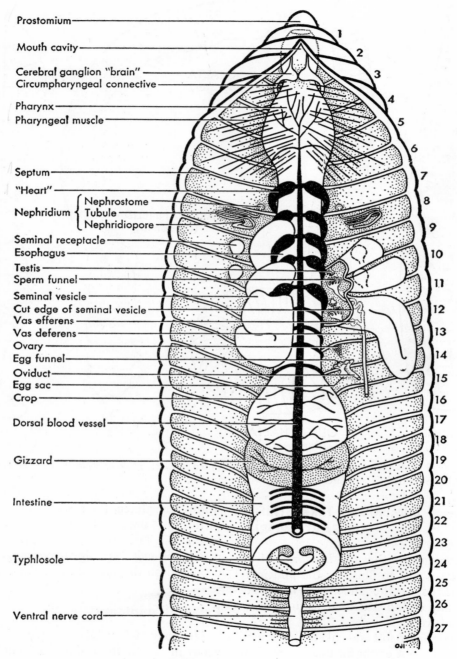

Prostomium

Mouth cavity

Cerebral ganglion "brain"
Circumpharyngeal connective

Pharynx
Pharyngeal muscle

Septum

"Heart"

Nephridium { Nephrostome
Tubule
Nephridiopore

Seminal receptacle
Esophagus

Testis
Sperm funnel

Seminal vesicle
Cut edge of seminal vesicle
Vas efferens
Vas deferens
Ovary
Egg funnel
Oviduct
Egg sac
Crop

Dorsal blood vessel

Gizzard

Intestine

Typhlosole

Ventral nerve cord

1
2
3
4
5
6
7
8
9
10
11
12
13
14
15
16
17
18
19
20
21
22
23
24
25
26
27

FIGURE 91. Anterior part of an earthworm with dorsal body wall removed to show the internal organs.

172

grooves extending around the body. At the anterior end a fleshy lobe, the **prostomium** (Fig. 94), projects over the **mouth;** this is not here considered a true segment, although some authors regard the prostomium as the first true segment. It is customary to number the segments, beginning at the anterior end, since both external and internal structures bear a constant relation to them. Segments 31 or 32 to 37 are swollen in mature worms, forming a saddle-shaped enlargement, the **clitellum,** of use during reproduction. Every segment, except the first and last, bears 4 pairs of chitinous bristles, the **setae** (Fig. 92); these may be moved by retractor and protractor muscles and are renewed if lost. The setae on segment 36, in mature worms, are modified for reproductive purposes.

The body is covered by a thin transparent **cuticle** secreted by the cells lying just beneath it. The cuticle protects the body from physical and chemical injury; it contains numerous **pores** to allow the secretions from unicellular glands to pass through; and it is marked with fine **striations,** causing the surface to appear iridescent.

A number of **external openings** of various sizes allow the entrance of food into the body, and the exit of feces, excretory products, reproductive cells, etc. (1) The mouth is a crescentic opening situated in the ventral half of the first segment (Fig. 94); it is overhung by the prostomium. (2) The oval **anal opening** lies in the last segment. (3) The openings of the sperm ducts or **vasa deferentia** are situated on each side of segment 15 (Fig. 91); they have swollen lips, and a slight ridge extends posteriorly from them to the clitellum. (4) The openings of the **oviducts** are small round pores, one on either side of segment 14; eggs pass out of the body through them. (5) The openings of the **seminal receptacles** appear as 2 pairs of minute pores concealed within the grooves which separate segments 9 and 10, and 10 and 11. (6) A pair of **nephridiopores** (Fig. 92), the external apertures of the excretory organs, open on every seg-

ment except the first 3 and the last. They are usually situated immediately anterior to the outer setae of the inner pair. (7) The body **cavity** or **coelom** communicates with the exterior by means of **dorsal pores.** One of these is located in the middorsal line at the anterior edge of each segment from 8 or 9 to the posterior end of the body.

Internal anatomy

If a specimen is cut open from the anterior to the posterior end by an incision passing through the body wall, a general view of the internal structures (Fig. 91) may be obtained. The body is essentially a double tube (Fig. 91); the body wall constituting the outer, and the straight digestive tract, the inner; between the two is a cavity, the **coelom.** The external segmentation corresponds to an internal division of the coelomic cavity into compartments by means of partitions called **septa,** which lie beneath the grooves (Fig. 91). The digestive tract passes through the center of the body and is suspended in the coelom by the partitions. Septa are absent between segments 1 and 2 and incomplete between segments 3 and 4, and 17 and 18. The walls of the coelom are lined with an **epithelium** termed the **peritoneum** (Fig. 92), which is derived from the mesoderm.

The coelomic cavity is filled with a colorless fluid which flows from one compartment to another when the body of the worm contracts, thus producing a sort of circulation. This is possible since a large opening is present in the median ventral part of each septum. In segments 9 to 16 are the reproductive organs; running along the upper surface of the digestive tract is the dorsal blood vessel; and just beneath it lie the ventral blood vessels and nerve cord. The body wall contains 2 layers of **muscles.** The outer layer lies beneath the epidermis and consists of **circular muscle** tissue. The muscle fibers are long and spindle-shaped; when they contract, the diam-

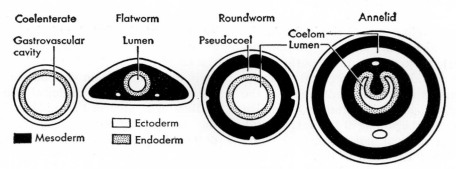

Coelenterate Flatworm Roundworm Annelid

Gastrovascular cavity Lumen Pseudocoel Coelom Lumen

■ Mesoderm □ Ectoderm ▨ Endoderm

The relationship of body cavities to germ cell layers

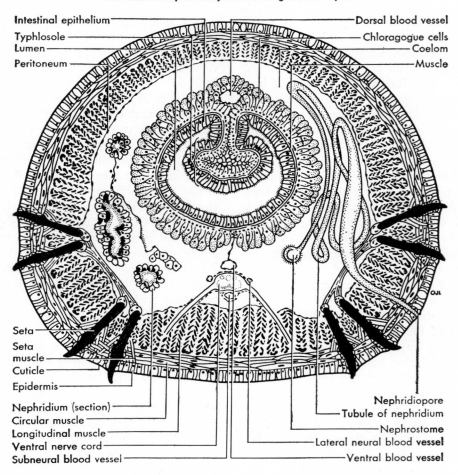

Intestinal epithelium
Typhlosole
Lumen
Peritoneum

Dorsal blood vessel
Chloragogue cells
Coelom
Muscle

Seta
Seta muscle
Cuticle
Epidermis

Nephridium (section)
Circular muscle
Longitudinal muscle
Ventral nerve cord
Subneural blood vessel

Nephridiopore
Tubule of nephridium
Nephrostome
Lateral neural blood vessel
Ventral blood vessel

FIGURE 92. *Top,* cross sections of a coelenterate, flatworm, roundworm, and annelid, designed to show the relationship of body cavities to the germ layers. *Bottom,* cross section of an earthworm, which illustrates the advances in complexity of structure, correlated with the appearance of a coelom and the development of systems of organs. *Left side* of drawing shows sectioned parts of nephridium as they actually appear, and *right side* shows an earthworm nephridium as it appears in a dissection. Rarely does a cross section show all four pairs of setae.

174

eter of the body becomes smaller and the worm longer. Under the circular layer is a thick **longitudinal layer** with muscle fibers lying parallel to the length of the worm; when these contract, the diameter of the body becomes greater and the worm shorter.

Digestive system

The digestive tract (Fig. 91) consists of (1) **a mouth (buccal) cavity** in segments 1 to 3; (2) a thick muscular **pharynx** lying in segments 4 and 5; (3) a narrow, straight tube, the **esophagus,** which extends through segments 6 to 14; (4) a thin-walled enlargement, the **crop (proventriculus),** in segments 15 and 16; (5) a thick muscular-walled **gizzard** in segments 17 and 18; and (6) a thin-walled **intestine** extending from segment 19 to the anal opening. The intestine is not a simple cylindrical tube, its dorsal wall is infolded, forming an internal longitudinal ridge, the **typhlosole** (Fig. 92); this increases the digestive surface. Surrounding the digestive tract and dorsal blood vessel is a layer of **chloragogue cells** (Fig. 92). The functions of these cells are not known with certainty, but in lumbricids and some other groups they nourish the developing eggs. Since chloragogue cells can synthesize urea, they are thought to be also excretory. Three pairs of **calciferous glands** lie at the sides of the esophagus in segments 10 to 12; actually, the first pair are storage pouches, but the second and third are true glands. Their primary function is excretion of calcium; neutralization of acid foods is probably an incidental function.

The **food** of the earthworm consists principally of pieces of leaves and other vegetation, particles of animal matter, and soil; this material is gathered at night, at which time the worms are active. They crawl out on the surface of the ground and hold fast to the tops of their burrows with their tails, exploring the neighborhood. Food particles are drawn into the mouth cavity by suction produced when the pharyngeal cavity is enlarged by the contraction of the muscles which extend from the pharynx to the body wall.

In the pharynx, the food receives a secretion from the pharyngeal glands; it then passes through the esophagus to the crop, where it is stored temporarily. The gizzard is a grinding organ; in it the food is broken up into minute fragments by being squeezed and rolled about. Solid particles, such as grains of sand, which are frequently swallowed, probably aid in this grinding process. The food then passes on to the intestine, where most of the digestion and absorption takes place.

Digestion in the earthworm is very similar to that of higher animals. Enzymes aid in the breakdown of food; these include **amylase** which acts upon carbohydrates, **cellulase** which acts upon cellulose, **pepsin** and **trypsin** which act upon proteins, and **lipase** which acts upon fats. The digested food is absorbed through the wall of the intestine, assisted by the amoeboid activity of some of the epithelial cells. Upon reaching the blood, the absorbed food is carried to various parts of the body. Absorbed food also makes its way into the coelomic cavity and is carried directly to those tissues bathed by the coelomic fluid. In one-celled animals, and in such metazoans as the hydra, planaria, and ascaris, no circulatory system is necessary, since the food is either digested within the cells or comes into direct contact with them; but in large complex animals, a special system of organs must be provided to bring about the proper distribution of digested food.

Circulatory system

The **blood** of the earthworm is contained in a complicated system of tubes which ramify to all parts of the body (Figs. 91 and 93). A number of these tubes are large and centrally located; these give off branches which likewise branch, finally ending in exceedingly thin tubules, the **capillaries.** The blood consists of a **plasma** in which are suspended a great number of colorless amoeboid cells (**corpuscles**), which correspond to white corpuscles in man. Its red color is due to a respiratory pigment termed **hemoglobin** which is dissolved in the plasma. In vertebrates the hemoglobin is located in the blood corpuscles.

There are **5 longitudinal blood vessels**. These main vessels and their connectives are shown in Fig. 93 and are as follows: (1) the **dorsal vessel**, (2) the **ventral** (subintestinal) vessel, (3) the **subneural vessel**, (4) two **lateral neural vessels**, (5) five pairs of **aortic arches** (**hearts**) in segments 7 to 11, (6) two **lateral esophageal vessels**, (7) **segmental vessels** from the ventral vessel to the nephridia, body wall, and intestine, (8) **parietal vessels** connecting the dorsal and subneural vessels in the intestinal region, (9) branches to the dorsal vessel from the intestine, and (10) a **typhlosolar vessel**

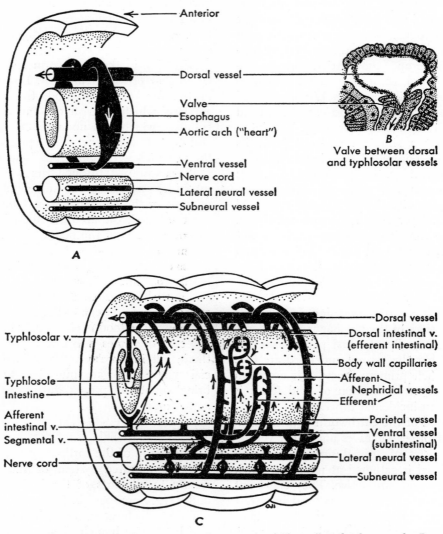

FIGURE 93. Earthworm circulatory system. *A*, one pair of "hearts" and other vessels. *B*, a section to show the structure of a valve. *C*, a third-dimensional view of two cuts through the earthworm to show the general scheme of the circulation. (*A* and *B* modified from Bell; *C*, after Bell, and a drawing by the Department of Zoology, Kansas State College.)

from the dorsal vessel supplies the dorsal half of the intestine.

The **dorsal vessel** (Fig. 93) serves the function of a true heart in that it is a pump with valves; and the aortic arches, the so-called hearts, act as a pressure-regulating mechanism, receiving blood in spurts from the dorsal vessel, and then contracting to force the blood under a steady pressure into the ventral vessel. Blood is forced forward by wavelike contractions of the dorsal vessel, beginning at the posterior end and traveling quickly anteriorly. These contractions are said to be **peristaltic**; they have been likened to the action of the fingers in the operation of milking a cow. **Valves** (Fig. 93) in the walls of the dorsal vessel prevent the return of blood from the anterior end. In segments 7 to 11, the blood passes from the dorsal vessel into the hearts, which force it forward and backward in the ventral trunk. Valves in the heart prevent the backward flow. From the ventral vessel the blood passes to the body wall, the intestine, and the nephridia. The flow in the subneural vessel is toward the posterior end, then dorsally through the parietal vessels into the dorsal vessel. The anterior region receives blood from the dorsal and ventral vessels. The blood which is carried to the body wall and the skin receives oxygen through the cuticle and is then returned to the dorsal vessel by way of the subneural vessel and the parietal connectives.

The exchange of materials between the blood and the tissue cells takes place in minute **tissue spaces.** Blood plasma and a few corpuscles, which constitute the tissue fluid, pass from the capillaries into these tissue spaces, where the cells are bathed and the interchange occurs. The tissue fluid collects waste products of cellular metabolism and makes its way back again into the blood stream.

Respiration

The earthworm possesses no organized respiratory system, but it obtains oxygen and gets rid of carbon dioxide through the moist skin. Respiration can be carried on in air and also in water as experiments have shown. Many capillaries lie just beneath the cuticle, making transfer of gases essentially as it is done in a gill or lung. The oxygen passes into the blood and combines with the hemoglobin. The hemoglobin of the earth-

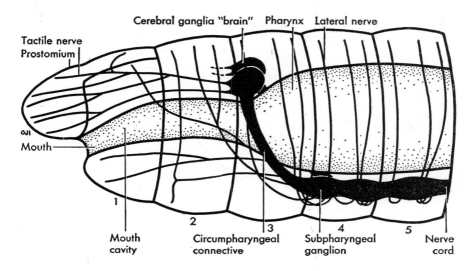

FIGURE 94. Earthworm. Side view of anterior end showing the cerebral ganglia and larger nerves. (After Hess.)

worm is inefficient as an oxygen-transporting substance compared to the hemoglobin of man.

Excretory system

Most of the excretory matter is carried out of the body by a number of coiled tubes termed **nephridia** (Figs. 91 and 92), a pair of which are present in every segment except the first three and the last. A nephridium occupies part of two successive segments; in one is a ciliated funnel, the **nephrostome,** which is connected by a thin ciliated tube with the major portion of the structure in the segment posterior to it. Three loops make up the coiled portion of the nephridium. The cilia on the nephrostome and in the nephridium create a current which draws in waste material from the coelomic fluid; other waste is received directly from blood vessels surrounding the nephridium. These excretory products (ammonia, urea, creatine) are eventually carried out through the **nephridiopore.** Chloragogue cells may store excretory matter temporarily before releasing it into the coelomic fluid. The nephridia serve the same function in the earthworm that the kidneys do in man.

Nervous system

The nervous system is concentrated (Figs. 91, 94, and 95). There is a bilobed mass of nervous tissue, the "brain" or **cerebral ganglia,** on the dorsal surface of the pharynx in segment 3. This is connected by 2 **circumpharyngeal connectives** with a pair of **subpharyngeal ganglia** which lie beneath the pharynx. From the latter, the **ventral nerve cord** extends posteriorly near the ventral body wall. The ventral nerve cord enlarges into a **ganglion** in each segment and gives off 3 pairs of nerves in every segment posterior to segment 4. Each ganglion really consists of 2 ganglia fused together. Near the dorsal surface of the ventral nerve cord are 3 longitudinal **giant fibers.** The brain and nerve cord constitute the **central nervous system;** the nerves which pass from and to them represent the **peripheral nervous system.**

The nerves of the peripheral nervous system are either motor or sensory. **Motor nerve fibers** (Fig. 95) are extensions from

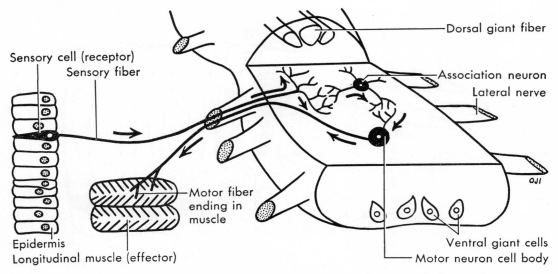

FIGURE 95. Diagram of sensory and motor neurons of the ventral nerve cord of an earthworm, showing their connections with the skin and the muscles to form a reflex arc.

cells in the ganglia of the central nervous system. They pass out to the muscles or other organs; and, since impulses sent along them give rise to movements, the cells of which they are a part are said to be **motor nerve cells.** The **sensory fibers** originate from nerve cells in the epidermis and carry impulses into the ventral nerve cord. The peripheral nervous system is composed of elements which have definite connections in the nerve cord.

The functions of nervous tissue are reception, conduction, and stimulation. These are usually performed by nerve cells called **neurons.** The neuron theory assumes that there is no nerve fiber independent of a nerve cell, that the nerve cell body with all of its processes is a unit, called the neuron. There is no protoplasmic continuity of one neuron with another; the relation between the neurons is probably contact of the terminals of one neuron with those of another.

The **reflex** is considered the functional unit of the nervous system. The apparatus required for a simple reflex in the body of an earthworm is represented in Fig. 95. A **sensory neuron,** lying at the surface of the body, sends a fiber into the ventral nerve cord, where it branches out; these branches meet but are not continuous with branches from an **association neuron** lying in the ventral nerve cord. The association neuron is in contact with a motor neuron that sends fibers into a reacting organ, which in this case is a muscle. These fibers extending to the reacting organ are called **motor fibers;** those leading to the ventral nerve cord are

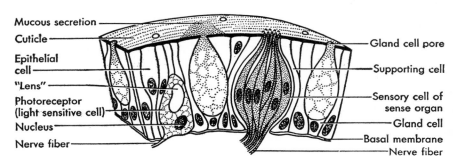

Mucous secretion
Cuticle
Epithelial cell
"Lens"
Photoreceptor (light-sensitive cell)
Nucleus
Nerve fiber

Gland cell pore
Supporting cell
Sensory cell of sense organ
Gland cell
Basal membrane
Nerve fiber

FIGURE 96. Diagram of the epidermis of the earthworm showing sense organs.

termed **sensory fibers.** The first neuron or **receptor** receives the stimulus and produces the nerve impulse which is carried on to the association neuron; the association neuron in turn transmits the impulse to a motor neuron which has processes extending to an **effector** such as a muscle or other organ.

Any action which takes place through such a reflex arc is termed a **reflex act.**

Within the ventral nerve cord are association neurons whose fibers serve to connect structures within one ganglion or two succeeding ganglia. These neurons are doubtless responsible for the muscular waves which pass from the anterior to the posterior end of the worm during locomotion. The three giant fibers, which lie in the dorsal part of the ventral nerve cord throughout almost its entire length, are connected by means of fibrils with nerve cells in the ganglia, and probably distribute the impulses that cause a worm to contract its entire body when stimulated. The earthworm's behavior is largely a matter of reflex acts.

Behavior due to simple reflexes are as mechanical as the reflection of light from a mirror, they often save animals from injury and even from death. Fortunately, we ourselves do not have to think before we pull our hand away from a hot stove, or before we close our eyes when we see an object about to strike us in the face.

Sense organs. The sensitiveness of the earthworm to light and other stimuli is due to the presence of a great number of epidermal sense organs. The two main types of epidermal receptors are the light-sensitive cells (**photoreceptor cells**) and the **sense organs** (Fig. 96), composed of a group of sensory cells surrounded by supporting cells. These sense organs are connected with the central nervous system by means of nerve fibers and communicate with the outside world through sense hairs which penetrate the cuticle. In addition to these sensory organs there are also free endings of nerve fibers between the cells of the epithelium. More of these sense organs occur at the anterior and posterior ends than in any other region of the body.

Reproductive system

The earthworm is not known to reproduce asexually although it has great powers of regeneration of lost parts. Mating takes place at night and requires two or three hours. Both male and female sexual organs occur in a single earthworm (Fig. 91). The **female system** consists of: (1) a pair of **ovaries** in segment 13; (2) a pair of **oviducts**, which open by a ciliated funnel in segment 13 and pass to the exterior in segment 14; (3) an **egg sac**, which is a small diverticulum of the septum associated with the funnel; and (4) two pairs of seminal receptacles, in segments 9 and 10. The male organs are: (1) two pairs of minute glove-shaped testes in segments 10 and 11, and back of each, (2) a ciliated **sperm funnel** which is connected to (3) a tiny duct, the **vas efferens.** The two ducts on each side connect to (4) a **vas deferens,** that leads to the outside. The testes and funnels are contained in (5) the **seminal vesicles,** conspicuous saclike structures which surround the testes and in which the sperms mature.

Self-fertilization does not take place, but sperms are transferred from one worm to another during a process called **copulation.** Two worms come together, as shown in Fig. 98; then spermatozoa from the seminal vesicles of each worm are expelled. They pass along the seminal grooves into the **seminal receptacles** of the other worm. The worms then separate. When the time for egg laying approaches, the glandular clitellum secretes a bandlike mucous tube which is forced forward by movements of the worm. Eggs are discharged through the oviducts, and sperms through the openings of the seminal receptacles into the space between this tube and the body wall. The tube is then forced forward over the anterior end; its ends become closed, and a cocoon, about the size of an apple seed, is thus formed containing fertilized eggs which develop within the cocoon into minute worms. The reciprocal fertilization insures cross-fertilization in the earthworm.

The **eggs** of the earthworm are **holoblastic,** but cleavage is unequal. A hollow blastula is formed, and a gastrula is produced by invagination. The mesoderm develops from two of the blastula cells called **mesoblasts.** These cells divide, forming two **mesoblastic bands** which later become the epithelial lining of the coelom. There is no swimming stage such as occurs in the marine annelids. The embryo escapes from the cocoon as a small worm in about two to three weeks.

Regeneration and grafting

Earthworms have considerable powers of regeneration. No more than 5 new segments will regenerate at the anterior end, and no "head" will regenerate if 15 or more segments have been cut off. A posterior piece may regenerate a "head" of 5 segments (Fig. 98B); or, in certain cases, a tail (Fig. 98C). Such a double-tailed worm slowly starves to death. An anterior piece regenerates a tail. Three pieces from several worms may be united to make a long worm (Fig. 98D); two pieces may fuse, forming a worm

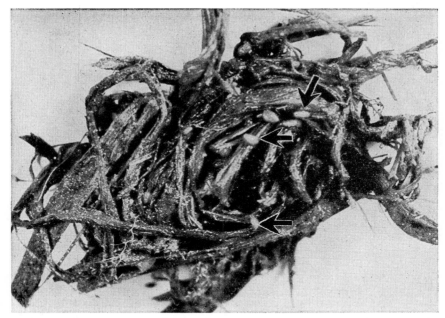

FIGURE 97. Earthworm cocoons deposited in cornstalk compost. Arrows point to cocoons. (Photo courtesy of R.C. Ball.)

with two tails; and an anterior piece may be united with a posterior piece to make a short worm. In such regeneration experiments, the parts are held together by threads until they become united. Regeneration probably does not contribute to the survival of the earthworm as much as it does to planarians and starfishes.

Behavior

The external stimuli that have been most frequently employed in studying the behavior of earthworms are those dealing with contact, chemicals, and light.

Reactions to mechanical stimuli

Mechanical stimulation, if continuous and not too strong, calls forth a positive reaction; the worms live where their bodies come in contact with solid objects; they respond to the stimulus of mechanical contact such as the walls of their burrows. Reactions to sounds are not due to the presence of a sense of hearing, but to the contact stimuli produced by vibrations. Darwin showed that musical tones produced no response; but if a flower pot containing earthworms was placed upon a piano and a note was struck, the worms immediately drew back into their burrows. This result was due to vibrations.

Reactions to chemicals

In certain cases, reactions to chemicals result in bringing the animal into regions of favorable food conditions or turning it away from unpleasant substances. Moisture, which is necessary for respiration and consequently for the life of the earthworm, causes a positive reaction, when it comes in contact with the body; no positive reactions are produced by chemical stimulation from a distance. Negative reactions, on the other hand, such as moving to one side or back into the burrow, are produced even when certain unpleasant chemical agents are still some distance from the body. These reactions are quite similar to those caused by contact stimuli. Darwin explained the preference of the earthworm for certain kinds of

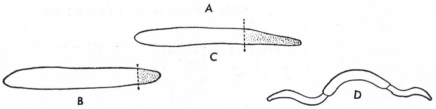

FIGURE 98. Earthworm. Diagrams illustrating copulation and regeneration. A, a pair in copulation. Because this usually occurs at night, it is not often observed. B, a new anterior end (dotted) that has regenerated in place of an anterior end removed. C, a new posterior end (dotted) that has regenerated in place of an anterior end removed. D, a long worm produced by grafting together parts of three worms. (A, courtesy of General Biological Supply House, Inc., Chicago; B, C, D after Morgan.)

food by supposing that the discrimination between edible and inedible substances was possible when they were in contact with the body. This would resemble the sense of taste as present in the higher animals.

Reactions to light

No definite visual organs such as eyes have been discovered in earthworms; nevertheless, these animals are very sensitive to light, as is proved by the fact that a sudden illumination at night will often cause them to quickly snap back into their burrows. This sensitiveness to light is due to the photoreceptor cells (Fig. 96) that are concentrated especially in the anterior and posterior ends, and are found in every segment of the body. Each of these light-sensitive cells contains a transparent "lens" that focuses light on the neurofibrils which ramify through the cell. By means of these photoreceptor cells, very slight differences in the intensity of the light are distinguished. If a choice of two illuminated regions is given, the one more faintly lighted is selected in the majority of cases. A positive reaction to faint light has been demonstrated for the manure worm, *Eisenia foe-*

tida; this positive reaction to faint light may account for the emergence of the worms from their burrows at night. It is an interesting fact that although the worms react negatively to sunlight, they respond positively to red light and may be collected at night with the use of such a light.

Physiologic state

From the foregoing account, it might be inferred that only external stimuli are factors in the behavior of the earthworm. This, however, is not the case, since the physiologic condition, which depends largely upon previous stimulation, determines the character of the response. Different physiologic states may be recognized, ranging from a state of rest in which slight stimuli are not effective, to a state of great excitement caused by long-continued and intense stimulation, in which condition, slight stimuli cause violent responses. By physiologic states we mean the varying internal physiologic conditions of the organism as distinguished from permanent anatomic conditions. Such different internal physiologic conditions can be inferred from the behavior of the animal.

Learning in earthworms

Whether or not learning occurs in protozoans, or in such simple metazoans as sponges and hydras, is uncertain. But at the stage in evolution represented by the earthworm, experiments indicate that this animal is capable of what psychologists call "latent memory," or the storing of impressions until a later time when they may be useful.

In one experiment, worms could escape from a lighted chamber by entering the bottom of a branched passageway constructed of glass tubing in the form of a "T." If the worms turned to the right at the top of the "T," they entered a dark moist chamber filled with damp earth and moss, a favorable environment for an earthworm. If they turned left, they encountered an electric shock. In the early trials, they turned to the left as often as to the right. At the end of 20 days, they turned to the left only 5 times out of 20, and at the end of 40 days they were turning left only once out of 20 trials.

OTHER ANNELIDA

Annelids differ from the other groups of "worms" in the following respects: (1) the body is divided into a linear series of similar segments, often visible externally because of grooves that encircle the body, and internally because of partitions called septa; (2) the body cavity between the digestive tract and body wall is a true coelom; (3) the mouth opens in the first segment and is overhung by the prostomium; (4) the nervous system consists of a preoral ganglion, the "brain," often bilobed, and a pair of ventral nerve cords, typically with a pair of ganglia in each segment; (5) usually, a nonchitinous cuticle on the surface of the body; chitinized bristles or setae are present.

The sandworm

Neanthes virens is a common polychaete that lives in burrows in the sand or mud of the seashore at tide level. By day it rests in its burrow, but at night it extends its body in search of food or may leave the burrow entirely.

The body is flattened dorsoventrally and may reach a length of 18 inches or more, with 100 to 200 or more segments. The head is well developed. Above the mouth is the **prostomium** (Fig. 99) which bears a pair of terminal **tentacles**, 2 pairs of **simple eyes**, and, on either side, a thick **palp**. The first segment is the **peristomium**; from each side of this arise 4 **tentacles**. Small animals are captured by a pair of strong chitinous **jaws** which are everted with part of the pharynx when *Neanthes* is feeding. Behind the head are a variable number of segments each bearing a fleshy outgrowth on either side, the **parapodium** (Fig. 99).

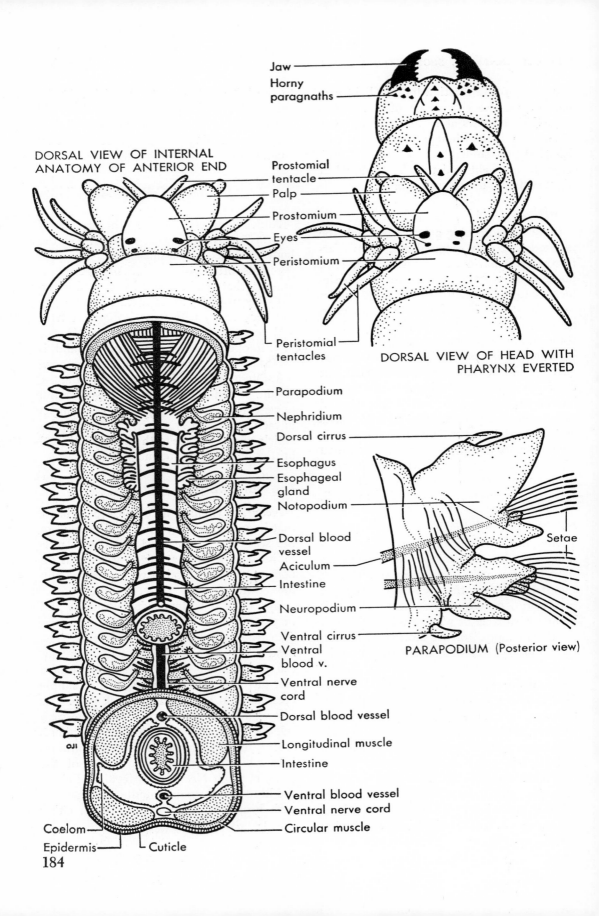

DORSAL VIEW OF INTERNAL
ANATOMY OF ANTERIOR END

Jaw
Horny
paragnaths

DORSAL VIEW OF HEAD WITH
PHARYNX EVERTED

Prostomial
tentacle
Palp
Prostomium
Eyes
Peristomium

Peristomial
tentacles

Parapodium
Nephridium
Dorsal cirrus
Esophagus
Esophageal
gland
Notopodium

Dorsal blood
vessel
Aciculum
Intestine

Neuropodium

Ventral cirrus
Ventral
blood v.

Ventral nerve
cord

Dorsal blood vessel

Longitudinal muscle

Intestine

Ventral blood vessel
Ventral nerve cord
Circular muscle

Coelom
Epidermis
Cuticle

Setae

PARAPODIUM (Posterior view)

184

The body wall consists of an outer **cuticle,** which is secreted by the cells of the epidermis just beneath it, and several muscular layers under the epidermis. The body cavity between the body wall and the intestine is a **coelom** lined with **peritoneal epithelium.** The **digestive system** (Fig. 99) consists of the **mouth, pharynx, esophagus,** with an **esophageal gland** on either side opening into it, and a straight **stomach-intestine** extending to the **anus.**

The **circulatory system** comprises a dorsal vessel and a ventral vessel, with branches to capillaries in the body wall and intestine. Almost every segment, except the peristomium and the anal segment, contains a pair of **nephridia.** In the head is a **cerebral ganglion,** the "**brain.**" This is joined by a pair of **circumesophageal connectives** to a pair of **subesophageal ganglia** and is followed by a **ventral nerve cord** with a pair of ganglia in each segment. The sexes are separate. Ova or sperms arise from the wall of the coelom. A **trochophore larva** develops from the fertilized egg.

Polychaetes

The principal characteristics of the classes Oligochaeta and Polychaeta are exhibited by the earthworm (Fig. 92) and the sandworm (Fig. 99) respectively. However, many variations from these types occur.

The polychaetes consist largely of free-living marine annelids in which typical annelidan characters occur. The body tends to be long and wormlike, and somewhat depressed to a cylindrical shape in cross section. It consists of a prostomial or head region, and a trunk. Segmentation is well marked both internally and externally. The outer cuticle is usually soft and moist and is dependent on a wet environment for the prevention of desiccation. The digestive system consists of a straight tube with an an-

teroventral mouth and a posterodorsal anus. The circulatory system has a dorsal vessel where the blood moves forward, and a ventral one where it moves backward, together with transverse vessels. The nervous system has a dorsal "brain" in or near the prostomium, and paired ventral ganglia in a ladderlike arrangement. A giant nerve fiber system is usually present, consisting of longitudinal strands that extend parallel to the ventral nerve cord and function for rapid response reactions. Nephridia are segmental and are present in most body segments. Most polychaetes are dioecious, with the two sexes resembling each other; gonads may occur in many segments, and ova may be produced in enormous numbers. The lateral appendages or parapodia are formed by outpocketings of the lateral body walls; they are usually conspicuous and variously provided with fleshy structures such as cirri, scales, and gills. The setae occur in bundles; they are formed from secretions of specialized cells, and they function in locomotion, tube building, food gathering, and other important ways. The fertilized egg develops into a **trochophore.**

In detail, however, there is remarkable diversity among the polychaetes so that the characters named above can be regarded only as generalizations. Such common names for families as the following illustrate the variations in shape and structure that may occur: sea mouse, scale worms, fireworms, glass worms, proboscis worms, bamboo worms, gold crowns, gooseberry worms, lugworms, feather dusters, and shield worms. The variable structure of polychaetes makes possible adaptations to many ocean habitats.

Most polychaetes are free-living, but many are partly or wholly parasitic; most are marine but many others live in water varying in saltiness from briny to fresh; a few are terrestrial. Metamerism may be homonymous (with successive rings alike), but usually there is considerable departure from this structure. In *Chaetopterus* (Fig. 100), parts of the parapodia are modified to function as suction disks, as a food-ball organ, as water-

FIGURE 99. *Facing page, Neanthes,* the sandworm. *Left,* anterior end of the body with dorsal wall removed. *Right,* some details of structure.

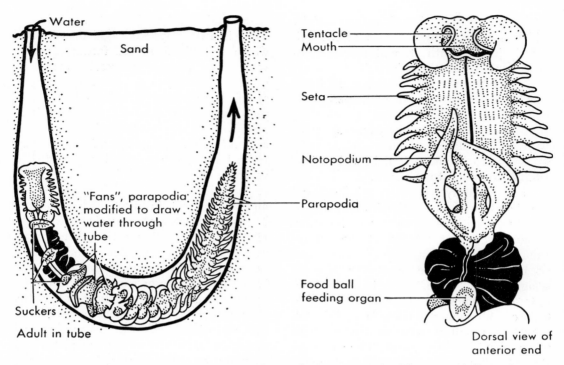

FIGURE 100. A marine polychaete (*Chaetopterus*) feeding in its tube. The arrows indicate the direction of water currents. (*Left* after Enders; *right* after Lankester.)

pumping fans, etc. In the feather duster worms the peristomium or first segment is enormously developed to form the feathery tentacular crown, or food-gathering organ, or to form also the operculum that serves to close the end of the tube when the animal is withdrawn. The tubes of the polychaetes are nearly as variable and characteristic of the different species as are the body parts; the basic structures formed by the worms may be spun threads (modified setal secretions as in some of the scale worms), transparent horny tubes, tough leathery tubes, calcareous tubes, or clear glasslike tubes (some serpulids). Extraneous materials such as sand particles, shells, and sticks, are frequently used and sometimes selected with precision in regard to size, color, and weight, so that some intelligence has been credited to certain tube-dwelling worms.

Polychaeta differ from Oligochaeta in being largely marine instead of fresh-water or terrestrial; parapodia are typically well developed, and the setae are numerous instead of few; the prostomium or some of the first few segments are often highly differentiated to form a cephalic region of considerable proportions; sexes are usually separate, with gonads present in a large and variable number of segments. Fertilization of ova is typically external; development is by spiral cleavage and through a pelagic trochophore. In certain species, for example *Autolytus*, the body, which is only 15 mm. long, may produce buds at the posterior ends, thus forming a linear row of offspring (Fig. 101), each of which acquires a head before separating from the parent. There are thousands of species of polychaetes. They are known in all seas and at all recorded depths, but they are most abundant in the upper 180 feet.

The Pacific palolo worm, *Eunice* (Fig. 102), first became known from the Samoan Islands, where it attracted the attention of

Autolytus, a Polychaete reproducing by budding at the posterior end.

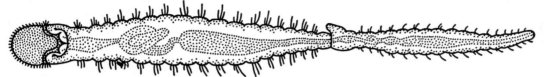

Aeolosoma, a fresh-water oligochaete reproducing by transverse division.

FIGURE 101. Asexual reproduction in annelids. *Top,* a marine polychaete budding at the posterior end. *Bottom,* a fresh-water oligochaete showing a budding segment. (After Mensch.)

the missionaries because it was eaten by the natives; also because it appeared periodically in certain localities in enormous numbers for only a few hours. It makes its appearance (swarms) almost invariably in the months of October and November, and usually at the time of the third quarter of the moon. Other important factors, such as the velocity of the wind and the stage of sexual maturity, may account for a departure from this time to produce lesser swarms at other moon phases during these two months. The pos-terior half of the worm breaks off from the parent worm and swims to the surface. The enclosed eggs and sperms are shed into the sea in the early morning, and in some localities in such enormous numbers that the surface of the sea has been likened to a thick noodle soup. The eggs develop into young larvae rapidly, and in three days sink to the bottom. Other palolo worms occur in different parts of the world, particularly in warm seas. The Atlantic palolo swarms in June and July.

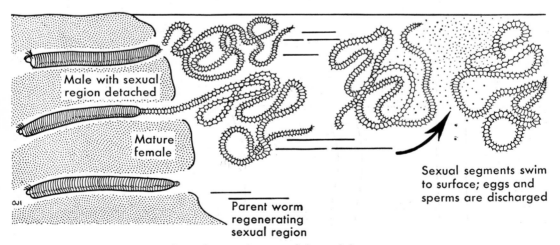

Male with sexual region detached

Mature female

Parent worm regenerating sexual region

Sexual segments swim to surface; eggs and sperms are discharged

Sexual reproduction of the palolo worm, *Eunice,* a polychaete

FIGURE 102. The Pacific palolo worm, *Eunice viridis,* has its burrows in coral reefs; it produces many posterior segments filled with eggs or sperms which are periodically cast off.

A tube-dwelling species is *Chaetopterus* (Fig. 100). When full grown it may reach 15 to 30 cm. (12 inches); the body is highly luminescent and consists of three distinct regions. The U-shaped, opaque, parchment-like tube may be 50 cm. long; it lies completely buried in mud or sand, except for the two distal orifices. The worm maintains its position in the spacious tube by means of the long anterior notopodia (Fig. 100) and three ventral suckers that are formed by the median fusion of three pairs of neuropodia. A powerful current of water may be set up by three muscular fan segments, formed by the median fusion of three pairs of notopodia. Other remarkable modifications include the food-ball organ (Fig. 100) that is formed by the fusion of a pair of notopodia and serves to carry mucous food balls to the mouth. This polychaete is world-wide in its distribution; it usually occurs where there are broad sand flats and little current. It is found along the Atlantic Coast from North Carolina to Cape Cod.

Archiannelida

The Archiannelida are aberrant marine polychaetes, characterized largely for the persistence of larval features such as ciliary rings and lack of setae, or reduction of organ systems. Whether these traits are primitive or degenerate is not known. *Polygordius appendiculatus* (Fig. 103) lives in the sandy shores of the Atlantic and Mediterranean coasts. It is about one inch long and indistinctly segmented externally. The prostomium bears a pair of cephalic tentacles, and the posterior end bears two anal tentacles. A pair of ciliated pits, one on either side of the prostomium, probably serve as sense organs. The development of *Polygordius* includes a trochophore stage. The adult develops from the trochophore by the growth and elongation of the anal end. This elongation becomes segmented; and, by continued growth the larva transforms into the adult.

The archiannelids number only about 45

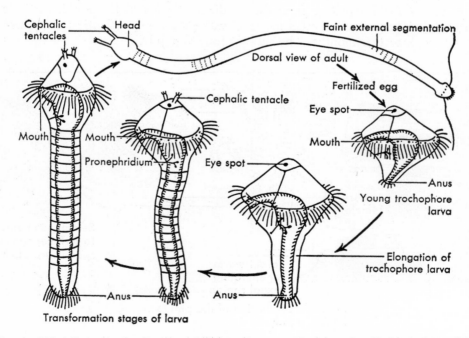

FIGURE 103. Stages in development of *Polygordius appendiculatus,* one of the Archiannelida. (After Fraipont.)

species in 10 genera; they have originated in various ways, and are thus a heterogeneous assemblage and not to be regarded as a unit.

Another aberrant group of polychaetes includes the family Myzostomidae. All are parasites of echinoderms, notably sea lilies (crinoids); in size they range from 0.5 to 9 mm. The body is oval and depressed with few segments. Individuals are protandric, that is, the smaller younger ones function as males, and later, with increase in size and age, become females; cross-fertilization is thus insured. The egg gives rise to a swimming trochophore.

Oligochaetes

The members of the class Oligochaeta are mostly terrestrial, but some inhabit fresh water; no parapodia, and few setae are present, and the head has no distinct appendages. They are hermaphroditic, but no trochophore larva develops from the egg. The earthworm is the best-known species. Among the interesting species of oligochaetes are those of *Aeolosoma* (Fig. 101), which are only 1 mm. long and spotted with red oil globules in the integument. They live among algae, consist of from 7 to 10 segments, and reproduce asexually by trans-

FIGURE 104. A giant earthworm is shown being pulled from its burrow in the wet river slopes of Gippsland, Australia. Although the giant earthworm, in popular accounts, is said to be 12 feet long, scientific reports give 7 feet as the length. (Courtesy of Australian News and Information Bureau.)

verse fission. *Nais* is light brown in color, 2 to 4 mm. long, and consists of from 15 to 37 segments. It lives among algae and may reproduce by budding. *Tubifex tubifex* is reddish in color and about 4 cm. long. It lives in a tube from which the posterior end projects and waves back and forth. Often large numbers occur in patches on muddy bottoms.

Among the smallest of oligochaetes are species of *Chaetogaster* that may be only 0.44 mm. long. The largest ones are known from South Australia, where *Megascolides australis* may attain a length of 7 feet. The number of segments in oligochaetes varies from 7 in *Aeolosoma* to over 600 in *Rhinodrilus*.

Leeches

The class Hirudinea contains annelids that are usually flattened dorsoventrally, but differ externally from the flatworms in being distinctly segmented. They differ from other annelids in the lack of setae (except in one genus), and in the presence of copulatory organs and genital openings on the ventral side. Leeches (Fig. 105) are abundant in fresh water but also occur in salt water and on land. Many of them are brilliantly colored and bear elaborate color patterns. We commonly think of leeches as bloodsuckers; large numbers, however, are predaceous, that is, they do not act as bloodsucking parasites, but devour other small animals such as earthworms and mollusks. They are themselves preyed upon by birds such as the bittern, reptiles, flatworms, and other animals.

External annulation is not indicative of the true number of segments; there may be several external annulations for every segment as shown by internal organs (Fig. 106).

The principal characteristics are exhibited by *Hirudo medicinalis*, which is about 4 inches long but is capable of great contraction and elongation. The **suckers** are used as organs of attachment. Figure 106 illustrates the principal structures of a leech. The **digestive tract** is fitted for digestion of the blood of vertebrates, which forms the principal food of some leeches. The mouth lies in the anterior sucker and is provided with three **jaws** armed with **chitinous teeth** for biting. Blood is sucked up by the dilatation of the **muscular pharynx**. The short esophagus leads from the pharynx into the **crop**, which has 11 pairs of lateral branches. Here the blood is stored until digested in the small globular stomach. Because of its enormous crop, a leech is able to ingest three times its own weight in blood; and, since it may take as long as 9 months to digest this amount, meals are few and far between.

Respiration is carried on mainly through the surface of the body. Waste products are extracted from the blood and coelomic fluid by 17 pairs of **nephridia**. Leeches are hermaphroditic, but the eggs of one animal are fertilized by sperms from another leech. Copulation and formation of a cocoon are similar to those processes in the earthworm. Other leeches carry their eggs on the ventral side, and some deposit them on stones.

Metamerism

The biological principle of body segmentation is called **metamerism**. This is exhibited in the true annelids and is here encountered for the first time. This type of structure is of considerable interest since the most successful groups in the animal kingdom, the Arthropoda and Vertebrata, have their parts metamerically arranged. How this condition has been brought about is still doubtful, but many theories have been proposed to account for it. According to one view, the body of a metameric animal has evolved from that of a non-segmented animal by transverse fission. The individuals thus produced remained united end to end and gradually became integrated both structurally and physiologically so that their individualities were united into one

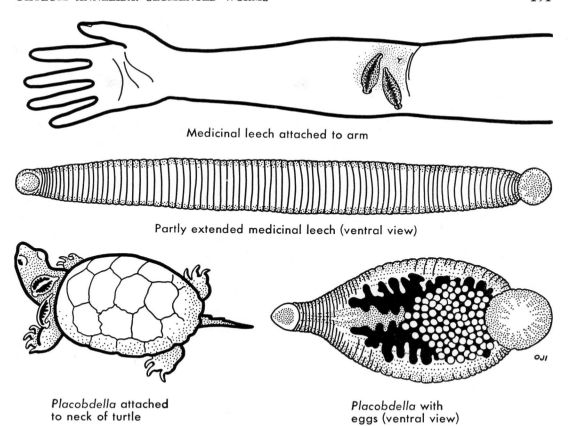

Medicinal leech attached to arm

Partly extended medicinal leech (ventral view)

Placobdella attached
to neck of turtle

Placobdella with
eggs (ventral view)

FIGURE 105. Leeches are commonly called bloodsuckers. A full-grown medicinal leech is four inches in length. *Placobdella*, common on turtles, is about one inch long.

complex individuality. Some zoologists maintain that the segmental arrangement of organs, such as nephridia, blood vessels, and reproductive organs, has arisen by division of a single ancestral organ, and not by formation of new organs as the fission theory demands.

The coelom

The coelom (Fig. 92) is a body cavity lined with tissue of mesodermal origin; from it the excretory organs open; and from its embryonic walls, the reproductive cells originate. The importance of the coelom should be clearly understood since it has played a prominent role in the progressive development of complexity of structure. The appearance of this cavity between the digestive tract and body wall brought about great physiologic changes; it is correlated with the origin of nephridia for transporting waste products out of the body, and of reproductive ducts for the exit of eggs and sperms. The coelom also affected the distribution of digested food within the body, since it contains a fluid which takes up material absorbed by the digestive tract and carries it to the tissues. Excretory matter finds its way into the coelomic fluid and thence out of the body through the nephridia.

So important is the coelom considered by most zoologists that the Metazoa are frequently separated into two groups: (1) the Acoelomata without a coelom, and (2) the Coelomata with a coelom. The Porifera,

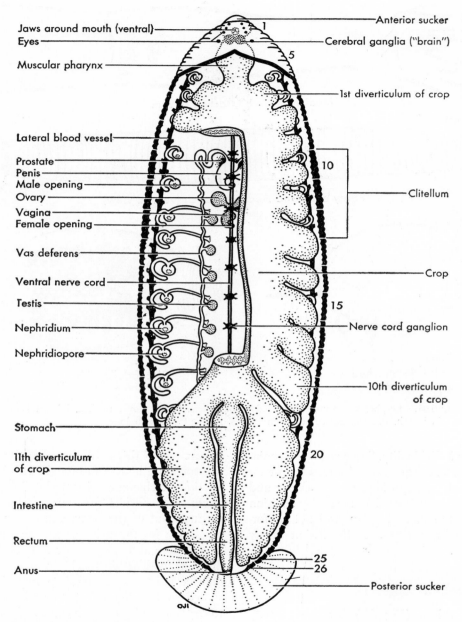

Jaws around mouth (ventral)
Eyes
Muscular pharynx
Anterior sucker
Cerebral ganglia ("brain")

1
5

1st diverticulum of crop

Lateral blood vessel
Prostate
Penis
Male opening
Ovary
Vagina
Female opening
Vas deferens
Ventral nerve cord
Testis
Nephridium
Nephridiopore

10

Clitellum

Crop

15

Nerve cord ganglion

10th diverticulum
of crop

20

Stomach
11th diverticulum
of crop
Intestine
Rectum
Anus

25
26

Posterior sucker

Figure 106. Dorsal view to show the segmentation and internal anatomy of the leech. Part of the crop is cut away on the left side to show the ventral nerve cord and reproductive organs. The numbers on the right indicate the internal segmentation or somites as shown by the nerve ganglia.

Coelenterata, Ctenophora, and Platyhelminthes are undoubtedly Acoelomata. Likewise the Annelida, Echinodermata, Arthropoda, Mollusca, and Chordata are certainly Coelomata. The Nemathelminthes and related phyla belong to the Pseudocoelomata.

Trochophore

The term **trochophore** has been applied to the larval stages of a number of marine animals. The figures of the trochophores of the polychaete *Eupomatus* (Fig. 107) and of *Polygordius* (Fig. 103) are sufficient to indicate the characteristics of this larva.

Many other marine annelids pass through a trochophore stage during their life history; those that do not are supposed to have lost this step during the course of evolution.

Since a trochophore also appears in the development of animals belonging to other phyla, for example, Mollusca and Bryozoa, and resembles very closely certain Rotifera, the conclusion has been reached by some embryologists that these groups of animals are all descended from a common hypothetical ancestor called a **trochozoan**. Strong arguments have been advanced both for and against this theory.

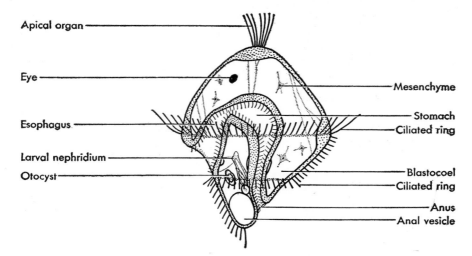

FIGURE 107. Trochophore larva of a polychaete, *Eupomatus*, side view.

ORIGIN AND RELATIONS OF THE ANNELIDA

The annelids comprise the polychaetes, archiannelids, oligochaetes, and leeches. Formerly the archiannelids were regarded as ancestral annelids. It was hypothesized that both polychaetes and oligochaetes evolved from them. Since the discovery that the archiannelids show some larval features that resemble larval polychaetes, it is not known whether they are primitive or degenerative. Hartman prefers to regard the Archiannelida as an Appendix of Polychaeta.

The polychaetes are by far the oldest, largest, and most diversified of the annelids. The origin of aquatic and terrestrial oligochaetes from an ancestral, generalized polychaete is likely. The leeches, in turn, have many features in common with oligochaetes; their peculiar modifications are the result of parasitism.

RELATIONS OF THE ANNELIDA TO MAN

Of the influence of segmented worms on human welfare, that of the earthworm and leeches is the most obvious. Earthworms are widely used as bait for fishing; various methods have been used to drive them out of their burrows so that they can be collected in large numbers. These include use of an electric current, jarring the soil by beating a stick driven into it, and pouring a solution of chemicals such as mercuric chloride (poison) on the ground. Raising earthworms as bait for fishing has become quite profitable in some resort districts.

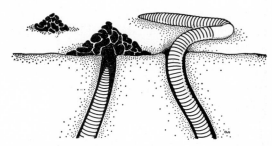

FIGURE 108. Diagram showing the burrow and castings of an earthworm.

Charles Darwin demonstrated, by careful observations extending over a period of 40 years, the great economic importance of earthworms. One acre of ground may contain over 50,000 earthworms. The feces of these worms are the little heaps of black earth called castings (Fig. 108) which strew the ground; they are especially noticeable early in the morning. Darwin estimated that more than 18 tons of earthly castings may be carried to the surface in a single year on one acre of ground; and in 20 years, a layer three inches thick would be transferred from the subsoil to the surface. By this means objects are covered up in the course of a few years. The continuous honeycombing of the soil by earthworms makes the land more porous and insures better penetration of air and moisture. The mixing of soil and organic matter in the digestive tract of the earthworm should contribute something to increasing humus; however, the claim that the addition of earthworms to an unproductive soil will greatly increase its fertility is false.

Earthworms may also be harmful. They disfigure lawns and golf courses with their castings and may serve as intermediate hosts of parasitic worms. For example, they are intermediate hosts in the life cycle of a cestode of chickens, *Amoebotaenia*, and in that of a pig lungworm of the nematode genus *Metastrongylus*; and they are passive carriers of the nematode worm *Syngamus trachea*, which causes gapes in fowls.

As a transporter of soil, the **lugworm**, a species of *Arenicola* (Fig. 90), a polychaete, is even more effective than the earthworm. The amount of sand brought to the surface on 19 measured areas was 82,423 castings to an acre; the average amount of sand brought up to the surface each year on these areas was about 1911 tons to the acre, which, if spread evenly, would form a layer about 13 inches deep. Other observations made at different places showed about 34 to 38 castings to the square yard; the amount brought up was estimated to be about 3700 tons to the acre in a year, or equivalent to a layer about 24 inches thick. Species of lugworms are widely used as bait in all places where they are found. A bed where fishermen constantly dig may contain about three million worms; removal of a few thousand a day produces no noticeable effect. In certain bays of New England, it is estimated that 12½ million worms (species of *Neanthes* and *Glycera*) are picked up by diggers in one year. At one time, a digger may collect about 350 worms.

Oyster pests include polychaete worms of the genus *Polydora*; they cause mud blisters in the nacreous layers of the shells and render the oysters unsalable; or the oyster may be weakened, if not actually killed. Oyster growers call it "worm disease." In some regions where oyster culture once flourished, it had to be discontinued, or different methods had to be introduced, such as rearing the spat (young oysters) on elevated or only partially submerged surfaces. Not only oysters, but other bivalved mollusks may be attacked; also years of low infestation may be followed by years of heavy mortality.

Sedentary polychaetes are among the more conspicuous agents that cause fouling on the bottoms of ships, dikes, and various harbor installations. They not only cause destruction of the building materials, but add to the submerged weight so that the speed of a vessel is materially lessened. Periodic drydocking of vessels in harbor cities is required to clear the hulls of fouling organisms.

As reef-building agents, some sand- and lime-concreting, tube-building polychaetes are important in some parts of the world, changing shore contours, building up land masses, and transporting vast amounts of inert materials. As a result of selective action in the construction of tubes or matrices, some reefs or bars are likely to be pure sand or lime particles of homogeneous size.

Use of certain polychaetes as food, such as the palolo, is of interest since there are certain traditional rites attending such feasts. The annual occurrence of swarms is predictable within narrow limits in certain regions of the south Pacific. Since the portions taken consist of almost pure yolk-laden eggs, a highly nutritive food is available. In oriental countries a large echiurid worm is collected, dried, and used as food.

The widespread occurrence of fireworms (species of the polychaete family Amphinomidae) found along tropical shores is of interest to man largely because of the injuries that may be inflicted. The worms are sometimes large, as much as a foot long, with striking color patterns and brilliant displays, creeping conspicuously over rocky surfaces. The unwary collector who picks them up is startled by severe burning from the contact. The injuries are produced by the harpoonlike bristles that penetrate human skin.

The use of the leech (Fig. 105) in medicine was based on the theory that many illnesses were due to "bad blood," either locally or generally; bloodletting, as the practice is called, was thus considered a cure for many ailments. Today in modern medical practice, transfusions of blood into the body are a common procedure, instead of bloodletting, to get rid of "bad blood." However, so common was leeching in olden times that doctors were often called leeches. Not only *Hirudo medicinalis* but other species were used in various parts of the world. Wordsworth's interesting poem, "The Leech Gatherer" was based on the medicinal use of the leech. Bloodletting by leeches is now extremely rare in this country. In addition to such therapeutic use, the leech has been used as a drug, supposedly, to cure loss or graying of hair and other symptoms of old age.

Leeches may be very annoying, especially in tropical regions where they live among dense vegetation and may attach themselves in large numbers to human beings and other animals. It has been said that such leeches caused much discomfort to the soldiers of Napoleon when they invaded North Africa. The salivary glands of leeches produce a substance termed **hirudin**, which prevents clotting of blood while the leech is feeding. For this reason a wound made by a leech may bleed for some time after the leech has detached itself. Hirudin is used in modern medicine as an anticoagulant.

CLASSIFICATION OF THE PHYLUM ANNELIDA

(For reference purposes only)

Phylum Annelida. Annelids are bilaterally symmetrical, segmented worms; the body cavity is a true coelom; the nervous system consists of a dorsal brain and a pair of ventral nerve cords with, typically, a pair of ganglia in each segment; the digestive tract is a straight tube with a mouth that is anterior and ventral, and an anus that is posterior and dorsal; the muscular system consists of an outer circular and an inner longitudinal series. The sperms and eggs are derived from mesoderm. Cleavage of the egg is spiral unless obscured by excessive yolk. Four classes are recognized as follows:

Class 1. Polychaeta. Marine; parapodia well developed and provided with setae that are variously modified; prostomium and first few segments sometimes highly cephalized; sexes usually separate; larva typically a trochophore. Ex. *Neanthes virens* (Fig. 99).

Class 2. Archiannelida. A small heterogeneous group, most nearly related to Polychaeta; therefore some zoologists prefer to make it an appendix to the class Polychaeta rather than give it a separate class status. It is characterized largely for loss of morphologic characters such as distinct parapodia or setae, and retention of larval ones such as ciliary rows. Mainly marine, littoral, and sometimes living in brackish to fresh water. Usually dioecious or sometimes hermaphroditic larva, a trochophore, or development direct. Ex. *Dinophilus* (Fig. 90).

Class 3. Oligochaeta. Terrestrial or freshwater; without parapodia, and setae few; head not well developed; hermaphroditic; no trochophore larva. Ex. *Lumbricus terrestris* (Fig. 90).

Class 4. Hirudinea. Parasitic or predaceous; mostly fresh-water or terrestrial; without parapodia or setae; body with 33 segments plus prostomium; posterior and often an anterior sucker; hermaphroditic; coelom reduced by encroachment of connective tissue. Ex. *Hirudo medicinalis* (Fig. 105).

SELECTED COLLATERAL READINGS

Bahl, K.N. *Pheretima, An Indian Earthworm.* Lucknow Publishing House, Lucknow, India, 1947.

Ball, R.C., and Curry, L.L. "Culture and Agricultural Worth of Earthworms." *Bull. 222,* Michigan State Univ., East Lansing, Mich., 1956.

Beddard, F.E. "Oligochaetes (Earthworms, etc.) and Hirudinea (Leeches)." *Cambridge Natural History.* Macmillan, London, 1896.

Bell, A.W. "The Earthworm Circulatory System." *Turtox News,* 25:89–94, 1947.

Borradaile, L.A. and Potts, F.A. *The Invertebrata.* Cambridge Univ. Press, New York, 1958.

Buchsbaum, Ralph. *Animals Without Backbones.* Univ. Chicago Press, Chicago, 1948.

Darwin, C. *The Formation of Vegetable Mould Through the Action of Worms, with Observations on Their Habits.* Murray, London, 1881.

Grove, A.J. "On the Reproductive Processes of the Earthworm, *Lumbricus terrestris.*" *Quart. J. Microscop. Sci.,* 69:245–290, 1925.

Harvey, E.N. *Bioluminescence.* Academic Press, New York, 1952.

Miner, R.W. *Field Book of Seashore Life.* Putnam, New York, 1950.

Moore, J.P. "The Control of Blood-sucking Leeches, with an Account of the Leeches of Palisades Interstate Park." *Roosevelt Wild Life Bull.,* Syracuse Univ., 2:1–55, 1923.

Robertson, J.D. "The Function of the Calciferous Glands of Earthworms." *J. of Exper. Biol.* (British), 13:279–297, 1936.

Stephenson, J. *The Oligochaeta.* Clarendon Press, Oxford, 1930.

Wilson, E.B. "The Embryology of the Earthworm." *J. of Morph.,* 3:387–462, 1889.

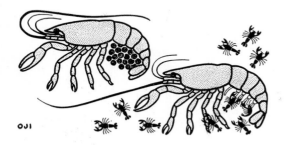

CHAPTER 16

Phylum Arthropoda. Crayfish, Crabs, Barnacles, Water Fleas, Sow Bugs, and Others

THE arthropods are joint-footed animals. To this phylum belong the lobsters, crabs, water fleas, barnacles, millipedes, centipedes, scorpions, spiders, mites, and insects (Fig. 109). An arthropod is **bilaterally symmetrical,** and consists of a longitudinal series of segments; on all or some is a **pair of appendages.** An animal of this phylum is covered with a **hardened exoskeleton,** containing **chitin** which is flexible at intervals to provide movable joints. It possesses a **nervous system** of the annelid type and has a coelom which is small or absent in the adult; the body cavity is a hemocoel filled with blood.

The arthropods comprise about 78 per cent of all known species of animals (Fig. 1). They are the dominant animals on the earth, if numbers of different species are accepted as criteria of dominance. The variety of the multitudes of arthropods seems infinite, but the fundamental plan of structure is the same. The common crayfish exhibits to excellent advantage the characteristics of the class Crustacea as well as of arthropods in general. The segmented appendages of the crayfish are particularly interesting since they seem to have developed from a common type but have become greatly modified for the performance of various functions. Many arthropods, including the crayfish, possess compound eyes—a type of visual organ very different from those of other invertebrates and vertebrates. Other biological phenomena exhibited by the crayfish and worthy of special mention are the power of regeneration, autotomy, habit formation, and superficial cleavage of the fertilized egg. Many other Crustacea are of great biological interest and of economic importance.

CAMBARUS—A CRAYFISH

The crayfish (crawfish) is found in fresh-water lakes, streams, ponds, and swamps over most of the world. The genus *Cambarus* is common in the central and eastern

197

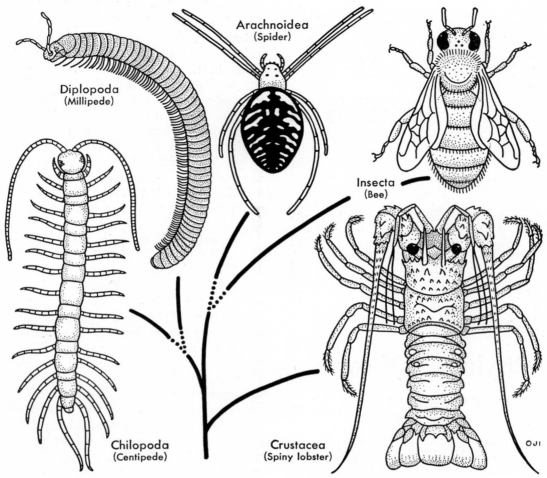

FIGURE 109. Representatives of the major classes of arthropods, showing body divisions and appendages. The lines suggest possible relationships. The figures are not drawn to scale.

states, and *Astacus* in the western United States. The lobster *Homarus americanus,* differs in structure from the crayfish only in minor details. In Europe the most common crayfish is *Astacus fluviatilis.*

External anatomy

Exoskeleton

The outside of the body is covered by a hard **cuticle** containing chitin* and impreg-

* The best-known component of the cuticle is chitin, a nitrogenous polysaccharide; it is a very re-

nated with lime salts. This exoskeleton (Fig. 112) is thinner and flexible at the joints, allowing movement.

sistant substance that is insoluble in water, alcohol, dilute acids, alkalies, and the digestive juices of many animals. Formerly it was thought that the chitin was responsible for the hardness of the cuticle; now, however, it is definitely known that the hardness of the cuticle is due to nonchitinous substances. The softer parts of the cuticle usually contain more chitin than the harder parts. The hard parts of the cuticle are said to be "sclerotized," not chitinized.

Chitin also occurs in some sponges, hydroids, bryozoans, brachiopods, annelids, and mollusks.

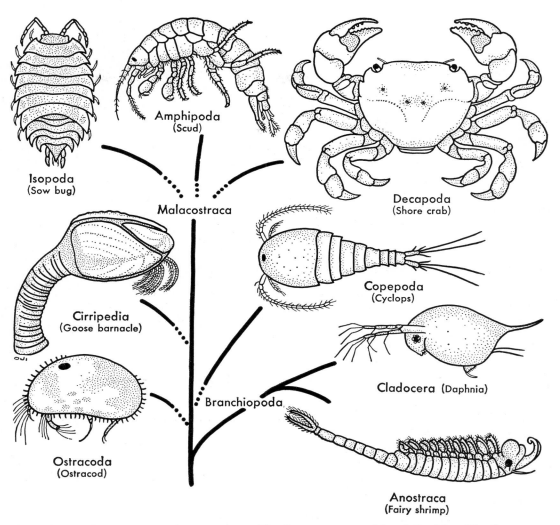

Isopoda
(Sow bug)

Amphipoda
(Scud)

Malacostraca

Decapoda
(Shore crab)

Cirripedia
(Goose barnacle)

Copepoda
(Cyclops)

Cladocera (Daphnia)

Branchiopoda

Ostracoda
(Ostracod)

Anostraca
(Fairy shrimp)

FIGURE 110. Representative crustaceans. The lines suggest possible relationships. The figures are not drawn to scale.

Regions of the body

The body consists of two distinct regions, an anterior rigid portion, the **cephalothorax,** and a posterior series of segments, the abdomen. The entire body is segmented, but the joints, except one, have been obliterated on the dorsal surface of the cephalothorax.

Exoskeletal structures of a segment

A typical segment consists of a convex dorsal plate, the **tergum,** a ventral transverse bar, the **sternum,** and plates projecting down at the sides, the **pleura** (Fig. 113).

Cephalothorax

The cephalothorax consists of segments 1-12,* which are enclosed dorsally and later-

* Many textbooks give 13 segments; but according to Snodgrass and other authorities, the antennules of arthropods are developmentally and phylogenetically different from the appendages posterior to them. The antennules arise from a structure which appears to be a homologue of the prostomium

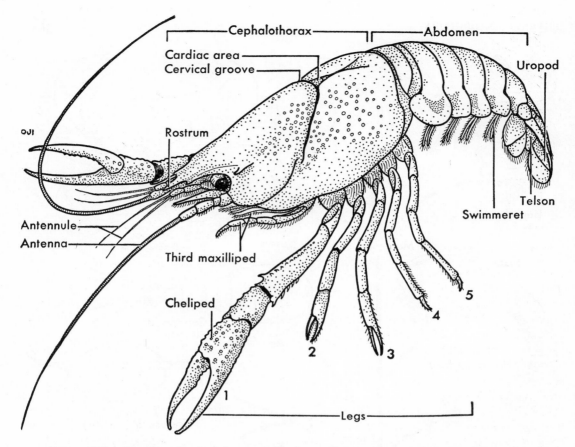

FIGURE 111. Crayfish, showing the external characteristic structures of most of the class Crustacea.

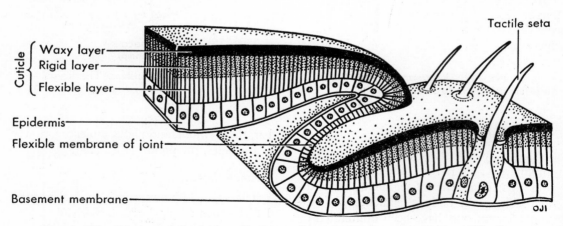

FIGURE 112. Diagram of the body wall of an arthropod, showing some of its modifications. The rigid layer is replaced by a flexible membrane in places where movement occurs.

200

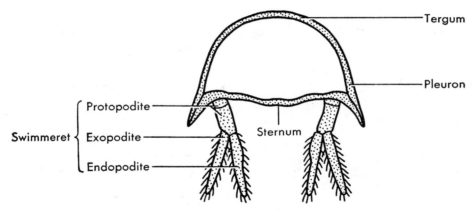

FIGURE 113. Diagram of a cross section of the third abdominal segment of the crayfish.

ally by a cuticular shield, the **carapace.** An indentation, termed the **cervical groove,** runs across the middorsal region of the carapace and obliquely forward on either side. The anterior pointed extension of the carapace is known as the **rostrum.** Beneath this on either side is an **eye** at the end of a movable stalk. The **mouth** is situated on the ventral surface near the posterior end of the head region. It is partly obscured by the neighboring appendages. The carapace of the thorax is separated into three parts by **branchiocardiac grooves:** a median dorsal longitudinal strip, the **areola,** and two large convex flaps, one on either side, the **branchiostegites,** which protect the gills beneath them.

Abdomen

In the abdomen there are 6 segments and a terminal body extension, the **telson,** bearing on its ventral surface the longitudinal anal opening. Whether or not the tel-

son is a true segment is still in dispute; we shall adopt the view that it is not. The first abdominal segment (13) is smaller than the others and lacks the pleura. Segments 14–18 are sheathed as described above.

Appendages

Every segment of the body bears a pair of jointed appendages. These are all variations of a common type consisting of a basal region, the **protopodite,** which bears 2 branches, an inner **endopodite,** and an outer **exopodite.** Beginning at the anterior end, the appendages are arranged as follows (Fig. 115). In front of the mouth are the **antennae;** the mouth possesses a pair of **mandibles,** behind which are the first and second **maxillae;** the thoracic region bears the first, second, and third **maxillipeds,** the **chelipeds** (pincers), and 4 other pairs of **walking legs;** beneath the abdomen are 5 pairs of **swimmerets,** some of which are much modified. The sixth abdominal segment bears greatly flattened appendages termed **uropods.** The accompanying table (pp. 206) gives brief descriptions of the different appendages, and shows the modifications concerned with differences in function. The functions of some of the appendages are still in doubt.

Three kinds of appendages can be distinguished in the adult crayfish: (1) **foliace-**

of the annelids and is a region, in a phylogenetic sense, that has not come under the influence of metamerism; therefore the first pair of serially metameric appendages of the crayfish is the antennae. The antennules are actually prostomial sense organs, like the eyes, and hence not homologous with the other true appendages. It will be noted that the numbers used in the discussion of the appendages are 1 less in value than those of texts which list 19 pairs of homologous appendages.

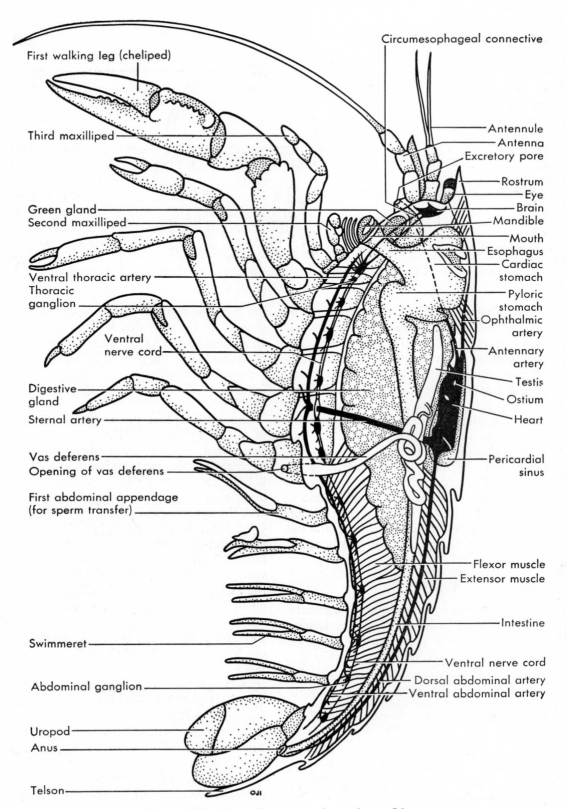

Figure 114. Internal structure of a male crayfish.

202

ous, the second maxilla, (2) **biramous**, the swimmerets, and (3) **uniramous**, the walking legs. All these appendages have probably been derived from a single type, the modifications being correlated with the functions performed by them. The biramous type may represent the condition from which the other types developed as shown in Fig. 115. The uniramous walking legs, for example, pass through a biramous stage during their embryologic development. Again, the biramous embryonic maxillipeds are converted into the foliaceous type by expansion of

their basal segments. Other types of appendages undergo similar changes.

Structures that have a similar fundamental structure, regardless of function, due to descent from a common ancestor, are said to be **homologous.** The highly specialized chelipeds, walking legs, jaws, and other structures of the crayfish have evidently developed from a fundamental type and have become different in function. When homologous structures are repeated in a series the condition is known as **serial homology.** This is a most striking example of serial homology

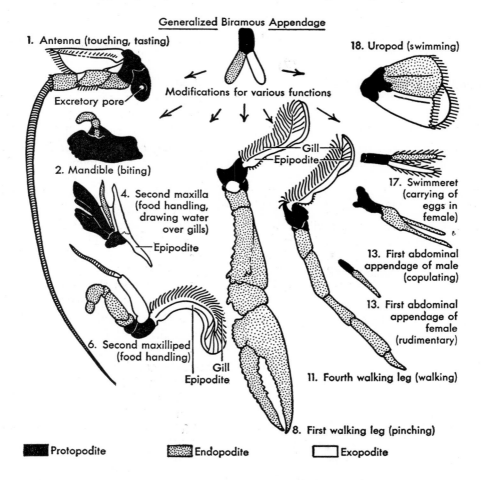

FIGURE 115. Homology and evolution of crayfish appendages. All are believed to have been derived from a generalized two-branched (biramous) appendage consisting of protopodite, endopodite, and exopodite. This basic plan of structure has been modified (specialized) for the various uses noted. The appendages demonstrate in a striking way the changes that occur in the evolution of structures.

and is one of the reasons why crayfish appendages are usually studied in some detail.

Internal anatomy

The body of the crayfish (Fig. 114) contains all of the important systems of organs characteristic of the higher animals. The coelom is not large but is restricted to the cavities enclosing the gonads and the excretory green glands. Certain organs are metamerically arranged, such as the **nervous system**; others, like the **excretory organs**, are concentrated into a small space. The systems of organs and their functions will be presented in the following order: (1) digestive, (2) circulatory, (3) respiratory, (4) excretory, (5) nervous, (6) sense, (7) muscular, and (8) reproductive.

Digestive system

The digestive tract of *Cambarus* consists of the following parts:

1. The **mouth** opens on the ventral surface between the jaws.

2. The **esophagus** is a short tube leading from the mouth to the stomach.

3. The **stomach** is a large cavity divided by a constriction into an anterior **cardiac chamber** and a smaller posterior **pyloric chamber**. In the cardiac chamber are three hard **teeth** (chitinous ossicles) of use in grinding the food and collectively known as the **gastric mill**. The teeth are able to move one upon another; and, being connected with powerful muscles, are effective in grinding up the food. On either side of the pyloric chamber a duct enters from the digestive glands and above is the opening of the small **cecum**.

About 10 to 30 days before molting, two calcareous bodies, known as **gastroliths**, are present in the lateral walls of the cardiac chamber of the stomach. During the molt these are shed into the stomach where they may be dissolved. When this occurs they are probably used in the calcification of the new exoskeleton. However, a high percentage of the gastroliths are lost in the shedding process, and in these cases there is no possibility of the re-use of the lime which they contain.

4. A short **midgut**.

5. The **intestine** is a small tube that passes through the abdomen and opens to the outside through the **anus** on the ventral surface of the telson.

6. The **digestive glands** ("liver") are situated in the thorax and abdomen, one on each side. Each consists of 3 lobes composed of a great number of small tubules. The glandular epithelium lining these tubules produces a pancreaticlike enzyme which may pass into the **hepatic ducts** and thence into the midgut.

Nutrition

Food. The food of the crayfish is made up principally of living animals such as snails, tadpoles, insect larvae, small fish, and frogs, but decaying organic matter is also eaten. Crayfishes also prey upon others of their kind. They feed at night, being more active at dusk and daybreak than at any other time. Their method of feeding may be observed in the laboratory if a little fresh meat is offered to them. The maxillipeds and maxillae hold the food while it is being torn and crushed into small pieces by the mandibles. It then passes through the esophagus into the stomach. The coarser parts are ejected through the mouth.

Digestion. In the cardiac chamber of the stomach, the food is ground up by the teeth of the gastric mill. When fine enough, it passes through the **strainer** which lies between the cardiac and pyloric portions of the stomach. This strainer consists of two lateral folds and a median ventral one which bear hairlike processes and allow passage of only liquids or very fine particles. In the midgut, the food is mixed with the secretion from the digestive glands brought in by way of the hepatic ducts. From the midgut some of the dissolved or partially digested food passes into the digestive glands,

DESCRIPTIVE TABLE OF THE HOMOLOGOUS APPENDAGES OF THE CRAYFISH *

SEGMENT NUMBER AND NAME OF APPENDAGE	PROTOPODITE	EXOPODITE	ENDOPODITE	FUNCTION
1 Antenna	2 segments; excretory pore in basal segment	Broad, thin, dagger-like lateral projection	Three basal segments, and long many-jointed "feeler"	Touch; taste
2 Mandible	1 segment; a heavy jaw	Not present	Small; 3 segments of palp	Biting food
3 1st Maxilla	2 thin lamellae extending inward	Not present	A small outer lamella	Food handling
4 2d Maxilla	2 bilobed lamellae; a broad plate, the epipodite	Dorsal half of plate, the scaphognathite	1 segment; small, pointed	Creates current of water in gill chamber; food handling
5 1st Maxilliped	2 thin segments extending inward; epipodite extending outward	A long basal segment bearing a many-jointed filament	Small; 2 segments	Taste; touch; holds food
6 2d Maxilliped	2 segments; a basal coxopodite bearing a gill, and a basipodite bearing the exopodite and endopodite	Similar to 5	5 segments; the basal one long and fused with the basipodite	Similar to 5
7 3d Maxilliped	Similar to 6	Similar to 5	Similar to 6; but larger	Similar to 5
8 1st Walking Leg (Chela, Cheliped or Pincer)	2 segments; coxopodite, and basipodite	Not present	5 segments, the terminal two forming a powerful pincer	Pincer for offense and defense; aids in walking; touch
9 2d Walking Leg (Pereiopod)	Similar to 8	Not present	As in 8, but not so heavy	Walking; grasping
10 3d Walking Leg	Similar to 8; coxopodite of female contains genital pore	Not present	Similar to 9	Similar to 9
11 4th Walking Leg	Similar to 8	Not present	Similar to 9, but no pincer at end	Walking
12 5th Walking Leg	Similar to 8; coxopodite of male bears genital pore	Not present	Similar to 11	Walking; cleaning abdomen and eggs
13 1st Abdominal (1st Pleopod or Swimmeret)				Reduced in female; in male, protopodite and endopodite, fused together, forming an organ for transfering sperm

DESCRIPTIVE TABLE OF THE HOMOLOGOUS APPENDAGES OF THE CRAYFISH *
(Continued)

SEGMENT NUMBER AND NAME OF APPENDAGE	PROTOPODITE	EXOPODITE	ENDOPODITE	FUNCTION
14 2d Abdominal (2d Pleopod or Swimmeret)	In female 2 segments	In female many-jointed filament	In female many-jointed filament	In female as in 15; in male modified for transferring sperm to female
15 3d Abdominal (3d Pleopod or Swimmeret)	2 segments	Many-jointed filament	Many-jointed filament	Creates current of water; in female used for attachment of eggs and young
16 4th Abdominal (4th Pleopod or Swimmeret)	2 segments	As in 15	As in 15	As in 15
17 5th Abdominal (5th Pleopod or Swimmeret)	As in 16	As in 15	As in 15	As in 15
18 6th Abdominal (Uropod)	1 short, broad segment	Flat oval plate divided by transverse groove into two parts	Flat oval plate	Swimming

* The antennules are not included in this table because they are considered by Snodgrass and other authorities as prostomial sense organs, as are the eyes.

which not only form the digestive enzymes but also absorb some of the products of digestion. Undigested particles pass on into the posterior end of the intestine, where they are gathered together into feces and pass through the anus.

Circulatory system

Blood. The **blood plasma**, into which the absorbed food passes, is an almost colorless liquid, but contains **hemocyanin**, a bluish respiratory pigment that contains copper instead of iron. There are suspended in the plasma a number of amoeboid cells, the **blood corpuscles.** The principal **functions** of the blood are transportation: it transports food materials from one part of the body to another, oxygen from the gills to the various tissues, carbon dioxide to the gills, and waste products to the excretory organs.

If a crayfish is wounded, the blood thickens, forming a clot; it is said to **coagulate.** This clogs the opening and prevents loss of blood.

Blood vessels. The principal blood vessels (Figs. 114 and 116) are a heart, 7 main arteries, and a number of spaces called sinuses.

Heart. The **heart** is a muscular-walled, saddle-shaped sac lying in the **pericardial sinus** in the median dorsal part of the thorax. It may be considered a dilatation of a dorsal vessel, resembling that of the earthworm. Blood enters the heart through three pairs of valves called **ostia,** one dorsal, one lateral, and one ventral.

Arteries. Five arteries arise from the anterior end of the heart.

1. The **ophthalmic artery** is a median dorsal tube passing forward over the stomach

and supplying the cardiac portion, the esophagus, and the head.

2, 3. The two **antennary arteries** arise one on each side of the ophthalmic artery. They pass forward, outward, and downward, and then branch, sending a **gastric artery** to the cardiac part of the stomach, and arteries to the antennae, excretory organs, muscles, and to other cephalic tissues.

4, 5. The two **hepatic arteries** leave the heart below the antennary arteries. They lead directly to the digestive glands.

6. The **dorsal abdominal artery** is a median tube leading backward from the ventral part of the heart and supplying the dorsal region of the abdomen. It branches near its point of origin, giving rise to the **sternal artery**; this leads directly downward, and, passing between the nerve cords connecting the fourth and fifth pairs of thoracic ganglia, it divides into two arteries (Fig. 114). One of these, the **ventral thoracic artery**, runs forward beneath the nerve chain and sends branches to the ventral thoracic region and to appendages 2 to 12; the other, the **ventral abdominal artery**, runs backward beneath the nerve chain and sends branches to the ventral abdominal region.

Sinuses. The blood passes from the smallest arteries into spaces lying in the midst of the tissues, called **sinuses**. The pericardial sinus has already been mentioned. The thorax contains a large ventral blood space, the **sternal sinus**, and a number of **branchiocardiac sinuses** that lead from the bases of the gills, up the inner sides of the thoracic wall, to the pericardial sinus. A **perivisceral sinus** surrounds the digestive tract in the **cephalothorax**.

Blood flow. The heart by means of rhythmic contractions forces the blood through the arteries to all parts of the body. Valves are present in every artery where it leaves the heart; they prevent the blood from flowing back. The finest branches of these arteries, open into spaces between the tissues, and the blood eventually reaches the **sternal sinus**. From here it passes into

afferent channels of the gills and into the gill filaments, where the carbon dioxide is given off and oxygen is taken in from the water in the branchial chambers. It then returns by way of the **efferent gill channels**, passes into the branchiocardiac sinuses, thence to the pericardial sinus, and finally through the ostia into the heart. The valves of the ostia allow the blood to enter the heart, but prevent it from flowing back into the pericardial sinus.

The crayfish thus has an **open** (lacunar) **blood system** in which the blood is distributed to blood spaces (sinuses) before being returned to the heart. There are no veins as in vertebrates.

Respiratory system

Breathing in the crayfish is by means of plumy gills. Between the branchiostegites and the body wall are the branchial chambers containing the gills (Fig. 116). At the anterior end of the branchial chamber there is a channel in which the **gill bailer** (**scaphognathite**) of the second maxilla moves back and forth, forcing the water out through the anterior opening. Water flows in through the posterior opening of the branchial chamber and ventrally.

There are two rows of **gills**, named according to their points of attachment. The outermost, the **podobranchs**, are fastened to the **coxopodites** of certain appendages; and the inner double row, the **arthrobranchs**, arise from the membranes at the bases of these appendages. In *Astacus* there is a third row, the **pleurobranchs**, attached to the walls of the thorax. The podobranchs consist of a basal plate covered with delicate setae and a central axis bearing a thin, longitudinally folded, corrugated plate on its distal end, and a featherlike group of **branchial filaments**. Each arthrobranch has a central stem, on each side of which extends a number of filaments, causing the entire structure to resemble a plume. Attached to the base of the first maxilliped is a broad thin plate, the **epipodite** (Fig. 115), which has lost its

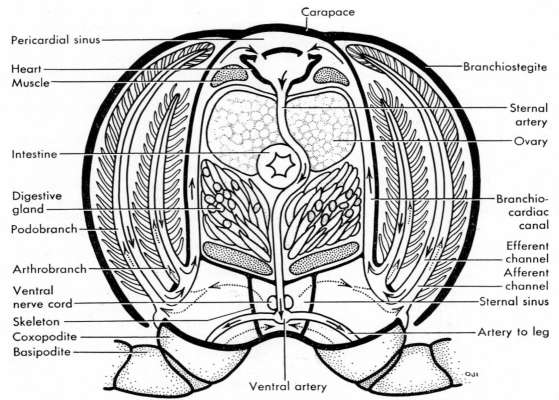

FIGURE 116. Cross section of a crayfish showing arrangement of the gills and some of the internal organs.

branchial filaments. Crayfishes do not drink when in water; the water diffuses through the gills into the body.

Excretory system

The excretory organs are a pair of rather large bodies, the **green glands** (Fig. 114), situated in the ventral part of the head anterior to the esophagus. Each green gland consists of a glandular portion which is green in color, a thin-walled dilatation, the bladder, and a duct opening to the exterior through an **excretory pore** on the basal segment of the antenna.

Nervous system

The general structure of the nervous system (Fig. 114) of the crayfish is in many respects similar to that of the earthworm but further developed in the head and thorax.

The **central nervous system** includes a dorsal ganglionic mass, the **brain (supraesophageal ganglia)**, in the head, and two **circumesophageal connectives** which pass to the **subesophageal ganglion**. This is the most anterior ganglion of the **ventral nerve cord**. Following the subesophageal are 6 ganglia in the **thorax** and 6 ganglia in the **abdomen**, all joined to each other by the ventral nerve cord.

The **brain** is a compact mass, larger than that of the earthworm, which supplies the eyes, antennules, and antennae with nerves.

The ganglia and connectives of the ventral nerve cord are more intimately fused than in the earthworm; it is difficult to make out the double nature of the connectives except between thoracic ganglia 4 and 5, where the sternal artery passes through.

The **visceral nervous system** consists of

an anterior visceral nerve which arises from the ventral surface of the brain; it is joined by a nerve from each circumesophageal connective, and, passing back, it branches upon the dorsal wall of the pyloric part of the stomach, sending a **lateral nerve** on each side to unite with an **inferolateral nerve** from the **stomatogastric ganglion.**

Sense organs

Eyes. The compound eyes of the crayfish are situated at the end of movable stalks which extend out, one from under each side of the rostrum (Fig. 114). The external convex surface of the eye is covered by a modified portion of the transparent cuticle called the **cornea.** This cornea is divided by a large number of fine lines into 4-sided areas termed **facets.** Each facet is but the external part of a long slender visual rod known as an **ommatidium.**

Sections (Fig. 117, A) show the compound eye to be made up of similar ommatidia lying side by side, but separated from one another by a layer of dark pigment cells. The average number of ommatidia in a single eye is 2500.

Two ommatidia are shown in Fig. 118.

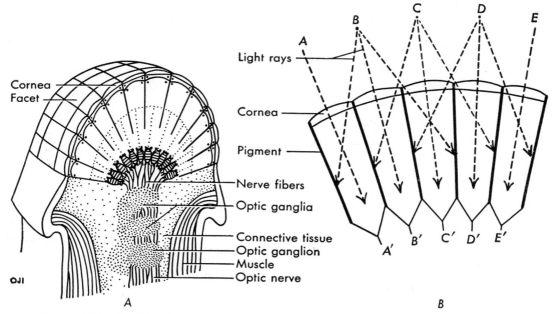

FIGURE 117. Crayfish. A, entire eye in longitudinal section to show its general structure. B, diagram of part of a compound eye showing in strong light how the light rays are absorbed by the pigment surrounding the ommatidia; only those that pass through the center such as A-A', B-B', etc., reach the nerve fibers. This results in a separate image from each ommatidium. (A after Borradaile and Potts; B after Lubbock.)

Beginning at the outer surface, each ommatidium consists of the following parts: (1) a **cornea (lens)**; (2) two **corneagen cells** which secrete the cornea; (3) a **crystalline cone** formed by four cone cells; (4) two **retinular cells** surrounding the crystalline cone; (5) several **retinular cells** which form a central **rhabdom** where they meet; and (6) a number of black **basal pigment cells** around the base of the retinular cells. Fibers from the **optic nerve** enter at the base of the ommatidium and communicate with the inner ends of the retinular cells.

Vision. The eyes of the crayfish are supposed to produce a **mosaic** or **apposition image;** this is illustrated in Fig. 117, B, where the ommatidia are represented by A–E, and the fibers from the optic nerve by A'–E'. The rays of light from any point, A, B, or C, will all encounter the dark pigment cells surrounding the ommatidia and be absorbed, except the ray which passes directly through the center of the cornea as D or E; this ray will penetrate to the retinulae and thence to the fibers of the optic nerve. Thus the retinula (plural, retinulae) of one ommatidium receives a single resultant impression from the light which reaches it. But the adjacent ommatidia, being directed to a different though adjoining region of the outer world, may transmit a different impression, and the stimuli from all of the ommatidia

which make up a compound eye will correspond in greater or less degree to the whole of the visible outer world which subtends their several optic axes. This means that each visual unit responds to a fragment of the total field and that these fragmentary images are fitted together into a single general picture. However, the image formed by this type of eye is never very good; it functions best at short distances—the arthropod is always near-sighted.

When the pigment surrounds the ommatidia (Fig. 118, A), vision is as described above; but it has been found that in weak light the pigment migrates partly toward the outer and partly toward the basal end of the

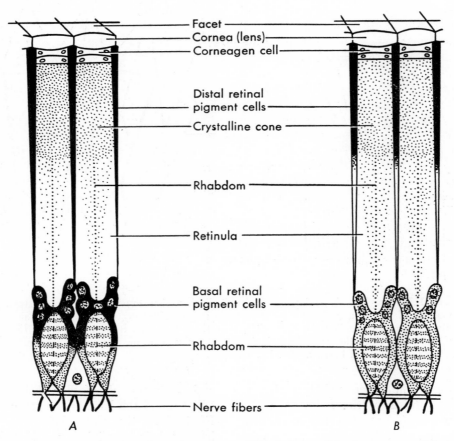

Facet
Cornea (lens)
Corneagen cell

Distal retinal pigment cells
Crystalline cone

Rhabdom

Retinula

Basal retinal pigment cells

Rhabdom

Nerve fibers

A   B

Figure 118. Longitudinal sections of two ommatidia of the crayfish. A, one ommatidium in the light; pigment extended so that it completely surrounds the ommatidium, isolating it from its neighbors. B, ommatidium in the dark; pigment in the basal pigment cells is withdrawn. (After Bernhards, from Parker.)

ommatidia (Fig. 118, *B*). When this occurs the ommatidia no longer act separately, but a continuous image is thrown on the retinular layer. This is called a **superposition image,** which is much less distinct than the apposition image, but it is more sensitive to weak intensities of light.

Statocysts. The statocysts of *Cambarus* are chitin-lined sacs situated one in the basal segment of each antennule. In the base of the statocyst is a ridge with many fine sensory hairs which are innervated by a single nerve fiber. Among these hairs are a number of large grains of sand, the **statoliths,** which are placed there by the crayfish. Beneath the sensory cushion are glands which secrete a substance for the attachment of the statoliths to the hairs.

The statocyst for many years was considered an auditory organ, but later investigations have proved that it is an organ of **equilibrium.** The contact of the statoliths with the statocyst hairs determines the orientation of the body while swimming, since any change in the position of the animal causes a change in the position of the statoliths under the influence of gravity. When the crayfish changes its exoskeleton in the process of molting, the statocyst is also shed. Individuals that have just molted, or have had their statocysts removed, lose much of their powers of orientation. Perhaps the most convincing proof of the function of equilibrium is that furnished by experiments. Shrimps, which had just molted and were therefore without statoliths, were placed in filtered water. When supplied with iron filings, the animals filled their statocysts with them. A strong electromagnet was then held near the statocyst, and the shrimp took up a position corresponding to the resultant of the two pulls, that of gravity and that of the magnet.

Endocrine glands

The **sinus gland** located in the base of the eye stalk produces two hormones, and possibly more. These hormones appear to control the spread of pigment granules in the chromatophores in the compound eyes and in the body epidermis. They govern to a greater or lesser extent, metabolic rate, growth and viability. They also regulate the frequency of molting, and are necessary for normal deposition of calcium salts in the exoskeleton. These hormones are distributed by the blood stream, as in the vertebrates. It has been observed in experimental animals that removal of the sinus glands shortened the life of crustaceans.

Muscular system

In the crayfish the complex muscles are all attached to the inner surface of the skeleton, instead of constituting a part of the body wall as in the coelenterates and annelids, or being external to the skeleton as in man. The largest muscles in the body of the crayfish are situated in the abdomen (Fig. 114) and are used to bend that part of the animal forward upon the ventral surface of the thorax, thus producing backward locomotion in swimming. Other muscles extend the abdomen in preparation for another stroke. Muscles of considerable size are situated in the thorax and within the tubular appendages, especially the chelipeds. A comparison of the skeleton and muscles of the crayfish with those of man is interesting.

Reproductive system

Sexes are normally separate in the crayfish, there being only a few cases on record where both male and female reproductive organs were found in a single specimen.

Male reproductive organs. The male organs consist of two white **testes** partially fused into three lobes and on each side a long coiled sperm duct, the **vas deferens,** which opens through the base of the fifth walking leg. The testes lie just beneath the heart (Fig. 114). They constitute a soft body possessing two anterior lobes and a median posterior extension.

Spermatogenesis. The primitive germ cells within the testis pass through two

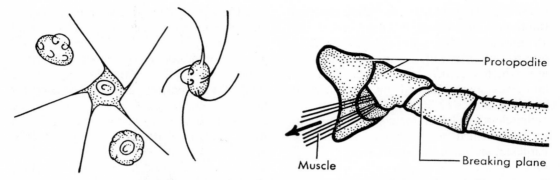

FIGURE 119. *Left*, different views of crayfish sperms, greatly magnified. *Right*, posterior view of basal region of second walking leg of the crayfish, showing the line where the break occurs in autotomy, and the special muscle concerned. Arrow indicates the direction of pull of the muscle involved in the reflex.

maturation divisions and then develop into sperms. These are flattened spheroidal bodies when enclosed within the testis or vas deferens; but, if examined in water or some other liquid, they are seen to uncoil, finally becoming star-shaped (Fig. 119).

The sperms remain in the testes and vasa deferentia until copulation takes place. As many as two million sperms are contained in the vasa deferentia of a single specimen.

Female reproductive organs. The two **ovaries** resemble the testes in form and are similarly located in the body (Fig. 116). A short **oviduct** leads from near the center of the side of each ovary to the external opening in the base of the third walking leg.

Oogenesis. The primitive germ cells in the walls of the ovary grow in size and become surrounded by a layer of small cells, the follicle, which eventually breaks down, allowing the eggs to escape into the central cavity of the ovary. At the time of laying, the ova pass out through the oviduct.

Fertilization and development. The sperms are transferred from the male to the seminal receptacle of the female during copulation, which usually takes place between early spring and autumn. The **seminal receptacle** is a cavity in a fold of cuticle between the fourth and fifth pairs of walking legs. The female lays her eggs several weeks to several months after copulation; the ova

are fertilized by the sperms when laid. The eggs are fastened to the swimmerets with a sticky substance and are aerated by being moved back and forth through the water.

The **cleavage** of the egg is superficial, and the embryo appears first as a thickening on one side. The eggs hatch in 2 to 20 weeks, and the larvae cling to the egg stalk. In about 2 to 7 days they shed their cuticular covering, a process known as **molting.** Casting off the covering of the body is not peculiar to the young, but occurs in adult crayfishes as well as in young and adults of many other arthropods. In the larval crayfish the cuticle of the first stage becomes loosened and drops off. In the meantime, the epidermal cells have secreted a new covering. Molting is necessary before growth can proceed since the exoskeleton is hard and nonelastic. In adults it also is a means of getting rid of an old worn-out coat and acquiring a new one. Over a period of some time before the molt, a quantity of calcium from the old exoskeleton is absorbed and distributed by the blood, especially to the stomach, where it is deposited in calcareous bodies, the **gastroliths.** The formation of gastroliths is under the control of an endocrine gland. The young stay with the mother, attached to her swimmerets with their chelae (see headpiece at beginning of this chapter) until they can shift for themselves.

They molt at least 6 times during the first summer. Before the new exoskeleton hardens an increase in body bulk occurs, probably due to absorption of unusual quantities of water before molting. Several days after a molt, the animal remains in hiding, thus avoiding enemies while it is in a relatively defenseless condition. It takes several weeks for the new shell to become as completely hardened as the one cast off.

Regeneration

The crayfish and many other crustaceans have the power of regenerating lost parts, but to a much more limited extent than such animals as the hydra and earthworm. Experiments have been performed upon almost every one of the appendages as well as the eye. The second and third maxillipeds, the walking legs, the swimmerets, and the eye have all been injured or cut off at various times, and the lost parts were subsequently renewed. Many species of crayfish of various ages have been used for these experiments. The growth of regenerated tissue is more frequent and rapid in young specimens than in adults.

The new structure is not always like that of the one removed. For example, when the annulus containing the seminal receptacle of an adult is extirpated, another is regenerated; although this is as large as that of the adult, it is comparable in complexity only to that of an early larval stage. A more remarkable phenomenon is the regeneration of an apparently functional antennalike organ in place of a degenerate eye which was removed from the blind crayfish *Cambarus pellucidus testii*. In this case a nonfunctional organ was replaced by a functional one of a different character. The regeneration of a new part which differs from the part removed is termed **heteromorphosis**.

Self-amputation (autotomy)

Perhaps the most interesting anatomic structure connected with the regenerative process in *Cambarus* is the definite breaking point near the bases of the walking legs (Fig. 119). If a cheliped is grasped or injured, it is broken off by the crayfish at the breaking plane. The other walking legs, if injured, may be thrown off at the free joint between the second and third segments. A new leg as large as the one lost develops from the end of the remaining stump. This breaking off of the legs at a definite point is known as **autotomy**, a phenomenon that occurs also in a number of other animals. The breaking plane in decapod crustaceans is near the base of the legs. The leg is flexed by a special (autotomizer) muscle; continued pull of this muscle separates the leg at the breaking point. The muscles are not damaged, and a membrane develops across the inside of the leg on the proximal side of the breaking place. There is a small hole in the membrane through which nerves and blood vessels pass, but this hole is quickly stopped by a blood clot. About 5 days later regeneration begins by an outward growth of the cells which lined the exoskeleton.

Autotomy is an adaptation which prevents undue loss of blood when a leg is sacrificed to escape an enemy.

As in the earthworm, the **rate of regeneration** depends upon the amount of tissue removed. If one cheliped is amputated, a new one regenerates less rapidly than if both chelipeds and some of the other walking legs are removed.

Behavior

When at rest, the crayfish usually faces outward from its place of concealment and extends its antennae. In this position it may learn the nature of any approaching object without being detected. Activity at this time is reduced to the movements of a few of the appendages and the gills; the gill bailers of the second maxillae move back and forth bailing water out of the forward end of the gill chambers; the swimmerets are in constant motion creating a current of water; the maxillipeds are likewise kept moving; and the antennules and antennae are in continual motion exploring the surroundings.

Crayfishes are more active between dusk and dawn than during the daytime. At this time they venture out of their hiding places in search of food.

Locomotion

Locomotion is accomplished by either walking or swimming. Crayfishes are able to walk in any direction, forward usually, but also sidewise, obliquely, or backward. In walking, the fourth pair of legs is most effective and bears nearly the entire weight of the animal; the fifth pair serves as props and to push the body forward; the second and third pairs are less efficient for walking since they are modified to serve as grasping organs and as toilet implements. Swimming is not resorted to under ordinary conditions, but only when the animal is frightened or shocked. In such a case the crayfish extends the abdomen, spreads out the uropods and telson, and, by sudden contractions of the flexor abdominal muscles, bends the abdomen and darts backward. The swimming reaction apparently is not voluntary, but is almost entirely reflex.

Equilibrium

The crayfish, either at rest or in motion, is in a state of unstable equilibrium and must maintain its body in the normal position by its own efforts. The force of gravity tends to turn the body over. From a large number of experiments, it has been proved that the statocysts are the organs of equilibrium. The structure of these organs is described on page 211. The contact of the statoliths with the sensory hairs furnishes the stimulus which causes the animal to maintain an upright position.

When placed on its back, the crayfish has some difficulty in righting itself. Two methods of regaining its normal position are employed. The usual method is that of rais-

ing itself on one side and allowing the body to tip over by the force of gravity. The second method is that of contracting the flexor abdominal muscles, which causes a quick backward flop, bringing the body right side up. In general, the animals right themselves by the easiest method when placed on their backs; and this is found to depend usually upon the relative weight of the two sides of the body. When placed upon a surface which is not level, they take advantage, after a few experiences, of the inclination by turning toward the lower side.

Senses and their location

The crayfish has more highly developed sense organs than the annelids. The sense of **touch** in crayfishes is perhaps the most valuable, since it aids them in finding food, avoiding obstacles, and in many other ways. Touch organs are located in specialized hairlike bristles or setae (Fig. 112) on various parts of the body. These are especially abundant on the mouth parts, chelae, chelipeds, and edge of telson. **Vision** in crayfishes is undoubtedly of real value to the animal in detecting moving objects. No reactions to **sound** have ever been observed in crayfishes, and apparently they do not hear. The reactions formerly attributed to hearing are probably due to touch reflexes. In aquatic animals it is so difficult to distinguish between reactions of **taste** and **smell** that these senses are both included in the term **chemical sense**. The end organs of this sense are found in hairs located on the antennules, tip of antennae, mouth parts, and other places.

Reactions to stimuli

Contact. **Positive reactions** to contact are exhibited to a marked degree by crayfishes; the animals seek to place their bodies in contact with a solid object if possible. The normal position of the crayfish when at rest under a stone is such as to bring its side or dorsal surface in contact with the walls of its hiding place. This, no doubt, is of distinct advantage since it places the animal in a position of safety.

Light. Light of various intensities in the majority of cases causes the crayfish to retreat. Individuals prefer colored lights to white. **Negative reactions** to light play an important role in the animal's life, since they influence it to seek a dark place where it is concealed from its enemies.

Chemicals. The reactions of the crayfish to food are due in part to a **chemical sense.** **Positive reactions** result from stimulation by food substances. For example, if meat juice is placed in the water near an animal, the antennae move slightly and the mouth parts perform vigorous chewing movements. The meat juice causes general restlessness and movements toward the source of the stimulation, but the animals seem to depend chiefly on touch for the accurate localization of food. Acids, salts, sugar, and other chemicals produce a sort of **negative reaction,** indicated by the animal scratching the carapace, rubbing the chelae, or pulling at the part stimulated.

Habit forming

It has been shown by certain simple experiments that crayfishes are able to form habits and to modify them. They learn by experience and modify their behavior slowly or quickly, depending upon their familiarity with the situation. The chief factors in the formation of such habits are the chemical sense (probably both smell and taste), touch, sight, and the muscular sensations resulting from the direction of turning. Experiments show that the animals are able to learn a path even when the possibility of following a scent is excluded.

Cave crayfishes

There are at least 12 different species of cave crayfishes in the United States; some are restricted to the waters of a single cave, such as Mammoth Cave, Kentucky.

Cave species are interesting because of their striking modifications. All are blind, the eyes are atrophied and the eye stalks are more or less undeveloped. Pigmentation is absent, and the body is light-colored. They are mostly small species; the chelae are not well developed. The antennae are long and highly specialized as tactile organs.

OTHER CRUSTACEA

Almost every pond, lake, or stream contains crustaceans of many species, and salt water is likewise inhabited by a large variety of forms. A few live on land. Often crustaceans are very abundant. Only a few of the more common or more interesting species can be mentioned here.

Fairy shrimps, *Eubranchipus,* reach a length of about one inch, live in fresh-water pools, and are common. They are semitransparent, pinkish, and swim on their backs (Fig. 110). Eggs laid in the summer become buried in the mud and are able to withstand drying and the winter cold. They hatch the following spring. One species of fairy shrimp lives in water more salty than that of the sea.

Water fleas, *Daphnia,* are oval, laterally compressed crustaceans with a prominent beak on the under side of the head, and a sharp caudal spine (Fig. 110). They are about 2 mm. long and are very common in fresh water. The soft body is enclosed in a bivalve shell through which can be seen a regularly beating heart, in front of which is a single eye, and behind which is a brood chamber full of eggs.

The ostracods are common in fresh and salt water and widely distributed. The bivalve shell (Fig. 110) makes it appear like a microscopic clam if the appendages are not seen. They swim with the first pair of legs. Only females are known in certain genera; these lay eggs which develop without fertilization, that is, they are parthenogenetic.

The modern cyclops is not a giant with a single eye in his forehead like the Cyclops of

Greek mythology, but is a very successful one-eyed little crustacean that lives in fresh water or in the sea (Fig. 110). *Cyclops viridis* is common in small fresh-water ponds, measures from 1.5 to 5 mm. in length, and is usually greenish in color. The eye is red. Often on each side of the tail is a sac full of eggs. Certain relatives of the cyclops live in the sea; although minute in size, they are often so numerous that they color the water pink and furnish the principal food of certain whales. Cyclops serve as the intermediate host for the broad tapeworm of man and the guinea worm.

Goose barnacles (Fig. 110), so called because barnacle geese were once supposed to have hatched from them, often attaching themselves to the bottoms of ships. They are fringe-legged crustaceans. They were considered by early zoologists to be mollusks because they live within a calcareous shell that they secrete. This barnacle possesses a long stalk by which it is attached to seaweed or other floating objects. It is found in both the Atlantic and Pacific oceans.

The rock barnacles, *Balanus*, possess a thick shell but no stalk (Fig. 120). They attach themselves to rocks and other stationary objects, to the shells in which hermit crabs live, and to other animals; the body of the whale often becomes intensely irritated by them. When the tide goes out, they close the 6 plates of their shells for protection. While under water they thrust out their delicate fringed legs and kick minute organisms into their mouths.

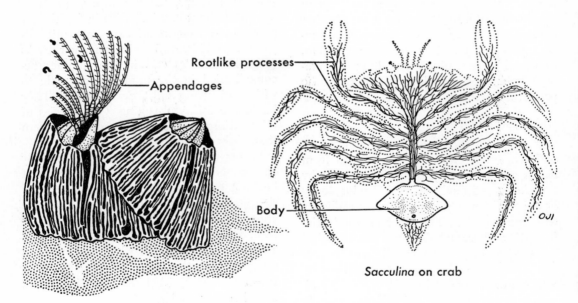

Balanus (rock barnacle)

FIGURE 120. Highly magnified crustaceans. *Left,* rock barnacles are common marine crustaceans which live permanently attached. One is shown with appendages extended and feeding. The other is withdrawn into its shell for protection from enemies. *Right, Sacculina,* a curious marine crustacean, which in the adult stage is parasitic on a crab. The crab is represented by dotted lines, and the parasite body from which the roots penetrate the tissues of the host by solid lines.

The root-headed barnacles are parasitic. The best-known species, *Sacculina* (Fig. 120), attaches itself when young to a marine crab, between the thorax and abdomen, on the ventral surface. It then loses most of its organs, sends rootlike processes into the body of the crab, and becomes a mere sac. The host's body becomes so completely parasitized that the whole physiology is seriously affected.

Many interesting crustaceans belong to the subclass Malacostraca. A few will be described here, beginning with the sow bugs. A terrestrial species *Oniscus* (Fig. 110), about 16 mm. long, is slate-colored, spotted with white, and is common under stones, bark of logs, etc. It breathes with gills and must therefore live in a moist place. The body is oval and flat, which enables it to creep into crevices; and the "legs" are approximately equal in size.

Beach fleas live on beaches where they bury themselves in the sand. They can leap with agility but do not bite. The common, long-horned, beach flea (Fig. 121), is about one inch long, has a laterally flattened body like that of a flea, and has legs adapted for leaping. It feeds on decaying animal and vegetable matter and is a valuable scavenger on many sand beaches.

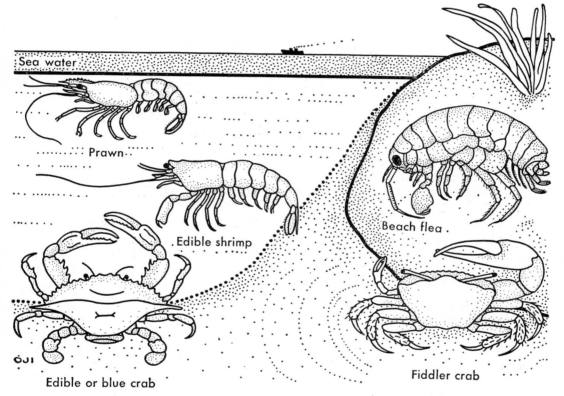

FIGURE 121.   Representative malacostracans in their respective habitats.

The fresh-water scud, *Gammarus* (Fig. 110), is also an amphipod, but lives in fresh-water ponds and streams and swims instead of leaps. It is whitish and about 15 mm. long.

Our most important edible crustacean is the American lobster, *Homarus*, a near relative of the crayfish. The American lobster has probably been more intensively studied than any other marine animal with the possible exception of the American oyster (*Ostrea*). These lobsters live in the sea along the Atlantic Coast. They are not red when alive, but usually dark green with darker spots and yellowish underneath. They may grow to a length of over 2 feet and to a weight of over 30 pounds, but most of those caught in lobster pots are less than

10 inches long and weigh less than 2 pounds. The west coast lobster (*Panulirus*) is commonly called a spiny lobster because its skeleton is provided with many needle-sharp spines.

Shrimps and prawns are also decapods. The edible shrimp is slender, with whiplike antennae, and is about 5 cm. long. It is very agile, swimming backward with quick jerks of the fin at the posterior end of the body. It eats both animal and vegetable matter. Shrimps are constantly being preyed upon by fish and other marine animals as well as by man. Prawns are smaller than shrimps. A common species, which is displayed in Fig. 121, lives among rock weed and eel grass on muddy bottoms along the Atlantic Coast from Massachusetts to Florida.

Hermit crabs (see colored frontispiece at beginning of text) are famous because they live in the empty shells of marine snails. As they grow larger, they must move from one shell into a larger one. Frequently the shell is covered with coelenterates. The abdomen of the crab within the shell is soft and twisted to fit the coils, and one pair of abdominal appendages develops into hooks which anchor the body in the shell; the other abdominal appendages become degenerate. The right-hand pincer, which is used to capture and crush its prey, is constructed so as to close the opening in the shell. The other smaller pincer fills any crevice in the opening left by the other claw. A common one is *Pagurus*, which lives in rock pools and shallow water along the beach from Maine to South Carolina.

Many species of crabs are edible, but one species, *Callinectes sapidus* (Fig. 121), is usually given this doubtful honor. The short and broad body is about 7 cm. long and 17 cm. wide. The shell is dark green and the feet are blue. Edible crabs are common on muddy bottoms in shallow water from Cape Cod to Louisiana. In California the most important edible crab is *Cancer magister*. Crabs that are considered edible in one locality may not be eaten in other regions.

Spider crabs are noted for their long spidery legs. The common species, *Libinia emarginata*, is about 7 cm. long and lives on mud flats and oyster beds along the Atlantic Coast from Maine to Florida, and in California. The shell is pointed in front and covered with a dense growth of chitinous "hairs" which give it a furry appearance. The legs of a Japanese spider crab reach an enormous length; individuals of this species may measure 12 feet across when spread out.

Fiddler crabs (Fig. 121) are accustomed to wave their large claw back and forth as though playing a violin, hence the common name. They form colonies which live in burrows that are dug in the mud or sand in salt marshes. In certain species, the males are very pugnacious and fight each other with great vigor.

ORIGIN AND RELATIONS OF THE ARTHROPODA

The Arthropoda probably evolved from an annelidlike ancestor.

The Onychophora (Fig. 124) seem to resemble most closely this ancestral condition. They possess a thin cuticle, a continuous and muscular body wall, no joints, one pair of jaws, and appendages on the first segment. In the other groups of arthropods, development of a rigid exoskeleton with joints brought about a change in the distribution of the muscles from the continuous type forming a muscular body wall, as in the annelids, to the discontinuous type in which the muscles are separately and diversely developed for the movement of special segments.

The crustaceans, insects, centipedes, and millipedes appear to have developed along one line, since they have so much in common; and the arachnids along another line, since none of their appendages have developed into antennae, and none possess mandibles. The classes of crustaceans have become different from one another, principally as a result of specialization of appendages, shortening of the body, and development of a carapace. Internal changes are associated with these external modifications. Orders of insects are arranged in the phylogenetic tree (p. 229) to suggest possible relationships. The centipedes are more closely related to the insects than are the millipedes.

Trilobites

The name trilobite (Fig. 122) means "three-lobed" and refers to the fact that the dorsal surface is divided by longitudinal furrows into three lobes. They were covered by a hard shell. On the head was a pair of antennae, 4 pairs of two-branched appendages, and often a pair of compound eyes.

These primitive fossil arthropods date from early geologic time. Although trilobites

FIGURE 122. Fossil trilobites; these extinct arthropods lived in warm primeval seas about 500,000 million years ago. They dominated life on earth for a span many, many times as long as man's whole existence. (Courtesy of American Museum of Natural History.)

probably did not give rise directly to any other group of arthropods, they appear to be most closely related to crustaceans.

RELATIONS OF CRUSTACEA TO MAN

Crustacea are of considerable value as food for man, either directly or indirectly. The smaller species may be present in enormous numbers in both fresh water and salt water and constitute an important part of the food chain of many fish and other aquatic animals that eventually come to our table. Commercially, the shrimp is the most important of the crustaceans as human food; crabs, lobsters, and crayfishes follow in this order. Blue or edible crabs are eaten extensively in certain regions; they are called hard-shelled crabs except just after molting, when they become soft-shelled. The crayfish, especially the soft-shelled individual, is very popular among fishermen as bait. The soft-shelled crayfishes may be kept soft for a week or more on ice. Refrigeration slows metabolism so that the shell develops slowly.

The crayfish is used for food, especially in Europe and on the Pacific Coast. The spiny lobster of the Pacific Coast may reach a weight of 10 pounds. Shrimps and prawns

FIGURE 123. A Cape Cod lobsterman removing a prize lobster from a wooden trap. These traps are baited, weighted with a brick, tied to the frame, as shown, and set in the ocean to harvest the lobster crop. (Courtesy of Mike Roberts Color Productions.)

are marine species whose large abdominal muscles are sold in the fresh condition or canned. The shrimp industry in the United States is especially important in Louisiana and California. Certain crustaceans may become pests when present in large numbers. Thus in some parts of our southern states, crayfishes damage cotton and other crops by devouring the plants; they occasionally burrow into levees and weaken them. Sow bugs, which also feed on vegeta-tion, may become pests in greenhouses and fields when sufficiently numerous.

Although some crustaceans are parasites of aquatic animals, none is a parasite of man or other land animals. Copepods serve as intermediate hosts of several parasitic worms in man; for example, certain species of *Cyclops* for the guinea worm and other species of *Cyclops* for tapeworms. Crayfish and crabs act as second intermediate hosts for the lung flukes.

CLASSIFICATION OF
THE CRUSTACEA

(For reference purposes only)

Class Crustacea are arthropods, most of which live in water and breathe by means of gills. Symmetry is bilateral; they are triploblastic, and the body consists of a longitudinal series of segments. The body is divided into **head, thorax,** and **abdomen,** or the head and thorax may be fused, forming a **cephalothorax.** The head consists of different numbers of fused segments in different groups; it bears two pairs of **antennae** (feelers), one pair of **mandibles** (jaws), and two pairs of **maxillae.** The appendages are jointed. Only five subclasses and one order are listed here.

Subclass 1. **Branchiopoda.** This is the most primitive group of crustaceans. Free-swimming; thoracic appendages leaflike and respiratory; usually a carapace. Ex. *Eubranchipus vernalis* (Fig. 110).

Subclass 2. **Ostracoda.** Free-swimming, carapace bivalved; appendages not leaflike. Ex. *Eucypris virens* (Fig. 110).

Subclass 3. **Copepoda.** Free-swimming, parasitic, or commensal; no compound eyes; typically with 6 pairs of thoracic legs. Ex. *Cyclops* (Fig. 110).

Subclass 4. **Cirripedia.** Barnacles. Adults sessile and attached, or parasitic; no compound eyes in adults; carapace enclosing body, usually with limb plates; mostly hermaphroditic. Ex. *Lepas* (Fig. 110).

Subclass 5. **Malacostraca** (Fig. 121). Mostly large, but some small, such as the sow bugs, Fig. 110; usually 4 segments in head, 8 in thorax, and 6 in abdomen; gastric mill in stomach. Only one order listed here.

Order **Decapoda.** Lobsters, crayfish, shrimps, crabs, etc. Carapace large, covering thorax; eyes on stalks; 5 pairs of walking legs. Ex. *Orconectes,* crayfish (Fig. 111); *Homarus,* lobster.

Class Trilobita. The trilobites (Fig. 122) were marine animals, probably allied to the crustaceans; they are all extinct. The best-known species, *Triarthrus becki,* occurs in the Utica shale (Lower Silurian) of New York State.

SELECTED COLLATERAL
READINGS

Borradaile, L.A., and Yapp, W.B. *Manual of Elementary Zoology.* Oxford Univ. Press, New York, 1958.

Huxley, T.H. *The Crayfish, an Introduction to the Study of Zoology.* Kegan, Paul, Trench, Trubner, London, 1880.

Pennak, R.W. *Freshwater Invertebrates of the United States.* Ronald Press, New York, 1953.

Pratt, H.S. A *Manual of Common Invertebrate Animals.* Blakiston, Philadelphia, 1935.

Snodgrass, R.E. "Evolution of the Annelida, Onychophora, and Arthropoda." *Smithsonian Misc. Collections,* 97:1–159, 1938.

Snodgrass, R.E. A *Textbook of Arthropod Anatomy.* Comstock Publishing Associates, Ithaca, N.Y., 1952.

Ward, H.B., and Whipple, G.C. *Fresh-water Biology.* Wiley, New York, 1918.

Wilson, R.C. "A Review of the Southern California Spring Lobster Fishery." *California Fish and Game,* 34:71–80, 1948.

CHAPTER 17

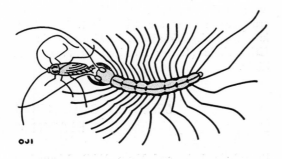

Phylum Arthropoda. Peripatus, Centipedes, and Millipedes

For convenience, three classes of arthropods are considered together in this chapter. The Onychophora (the name means claw-bearing) are rare; and, although the Chilopoda (centipedes) and Diplopoda (millipedes) are abundant in certain localities, other types of arthropods considered in Chapter 18 reveal the characteristics of this phylum to better advantage.

The onychophorans resemble more closely than any other animals what is believed to have been the ancestral condition of the arthropods. They possess a thin cuticle, a continuous muscular body wall, no joints, one pair of jaws, a tracheal respiratory system, and a series of nephridial openings.

CLASS ONYCHOPHORA

Peripatus (Fig. 124), a representative species, is about two or three inches in length, with a cylindrical body, but without a distinct head. These animals are especially interesting because they obviously exhibit both arthropod and annelid characteristics, as well as peculiarities of their own. Unfortunately, they are gradually disappearing and hence becoming more difficult to observe. However, the group furnishes an excellent example of **discontinuous distribution**. Species have been reported from Central America, Mexico, the West Indies, and the southern hemisphere. Even in the area where a species occurs, specimens are

FIGURE 124. *Facing page, Peripatus, an onychophoran. Top, drawing to show external structure. Bottom, photo of living animal. It is a walking wormlike animal, which is neither an annelid nor a typical arthropod. Because it has both annelid and arthropod characteristics, it is the only living animal that comes near to being a common relative to annelids and arthropods. Therefore it is considered by some as a connecting link between the two phyla.* (Photo reproduced by permission from *The Biotic World and Man*, by L.J. and M.J. Milne, p. 498. Copyright, 1952, by Prentice-Hall, Inc., Englewood Cliffs, N.J.)

222

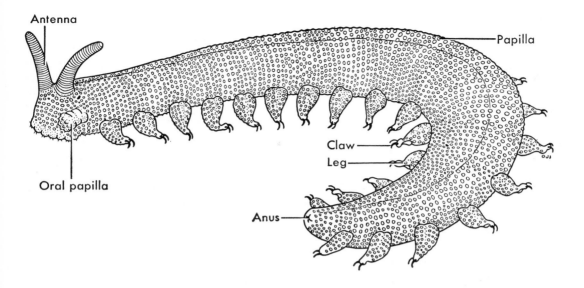

Antenna

Papilla

Oral papilla

Claw

Leg

Anus

present in only a few of the many available habitats. This seems to indicate that this group once had a continuous distribution but that it has disappeared throughout most of its range and is on the road to extinction.

Peripatus lives in crevices of rock, under bark and stones, and in other dark moist places and is active only at night. When irritated, it throws a jet of slime, sometimes to a distance of almost a foot, from a pair of glands which open on the **oral papillae**.

This slime sticks to everything but the body of the animal itself; it is used principally to capture flies, wood lice, termites, and other small animals; and, in addition, is a weapon of defense. A pair of modified appendages serve as **jaws** and tear the food to pieces.

Most of the 70 known species are viviparous, and a single large female may produce 30 or 40 young in a year. These young resemble the adult when born, differing mainly in size and color.

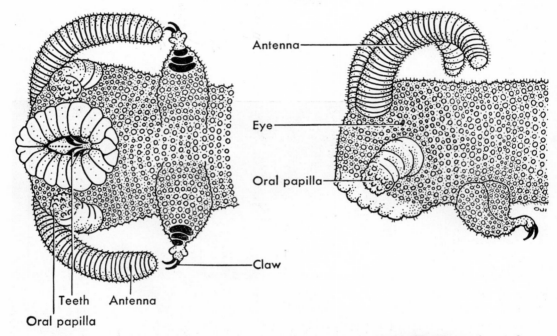

FIGURE 125. *Peripatus. Left,* ventral view, the legs are stubby and unlike those of typical arthropods, but the claws are arthropodlike. In each jaw are embedded two backward-pointing, clawlike teeth. *Right,* lateral view, the "head" bears two extensible antennae, near the base of which is a pair of simple eyes. The numerous papillae which cover the whole body give it a velvety texture.

The internal anatomy is a combination of annelidlike and arthropodlike structures. The chief systems of organs are arranged as in **annelids;** the **nephridia** are paired and segmental in distribution, and the **reproductive organs** are supplied with cilia. Cilia do not occur in arthropods. The **arthropod characteristics** include **jaws** derived from appendages, a body cavity that is a **hemocoel,**

tracheae, and the almost complete absence of a coelom around the digestive tract. *Peripatus* differs from both annelids and other arthropods in the possession of a single pair of jaws, in scant metamerism, in the arrangement of the tracheal openings, in the texture of the skin, and in the separate nerve cords with no well-developed ganglia. Hence, the onychophorans do not fit the phylum Arthropoda very well, and are, therefore, sometimes placed in a separate phylum.

CLASS CHILOPODA

The Chilopoda are called **centipedes** (Fig. 126). The body is flattened dorsoventrally and, in different species, consists of from 15 to 173 segments, each of which bears **one** pair of legs, except the first which has legs modified as **poison claws**, and the last two, which usually lack appendages. Their prey consists of insects, worms, mollusks, and other small animals which are killed with their poison claws and then chewed with their mandibles. The antennae are long, consisting of at least 12 segments. The internal anatomy of a common centipede is shown in Fig. 127.

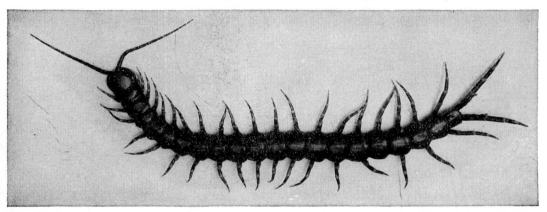

FIGURE 126. Centipedes have many legs. In the East Indies there is a giant centipede nearly a foot long. The photo shows a smaller form, common in the United States. (Courtesy of N.Y. Zoological Society.)

Centipedes are swift-moving creatures. Many of them live under the bark of logs, or under stones. Some of the **poisonous centipedes** of tropical countries belong to the genus *Scolopendra*. They may reach a foot in length, and their bite is painful and even dangerous to man. The common house centipede (*Scutigera*) has 15 pairs of very long legs, and lives in damp places such as basements. It is not only harmless to man, but really beneficial for it feeds on insects.

CLASS DIPLOPODA

The Diplopoda are the millipedes. The body is subcylindrical and consists of from about 25 to more than 100 segments, according to the species (Fig. 128). All segments bear two pairs of legs except the thorax, on which the number is reduced to one pair.

The mouth parts are a pair of **mandibles** and a pair of **maxillae**. One pair of short **antennae** and clumps of simple **eyes** are usually present. There are **olfactory hairs** on the antennae and a series of **scent glands** that secrete an objectionable fluid which is used in defense. In fact, there is a species in Micronesia that ejects for several inches such a highly irritating fluid that it will cause temporary blindness. The breathing tubes (**tracheae**) are usually unbranched; they develop in tufts from pouches which open just in front of the legs.

Millipedes move very slowly in spite of their numerous legs. Some are able to roll themselves into a spiral or ball. They live in dark, moist places, and feed, principally, on

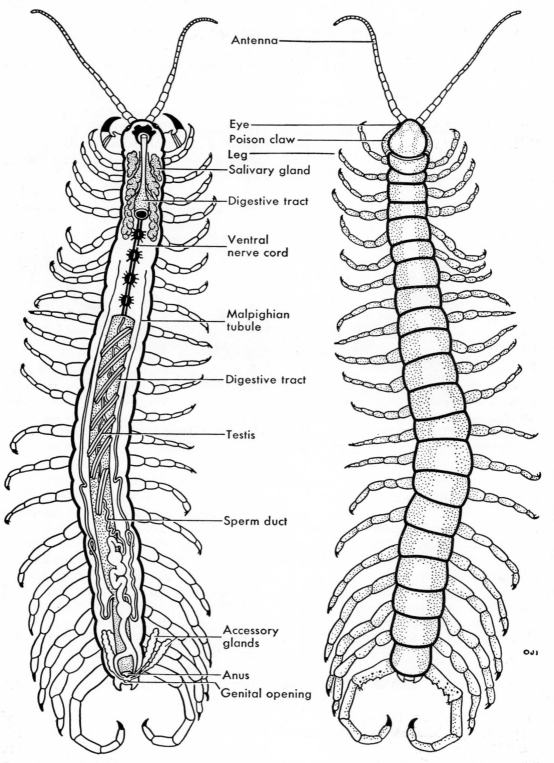

Antenna

Eye
Poison claw
Leg
Salivary gland

Digestive tract

Ventral
nerve cord

Malpighian
tubule

Digestive tract

Testis

Sperm duct

Accessory
glands

Anus
Genital opening

FIGURE 127. Drawings of centipede showing the internal organs and external features of *Scolopendra*.

226

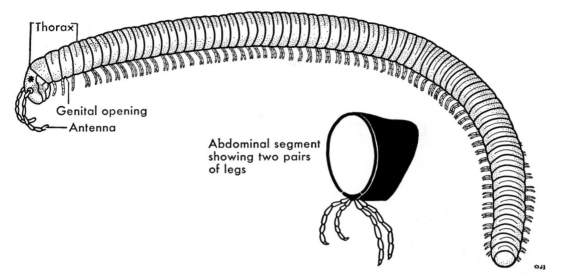

Thorax

Genital opening

Antenna

Abdominal segment
showing two pairs
of legs

FIGURE 128. A millipede, the name means "thousand-legged" but there are never that many legs. Millipedes are shy animals which hide in dark places to avoid the light. They can easily be distinguished from centipedes by the subcylindrical body and the two pairs of legs on most segments.

decaying vegetable matter, but sometimes on living plants, and may thus be destructive to gardens. The sexes are separate, and the eggs are laid in a nest made of damp earth. The young have 6 segments and only three pairs of legs when they hatch, and resemble wingless insects. Other segments are added just in front of the anal segment at successive molts during growth. Common examples of this class are *Spirobolus* and *Julus*; the latter occurs all over the United States, especially in meadows and gardens.

CHAPTER 18

Phylum Arthropoda.

Insects

INSECTS are more numerous in species than all other animals combined. Over 850,000 species have been described; and, no doubt, hundreds of thousands remain to be discovered (Fig. 130). They live in almost every conceivable type of environment: on land and in water, from the Arctic to the tropics; and their structure, habits, and life cycles are correspondingly modified. Nevertheless, it is possible to separate this vast assemblage into orders, families, etc., although there is no unanimity of opinion with respect to the number that should be recognized and the names that should be applied (Fig. 129).

The insects are such a large and varied group that many specialties have grown up in the general field of entomology, for example, medical and economic entomology. Because insects differ so widely in habit, physiology, and morphology and exhibit so many interesting adaptations, only those areas of entomology are included that deal briefly with life cycles, adaptive modifications, types of coloration, and social life.

The class Insecta are air-breathing arthropods with bodies divided into head, thorax, and abdomen. The head bears one pair of antennae, and the thorax three pairs of legs, and usually one or two pairs of wings in the adult stage.

In many ways the grasshopper is a very favorable species as a type for detailed study. It is abundant and easily secured; it is comparatively large and hence excellent material for dissection; it is one of the least specialized of all insects, and, therefore, exhibits better than most other forms the essential features of insects, both externally and internally. The grasshopper also has several conspicuous adaptations, such as leathery

FIGURE 129. *Facing page*, representatives of some orders of insects. The lines suggest possible relationships. The figures are not drawn to scale. (Drawn specifically for this text from a diagram prepared by R.L. Fischer, Curator of Insects, Michigan State University.)

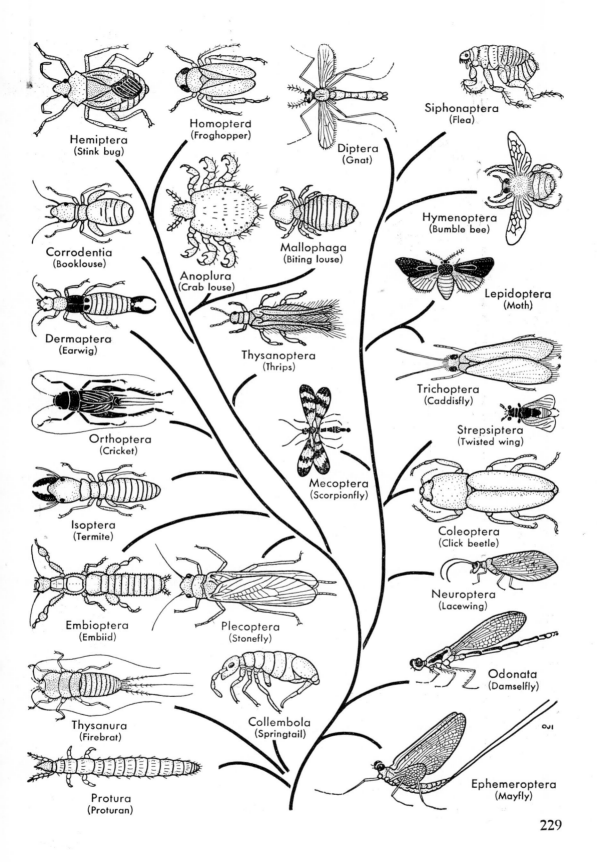

Hemiptera
(Stink bug)

Homoptera
(Froghopper)

Diptera
(Gnat)

Siphonaptera
(Flea)

Hymenoptera
(Bumble bee)

Corrodentia
(Booklouse)

Anoplura
(Crab louse)

Mallophaga
(Biting louse)

Lepidoptera
(Moth)

Dermaptera
(Earwig)

Thysanoptera
(Thrips)

Trichoptera
(Caddisfly)

Orthoptera
(Cricket)

Mecoptera
(Scorpionfly)

Strepsiptera
(Twisted wing)

Isoptera
(Termite)

Coleoptera
(Click beetle)

Embioptera
(Embiid)

Plecoptera
(Stonefly)

Neuroptera
(Lacewing)

Thysanura
(Firebrat)

Collembola
(Springtail)

Odonata
(Damselfly)

Protura
(Proturan)

Ephemeroptera
(Mayfly)

229

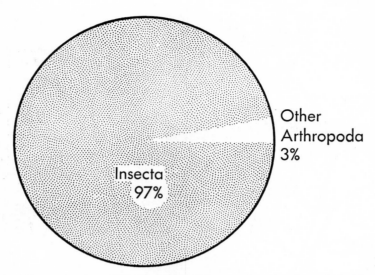

Figure 130. There are about 875,000 known living species of arthropods in the world. Of these approximately 850,000 species are insects, and 25,000 species are other arthropods. Insects comprise about 97 per cent of the species of known arthropods.

forewings, enlarged hindlimbs, auditory organs, and structures for making sounds. It is of considerable economic importance.

THE GRASSHOPPER

External anatomy

Like the crayfish, the grasshopper is covered by an **exoskeleton** (Fig. 131) which protects the delicate systems of organs within. This exoskeleton is the **cuticle,** which contains chitin and is divided into a linear row of **segments.** As in the crayfish, the cuticle is soft in certain regions, thus allowing movements of such structures as the abdomen, wings, legs, and antennae. These softer regions are known as **sutures.** The body wall consists of the cuticle beneath which is a layer of cells, the **epidermis,** which secretes it, and under this is a **basement membrane.** Each segment is made up of separate plates (pieces), which are known as **sclerites;** usually some of the sclerites of a typical segment cannot be distinguished because the sutures are indistinct or absent.

In the grasshopper the body is divided into three groups of segments that constitute the **head, thorax,** and **abdomen.**

Head

The head is composed of fused segments (Fig. 132). These are not visible in the adult, but may be observed in the embryo, and are indicated by the paired appendages of the adult. The dorsal region of the head is known as the **vertex;** the front portion is called the **frons;** and the sides are the cheeks or **genae.** The rectangular sclerite below the frons is the **clypeus.** On either side of the head is a **compound eye,** and on top of the head and near the inner edge of each compound eye is a simple eye (**ocellus**).

Mouth parts

The **food** of the grasshopper consists of vegetation which it bites off and grinds up by means of its chewing **mouth parts** (Fig. 132). There is a **labrum** or upper lip attached to the ventral edge of the **clypeus.** Beneath this is the membranous tonguelike organ, the **hypopharynx.** On either side is a hard jaw or **mandible,** with a toothed sur-

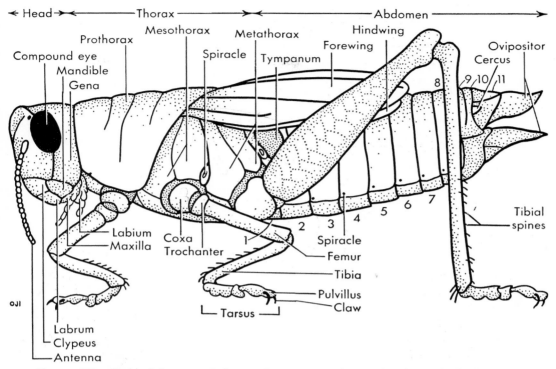

FIGURE 131. External features of the grasshopper, a good example of a generalized insect. This is a female.

face fitted for grinding. Behind the mandibles are a pair of **maxillae,** consisting of several parts and with sensory palps at the sides. The **labium** or lower lip has slender palps at the sides. The labium of insects appears to have evolved from the lateral union of two appendages resembling the biramous limbs of a crustacean. The **maxillae** obviously have also arisen from this type of appendage. The labrum and labium serve to hold food between the mandibles and maxillae, which move laterally and grind it. The maxillary and labial palpi are supplied with sense organs that probably serve to distinguish different kinds of food.

Ocellus

The simple eye (Fig. 133) consists of a group of visual cells, the **retina,** pigment, and a transparent **lens,** a modification of the cuticle.

Compound eye

The compound eye (Fig. 132) is covered by a transparent part of the cuticle, the **cornea,** which is divided into a large number of hexagonal pieces, the **facets.** Each facet is the outer end of a unit known as an **ommatidium.** Such a structure gives mosaic vision as described in the crayfish (p. 209). Some insects, possibly the grasshopper, are able to distinguish colors.

Antennae

These are threadlike in form and consist of many segments. **Tactile hairs** and **olfactory pits** are present on them; and this condition, combined with the ability of the insect to move them about, makes them efficient sense organs.

Thorax

This portion of the body is separated from the head and abdomen by flexible joints and

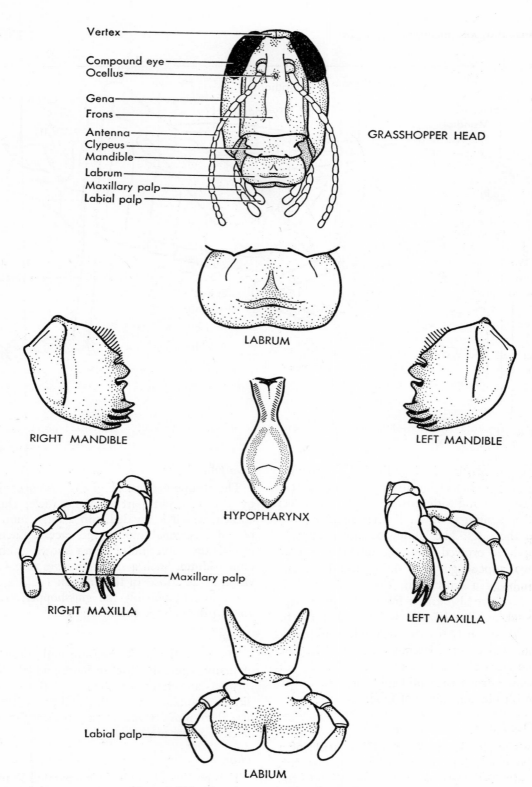

Vertex

Compound eye
Ocellus

Gena
Frons

Antenna
Clypeus
Mandible

Labrum
Maxillary palp
Labial palp

GRASSHOPPER HEAD

LABRUM

RIGHT MANDIBLE

LEFT MANDIBLE

HYPOPHARYNX

Maxillary palp

RIGHT MAXILLA

LEFT MAXILLA

Labial palp

LABIUM

FIGURE 132. Grasshopper head and mouth parts.

232

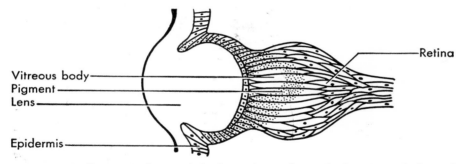

Vitreous body

Pigment

Lens

Epidermis

Retina

FIGURE 133. Ocellus or simple eye of the honey bee in longitudinal section. (Redrawn from *Entomology*, by J.W. Folsom. Copyright 1906 by The Blakiston Company.)

consists of three segments: an anterior **prothorax**, a middle **mesothorax**, and a posterior **metathorax**. Each segment bears a pair of **legs**; and the mesothorax and metathorax each bear a pair of **wings**. On either side of the mesothorax and metathorax is a **spiracle**, an opening into the respiratory system. A typical segment consists of the dorsal **tergum** composed of 4 fused **sclerites** in a row; a lateral **pleuron** made up of 3 sclerites on each side, and a single ventral sclerite, the **sternum**.

Prothorax. The saddlelike **pronotum** of the prothorax is large and extends down on either side; its 4 sclerites are indicated by tranverse grooves. The sternum bears a spine.

Mesothorax. In this segment the tergum is small, but the sclerites of the pleuron are distinct. The sternum is large.

Metathorax. This resembles the mesothorax.

Legs

Each leg (Fig. 131) consists of a longitudinal series of segments as follows: the **coxa** articulates with the body; then comes the small **trochanter** fused with the **femur**, the **tibia**, and the **tarsus**. The femora of the metathoracic legs are enlarged to contain the muscles used in jumping. The tarsus at the end of each leg consists of three visible segments; the one adjoining the tibia has three pads on the ventral surface, and the terminal segment bears a pair of **claws** be-

tween which is a fleshy pad or lobe, the **pulvillus**. The claws and pulvilli are used in clinging to any kind of surface.

Wings

The wings of insects (Figs. 134 and 135) arise from the region between the tergum and pleuron as a double layer of epidermis, which secretes the upper and lower cuticular surfaces. Between these are tracheae, around which spaces occur, and the cuticle thickens; they (Fig. 134C) later become the longitudinal wing veins. The **veins** are of value in strengthening the wings. They differ in number and arrangement in different species of insects but are so constant in individuals of certain species that they are very useful for purposes of classification. The mesothoracic wings of the grasshopper are leathery and not folded; they serve as covers for the metathoracic wings which lie beneath them. The latter are thin and folded like a fan.

Abdomen

The slender **abdomen** consists dorsally of 11 segments; those at the posterior extremity being modified for copulation or egg laying. Along the lower sides of the abdomen, there are 8 pairs of small openings (**spiracles**) through which the animal breathes. In the grasshopper, the sternum of segment one is fused with the metathorax; on either side of this segment there is an oval **tympanic membrane** covering an **auditory sac.** Segments 2

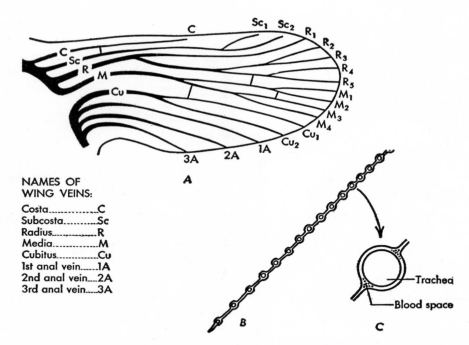

NAMES OF
WING VEINS:

Costa..............C
Subcosta..........Sc
Radius............R
Media............M
Cubitus...........Cu
1st anal vein.....1A
2nd anal vein....2A
3rd anal vein....3A

FIGURE 134. A, generalized insect wing showing the chief veins. B, cross section of wing. C, enlarged cross section of wing showing a vein which consists of the outer surface of the wing, blood space, and trachea. (A from *The Wings of Insects*, by J.H. Comstock. Copyright 1916 by The Comstock Publishing Company.)

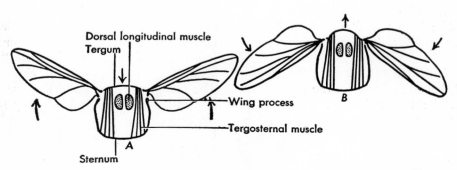

FIGURE 135. Movement of wings in flight. A, the wings are elevated on the pleural wing processes by the depression of the tergum due to the contraction of the tergosternal muscles. The hind margins of the wings are deflected. B, the wings are lowered by the elevation of the tergum due to the contraction of the dorsal, longitudinal muscles. Hind margins of wings are elevated. (After Snodgrass.)

to 8 are unmodified. In the **male**, the sternum of segment 9 is elongated ventrally, giving an upward twist to the abdomen. The end of the **female** abdomen is more tapering than that of the male and forms the **ovipositor**, an egg-laying apparatus.

Internal anatomy and physiology

The systems of organs within the body of the insect (Fig. 136) lie in the body cavity, which is filled with blood and is a

hemocoel, not a coelom. All of the systems characteristic of higher animals are represented.

Muscular system

The muscles are of the **striated type,** very soft and delicate, but strong. They are segmentally arranged in the abdomen but not in the head and thorax. The most conspicuous muscles are those that move the mandibles, the wings, the metathoracic legs, and the ovipositor.

Digestive system

The principal parts of the digestive tract (Fig. 136) are the foregut, midgut, and hindgut. The **foregut** consists of (1) the **mouth,** on each side of which opens a **salivary gland** that produces an enzyme-containing secretion; (2) a tubular **esophagus,** which enlarges into (3) a **crop** in the mesothoracic and metathoracic segments. This leads into (4) the **proventriculus,** which is a grinding organ (**gizzard**). Next is the **midgut,** which is the **ventriculus** (**stomach**), reaching posteriorly into the abdomen; and into it, 6 double cone-shaped pouches, the **gastric ceca,** pour the digestive enzymes they secrete. The products of digestion are absorbed through the wall of the stomach and pass into the blood around it. From this point, the food is carried through the circulatory system to the cells, where it is utilized. Then the **hindgut** is made up of (1) the **ileum,** into the anterior end of which the delicate **Malpighian tubules** open and (2) the **colon,** which expands into the (3) **rectum** and opens through the (4) **anus.** Since both the foregut and the hindgut are lined with cuticle, little absorption takes place in them.

Circulatory system

This (Fig. 136) is not a closed system of blood vessels as in vertebrates and some invertebrates, but consists of a single tube located in the abdomen just under the body wall in the middorsal line, and of spaces (sinuses). The **heart** is divided into a row of chambers; into the base of each opens a pair of **ostia.** These ostia are closed by **valves** when the heart contracts. The **pericardial cavity,** in which the heart lies, is formed by a transverse **diaphragm** beneath it. Blood enters the heart and is forced anteriorly through the **aorta** into the hemocoel, where it bathes all the organs. The blood system is an open one, as is that of other arthropods, for there are no capillaries or veins. The blood serves chiefly to carry food and wastes; there is a separate respiratory system. The blood consists of a clear **plasma** in which are suspended **white blood cells** that act as phagocytes to remove foreign organisms and other substances.

Respiratory system

The respiratory system (Fig. 137) consists of a network of tubes, the **tracheae,** that communicate with every part of the body. The tracheae consist of a single layer of cells lined with a layer of cuticle, which is thickened to form **spiral rings** that prevent the tracheae from collapsing. A tracheal branch extends from each **spiracle** to a longitudinal trunk on each side of the body. The finest tracheae, the **tracheoles,** are connected directly with the tissue to which they supply oxygen and from which they carry away carbon dioxide. The smallest tracheoles contain fluid in which oxygen dissolves before actually reaching the cells; this fluid serves in internal respiration like the blood in other animals. In the grasshopper and certain other insects, some of the tracheae become expanded into thin-walled air sacs which are easily compressed and thus aid in the movement of air. Contraction and expansion of the body expels air from and draws it into the tracheal system.

The utilization of oxygen in the metabolic processes of the cell, with the production of carbon dioxide, is accomplished through the action of respiratory enzymes called the cytochrome system. The cytochrome sys-

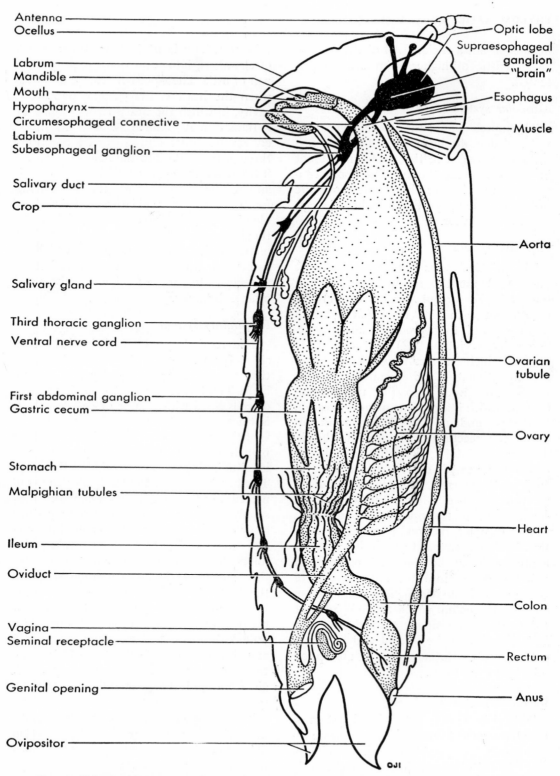

Antenna

Ocellus

Labrum

Mandible

Mouth

Hypopharynx

Circumesophageal connective

Labium

Subesophageal ganglion

Salivary duct

Crop

Salivary gland

Third thoracic ganglion

Ventral nerve cord

First abdominal ganglion

Gastric cecum

Stomach

Malpighian tubules

Ileum

Oviduct

Vagina

Seminal receptacle

Genital opening

Ovipositor

Optic lobe

Supraesophageal ganglion "brain"

Esophagus

Muscle

Aorta

Ovarian tubule

Ovary

Heart

Colon

Rectum

Anus

OJI

FIGURE 136. Internal organs of a grasshopper as seen with the left side of the body wall removed; tracheae not included.

236

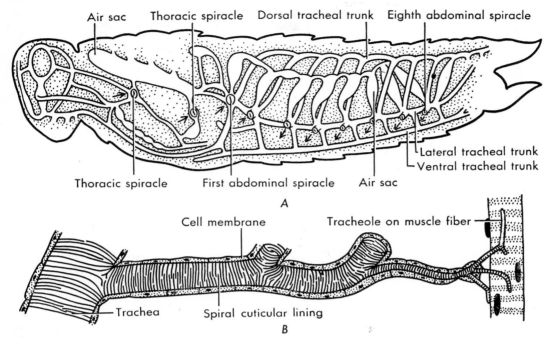

FIGURE 137. A, diagram of the tracheae in the body of a grasshopper. The tracheal system consists of air-filled tubes which branch into others. The arrows indicate that the grasshopper inhales through spiracles located in the anterior part of the body and exhales through those limited to its abdomen. B, a large tracheal trunk and some of its branches. (A redrawn from *College Entomology*, by E.O. Essig. Copyright 1942 by The Macmillan Company.)

tem is localized in the mitochondria of the cell.

Excretory system

The organs of excretion (Fig. 136) are the **Malpighian tubules** that are coiled about in the hemocoel and open into the anterior end of the hindgut. These tubules remove metabolic wastes; for example, uric acid is taken from the blood that fills the hemocoel, condensed in the tubules to crystals and discharged into the hindgut for evacuation through the anus. The conservation of water in this process results from its reabsorption through the tubules. The removal of wastes in the dry state is characteristic of small land animals that have only a limited water supply.

Nervous system

The nervous system (Fig. 138) includes a **brain** (supraesophageal ganglion), dorsally located in the head, consisting of three pairs of ganglia fused together. These ganglia supply the eyes, antennae, and other head organs. The brain joins, by two connectives around the esophagus, to the **subesophageal ganglion.** This ganglion consists of the three anterior pairs of ganglia of the ventral nerve chain fused together and supplies the mouth parts. The ventral nerve chain continues with a pair of large ganglia in each thoracic segment. The ganglia in the metathoracic segment are particularly large and represent the ganglia of this segment and of the first abdominal segment fused. Five pairs of ganglia are present in the abdomen. The pair in the second abdominal segment comprises the pairs from the second and third abdominal segments fused together, and the pair in the seventh segment represents the ganglia of the seventh to the eleventh segments combined. Connected with the brain are ganglia of the so-called **sympathetic** (autonomic) **nervous system** which controls the "involuntary" movements of the digestive tract, heart, aorta, and reproductive system.

Sense organs. Grasshoppers possess organs of sight, hearing, touch, taste, and smell. The **compound eye** and **ocellus** (Fig. 132) have already been noted. Vision by

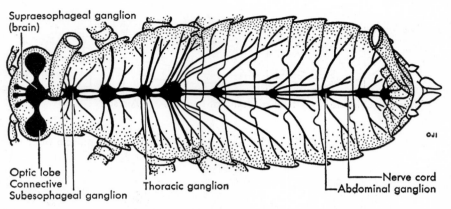

FIGURE 138. The grasshopper nervous system in dorsal view. (Redrawn from *Principles of Insect Morphology,* by R.E. Snodgrass. Copyright 1935 by McGraw-Hill Book Co., Inc.)

means of the compound eyes has been described in the crayfish. The ocelli are thought to be primarily organs of light perception, although it is possible that they may form crude images at close range. The pair of **auditory organs** are located on the sides of the tergite of the first abdominal segment. Each consists of a tympanic membrane (tympanum) stretched with an almost circular sclerotized ring; sound vibrations in the air set the tympanic membrane in motion, and this in turn affects a slender point beneath the membrane which is connected to sensory nerve fibers. Some of the insects hear sounds beyond the range of the human ear. Sound is produced by grasshoppers by rubbing the tibia of the hindleg with its rough surface against a wing vein which causes it to vibrate. The **antennae** are supplied with the principal organs of smell. Organs of **taste** are located on the mouth parts. The hairlike organs of **touch** are present on various parts of the body but particularly on the antennae.

Reproductive system

Female grasshoppers can easily be distinguished from males because of the pres-

ence of the **ovipositor** (Fig. 136). In the female there are two **ovaries.** Each consists of several tapering egg tubules called **ovarioles,** which, however, do not possess a lumen (Fig. 139). The ovarioles contain **oogonia** and **oocytes** arranged in a linear series, **nurse cells,** and other tissue cells. The oocytes grow as they proceed posteriorly down the ovariole, hence the ovariole becomes gradually larger toward the posterior end. The ovarioles of each ovary are attached posteriorly to an **oviduct** into which the eggs are discharged. The two oviducts unite to form a short **vagina** which leads to the **genital opening** between the plates of the ovipositor. A tubular **seminal receptacle** (spermatheca), which connects with the dorsal wall of the vagina, receives the **spermatozoa** during copulation and releases them when the eggs are fertilized.

In the **male** are two **testes** in which spermatozoa develop (Fig. 139). These are discharged into a **vas deferens.** The two vasa deferentia unite to form an **ejaculatory duct** which runs through the penis, at the end of which is the sperm-escape opening. **Accessory glands** are present at the anterior end of the ejaculatory duct.

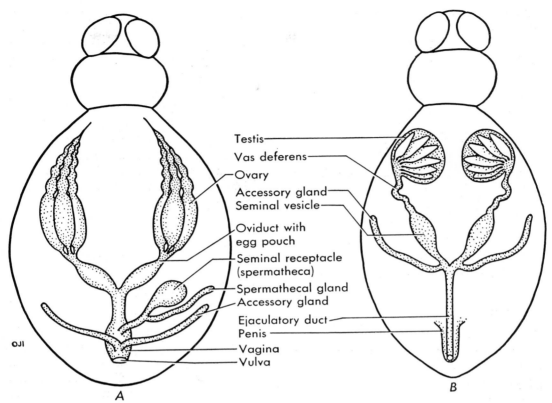

Testis
Vas deferens
Ovary
Accessory gland
Seminal vesicle
Oviduct with egg pouch
Seminal receptacle (spermatheca)
Spermathecal gland
Accessory gland
Ejaculatory duct
Penis
Vagina
Vulva

A   B

Figure 139. Diagrams of the reproductive systems of insects in general, that is, typical reproductive organs found in various insects; but all the organs shown are not present in all species.

Embryonic development and growth

The eggs are fertilized at the time they are deposited by the entrance of spermatozoa through an opening called the **micropyle** in one end of the eggshell. One sperm nucleus unites with the nucleus of the mature egg; a **blastoderm** is formed around the periphery of the egg from which an **embryo** develops (Fig. 41). The young grasshopper that hatches from the egg is called a **nymph** (Fig. 140). It resembles its parent but has a large head compared with the rest of the body and lacks wings. As it grows its body becomes too large for the inflexible exoskeleton, and the latter is shed periodically. Wings are gradually developed from wing buds, and the adult condition is finally assumed. This type of development is called gradual metamorphosis.

LIFE CYCLES OF INSECTS

The most conspicuous differences in the life cycles of various types of insects are associated with the kind of metamorphosis involved. There is **no metamorphosis** in certain species, a **gradual metamorphosis** in some as the grasshopper, **incomplete metamorphosis** in others (dragonfly or mayfly), and a **complete metamorphosis** in the most specialized groups. As variations in insect life cycles are almost infinite, we select a few typical common species for descriptive purposes.

A primitive wingless insect without metamorphosis

Campodea staphylinus (order Thysanura) is a delicate, whitish species (Fig. 140) about ⅛ inch long, that lives under stones and leaves, in rotten wood, humus, and other damp places. The young that hatch from the eggs look like miniature adults. As they grow they molt a number of times, finally reaching sexual maturity and adult functions.

A grasshopper with gradual metamorphosis

This is a type of development in which the young are strikingly like the adult in general form of body and in manner of life. However, there is a gradual growth of the body and wings, but these changes take place gradually and are not very great between any successive stages (Fig. 140).

A dragonfly and mayfly with incomplete metamorphosis

This is a type of metamorphosis in which accessory organs or gills occur in the aquatic naiads, and the adults are aerial. In this type of metamorphosis the changes that take place in the form of the body are greater than in gradual metamorphosis, but much less marked than in complete metamorphosis. The metamorphosis of a dragonfly (order Odonata) is **incomplete**. The naiad stage of the dragonfly does not have external gills, but has rectal gills and breathes by alternately drawing in and expelling water.

The metamorphosis of the mayfly is incomplete. Mating takes place during flight, after which the female lays several masses on a stone in the water; each mass contains from 80 to 300 eggs. The eggs hatch in about a month and the young that emerge are called **naiads**. The naiads live under the water, where they breathe by means of tracheal gills and feed on minute plants (diatoms and algae). Growth is accompanied by 27 molts and requires from 6 to 9 months. When ready to venture into the air, the naiad swims to the surface; a split appears along the back; and a gauzy-winged

adult flies out to a nearby object where it rests from 18 to 24 hours. Then it molts again and is ready to fly into the air and find a mate. The adult life of both males and females is but a few hours or days. Therefore, the scientific name of the order, which means "living but a day," was well chosen. The mayflies fly to lights in immense numbers, in towns along rivers or lakes. One river town has an authentic record of a pile of dead mayflies 8 feet deep, which formed in one night around an electric light pole.

A butterfly with complete metamorphosis

Pieris rapae (order Lepidoptera), the white cabbage butterfly, is one of our commonest species. The larvae or caterpillars (Fig. 143) feed on the leaves of certain plants, and therefore the eggs must be laid on them. These plants are cabbage, turnip, mustard, horse-radish, radish, etc. The larvae will die if they hatch out on the wrong type of plant. The butterfly probably distinguishes one plant from another by means of an olfactory sense. The **eggs** are laid, one by one, few in number, on a single plant. The eggs are bullet-shaped and covered with ridges and depressions. They are fastened to the leaf by the flat end. The **larva** eats its way out of the distal end of the egg shell and then proceeds to devour the rest of the shell. It begins at once to chew holes in the leaves of the host plant with its jaws, and when it can grow no larger within its cuticular covering, a split appears in the back near the anterior end, and the larva crawls out and expands because of the elasticity of the new exoskeleton. The caterpillar's legs are of two kinds: 3 jointed pairs on the thorax, and 5 unjointed, temporary **prolegs** on the abdo-

FIGURE 140. *Facing page*, three types of life cycles found in insects: without metamorphosis, gradual metamorphosis, and incomplete metamorphosis. See Fig. 141 for complete metamorphosis, a fourth type of life cycle.

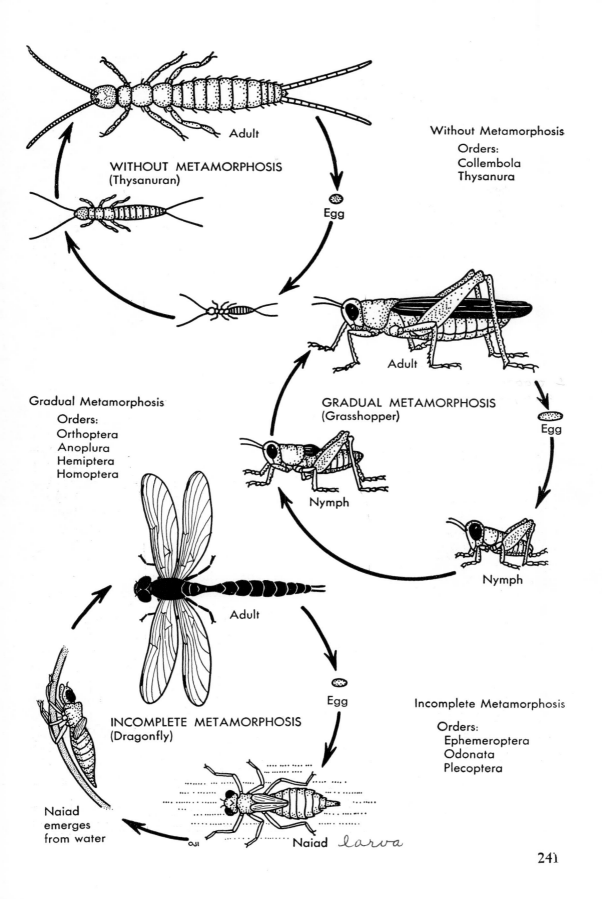

Adult

WITHOUT METAMORPHOSIS
(Thysanuran)

Egg

Without Metamorphosis
Orders:
Collembola
Thysanura

Adult

GRADUAL METAMORPHOSIS
(Grasshopper)

Egg

Gradual Metamorphosis
Orders:
Orthoptera
Anoplura
Hemiptera
Homoptera

Nymph

Nymph

Adult

INCOMPLETE METAMORPHOSIS
(Dragonfly)

Egg

Incomplete Metamorphosis
Orders:
Ephemeroptera
Odonata
Plecoptera

Naiad
emerges
from water

Naiad larva

241

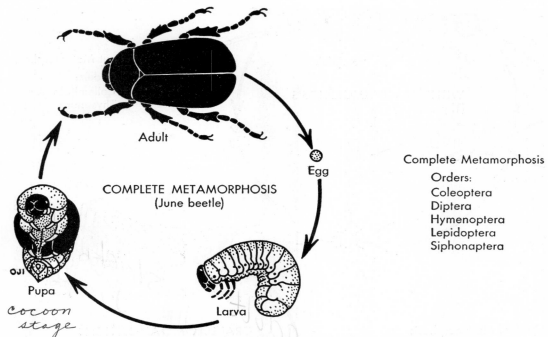

Adult

Egg

COMPLETE METAMORPHOSIS
(June beetle)

Complete Metamorphosis
Orders:
Coleoptera
Diptera
Hymenoptera
Lepidoptera
Siphonaptera

Pupa

cocoon
stage

Larva

FIGURE 141. An insect with complete metamorphosis, June beetle.

men. It possesses 6 small **simple eyes** on the head but no compound eyes. The green cabbage caterpillars resemble very closely the leaves on which they feed and are therefore difficult to detect by birds and other enemies (probably protective coloration).

When full grown (about 1¼ inches in length), the caterpillars attach themselves with a silken thread from their silk glands to the underside of a leaf of the host plant or beneath some other object. Butterfly caterpillars do not spin cocoons as many moth caterpillars do. After a time the body becomes shorter and thicker; the skin splits down the back and is pushed off at the posterior end; and a greenish-colored **pupa** is revealed (Fig. 143). The pupa does not feed; but, within it, violent activity is going on. The digestive system changes from one fitted for solid food to one that can utilize liquid food; the muscular system of the crawling larva becomes modified for purposes of flight; the nervous system is made over; wings grow out from pads of larval tissue; and the reproductive organs grow to

maturity. For these purposes, fat stored up by the larva is largely utilized. When this is all accomplished, requiring about 10 days, the pupal skin splits, the adult butterfly emerges, spreads its wings, and after they have become dry, flies away. The adult butterfly possesses a long proboscis coiled beneath the head that can be extended so as to probe the corollas of flowers for nectar, which is sucked into the food reservoir.

Many variations occur in the 4 types of metamorphosis just described. For example, among the termites one caste contains nymphs that are sexually mature; the naiads of mayflies, dragonflies, damsel flies, and stone flies are aquatic; the nymphs of grasshoppers, crickets, cockroaches, and chinch bugs are terrestrial; the nymphs of the "seventeen-year locust" live in the ground for 13 to 17 years before becoming adult; aphids may be ovoviviparous or oviparous, and their eggs may be fertilized or may develop without fertilization; the larvae of many beetles are called grubs; many moth caterpillars spin cocoons in which to pupate;

FIGURE 142. Millions of mayflies swarmed up from the river in St. Paul, Minnesota, to "plaster" lighted objects in the area. An attendant at a gas filling station covered his head for protection while servicing cars. The next morning, the short-lived flies were piled up seven inches high around the station. Their dead bodies were removed from the premises with a snow pusher. (Courtesy of Wide World Photos.)

the cockroach secretes an egg case to protect her eggs; the larvae of flies are known as maggots; and certain species, especially certain hymenopeterans, stimulate the formation of plant galls in which the larvae live.

ADAPTIVE MODIFICATIONS

The wings, legs, mouth parts, antennae, digestive tract, and respiratory system are among the structures most conspicuously

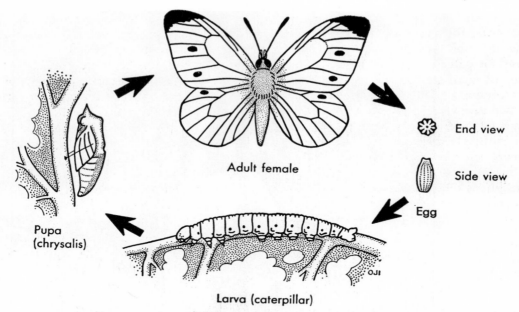

End view

Side view

Egg

Adult female

Pupa
(chrysalis)

Larva (caterpillar)

FIGURE 143. The life cycle of the imported cabbage butterfly.

modified so as to adapt insects to their environments.

Wings

The mesothorax and metathorax, each, bear a pair of wings in most insects. Certain simple species (Thysanura, Fig. 129) do not possess wings; others (lice and fleas, Fig. 160) are adapted to parasitic life and the wings are degenerate. The flies (Diptera) each have a pair of clubbed threads called balancers (halteres) in place of the metathoracic wings. Wings enable their owners to fly rapidly from place to place, to escape from enemies, and to find a bountiful food supply. The success of insects in the struggle for existence is in part attributable to the presence of wings. Modifications in wing venation come about by reduction or by addition. In the beetles (Coleoptera, Fig. 131) the forewings are sheathlike and are called elytra. The forewings of Orthoptera (grasshoppers, etc., Fig. 131) are leathery and are known as tegmina. The number of wing beats differs according to the species. Thus yellow swallow-tailed butterflies aver-

age about 6 beats per second, dragonflies about 30, house flies about 160, honey bees about 400 and the wings of the humming-birds make about 750 beats per second in forward flight. In contrast, man can perform a fast-finger piano trill at about 10 beats per second.

Legs

Legs are used for various purposes and are highly modified for special functions. Running insects, such as the ground beetle, possess long, slender legs (Fig. 154); the mantis has its forelegs fitted for grasping (Fig. 154); the hindlegs of the grasshopper are used in leaping (Fig. 131); the forelegs of the mole cricket are modified for digging; and the legs of the water bug are fitted for swimming. Many other types of modifications could be mentioned.

The legs of the honey bee (Fig. 144) are perhaps as remarkably adapted for a variety of purposes as those of any living insect. Honey bees are easily obtained and studied in the laboratory, and hence are selected here for further description. The **prothoracic** legs possess two useful structures, the **pollen brush** and the **antenna cleaner.** The femur and the tibia are clothed with branched hairs for gathering pollen. The surface of the first tarsal joint is covered with bristles, constituting a cylindrical pollen brush which is used to brush up and collect pollen within reach of these legs. On the anterior edge of the tibia is a flattened movable spine, the **velum,** which fits over a curved indentation in the proximal tarsal segment. This entire structure is called the antenna cleaner, and the row of teeth which lines the indentation is known as the **antenna comb.** The last

tarsal joint of every leg bears a pair of notched claws which enable the bee to obtain a foothold on rough surfaces. Between the claws is a fleshy glandular lobe, the **pulvillus;** its sticky secretion makes it possible for the bee to cling to smooth objects. Tactile hairs are also present.

The middle or **mesothoracic legs** are provided with a **pollen brush,** but instead of an antenna cleaner, a **spur** is present at the distal end of the tibia. This spur is used to dislodge wax from the wax pockets on the ventral side of the abdomen and to remove pollen from the pollen basket.

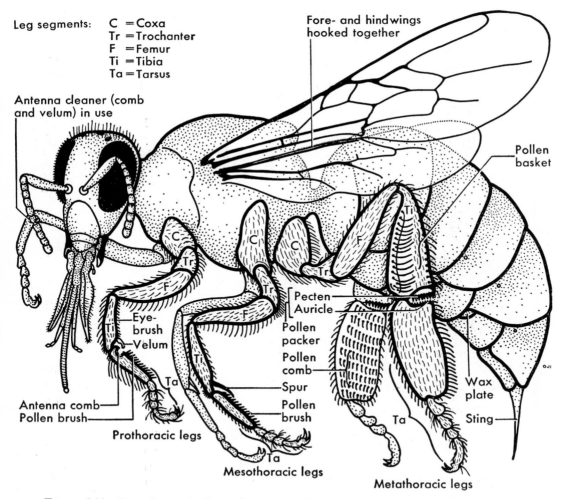

Leg segments: C = Coxa
Tr = Trochanter
F = Femur
Ti = Tibia
Ta = Tarsus

Fore- and hindwings hooked together

Antenna cleaner (comb and velum) in use

Pollen basket

Pecten
Auricle
Pollen packer
Pollen comb
Spur
Pollen brush

Eye-brush
Velum

Antenna comb
Pollen brush
Prothoracic legs

Mesothoracic legs

Wax plate
Sting

Metathoracic legs

FIGURE 144. Bee adaptations. Legs of the honey bee worker showing many of the structural modifications adapting them for gathering pollen, manipulating wax, cleaning the antennae, and other functions.

The hind- or **metathoracic legs** possess three very remarkable structures, the **pollen basket**, the **pollen packer**, and the **pollen combs**. The pollen basket consists of a concavity in the outer surface of the tibia with rows of curved bristles along the edges. By storing pollen in this basketlike structure, it is possible for the bee to spend more time in the field, and to carry a larger load on each trip. On the inner edge of the distal end of the tibia is a row of stout bristles, the **pecten.** Opposing the distal end of the tibia is the proximal end of the metatarsus bearing a plate or lip, the **auricle.** The auricle glides over the outer surface of the pecten and presses against the oblique outer surface of the end of the tibia when the joint between these structures is flexed backward. The auricle and the pecten, working together, constitute the **pollen packer**, since their manipulations force the sticky pollen masses into the pollen basket. In loading the pollen baskets, the pollen brushes of the mesothoracic pair of legs collect pollen from the brushes of the front legs and from other parts of the body, and are themselves cleaned by being drawn between the pollen combs of the hindlegs. Each **pollen comb** is then scraped over the pecten of the opposite leg, the sticky pollen being deposited on the outer surface of the pecten or falling on the upper surface of the auricle. The leg is then flexed backward at this joint, the auricle squeezing the pollen outward and upward, and thus packing it into the pollen basket.

Mouth parts

The mouth parts of insects are in most cases fitted either for chewing (mandibulate) or sucking (suctorial). The grasshopper possesses typical mandibulate mouth parts (Fig. 145). The mandibles of insects that live on vegetation are adapted for crushing; those of carnivorous species are usually

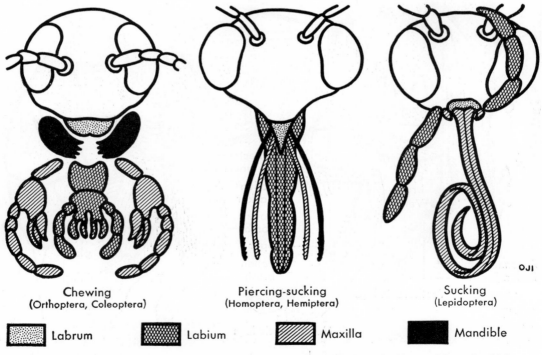

Chewing	Piercing-sucking	Sucking
(Orthoptera, Coleoptera)	(Homoptera, Hemiptera)	(Lepidoptera)

▓ Labrum   ▓ Labium   ▨ Maxilla   ■ Mandible

Figure 145. Some modifications of the fundamental mouth parts in insects. Note the high degree of specialization which adapts the animals to different methods of feeding.

sharp and pointed, being fitted for piercing and sucking. Suctorial mouth parts are adapted for piercing the tissues of plants or animals and sucking juices. The mouth parts of the honey bee are suctorial, but highly modified. In the female mosquito (Fig. 146), the labrum and hypopharynx com-bined form a sucking tube; the mandibles and maxillae are piercing organs; the hypopharynx carries saliva; and the labium consti-tutes a sheath in which the other mouth parts lie when not in use. The proboscis of the butterflies and moths is a sucking tube formed by the maxillae (Fig. 145).

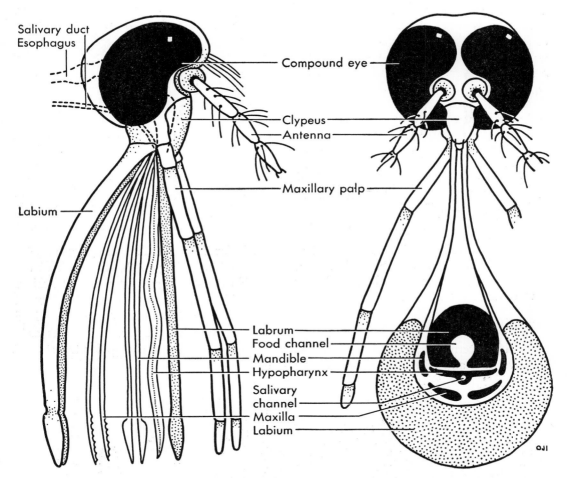

FIGURE 146. Mouth parts of a female mosquito showing the modifications adapting them for piercing and sucking. The mouth parts which are shown in solid black are those used in stinging.

The mouth parts of insects are of con-siderable importance from an economic standpoint, since insects that eat solid food can be destroyed by spraying the food with poisonous mixtures, whereas those that suck juices must be smothered with gases or killed by substances acting as direct contact poisons. The newer insecticides known as general purpose compounds are very effec-tive for they act either as a stomach or a con-tact poison, depending on the manner in which the insect encounters them.

Antennae

The antennae of insects are usually tactile, auditory, or olfactory in function. Interesting experiments by von Frisch have led him to the conclusion that bees can select certain odors; for example, they can select an odor derived from orange peel from among 43 others. He has also demonstrated that bees can find feeding places through a sense of smell. Experiments based on the removal of antennae indicate that the olfactory sense

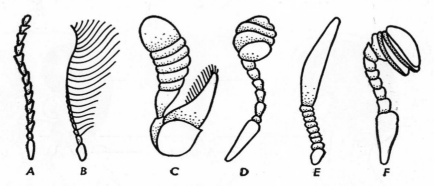

FIGURE 147. Antenna of Coleoptera showing variations within a single order of insects. *A,* Elateridae, click beetle. *B,* Lampyridae, firefly. *C,* Gyrinidae, whirligig beetle. *D,* Silphidae, *Necrophorus,* burying beetle. *E,* Curculionidae, weevil. *F,* Scarabaeidae, lamellicorn beetle. All highly magnified.

organs are located on this structure. Antennae differ in form and structure (Fig. 147), and often the antennae of the male differ from those of the female.

Digestive tract

Of the internal organs of insects, the digestive tract and respiratory system are of particular interest. The digestive tract is modified according to the character of the food; that of the grasshopper is typical of vegetable-eating insects. Suctorial insects, like the butterflies and moths, are provided with a muscular pharynx which acts as a pumping organ, and a crop for the storage of juices.

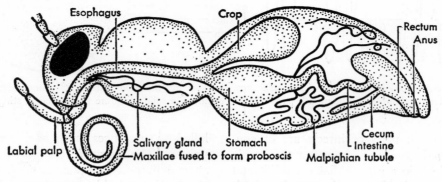

FIGURE 148. Digestive tract of a sucking insect. Diagram of the internal organs from the left side.

Respiratory system

The respiratory system of insects (Fig. 137) is in general like that of the grasshopper, but modifications occur in many species, especially in the larvae of those that live in water. Aquatic naiads, in many cases, do not have spiracles but get oxygen by means of threadlike or leaflike outgrowths at the sides or posterior end of the body, termed tracheal gills.

Special adaptations

One has only to study the structure, physiology, and behavior of an insect to discover adaptive modifications. A few interesting examples are: (1) the walking stick (Fig. 149) not only resembles a dead twig but has the habit of feigning death; (2) the male cricket possesses a highly differentiated sound-producing apparatus consisting of a file (Fig. 149) on the base of one wing and a scraper on the other; when the wings are held up over the body, the file is rubbed over the scraper, producing the pleasant call of the cricket. The rate at which these calls are made is proportional to the temperature. The significant part of the sounds produced by some classes of insects is a frequency so high as to be inaudible to the human ear; (3) dragonfly naiads breathe by means of rectal gills which line the enlarged posterior end of the digestive tract and remove oxygen from the water that is drawn in and expelled from this cavity; the labium of the naiad (Fig. 149) is much elongated and can be extended rapidly from its folded resting position beneath the head so as to impale its prey on the hooks at the end; (4) mosquito larvae obtain air through a tube that is thrust through the surface of the water; (5) water striders (Fig. 149) have long, slender legs which do not break through the surface film as they skim about over the water; (6) fireflies are provided with an organ capable of emitting light; the females

and larvae, known as glowworms, are also luminescent; (7) click beetles leap (click) by means of the action of a prosternal process in a metasternal groove; (8) dung beetles, including the sacred scarab of the Egyptians (Fig. 149), roll up balls of dung in which an egg is laid and on which the larva feeds; (9) the larvae of most caddisflies (Fig. 149) build portable protective cases of sand grains or vegetable matter fastened together with silk; (10) certain hornets build nests of wood pulp (Fig. 149) —they were the first papermakers; and (11) gall wasps stimulate plants to develop abnormal growths called galls, presumably caused by growth-stimulating substances secreted by the insect.

Hormones

It is now well established that **hormones** play an important part in the regulation of the activities of insects, for example, hormones control both metamorphosis and molting. Experiments have shown that the retention of juvenile characters and development of adult structures are controlled by **hormones** secreted by the brain, prothoracic gland, and corpora allata. The **corpus allatum** is a gland which lies behind the brain. If this gland is removed from the nymph of the bug *Rhodnius*, at a certain time, molting is prevented.

COLORATION

Everyone knows that many insects are brilliantly colored, especially the butterflies, moths, and beetles. Coloration of some insects differs with the season, and one brood may have one color pattern and a later brood a very different one. Such insects are said to be **seasonally dimorphic** (two types), **trimorphic** (three types), or **polymorphic** (more than three types). In certain species the males and females are differently colored;

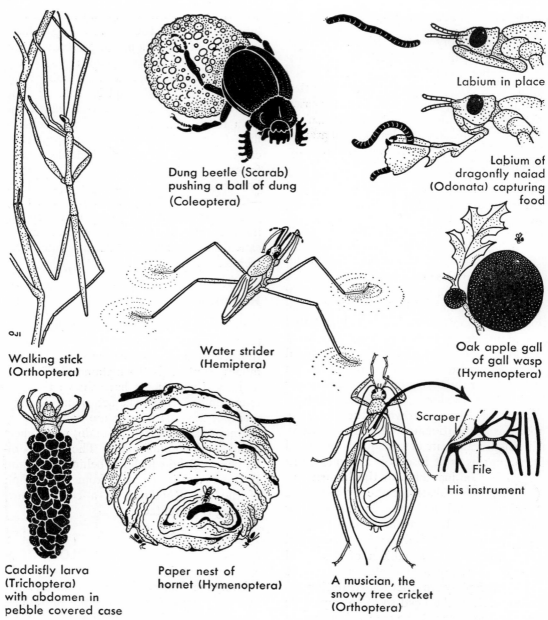

Dung beetle (Scarab)
pushing a ball of dung
(Coleoptera)

Labium in place

Labium of
dragonfly naiad
(Odonata) capturing
food

Walking stick
(Orthoptera)

Water strider
(Hemiptera)

Oak apple gall
of gall wasp
(Hymenoptera)

Scraper

File

His instrument

Caddisfly larva
(Trichoptera)
with abdomen in
pebble covered case

Paper nest of
hornet (Hymenoptera)

A musician, the
snowy tree cricket
(Orthoptera)

Figure 149. Special structural and physiologic adaptations of insects.

that is, they are **sexually dimorphic.** This often occurs, for example, in butterflies of the genus *Papilio*. Often insects are protected from their enemies by their coloration. Examples of what are known as protective coloration, protective mimicry, etc., are common among insects.

SOCIAL INSECTS

Various types of association occur among animals. Many protozoans live in colonies. The same is true of coelenterates, where the members of a colony may differ conspicuously from one another. In many cases animals band together for mutual defense, or congregate in one place for breeding purposes, or are attracted to a limited area because of the presence of food. Birds are often gregarious during the breeding season and migration. Certain mammals unite in herds partly for protection; for example, male bison, when attacked, form a circle around the cows and calves. The more complex societies involve **division of labor;** the principal types of activity are (1) reproduction, (2) obtaining food, and (3) defending the colony. Many of the most interesting examples of social life occur among the wasps, bees, ants, and termites.

Wasps and bees

Wasps and bees may be solitary or social. Solitary wasps and bees dig a hole in the ground or in wood, or construct a nest of mud. Wasps provision their nests with caterpillars or other arthropods that they have paralyzed; and bees provide pollen ("bee bread") to furnish proteins for the growth of the larvae. After laying an egg in the nest, they close the entrance and give their offspring no more parental care.

Bees

Bumble bees (Fig. 129) and honey bees (Fig. 150) are types of social bees. The fertilized queen bumble bee lives through the winter. In the spring she lays a few eggs in a cavity in the ground, from which workers develop. The workers are infertile females. They carry on all of the activities of the colony except laying eggs. At the end of the summer, males (drones) and fertile

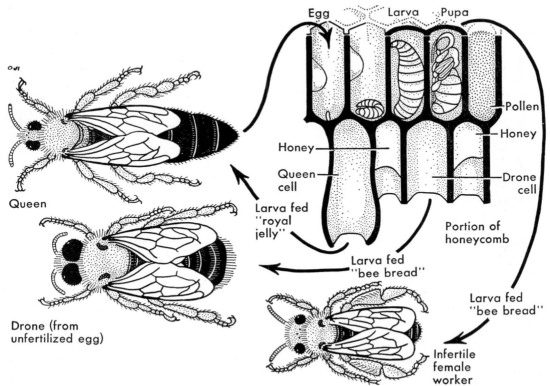

FIGURE 150. Life cycle of the honey bee showing growth stages and three adult castes, consisting of worker, drone, and queen. Cells of honeycomb in nature are arranged parallel to floor of hive.

females (queens) hatch from some of the eggs. These mate and the sperm receptacles of the queens are filled with sperms. The workers and drones then die, and the race is maintained during the winter by the queens alone. Honey bees exhibit an even more complex social organization.

"Language" of the honey bee

Our knowledge of how bees communicate is a fascinating discovery, and one that has astonished everyone. Observers of honey bees have always realized that they had some system of communicating with each other. However, it remained for the brilliant Austrian zoologist, von Frisch, to show clearly that their main method of broadcasting a source of nectar or pollen is not verbal, but depends on rhythmic movements and odors.

A bee informs other bees in her hive of a rich source of nectar found near it by means of a round dance (Fig. 151). This dance gives no indication of direction, but the bees know the food is to be found close to the hive. The specific odor of the plant visited, which is on the body of the informing bee, tells her companions the kind of flower for which to search.

If food is farther away than about 165 to 330 feet, the round dance is replaced by the tail-wagging dance (Fig. 151). This dance not only informs hive mates of a good source of food and its characteristic odor, but also the distance and direction in which it will be found. As the distance between feeding place and hive increases, the number of straight runs within the tail-wagging dance decreases. The direction of the straight run on the honeycomb indicates the direction of the nectar source in relation to the sun.

The dances are closely watched by other bees in the hive, who then go out to find the source of food.

Remarkable as the dance "language" of the bees is, other studies in progress on bee behavior may prove even more interesting. Many other social insects besides the honey bees undoubtedly have a means of communication, but its exact nature awaits discovery through further studies.

Round dance

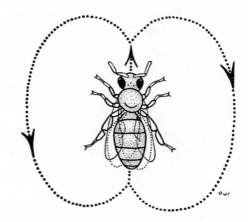

Tail-wagging dance

FIGURE 151. The behavior of the bee during the round and tail-wagging dance. When the round dance is performed, the bee turns in a circle, once to the left, then once to the right, repeating the dance in one place for about one-half minute. During the tail-wagging dance, the bee runs a short distance straight ahead wagging the abdomen, then makes a complete 360-degree turn to the left, runs ahead once more and turns right; this is repeated over and over. (After von Frisch.)

Other senses of honey bees

Are bees sensitive to colors? Apparently they can distinguish four colors: blue-green, yellow-green, blue-violet, and ultraviolet. Ultraviolet is invisible to man. This emphasizes the well-established fact that color vision in the honey bee is different from that in man. Too often biologists have made the false assumption that a red flower would appear red to all other animals.

Something is known about taste in bees. They can distinguish salt, sour, sweet, and bitter. Honey bees are able to determine different degrees of sweetness.

It is also known that bees can distinguish solid objects, that is, a solid triangle from three parallel lines.

Ants

Many ants live a complicated social life. The colony, unlike bees, contains several fertile females, the queens, and at certain periods fertile males, the drones. Infertile females may be of several types: (1) soldiers to guard the colony, (2) workers to gather food, (3) workers to care for the eggs and young, etc. These different types of individuals are morphologically different, the species being very polymorphic.

Termites

The most complex social life of all insects is that of the termites (Fig. 152). The colony contains three principal types or

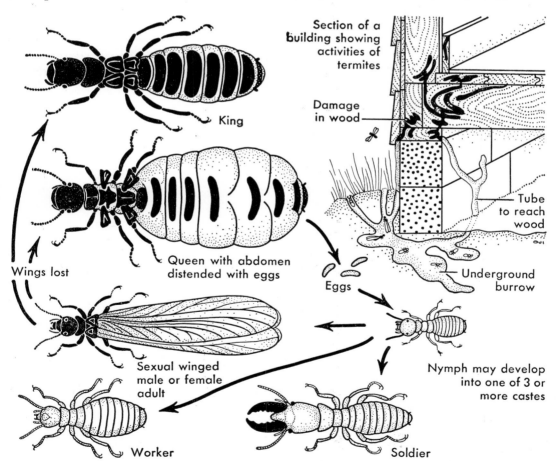

King

Wings lost

Queen with abdomen distended with eggs

Sexual winged male or female adult

Worker

Soldier

Section of a building showing activities of termites

Damage in wood

Tube to reach wood

Eggs

Underground burrow

Nymph may develop into one of 3 or more castes

FIGURE 152. Castes and life cycle of the termite. Note that it feeds on dead wood (p. 638); every year termites do great damage to buildings and books in their search for cellulose to eat.

castes: (1) **sexuals** (kings and queens), (2) **workers,** and (3) **soldiers.** The first type, the reproductive individuals, may possess functional wings, small nonfunctional wings, or no wings. The winged kings (males) and queens (females) leave the colony, mate, lose their wings at a particular breaking point, and start a new colony.

The second caste consists of the male and female **workers,** and the third caste of male and female **soldiers.** They have no wings and no functional sex organs. The workers are more numerous than any other caste. They care for the eggs and young, feed and tend the queen, obtain food, cultivate fungus in special chambers in certain species, excavate tunnels and galleries, construct mounds, and perform other duties.

The soldiers are the most highly specialized. Two castes may be present: one has a large body, strong head, and huge mandi-

bles for driving away intruders; the other carries on chemical warfare by means of a pore in the head through which a repellent fluid may be ejected. That the soldiers are not very successful is indicated by the fact that over 100 species of other insects, arachnids, centipedes, and millipedes live regularly as guests in the nests of termites.

RELATIONS OF INSECTS TO MAN

Beneficial insects

Insects of importance to human welfare have been mentioned in the preceding pages. Some of them are beneficial, but more are injurious. Among the beneficial insects are those that produce honey, wax, silk, lac, and cochineal; those that cross-fertilize (pol-

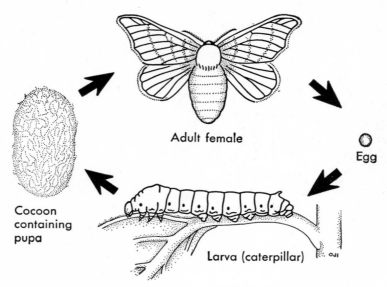

Adult female

Egg

Cocoon containing pupa

Larva (caterpillar)

Figure 153. A beneficial insect, the silkworm.

lenize) flowers; and those that destroy injurious insects either by devouring or parasitizing them. Injurious insects include farm and household pests, and species that transmit disease agents.

The **honey bee** (Fig. 150) produces about

250,000,000 pounds of honey in the United States every year. We also use about 10 million pounds of beeswax annually. **Silkworms** (Fig. 153) spin about 1000 feet of thread to make each cocoon, and about 25,000 cocoons are necessary to manufacture one pound of silk. The number of silkworms that are working for man is indicated by the fact that about 50 million pounds of silk are used in the world every year. **Lac insects** belong to the family Coccidae; they secrete a wax known as shellac. The dye known as cochineal is made from the dried bodies of a scale insect that lives on cactus; it is no

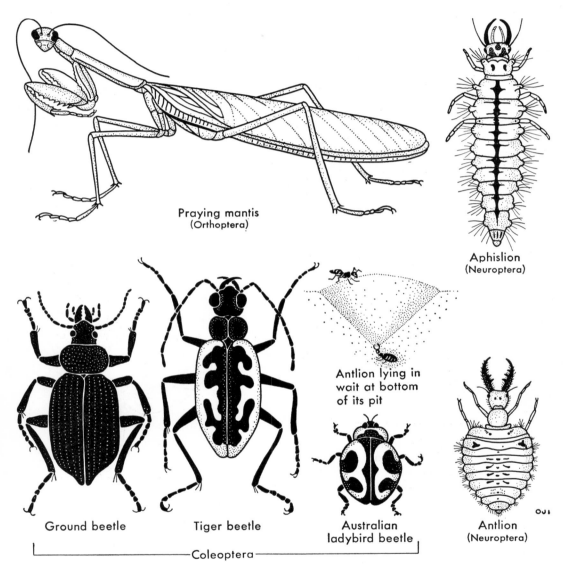

Praying mantis
(Orthoptera)

Aphislion
(Neuroptera)

Antlion lying in
wait at bottom
of its pit

Ground beetle   Tiger beetle   Australian
                                ladybird beetle

Antlion
(Neuroptera)

Coleoptera

FIGURE 154. Beneficial insects. The figures are not drawn to scale. (After U.S. Department of Agriculture *Yearbook*, 1952.)

longer of much value, aniline dyes having largely taken its place.

Bees are among the most valuable of the insects that **pollenize flowers.** For example, apples, pears, blackberries, raspberries, and clover depend upon them. Certain other insects also perform this important function. This means that many of our important food plants could not exist without insects. An interesting example is furnished by the Smyrna fig which could not be grown in California until the minute fig insect (Fig. 448) was introduced to pollenize the flowers.

Predaceous insects

Predaceous insects are of benefit because they devour vast numbers of other insects, most of which are injurious. Ground beetles, tiger beetles, antlions, and lady beetles, all

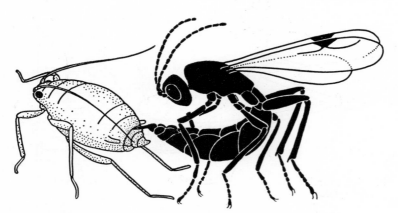

Hymenopteran ovipositing in an aphid (Homoptera)

Hymenopteran ovipositing in egg of codling moth (Lepidoptera)

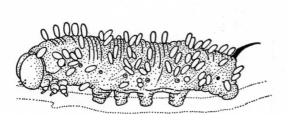

Cocoons (pupae) of a braconid fly (Hymenoptera) on the larva (hornworm) of the tomato sphinx moth (Lepidoptera)

Pyrgota fly (Diptera) ovipositing in abdomen of June beetle (Coleoptera)

FIGURE 155. Some insects that show a parasite-host relationship. It is roughly estimated that there are about 11,000 species of parasitic insects in North America. Insects are probably their own worst enemies. (After U.S. Department of Agriculture *Yearbook*, 1952.)

shown in Fig. 154, are common types. The Australian ladybird beetle (Fig. 154) was introduced into California because it was known to devour the fluted scale and to protect successfully the orange and lemon trees from this species. Other predaceous

species have also been introduced with favorable results.

Insects that live as **parasites** (Fig. 155) on other insects are also beneficial to man. They usually lay their eggs in the larvae, and the young that hatch from these eggs slowly devour and finally kill their host before it becomes an adult. Some parasitic insects furnish examples of what is known as **polyembryony**; each of their eggs produces not one but many larvae, as many as 395 having been reported from a single egg. Sometimes parasitic insects parasitize other parasitic insects and these in turn may be parasitized, and so on. Thus we have primary, secondary, tertiary, and quaternary parasites, a condition known as **hyperparasitism**. There is certainly truth in the following humorous lines:

Big fleas have little fleas
Upon their backs to bite 'em
And little fleas have lesser fleas,
And so *ad infinitum*.

Many insects are of the **scavenger** type, and vast quantities of dead animal and vegetable materials are eaten by them, thus preventing decay and obnoxious odors. Blow flies are especially effective, since they lay enormous numbers of eggs, and the larvae that hatch from them are extremely voracious. As Linnaeus remarked, a fly can devour the carcass of a horse more quickly than a

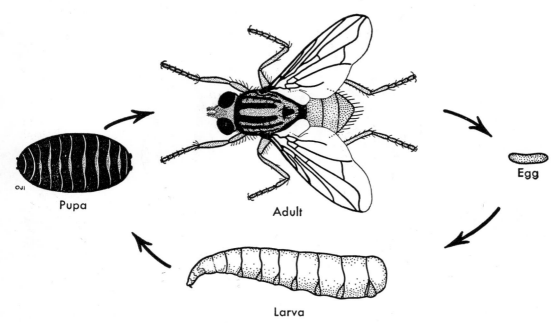

FIGURE 156. Life cycle of the housefly (*Musca domestica*). This fly, like insects in general, has a tremendous reproductive potential. It has been said that if this potential were unchecked, the descendants of a pair of flies in 10 years would weigh more than the earth.

lion can. Water-scavenger beetles, burying beetles, and dung beetles (Fig. 149), including the sacred scarab of the Egyptians are all scavengers.

A study of the effects of certain maggots as an aid in the healing of wounds has led from maggot therapy to chemical therapy in which synthetic allantoin is used directly in treatment.

Insects harmful to plants

Insect pests, according to estimates by the United States Department of Agriculture, do about $4,000,000,000 damage annually to farm crops, forests, stored foodstuffs, and domesticated animals. Some are **native pests**, such as the potato beetle (Fig. 157), Rocky Mountain locust, and army worm; others

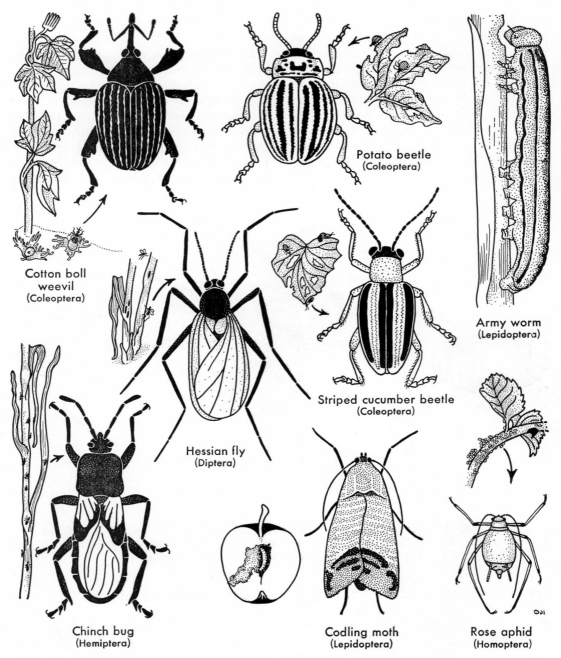

Cotton boll weevil (Coleoptera)

Potato beetle (Coleoptera)

Army worm (Lepidoptera)

Hessian fly (Diptera)

Striped cucumber beetle (Coleoptera)

Chinch bug (Hemiptera)

Codling moth (Lepidoptera)

Rose aphid (Homoptera)

FIGURE 157. Insects harmful to plants.

have been **introduced** from other countries, such as the San José scale, European corn borer, cotton boll weevil, Japanese beetle, and Mediterranean fruit fly. Among the **sucking insects** that may be classified as farm pests are the aphids, scale insects, stink bugs, Hessian fly maggots, and leafhoppers. The chinch bug is especially notorious because of its injuries to corn and small grain. **Chewing insects** of importance include wireworms, white grubs, the European corn borer, flat-headed borers, bark borers, alfalfa weevils, corn-ear worms, and cotton boll weevils. Stored grain is destroyed in large quantities by beetles of various kinds, especially by weevils and by caterpillars of moths.

Insects injurious to domestic animals

Domestic animals are often seriously injured by insects. Biting lice, such as the chicken louse (Fig. 158) may feed on feathers and cause loss of flesh by their constant irritation. Sucking lice are even more injurious. Among the flies, the horn fly is a bloodsucking species and a serious pest of cattle. The larvae of the horse botflies (Fig. 158) may cause series disturbances to the

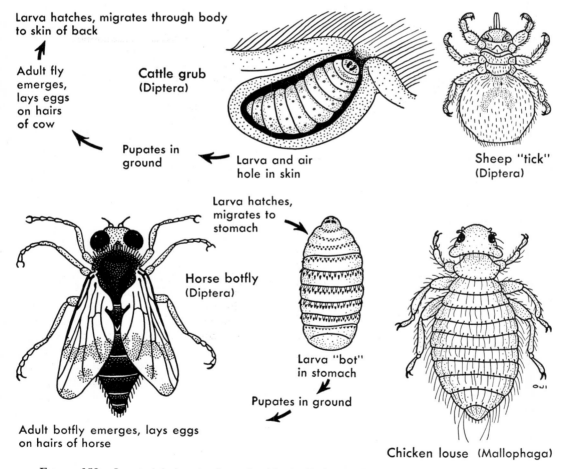

Larva hatches, migrates through body to skin of back

Adult fly emerges, lays eggs on hairs of cow

Cattle grub (Diptera)

Pupates in ground

Larva and air hole in skin

Sheep "tick" (Diptera)

Larva hatches, migrates to stomach

Horse botfly (Diptera)

Larva "bot" in stomach

Pupates in ground

Adult botfly emerges, lays eggs on hairs of horse

Chicken louse (Mallophaga)

FIGURE 158. Insects injurious to domestic animals. Each year livestock pests cost this country about $500,000,000. Figures of insects are not drawn to scale.

stomach. The cattle grubs of the ox warble fly (Fig. 158) cut holes in the skin of cattle and damage the hide; the animals also lose flesh.

Household insect pests

Insects that are **unwelcome guests** in the house (Fig. 159) are sometimes only annoying, but they may become destructive. Food may be spoiled by cockroaches, ants, fruit flies, and weevils; clothing, carpets, furs, and feathers may be injured by clothes moths and carpet beetles. Among the piercing insects that are annoying are stable flies, bedbugs, and mosquitoes.

Chemical control of household insect pests involves the use of chemicals that kill or repel them.

Insects that transmit human diseases

No doubt insects that carry diseases (Fig. 160) are one of the greatest enemies of man and affect human welfare most profoundly. Some of the more important species are the house flies that spread the bacteria of typhoid and of summer diarrhea; mosquitoes that transmit malaria, yellow fever, dengue, and filariasis; fleas that convey the bacteria of bubonic plague from rat or ground squirrel to man; body lice (cooties) that are responsible for transmission of typhus fever; and tsetse flies that are the vectors of African sleeping sickness in man, and nagana and other diseases in domestic animals.

Our federal and state governments and educational institutions all recognize the necessity of controlling injurious insects, and hence **economic entomology** has become one of the most important activities in the scientific field, both pure and applied. Departments of health devote a considerable part of their funds and efforts to the subject of insect control, especially the control of house flies and mosquitoes.

CLASSIFICATION OF THE INSECTS

(For reference purposes only)

Insects are divided into orders principally on the basis of the following characteristics: (1) with or without metamorphosis; if metamorphosis occurs, whether gradual, incomplete, or complete; (2) type of mouth parts, and (3) number and type of wings. Minor features are also of service. Some of the entomologists divide a few of the orders listed below still further, but to simplify we are giving only 25 as follows:

1. **Protura.**
2. **Thysanura.** Bristletails, etc.
3. **Collembola.** Springtails
4. **Orthoptera.** Grasshoppers, etc.
5. **Isoptera.** Termites
6. **Neuroptera.** Aphislions, etc.
7. **Ephemeroptera.** Mayflies.
8. **Odonata.** Dragonflies
9. **Plecoptera.** Stoneflies
10. **Corrodentia.** Booklice, etc.
11. **Mallophaga.** Bird and other biting lice
12. **Embioptera.** Embiids
13. **Thysanoptera.** Thrips
14. **Anoplura.** Sucking lice
15. **Hemiptera.** Bugs
16. **Homoptera.** Plant lice, etc.
17. **Dermaptera.** Earwigs
18. **Coleoptera.** Beetles
19. **Strepsiptera.** Stylopids
20. **Mecoptera.** Scorpionflies and others
21. **Trichoptera.** Caddisflies
22. **Lepidoptera.** Moths and butterflies
23. **Diptera.** Flies
24. **Siphonaptera.** Fleas
25. **Hymenoptera.** Bees, wasps, ants, etc.

Order 1. Protura (Gr. *proto*, first; *uro*, tail). Primitive; wingless; no metamorphosis; mouth parts insectlike; without antennae or true eyes; abdomen of 12 segments; live in damp places; about 30 species. Ex. *Acerentulus barberi*.

Order 2. Thysanura (Gr. *thysanos*, tassel). Firebrat (Fig. 129). Primitive, wingless; no metamorphosis; chewing mouth parts; 11 ab-

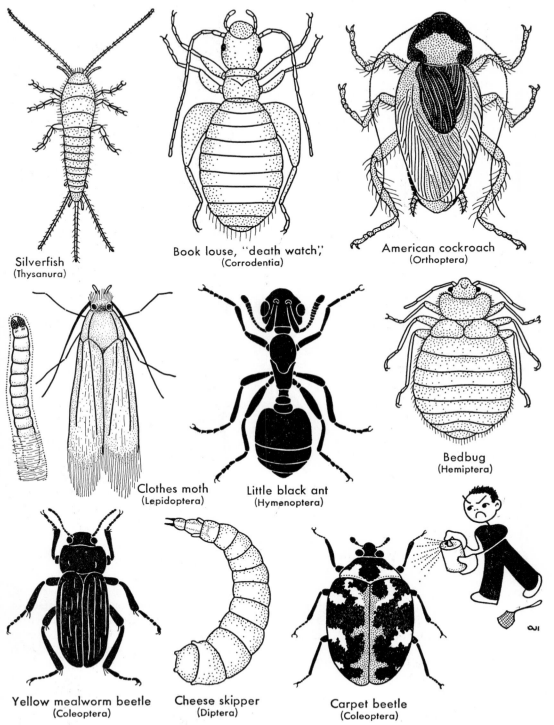

Silverfish
(Thysanura)

Book louse, "death watch,"
(Corrodentia)

American cockroach
(Orthoptera)

Clothes moth
(Lepidoptera)

Little black ant
(Hymenoptera)

Bedbug
(Hemiptera)

Yellow mealworm beetle
(Coleoptera)

Cheese skipper
(Diptera)

Carpet beetle
(Coleoptera)

FIGURE 159. Household insect pests. Figures are not drawn to scale.

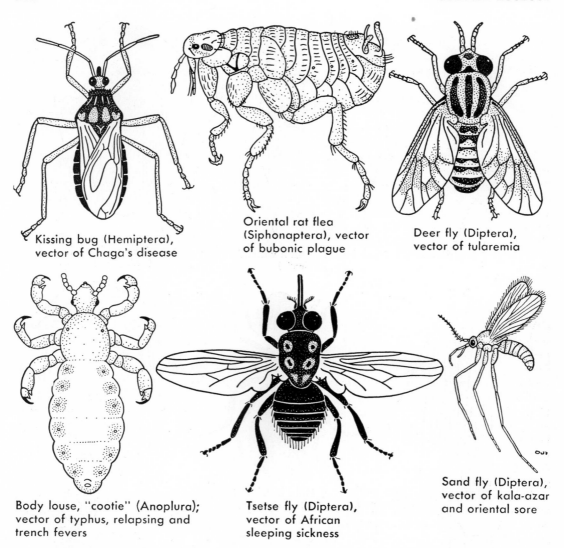

Kissing bug (Hemiptera), vector of Chaga's disease

Oriental rat flea (Siphonaptera), vector of bubonic plague

Deer fly (Diptera), vector of tularemia

Body louse, "cootie" (Anoplura); vector of typhus, relapsing and trench fevers

Tsetse fly (Diptera), vector of African sleeping sickness

Sand fly (Diptera), vector of kala-azar and oriental sore

FIGURE 160. Some insects that transmit human diseases. The figures are not drawn to scale.

dominal segments; usually two or three long, filiform, segmented, caudal appendages; less than 20 species known from the United States. Ex. *Lepisma saccharina* (Fig. 159), silverfish.

Order 3. Collembola (Gr. *kolla*, glue; *ballo*, put). Springtails (Fig. 129). Primitive wingless insects; chewing or sucking mouth parts; 4 segments in antennae; no metamorphosis; usually no tracheae, compound eyes, Malpighian tubules, nor tarsi; 6 abdominal segments; springing organ present in most species

on ventral side of fourth abdominal segment; sticky tubelike projection on ventral surface of first abdominal segment. Ex. *Achorutes nivicola*, snow flea.

Order 4. Orthoptera (Gr. *orthos*, straight; *pteron*, wing). Grasshoppers, etc. Metamorphosis gradual; chewing mouth parts; typically two pairs of wings; forewings often thickened and parchmentlike, called tegmina (singular, tegmen); hindwings folded like fan beneath forewings; in some, wings vestigial or absent; 6 common families as follows:

Cursoria. Walking or running
  Phasmatidae. Walkingsticks (Fig. 149)
  Mantidae. Mantes (Fig. 154)
  Blattidae. Cockroaches (Fig. 159)
Saltatoria. Leaping
  Tettigoniidae. Long-horned grasshoppers
  Gryllidae. Crickets
  Locustidae. Short-horned grasshoppers

Order 5. Isoptera (Gr. *isos*, equal; *pteron*, wing). Termites or "white ants." Metamorphosis gradual; chewing mouth parts; two pairs of long, narrow wings laid flat on back, or wingless; abdomen joined broadly to thorax; social insects living in colonies (p. 253). Ex. *Reticulitermes flavipes* (Fig. 152).

Order 6. Neuroptera (Gr. *neuron*, nerve). Dobson or hellgrammite, aphislions, antlions, and others. Metamorphosis complete; chewing mouth parts; 4 similar membranous wings, usually with many veins and cross veins; no abdominal cerci; larvae carnivorous, some with suctorial mouth parts; tracheal gills usually present on aquatic larvae. Ex. *Lacewing* (Fig. 129).

Order 7. Ephemeroptera (Ephemerida) (Gr. *ephemeros*, living but a day). Mayflies (Fig. 129). Metamorphosis incomplete; mouth parts of adult, vestigial; two pairs of membranous, triangular wings; forewings larger than hindwings; caudal filament and cerci very long. Ex. *Ephemera simulans,* which is an important fish food.

Order 8. Odonata (Gr. *odous*, tooth). Dragonflies and damselflies. Metamorphosis incomplete; chewing mouth parts; two pairs of membranous wings; hindwings as large as or larger than forewings; large compound eyes; small antennae; no cerci; naiads aquatic; both naiads and adults, predaceous. Ex. *Anax junius.*

Order 9. Plecoptera (Gr. *pleko*, fold). Stoneflies (Fig. 129). Metamorphosis incomplete; chewing mouth parts, often undeveloped in adults; two pairs of wings, the hindwings usually larger and folded beneath forewings; tarsus with three segments; naiad aquatic, often with tufts of tracheal gills. Ex. *Allocapnia pygmaea.*

Order 10. Corrodentia (Psocoptera) (L. *corrodens*, gnawing). Psocids and booklice (Fig. 159). Metamorphosis gradual; chewing mouth parts; wingless or with two pairs of membranous wings that have few, prominent veins; forewings larger than hindwings; wings, when at rest, held over body like sides of a roof. Ex. *Liposcelis divinatorius.*

Order 11. Mallophaga (Gr. *mallos*, wool). Biting lice (Fig. 158). Gradual metamorphosis; chewing mouth parts; wings absent; eyes degenerate. Ex. *Menopon gallinae,* common chicken louse.

Order 12. Embioptera (Gr. *embios*, lively). Embiids (Fig. 129). Metamorphosis gradual; chewing mouth parts; wingless or with two pairs of delicate, membranous wings, containing few veins, and folded on the back when at rest; cerci of two segments. Ex. *Embia texana.*

Order 13. Thysanoptera (Gr. *thysanos*, fringe). Thrips (Fig. 129). Metamorphosis gradual; rasping mouth parts; wingless or with two pairs of similar, long, narrow, membranous wings with few or no veins, and fringed with long hairlike structures; prothorax large and free; tarsi with two or three segments terminating in a bladderlike, protrusible vesicle. Ex. *Thrips tabaci,* onion thrips.

Order 14. Anoplura (Gr. *anoplos*, unarmed; *oura*, tail). Sucking lice. Gradual metamorphosis; piercing and sucking mouth parts; wingless; ectoparasites on mammals; eyes poorly developed or absent; tarsus with one segment bearing a single, large, curved claw adapted for clinging to hair of host. Ex. *Pediculus humanus corporis* (Fig. 160), body louse.

Order 15. Hemiptera (Gr. *hemi*, half). True bugs. Metamorphosis gradual; piercing and sucking mouth parts; wingless or with two pairs of wings; forewings thickened at base; labium forms a jointed beak in which the slender, piercing maxillae and mandibles move; a few families as follows:

Aquatic

  Corixidae. Water boatmen
  Notonectidae. Back swimmers
  Belostomatidae. Water bugs
  Gerridae. Water striders (Fig. 149)

Terrestrial

  Miridae. Leaf bugs
  Cimicidae. Bedbugs (Fig. 159)
  Reduviidae. Kissing bugs (Fig. 160)
  Tingidae. Lace bugs
  Lygaeidae. Chinch bugs (Fig. 157)

Coreidae. Squash bugs
Pentatomidae. Stink bugs (Fig. 129)

Order 16. Homoptera (Gr. *homos*, same).
Cicadas, leafhoppers, aphids, scales (Fig. 157).
Metamorphosis gradual; mouth parts for piercing and sucking; usually two pairs of wings of uniform thickness held over back, like sides of roof; a few families as follows:

Cicadidae. Cicadas
Cercopidae. Spittle insects (Fig. 129)
Membracidae. Treehoppers
Cicadellidae. Leafhoppers
Aphididae. Plant lice (Fig. 157)
Phylloxeridae. Phylloxerids
Aleyrodidae. Whiteflies
Coccidae. Scale insects

Order 17. Dermaptera (Gr. *derma*, skin).
Earwigs (Fig. 129). Metamorphosis gradual; chewing mouth parts; wingless or with one or two pairs of wings; forewings small, leathery, and meeting in a straight line along back; hindwings large, membranous, and folded lengthwise and crosswise under forewings; forcepslike cerci at posterior end of abdomen. Ex. *Forficula auricularia*.

Order 18. Coleoptera (Gr. *koleos*, sheath).
Beetles (Figs. 149, 154 and 157). Metamorphosis complete; chewing mouth parts; wingless or usually with two pairs of wings; forewings hard and sheathlike (elytra) and hindwings membranous and folded under elytra; prothorax large and movable; some of the families are as follows:

Cicindelidae. Tiger beetles (Fig. 154)
Carabidae. Ground beetles (Fig. 154)
Hydrophilidae. Water scavengers
Silphidae. Carrion beetles
Staphylinidae. Rove beetles
Dermestidae. Dermestids
Tenebrionidae. Darkling beetles, such as yellow mealworm beetles (Fig. 159)
Coccinellidae. Ladybird beetles (Fig. 154)
Scarabaeidae. Lamellicorn beetles (Fig. 149
Dytiscidae. Diving beetles
Gyrinidae. Whirligig beetles
Lampyridae. Fireflies
Meloidae. Blister beetles
Elateridae. Click beetles
Buprestidae. Wood borers

Lucanidae. Stag beetles
Cerambycidae. Long-horned beetles
Chrysomelidae. Leaf beetles (Fig. 157)
Curculionidae. Snout beetles, such as cotton boll weevil (Fig. 157)
Scolytidae. Engraver beetles

Order 19. Strepsiptera (Gr. *strepsis*, a turning). Stylopids (Fig. 129). Hypermetamorphosis; mouth parts vestigial or absent; endoparasitic in other insects; male with raspberrylike eyes, tiny club-shaped forewings and large fan-shaped membranous hindwings; female, larvalike, eyeless, wingless, and legless; nutrition by absorption; life cycle complex. As the description indicates, the Strepsiptera are in many respects the most unique of all the insects. Ex. *Xenos wheeleri*, a parasite of the wasp *Polistes*.

Order 20. Mecoptera (Gr. *mekos*, length).
Scorpionflies (Fig. 129). Metamorphosis complete; chewing mouth parts; antennae long and slender; head prolonged into beak; wingless or with two pairs of long, narrow, membranous wings; some males with clasping organ at caudal end resembling sting of scorpion. Ex. *Panorpa rufescens*.

Order 21. Trichoptera (Gr. *thrix*, hair).
Caddisflies (Figs. 129 and 149). Metamorphosis complete; vestigial mouth parts in adult; two pairs of membranous wings clothed with long, silky hairs; many aquatic larvae build portable cases. Ex. *Phryganea interrupta*.

Order 22. Lepidoptera (Gr. *lepis*, scale).
Butterflies, skippers, and moths (Figs. 143, 157 and 159). Metamorphosis complete; sucking mouth parts; wingless or with two pairs of membranous wings covered with overlapping scales; sucking apparatus coiled underneath head; larvae have chewing mouth parts and are called caterpillars; sometimes spin cocoon; pupa often called a chrysalis. A few families are as follows:

Families of Moths

Tineidae. Clothes moth (Fig. 159)
Tortricidae. Leaf rollers
Sphingidae. Hawk moths
Geometridae. Measuring worms
Lymantriidae. Tussock moths
Phalaenidae (Noctuidae). Owlet moths
Arctiidae. Tiger moths
Citheroniidae. Regal moths

Saturniidae. Giant silkworm moths
Bombycidae. Silkworm moths (Fig. 153)

Families of Skippers, and Butterflies

Hesperiidae. Skippers
Papilionidae. Swallowtails
Pieridae. Whites and yellows (Fig. 143)
Nymphalidae. 4-footed butterflies
Lycaenidae. Gossamer-wings

Order 23. Diptera (Gr. *dis*, two). Flies (Fig. 156). Metamorphosis complete; piercing and sucking mouth parts forming proboscis; wingless or with one pair of membranous forewings; hindwings represented by knobbed threads called halteres; larvae known as maggots (Fig. 156); larval skin sometimes serves as a cocoon and called a puparium; some of the families are as follows:

Tipulidae. Crane flies
Tendipedidae (Chironomidae). Midges
Psychodidae. Sand flies (Fig. 160)
Culicidae. Mosquitoes
Cecidomyidae. Gall gnats
Syrphidae. Flower flies
Trypetidae. Fruit flies
Drosophilidae. Pomace flies
Oestridae. Bot flies (Fig. 158)
Calliphoridae. Blow flies
Simuliidae. Black flies
Tabanidae. Deer flies (Fig. 160)
Bombyliidae. Bee flies
Asilidae. Robber flies
Sarcophagidae. Flesh flies
Tachinidae. Tachinid flies
Muscidae. Houseflies (Fig. 156)
Hippoboscidae. Louse flies
Braulidae. Bee lice

Order 24. Siphonaptera (Gr. *siphon*, sucker; *a*, without; *pteron*, wing). Fleas. (Fig. 160). Metamorphosis complete; piercing and sucking mouth parts; wingless; body laterally compressed; head small; no compound eyes; legs adapted for leaping; ectoparasites of mammals, a few birds. Ex. *Ctenocephalides felis*, cat flea.

Order 25. Hymenoptera (Gr. *hymen*, membrane). Ants, bees, wasps, etc. Metamorphosis complete; chewing or sucking mouth parts; wingless or with two pairs of membranous wings, forewings larger, venation reduced; wings on each side held together by hooks (hamuli); females usually with sting, piercer, or saw; some parasitic on other insects; some of the families are as follows:

Tenthredinidae. Sawflies
Braconidae. Braconids
Ichneumonidae. Ichneumons
Cynipidae. Gall wasps
Chalcididae. Chalcids
Formicidae. Ants (Fig. 159)
Vespidae. Wasps
Sphecidae. Digger wasps
Andrenidae. Mining bees
Megachilidae. Leaf cutters
Bombidae. Bumble bees
Apidae. Honey bees (Fig. 150)

SELECTED COLLATERAL READINGS

Borror, D.J., and DeLong, D.M. *An Introduction to the Study of Insects*. Rinehart, New York, 1954.

Comstock, J.H. *Introduction to Entomology*. Comstock, Ithaca, N.Y., 1940.

Essig, E.O. *College Entomology*. Macmillan, New York, 1942.

Fernald, H.T., and Shepard, H.H. *Applied Entomology*. McGraw-Hill, New York, 1955.

Graham, S.A. *Forest Entomology*. McGraw-Hill, New York, 1952.

Herms, W.B. *Medical Entomolgy*. Macmillan, New York, 1950.

Jaques, H.E. *How to Know the Insects*. Brown, Dubuque, Iowa, 1941.

Little, V.A. *General and Applied Entomolgy*. Harpers, New York, 1957.

Lutz, F.E. *Field Book of Insects*. Putnam, New York, 1935.

Matheson, Robert. *Medical Entomology*. Comstock, Ithaca, N.Y., 1950.

Metcalf, C.L., Flint, W.F., and Metcalf, R.L. *Destructive and Useful Insects*. McGraw-Hill, New York, 1951.

Roeder, K.D. *Insect Physiology*. Wiley, New York, 1953.

Ross, H.H. *A Textbook of Entomology*. Wiley, New York, 1956.

Scheer, B.T. (ed.). *Recent Advances in Invertebrate Physiology*. Univ. of Oregon Publications, Eugene, Ore., 1957.

Snodgrass, R.E. *Principles of Insect Morphology*. McGraw-Hill, New York, 1935.

Steinhaus, E.A., and Smith, R.F. *Ann. Rev. of Entomol*. Annual Reviews, Inc., Stanford, 1956.

von Frisch, Karl. *The Dancing Bees*. Harcourt, Brace, New York, 1955.

————. *Bees, Their Vision, Chemical Senses, and Language*. Cornell Univ. Press, Ithaca, N.Y., 1950.

West, L.S. *The House Fly*. Comstock, Ithaca, N.Y., 1951.

Wheeler, W.M. *The Social Insects, Their Origin, and Evolution*. Harcourt, Brace, New York, 1928.

Wigglesworth, V.B. *The Principles of Insect Physiology*. Methuen, London, 1950.

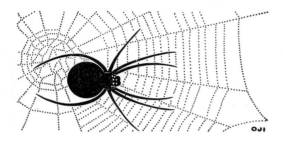

CHAPTER 19

Phylum Arthropoda. Spiders and Their Allies

The class Arachnoidea received its name from the Greek word *arachne*, which means spider. The name is appropriate since spiders are the most abundant members of the class. However, it is a heterogeneous group consisting of spiders, king crabs, scorpions, harvestmen, mites, ticks, and several minor groups. These animals differ markedly from one another, but agree in several important respects: (1) they have no antennae; (2) there are no true mandibles; (3) the first pair of appendages are nippers, termed chelicerae; and (4) usually the body can be divided into an anterior part, the cephalothorax, and a posterior part, the abdomen. Some have very interesting adaptations such as the spinning apparatus of the spiders.

The Arachnoidea, for convenience, are here classified into one class and four subclasses.

The spiders show interesting arthropod modifications, especially for breathing, for obtaining and digesting juices, and for spinning webs. A general knowledge of the other groups is worth while. Since king crabs represent an ancient group of animals, they are sometimes called "living fossils"; scorpions are poisonous to man and are often referred to in literature; harvestmen, or daddy long-legs, are frequently encountered in fields; and many mites and ticks are either directly injurious to man and domesticated animals, or they carry disease germs.

Ordinarly, arachnoids are not noticeable; and we would hardly know they existed were it not for the conspicuous webs spun by spiders.

SPIDERS

External anatomy

The body of the spider (Fig. 162) consists of a **cephalothorax** and an unsegmented **abdomen.**

There are 6 pairs of **appendages** attached to the cephalothorax. Antennae are absent; sensory functions are in part performed by

267

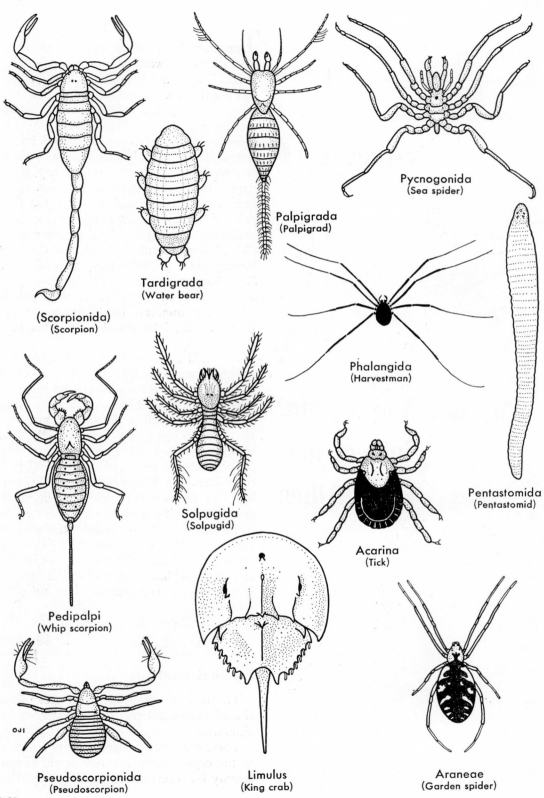

Pycnogonida
(Sea spider)

Palpigrada
(Palpigrad)

Tardigrada
(Water bear)

(Scorpionida)
(Scorpion)

Phalangida
(Harvestman)

Pentastomida
(Pentastomid)

Solpugida
(Solpugid)

Acarina
(Tick)

Pedipalpi
(Whip scorpion)

Pseudoscorpionida
(Pseudoscorpion)

Limulus
(King crab)

Araneae
(Garden spider)

the pedipalps and walking legs. The first pair of appendages are called **chelicerae** (Figs. 162 and 163). In many species, they are composed of two parts: a basal segment and

a terminal claw or **fang. Poison glands** are situated in the chelicerae of the tarantulas, but in most spiders they are in the cephalothorax. The poison (venom) they secrete

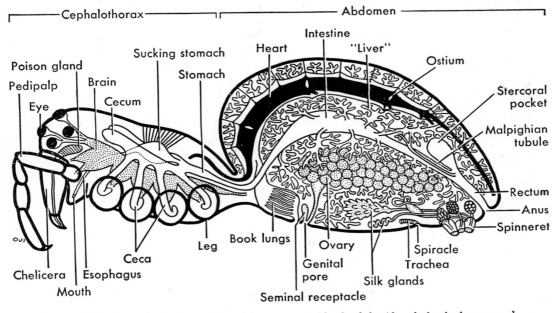

FIGURE 162. Internal structure of a spider as seen with the left side of the body removed. (Modified from Lueckart.)

passes through ducts that open on the fangs of the chelicerae; the venom is used to kill their prey and as a means of defense; it is strong enough to kill small animals and, in some species, to injure and kill larger animals. Although spiders in general have for centuries been considered very poisonous, the black widow is the only one in this country capable of causing death in man. The second pair of leglike appendages are the **pedipalpi**; their basal parts, called "maxillae," are used as jaws to press or chew the food. The pedipalpi of the mature male are also used to transfer sperms to the female.

There are 4 pairs of **walking legs** (Fig. 164). Each leg consists of 7 joints: (1) coxa, (2) trochanter, (3) femur, (4) patella, (5) tibia, (6) metatarsus, (7) tarsus. It is

terminated by two- or three-toothed claws (Fig. 163), and often a pad of hairs, the claw tuft, which enables the spider to run on ceilings and walls.

The **sternum** lies between the legs, and a **labium** is situated between the "maxillae." The **eyes**, usually 8, are on the front of the head (Fig. 163). The **mouth** is a minute opening between the bases of the pedipalpi; it serves for ingestion of liquids only.

The **abdomen** is connected with the cephalothorax by a slender waist (**peduncle**). Near the anterior end of the abdomen, on the ventral surface, is the **genital opening**, which in some female spiders is covered by a flat plate called the **epigynum**. On either side of the epigynum is the slitlike opening of the respiratory organs or **book lungs**. Some spiders also possess **tracheae** which open to the outside through **spiracles** near the posterior end of the ventral surface (Fig.

FIGURE 161. *Facing page*, some representatives of the class Arachnoidea. The figures are not drawn to scale.

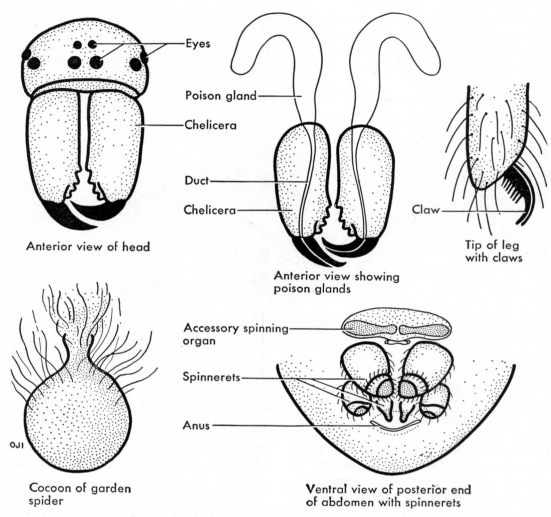

Anterior view of head

Poison gland

Chelicera

Eyes

Duct

Chelicera

Claw

Tip of leg
with claws

Anterior view showing
poison glands

Accessory spinning
organ

Spinnerets

Anus

OJI

Cocoon of garden
spider

Ventral view of posterior end
of abdomen with spinnerets

FIGURE 163.   Structural details of spiders and a cocoon.

162). Just back of the tracheal opening are three pairs of tubercles or **spinnerets** (Figs. 162 and 163) used for spinning threads. The anus lies posterior to the spinnerets.

Internal anatomy and physiology

The spider feeds mainly on insects; and because it can ingest only liquid food, the solid parts are liquefied by the action of powerful digestive enzymes contained in a fluid which is regurgitated into or over its prey. Actually, spiders ingest food in two

ways: (1) those with weak jaws puncture the body of the insect with their fangs, and then alternate between injecting digestive fluid through this hole, and sucking back the liquefied tissues, until only an exoskeleton remains; (2) those with strong jaws crush the insect into small pieces between their jaws as the digestive enzymes are regurgitated over them. Only a small mass of indigestible material, such as the sclerotized parts, remains to be discarded. In feeding, suction is produced mainly by the enlargement of the sucking stomach.

The **digestive system** is made up of a

mouth and pharynx, followed by the horizontal esophagus that leads into the sucking stomach, which in turn opens into the true stomach which gives off 5 pairs of ceca or blind tubes in the cephalothorax. The intestine passes almost straight through the abdomen; it is enlarged at a point where ducts bring into it a digestive fluid from the "liver," and again near the posterior end, where it forms a sac, the stercoral pocket, connected with the rectum, which terminates in the anus. Tubes called Malpighian tubes enter the intestine near the posterior end. The digestive tract in the abdomen is surrounded by a large digestive gland or "liver." This gland secretes a fluid resembling pancreatic juice, which pours into the intestine through ducts.

The circulatory system consists of a heart, arteries, veins, and a number of spaces or sinuses. The heart is situated in the abdomen and is dorsal to the digestive tract. It is a muscular contractile tube lying in a sheath, the pericardium. The heart opens into the pericardium, usually, by three pairs of openings (ostia). It gives off posteriorly a caudal artery, anteriorly an anterior aorta which branches and supplies the tissues in the cephalothorax, and three pairs of abdominal arteries. The blood, which is colorless and contains mostly amoeboid corpuscles, passes from the arteries into sinuses among the tissues, and is carried to the book lungs, where it is oxygenated; it then passes to the pericardium by way of the "pulmonary veins"; and finally enters the heart through the ostia.

Respiration is carried on by tracheae and book lungs; the latter are peculiar to arachnids. There are usually two book lungs, which, according to Kaston, have often been incorrectly described in textbooks. He states that each book lung consists of a blood-filled chamber with an air vestibule posterior to it. This air vestibule communicates to the outside through a slit in the body wall. From the front wall of the vestibule, there have been invaginated many parallel, narrow, air pockets, which have pushed forward into the blood-filled chamber; these may be considered tracheae which have a flattened fan shape instead of the tubular shape usually associated with tracheae. Air entering through the slit in the body wall circulates through the air pockets where oxygen is taken up by the blood. Tubular tracheae are also usually present but do not ramify to all parts of the body as in the insects.

The excretory organs are paired Malpighian tubules, which open into the intestine, and one or two pairs of coxal glands in the floor of the cephalothorax. The coxal glands are sometimes degenerate, and their openings are difficult to find; they are homologous with the green glands of the crayfish (Fig. 114).

The nervous system consists of a bilobed ganglion brain above the esophagus, a large subesophageal ganglionic mass, and the nerves which run to various organs. Sensory hairs, over the body and appendages, represent the principal sense organs. There are usually 8 simple eyes (Fig. 163), which differ in size and arrangement in different species. In only a few families are distinct images formed; in the others the eyes function primarily for perception of degrees of light, and moving objects such as prey.

Very fine, erect, hairlike processes set in sockets have been considered organs of hearing, but the evidence is still insufficient. The sense of smell is well developed, and an organ of taste is located in the pharynx.

The sexes are separate, and the testes or ovaries form a network of tubes in the abdomen. The sperms are ejected upon a special "sperm web," then picked up by the pedipalps and transferred to the seminal receptacles of the female in mating. There is courtship activity before mating which varies with the species. Sometimes the female kills and eats the male after mating. The eggs are not fertilized until laid; the sperms move from the seminal receptacle to fertilize the eggs as they pass through the "uterus externus" on their way out of the body of the female. The eggs are laid in a silk cocoon,

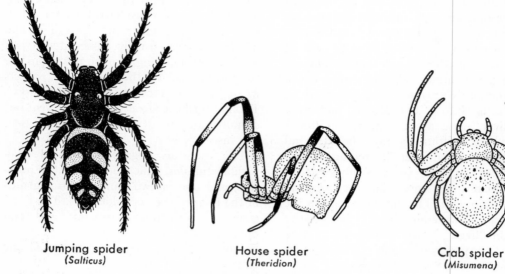

Jumping spider
(*Salticus*)

House spider
(*Theridion*)

Crab spider
(*Misumena*)

FIGURE 164.   Some common spiders.

which is attached to the web or to a plant, or carried about by the female. The young leave the cocoon after hatching, as soon as they

FIGURE 165.   The web of an orb-weaving spider. (Photo by Spencer. Courtesy of *Nature Magazine*.)

can run about. Several molts occur before maturity.

The **spinning organs** of spiders are three pairs of appendages called **spinnerets** (Figs. 162 and 163); they are pierced by hundreds of microscopic tubes through which a fluid, secreted by a number of abdominal **silk glands,** passes to the outside and hardens in the air, forming a thread. These threads are used to build snares, spin webs, and to form cocoons. Some spiders, while hunting, play out a dragline. Spiderlings disperse themselves by spinning a long thread on which they are carried away by the wind.

Many spiders possess an accessory spinning organ, the **cribellum** (Fig. 163) in addition to the spinnerets. A special kind of silk is emitted from this organ and is combed out by a row of bristles on the fourth metatarsus. The silk threads of spiders are stronger than steel threads of the same size. They are no longer used as cross hairs in the eye pieces of optical instruments; modern technology has produced better materials for the purpose.

An **orb web,** such as is shown in Fig. 165, is spun in the following manner. A thread is stretched across the space selected for the web; then from a point on this thread, other threads are drawn out and attached in radiating lines. These threads all become dry and smooth. On this foundation, a spiral of sticky thread is spun. The spider stands in the center of the web or retires to a nest at one side and waits for an insect to become entangled in the sticky thread; it then rushes out and spins threads about its prey until its struggles cease.

Many spiders do not spin webs, but wander about capturing insects, or lie in wait for them in some place of concealment.

Some spiders of special interest

Crab spiders (Fig. 164), although not all are shaped like crabs, have the habit of walking sideways. Some are white or yellow in color, and are said to favor flowers of similar color. Jumping spiders (Fig. 164) have stout front legs for capturing prey; they are famous for their peculiar antics during mating. Tarantulas (Fig. 169) are the giants of the spider world, reaching a body length of 2½ inches and a leg spread of 9 or 10 inches. Spiders of this size are able to capture small birds. Tarantulas, under laboratory conditions, are known to have lived over 20 years. The trap-door spider digs a tunnel in the ground about 6 inches deep and closes it with a hinged door, not for the purpose of trapping other animals, but to protect itself from intruders. Wolf spiders do not wait for prey to come to them, but go hunting for their victims. They care for their young by transporting them on their backs.

More than 30,000 species of spiders are known, of which about 3000 species live in the United States. Only the black widow and the tarantulas (Fig. 169) are harmful to man in this country; and contrary to popular belief, except for the tropical ones, the tarantulas are not particularly dangerous. The brightly colored garden spider is one of the more beautiful species. House spiders are considered a nuisance but are not dangerous.

OTHER ARACHNOIDEA

King or horseshoe crabs

Some of the strangest animals on earth are these peculiar "living fossils" (Fig. 166), whose close relatives died millions of years ago. The common name horseshoe crab refers to the heavy horseshoe-shaped carapace. Actually, it is not a crab. The horseshoe crab occurs along the Atlantic Coast from Maine to Yucatan. It lives in shallow water along the shores. Here it shoves its way through sand and mud, where it hunts for worms, bivalves, and other small animals on which it feeds.

Respiration is carried on with the aid of book gills. The respiratory pigment of the blood is hemocyanin which contains copper, although this metal is recoverable only in about a hundredth part in a million parts of sea water. Oxygen combines with the copper pigment to give the blood a blue color when it is exposed to the air.

Scorpions

Scorpions (Fig. 166) are rapacious arachnids measuring from ½ to 8 inches in length. They live in tropical and subtropical regions, hiding during the daytime, but running about actively at night. They capture insects, spiders, and other small animals. Larger animals are paralyzed by the sting on the end of the tail. This sting does not serve as a weapon of defense unless the scorpion is hard pressed; and it is not used to sting itself to death, as is often stated, since its poison has no effect upon its own body. The vital statistics of the Arizona State Department of Health show that during a twenty-year period, there were 64 deaths from scorpion sting. The state of Durango, Mexico, reports more than 1700 deaths from scorpions over a period of 41 years. These records indicate that some scorpions are killers and should be treated with respect.

The mating activities of scorpions are very

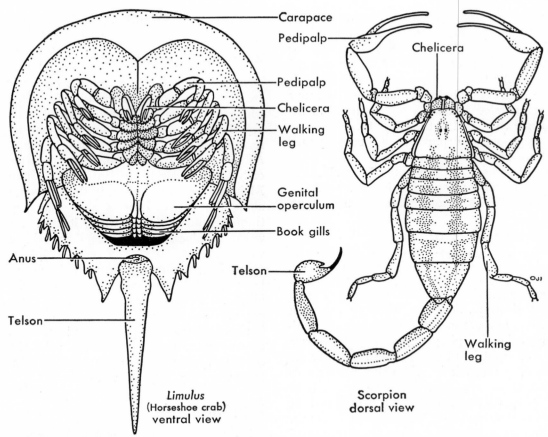

FIGURE 166. Horseshoe crab, *Limulus*, (formerly *Xiphosura*); ventral view. Natural size about 15 inches long. It is called a living fossil because it has undergone little change during long geologic periods. Scorpion, dorsal view. The poison gland is contained in the telson.

curious and include a sort of dance. Scorpions are viviparous. The young ride about upon the back of the female for about a week and then shift for themselves. They reach maturity in about 5 years.

Scorpions are one of the oldest forms of life still found on this earth. Fossilized specimens from many parts of the world show that they have remained essentially unchanged for hundreds of millions of years. Fossil scorpions resemble present-day forms (Fig. 166) in possessing a pair of chelicerae, a pair of pedipalps, four pairs of legs, and a poison gland. Thus it can be seen why modern scorpions may well be described as "living fossils."

Mites and ticks

Mites and ticks (Fig. 167) are found almost everywhere. Some live in fresh water, others in salt water; some live on the ground, others on vegetation; some live on the outside of the bodies of other animals, and others burrow into them. Animals and plants, either living or dead, serve as food for them; the parasitic species live largely on blood. The common names of certain families (p. 279) give some idea of the different types of ticks and mites. Some of those important to man are described below.

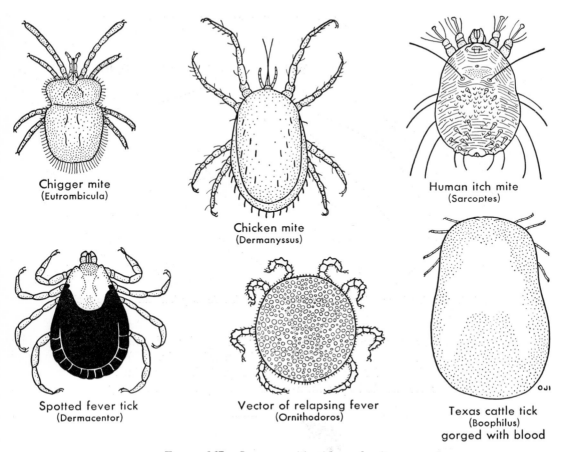

Chigger mite
(Eutrombicula)

Chicken mite
(Dermanyssus)

Human itch mite
(Sarcoptes)

Spotted fever tick
(Dermacentor)

Vector of relapsing fever
(Ornithodoros)

Texas cattle tick
(Boophilus)
gorged with blood

FIGURE 167. Some parasitic ticks and mites.

RELATIONS OF ARACHNOIDEA TO MAN

Most of the Arachnoidea are not only harmless, but they feed largely on injurious insects and are to a certain degree beneficial. A few species damage food plants; others attack man and domestic animals directly; and a few transmit disease germs. King crabs are trapped in great numbers and ground up for fertilizer.

The red spider, *Tetranychus*, is a greenhouse pest that is destructive to many species of plants; it may become a pest also in cotton fields. The clover mite injures clover and fruit trees, and the pear-leaf blister mite damages pears and apples.

Scorpions are noted for their poisonous sting; but they are mostly confined to the tropics and some are not very poisonous. The black widow spider, *Latrodectus* (Fig. 168), appears to be the only spider in the United States whose bite needs to be feared. The adult can be recognized by its glossy black color, globose abdomen, and the reddish spot on the under surface of the abdomen usually shaped like an hour glass, but sometimes like a triangle or two triangles.

Although not dangerous, the chigger mites or red bugs (Fig. 167) produce a very distressing itch which may continue for several days; an immunity may be acquired to their invasions of the skin. One of the itch mites,

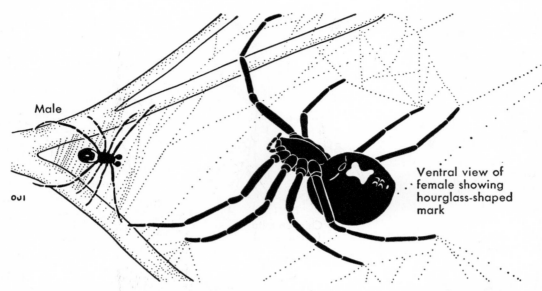

Male

Ventral view of female showing hourglass-shaped mark

FIGURE 168. Black widow spiders in their snare. The female may kill and eat the male after mating, but this is not always true.

Sarcoptes (Fig. 167), causes the so-called 7-year itch in man, as well as mange in dogs, cats, and many other kinds of animals.

Domestic animals are infested by a num-

ber of species of mites and ticks. The chicken mite (Fig. 167) is a serious pest of poultry. Scab mites attack horses, dogs, etc. The sheep scab mite may seriously injure

FIGURE 169. Tarantula, the largest of the spiders. The tarantula does not spin a web, but stalks its prey like a lion. It is found in our southwestern and western states. Although feared by many people, experiments on species in this country have shown their "bites" to be no more harmful than a bee sting. However, it is true that some South American tarantulas are more injurious. (Courtesy of N.Y. Zoological Society.)

sheep; it causes intense irritation, loss of wool, and decreased vitality. Unless these animals are properly treated, they may die.

Several important vectors of disease occur among the ticks. Rocky Mountain spotted fever of man is due to *Dermacentor*, which transmits germs (rickettsial organisms) from rodents and larger mammals to man; the female ticks pass the disease germs to their offspring through the egg. One symptom of this disease is the appearance of spots on the wrists, ankles, trunk, and face. An eastern variety of spotted fever occurs in country districts from New York to Florida; cases have also been found in the Middle West. A vaccine has been developed that confers immunity for about one year. The Rocky Mountain wood tick is also responsible for tick paralysis, which appears to be due to a poisonous salivary secretion (toxin) injected by the tick, and which may prove fatal to children. Another disease known to be transmitted by ticks as well as by certain insects (Fig. 160) is rabbit fever, or tularemia. Relapsing fever, characterized by alternating periods of fever and normal temperatures, occurs in various parts of the world, including Texas, Kansas, Montana, Utah, and California. Apparently a different species of tick of the genus *Ornithodoros* transmits the disease germs (spirochetes) in each locality. Texas fever in cattle is transmitted from diseased animals to healthy ones by the cattle tick (*Boophilus*) (Fig. 167) which passes the infective agent (sporozoan) to her offspring through the egg. Among the continents of the world, Africa is especially burdened with more than its share of different kinds of ticks.

CLASSIFICATION OF THE ARACHNOIDEA

(For reference purposes only)

Class Arachnoidea. No antennae; no true mandibles; body usually of 2 divisions, cephalothorax and abdomen; 6 pairs of appendages on cephalothorax; first pair of appendages are nippers, termed chelicerae; 1 pair of pedipalpi variously modified; and 4 pairs of legs.

Order 1. **Xiphosura** (Gr. *xiphos*, sword; *oura*, tail). King or horseshoe crabs (Fig. 166). Crablike; cephalothorax horseshoe-shaped; tail or telson long and spikelike. Ex. *Limulus polyphemus* (formerly *Xiphosura*).

Subclass 1. **Arachnida** (Gr. *arachne*, spider). Spiders, scorpions, mites, etc. No antennae; no true mandibles; first pair of appendages are chelicerae; cephalothorax and abdomen usually evident.

Order 1. **Scorpionida** (L. *scorpio*, scorpion). Scorpions (Fig. 166). Elongated; long abdomen of 13 segments; sting at end of tail. Ex. *Centruroides * gertsch*, Arizona.

Order 2. **Pedipalpi** (L. *pes*, foot; *palpo*, touch gently). Whip scorpions, etc. (Fig. 161). Pedipalps thick and strong; first pair walking legs with many-jointed tactile flagellum. Ex. *Mastigoproctus giganteus*, the garoon.

Order 3. **Araneae.** Spiders (Fig. 164). Cephalothorax distinct; abdomen usually unsegmented; cephalothorax and abdomen joined by a narrow waist; chelicerae small, a poison duct in the terminal fang; book lungs, some with tracheae; spinnerets on abdomen; chiefly terrestrial. Some of the common families are as follows:

1. Theraphosidae. Tarantulas. Large, hairy, hunting spiders, with 2 pairs of lungs, confined to the warmer regions of the globe, and hiding in holes in the ground or in crevices on tree trunks, etc. Sometimes brought to northern cities on bunches of bananas. Ex. *Dugesiella hentzi* of our south and southwest.

2. Ctenizidae. Trap-door spiders. Moderately large spiders with 2 pairs of lungs and with stout strong legs. They live in under-

* Formerly called *Centrurus*.

ground tunnels lined with silk and fitted with trap doors. Ex. *Pachylomerides audouini* of our south, and *Bothriocyrtum californicum* of the west coast.

3. Dictynidae. Hackled-band weavers. These spiders possess an accessory spinning organ, the cribellum (Fig. 163). The special silk emitted from this organ is combed out by the calamistrum of the fourth metatarsus. The irregular webs are constructed among plants or under debris. Ex. *Dictyna muraria* of wide distribution.

4. Pholcidae. Long-legged spiders. Most of these are pale, small-bodied, weak-jawed, long-legged spiders, which shun the light. Their irregular webs are built in basements and similar situations. Ex. *Pholcus phalangioides* of wide distribution.

5. Theridiidae. Comb-footed spiders. A very large family of spiders, most of whose members are small in size. The fourth tarsus is provided with a row of serrated bristles forming a comb, used for flinging a very viscid silk which swathes the prey captured in their irregular webs. Ex. *Theridion tepidariorum* (Fig. 164), the cosmopolitan and common house spider which builds cobwebs in the corners of rooms. *Latrodectus mactans* (Fig. 168), the black widow, which is found in most of North and South America, but commonest in the warmer regions.

6. Linyphiidae. Sheet-web weavers. Small spiders which build webs usually provided with a more or less horizontal or curved sheet from the under surface of which they suspend themselves upside down. Many build among plants, but large numbers are found among the dead leaves and other litter close to the forest ground. They are more abundant in temperate and arctic regions than in subtropical and warmer zones. Ex. *Linyphia marginata*, the filmy dome spider.

7. Araneidae. Orb weavers. A very large family of spiders, the members of which, if they build a web at all, construct a cartwheel-like structure known to all who have walked through the woods in late summer. While the foundation and radii lines are not sticky, the spiral thread is quite viscid and serves to snare the prey. The spiders have strong jaws and are usually beautifully marked. Ex. *Argiope aurantia* (Fig. 161), the black and orange garden spider, which builds its web in grass and among bushes exposed to sunlight, and in the hub of which it stands head down.

8. Agelenidae. Funnel-web weavers. These spiders build a more or less horizontal sheet web, over which they run in an upright position, and at one side of which they hide in a cone-shaped retreat. The threads are not sticky, and the spider does not swathe the prey, but depends upon lightning speed to run out and seize in its jaws any insect that happens to touch the threads. Ex. *Agelenopsis naevia*, which builds its web most commonly in grass, but also among shrubbery and stone fences.

9. Pisauridae. Nursery-web weavers. Most of these are large spiders which build no snares, but hunt their prey along water courses, in grassy areas, and forests. The large spherical egg sac is carried about by the mother under her sternum. Shortly before the emergence of the progeny, most species fasten the sac among some leaves and construct a nursery web around it, standing guard until the spiderlings emerge. Ex. *Pisaurina mira*.

10. Lycosidae. Wolf spiders. These are medium to very large spiders, with keen eyesight, strong legs, and powerful jaws. They run about actively, both day and night, hunting their prey. Some hide in natural cavities in the ground, others construct vertical burrows somewhat like those of the trap-door spiders. The males of many species go through elaborate courtship dances before the females. Ex. *Lycosa carolinensis*, our largest species.

11. Gnaphosidae. Ground spiders. The majority of these are medium-sized and run very rapidly over the ground, usually hiding under stones and logs. They build no snares, but may construct retreats in which they hide and in which the egg sac is fastened.

12. Thomisidae. Crab spiders. These spiders walk sidewise as readily as forward or backward, and many have short stocky bodies. While most are dark-colored and live on

bark, or among dead leaves on the ground, a few are conspicuously light-colored and frequent flowers. To some extent they can change from yellow to white, or vice versa, according to the color of the flower on which they wait to seize insects with their powerful front legs. Ex. *Misumena vatia* (Fig. 164).

13. Salticidae. Jumping spiders. These sun-loving spiders are more abundant in the tropics than in temperate regions. They have the largest eyes, the keenest vision, and are among the most beautifully adorned of all spiders. They build no snares, but stalk and pounce upon their prey, hunting only in daylight. There is much sexual dimorphism, and males perform elaborate courtship dances before the much duller-hued females. Ex. *Salticus scenicus* (Fig. 164), common on fences and the outside of buildings.

Order 4. **Palpigrada** (L. *palpo*, touch gently; *gradior*, walk). Palpigrada (Fig. 161). Minute; abdomen segmented; long caudal filament with bristles; 1 family. Ex. *Koenenia wheeleri*, Texas.

Order 5. **Pseudoscorpionida** (Gr. *pseudes*, false). Pseudoscorpions (Fig. 161). Small; flattened pedipalps scorpionlike. Ex. *Chelifer cancroides*, house scorpion.

Order 6. **Solpugida** (L. *solifuga*, sun-fleeing). Solpugids (Fig. 161). Head and thorax distinct; large chelate chelicerae; respiration by tracheae. Ex. *Eremobates pallipes*, southern states west of Mississippi.

Order 7. **Phalangida** (Gr. *phalangion*, long-legged spider). Harvestmen or daddy longlegs (Fig. 161). Body short and ovoid; cephalothorax unsegmented; abdomen segmented; pedipalps long and leglike; legs usually very long and slender. Ex. *Liobunum vittatum*.

Order 8. **Acarina** (Gr. *akares*, mite). Ticks and mites (Fig. 167). Small; body short and thick; cephalothorax and abdomen fused; abdomen unsegmented; larva with 3 pairs of legs, adult with 4 pairs; free-living or parasitic; world-wide. Some of the principal families are as follows:

1. Argasidae. Soft ticks. Ex. *Ornithodoros moubata*: vector of relapsing fever in man.
2. Ixodidae. Hard ticks. Ex. *Boophilus annulatus*: vector of Texas fever in cattle.
3. Eriophyidae. Gall mites. Ex. *Phyllocoptes pyri*: Pear-leaf blister mite.
4. Demodecidae. Skin mites. Ex. *Demodex folliculorum*: human face mite.
5. Dermanyssidae. Chicken mites and others. Ex. *Dermanyssus gallinae*: chicken mite.
6. Sarcoptidae. Itch mites. Ex. *Sarcoptes scabiei*: human 7-year itch mite.
7. Trombidiidae. Harvest mites and chiggers. Ex. *Eutrombicula alfreddugesi*: North American chigger mite or red bug.
8. Tetrarhynchidae. Red spiders. Ex. *Tetrarhynchus telarius*: red spider.
9. Hydrachnidae. Fresh-water mites. Ex. *Hydrachna geographica*: parasitic on aquatic insects.

Subclass 2. **Pycnogonida** (Gr. *pyknos*, thick; *gony*, joint). Sea spiders (Fig. 161). Marine; body small; legs very long; abdomen rudimentary. Ex. *Pycnogonum littorale*: sea spider.

Subclass 3. **Tardigrada** (L. *tardus*, slow; *gradior*, walk). Water bears (Fig. 161). Microscopic; usually aquatic; body cylindrical, unsegmented; 4 pairs of clawed legs; respiratory, excretory, and circulatory organs absent. Ex. *Macrobiotus hufelandi*: fresh-water water bear.

Subclass 4. **Pentastomida** (Gr. *pente*, five; *stoma*, mouth). Wormlike arachnids (Fig. 161). Parasitic; body long and ringed but not segmented; respiratory, excretory, and circulatory organs absent. Ex. *Linguatula serrata*: a parasite of mammals.

SELECTED COLLATERAL READINGS

Baker, E.W., and Wharton, G.W. *Introduction to Acarology*. Macmillan, New York, 1952.

Comstock, J.H., and Gertsch, W.J. *The Spider Book*. Doubleday, New York, 1940.

Emans, E.V. *About Spiders*. Dutton, New York, 1940.

Fabre, J.H. *The Life of the Spider*. Dodd Mead, New York, 1919.

Gertsch, W.J. *American Spiders*. Van Nostrand, New York, 1949.

Kaston, B.J., and Kaston, E. *How to Know the Spiders*. W. C. Brown, Dubuque, Iowa, 1953.

Savory, T.H. *The Biology of Spiders*. Sidgwick and Jackson, London, 1928.

CHAPTER 20

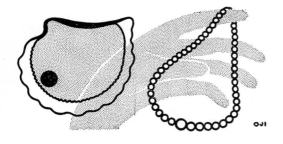

Phylum Mollusca. Snails, Squids, Octopuses, and Others

The soft-bodied animals, which comprise the phylum Mollusca, include the snails, slugs, clams, mussels, oysters, octopuses, and squids (Fig. 170). Most of them are bilaterally symmetrical; and, with the exception of one class, are unsegmented. Many possess shells of calcium carbonate. At first sight, mussels, clams, snails, and squids do not appear to have much in common, but closer examination reveals several structures which are possessed by all. One of these is an organ called the **foot,** which in the snail is usually used for creeping over surfaces; in the clam, generally, for plowing through the mud; and in the squid for seizing prey. In each there is a space called the **mantle cavity** between the main body and an enclosing envelope, the **mantle.** The anus opens into the mantle cavity.

Mollusks are among the most abundant of all animals and may be found on land, in fresh water, and in the sea. Many of the 90,000 species of this phylum are of economic importance. They serve as food for man—oysters, clams, and scallops; they provide material for making pearl buttons; and they produce pearls. Some species are injurious. Although the various types of mollusks differ widely in appearance and structure, they can be reduced to a single plan (Fig. 171). The varied activities of the different types indicate how well they are adapted to their environments both morphologically and physiologically. The larvae of all mollusks, except the cephalopods, are particularly interesting because they pass through trochophore and veliger stages, which suggests that they are related to the annelids and certain other phyla.

The mollusks are divided into 6 classes, according to symmetry and the character of the foot, shell, mantle, gills, muscles, radula, and nervous system. The mollusks follow the arthropods in this discussion, not because they are more complex or because they belong in this position, but for convenience. They could just as well come before the arthropods.

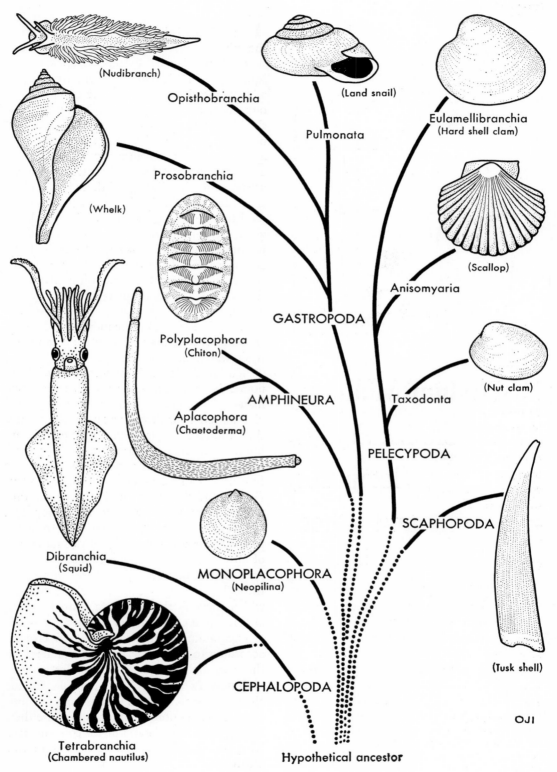

(Nudibranch)

Opisthobranchia

(Land snail)

Pulmonata

Eulamellibranchia
(Hard shell clam)

Prosobranchia

(Whelk)

(Scallop)

GASTROPODA

Anisomyaria

Polyplacophora
(Chiton)

AMPHINEURA

(Nut clam)

Aplacophora
(Chaetoderma)

Taxodonta

PELECYPODA

Dibranchia
(Squid)

SCAPHOPODA

MONOPLACOPHORA
(Neopilina)

Tetrabranchia
(Chambered nautilus)

CEPHALOPODA

(Tusk shell)

OJI

Hypothetical ancestor

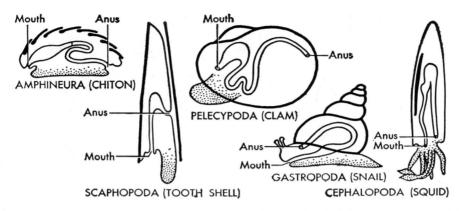

Mouth Anus
AMPHINEURA (CHITON)

Mouth
Anus
PELECYPODA (CLAM)

Anus
Mouth
SCAPHOPODA (TOOTH SHELL)

Anus
Mouth
GASTROPODA (SNAIL)

Anus
Mouth
CEPHALOPODA (SQUID)

FIGURE 171. Modifications in the molluscan body plan as illustrated by representatives of the 5 classes. Note how the shell (heavy lines), the foot (stippled), and the digestive tract vary in position in the different groups. (After *Animals Without Backbones*, by Ralph Buchsbaum. Second edition. Copyright 1948 by University of Chicago Press.)

ANODONTA—A FRESH-WATER CLAM

Clams usually lie partly buried in the muddy or sandy bottoms of lakes or streams. They burrow and move from place to place by means of the **foot** (Fig. 172), which can be extended from the anterior end of the **shell**. Water, loaded with oxygen and food material, is drawn in through a slitlike opening at the posterior end, called the **ventral** or **incurrent siphon**; and excretory substances and feces, along with deoxygenated water, are carried out through a smaller **dorsal** or **excurrent siphon**.

Shell

The shell consists of two parts called **valves**. Concentric ridges called **lines of growth** appear on the outside of each valve; these represent the intervals of rest between successive periods of growth, the annual lines being more conspicuous. The **umbo** is

FIGURE 170. *Facing page,* representative mollusks. The lines suggest possible relationships. The figures are not drawn to scale. (Based on a diagram by William J. Clench and Ruth D. Turner, Museum of Comparative Zoology, Harvard University. Made expressly for this book.)

the first part of the shell to develop and is produced in the late veliger stage; it is usually corroded by the carbonic and humic acids in water.

The outer epithelium of the mantle secretes the shell, which consists of three layers (Fig. 173): (1) an outer, thin, horny layer, the **periostracum** which serves to protect the underlying layers from the acids in the water and gives the exterior of the shell most of its color; (2) a middle portion of crystals of lime (calcium carbonate) called the **prismatic layer;** and (3) an inner **nacreous layer** (mother-of-pearl), which is made up of many horizontal layers of calcium carbonate, and produces an iridescent sheen.

Anatomy and physiology

The valves of the shell are held together by two large transverse **muscles** called **anterior** and **posterior adductors,** and a dorsal, ligamentous, elastic tissue hinge (Fig. 172). The two folds of the dorsal wall of the clam which line the valves are called the **mantle.** The space between the mantle flaps, containing the two pairs of gill plates, the foot, and the visceral mass is called the **mantle cavity.**

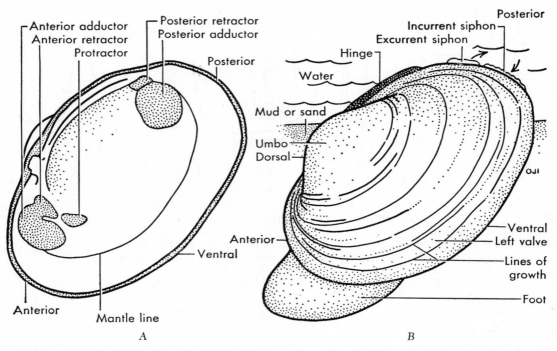

FIGURE 172. Fresh-water clam. A, inside view of a valve showing point of attachment of mantle and points of attachment of muscles. B, external view of a living animal with foot protruding from the shell and arrows showing direction of water flow through the siphons.

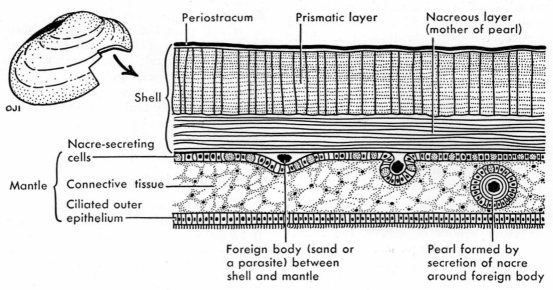

FIGURE 173. Enlarged cross section of the shell and mantle of a fresh-water clam. Note the pearl being formed between the shell and mantle by the nacre-secreting cells.

284

Digestion

Food is brought into the mantle cavity (Fig. 174) of the clam by the water circulating inward through the ventral incurrent siphon. Water containing suspended minute plants, animals, and debris passes over the gills, and the small suspended food particles adhere to the mucus which covers the gills. The smaller particles now caught in the mucus are carried by the beating cilia of the gills to the ventral edge, where this mass of material is transferred to the **labial palps.** These flaps of tissue which surround the mouth serve as a sorting mechanism that selects the materials to be utilized. These food materials are then carried into a deep groove between the labial palps and thence directly into the mouth. The food passes from the mouth through the short **esophagus** into the bulbous **stomach,** which is connected by ducts with a large **digestive gland** ("liver"). This gland surrounds the stomach and is the chief source of digestive enzymes. The **intestine** is given off from the ventral side of the stomach, descending into the visceral mass, where it makes a loop. Then it ascends parallel to its first portion and turns sharply backward and out of the visceral mass, through the pericardium and through the heart itself, where it becomes the **rectum.** It finally ends at the **anus** which opens near the excurrent siphon, and the feces are carried away in the outgoing current of water.

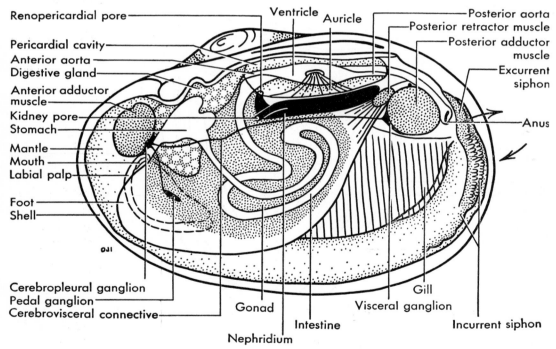

Figure 174. The internal anatomy of a fresh-water clam in the right valve as viewed from the left side.

The details of digestion in fresh-water clams are not very well known. However, as is true in most animals that eat fine particles of food, digestion appears to be partly intracellular.

Amoeboid cells are present throughout the digestive tract. From microscopic examinations, it is believed that such cells pass through the wall of the tract, engulf food particles, and digest it; then leave the intestine and return to the tissue spaces. The large digestive gland produces a digestive secretion containing the enzyme amylase; this secretion passes through ducts that empty into the stomach.

In one family (Unionidae) of the fresh-water clams, there is a carbohydrate-digesting enzyme set free in the stomach by dissolution of a gelatinous rod (crystalline style) which lies in a pouch off the intestine and projects into the stomach.

Circulation

The circulatory system consists of a dorsal heart, blood vessels, and spaces called sinuses. The **heart** lies in the **pericardium** (Fig. 175). The **ventricle** drives the blood forward through the **anterior aorta** and backward through the **posterior aorta**. Part of the blood passes into the mantle, where it is oxygenated, and then returns directly to the heart. The rest of the blood circulates through numerous spaces in the body and is finally collected by a vein, which lies just beneath the pericardium. From here the blood passes into the kidneys, then into the **gills**, and finally through the **auricles** into the ventricle. Nutriment and oxygen are carried by the blood to all parts of the body, and carbon dioxide is disposed of in the

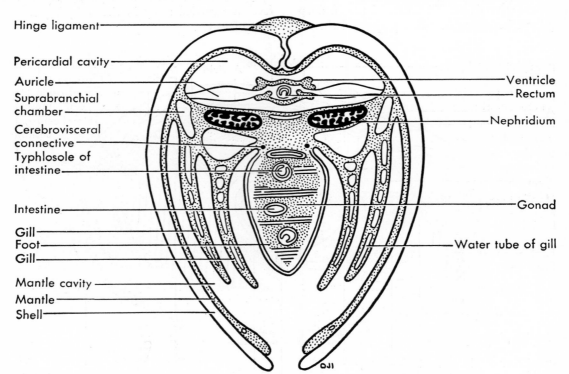

Hinge ligament
Pericardial cavity
Auricle
Suprabranchial chamber
Cerebrovisceral connective
Typhlosole of intestine
Intestine
Gill
Foot
Gill
Mantle cavity
Mantle
Shell
Ventricle
Rectum
Nephridium
Gonad
Water tube of gill

FIGURE 175. Cross-section of a fresh-water clam through the region of the heart.

mantle and gills; other waste products of metabolism are transported to the kidneys.

Respiration and excretion

Although the entire body surface is in contact with water and doubtless functions in respiration, the greater part of the oxygen–carbon dioxide exchange occurs in the gills and mantle. A pair of gills hang down into the mantle cavity on either side of the foot (Fig. 175). Each gill consists of two plates or **lamellae** made up of a large number of vertical **gill filaments** (Fig. 176), strengthened by chitinous rods and connected to one another by horizontal bars. Cross or **interlamellar partitions** between the two lamellae divide the gill into many vertical **water tubes.** Dorsally, the water tubes of each gill join a common **suprabranchial chamber.** The gills function in respiration by water circulating through their interiors. It enters through the incurrent siphon and flows over the gills. On the surfaces of the gills there are many microscopic openings, **water pores,** through which the water is driven by ciliary action into the water tubes. The water then passes dorsally in the water tubes to the suprabranchial chambers and along them to the excurrent siphon. Exchange of respiratory gases takes place

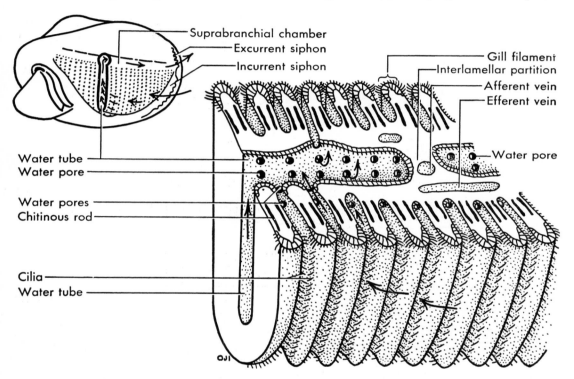

FIGURE 176. Respiratory system of a fresh-water clam. *Left,* a whole gill. *Right,* horizontal section through a gill showing arrangement of gill filaments, blood vessels, and water tubes. Arrow shows direction of water currents.

through the walls of blood spaces located in the partitions of the water tubes.

The two **kidneys (nephridia)** lie just beneath the pericardial cavity. Each nephridium is folded upon itself and differentiated into glandular (dark spongy mass) and bladderlike portions. The structure and relationships are such that one end of the nephridium opens into the pericardial cavity and the other end (external) opens into a suprabranchial chamber. Liquid wastes within the pericardial cavity may enter the tubule; or metabolic wastes carried by the circulating blood may be removed by the cells in the glandular portion of the nephridium.

Nervous system and sense organs

Three pairs of ganglia are present (Fig. 174): **cerebropleural ganglia, pedal ganglia,** and **visceral ganglia.** The sensory structures include **light receptors** in the siphon margins; a small vesicle (**statocyst**) containing a calcareous concretion (**statolith**) lies a short way behind the pedal ganglion; it is an **organ of equilibrium.** A thick patch of yellow epithelial cells (**osphradium**) covers each visceral ganglion. The osphradia are thought by most writers to be useful in detecting foreign materials in water. The edges of the mantle are provided with **sensory cells,** probably sensitive to contact and light.

Reproduction

Clams are usually either male or female; a few are hermaphroditic. The reproductive organs are situated in the visceral mass (Fig. 174). Some clams have interesting life

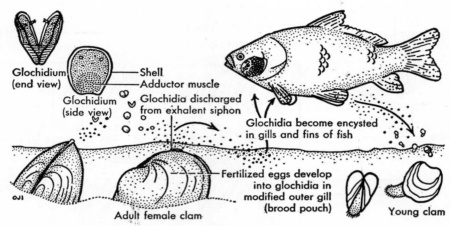

FIGURE 177. Life cycle of a fresh-water clam. The larval clam or glochidium passes out of the excurrent siphon of a female, attaches itself to the gills of a fish; finally, the glochidium drops from the fish host to take up a free-living existence as a young clam.

histories in which the young stage is parasitic on fish (Fig. 177). The eggs develop into a peculiar larva known as a **glochidium,** a modified veliger (Fig. 177). In *Anodonta* the eggs are usually fertilized in August, and the glochidia which develop from them remain in the gills of the mother all winter. In the following spring they are discharged; and, if they chance to come in contact with the external parts of a fish, this contact stimulus causes them to seize hold of it by closing the valves of their shells. The skin of the fish grows around them, forming "worms" or "blackheads." After a parasitic life within the tissues of the fish, from three to many weeks, the young clam is liberated and takes up a free existence. As a result of this parasitic habit, clams are widely dispersed by the migrations of the fish.

OTHER MOLLUSKS

General characteristics of mollusks

The bodies of mollusks are soft and generally covered by a moist integument. They are therefore fitted for life in water or in moist places. The **mantle** is a fold of the body wall which secretes the **shell.** If there are two lobes, a bivalve shell is produced as in the mussel. If only one lobe is present, a univalve shell is formed as in snails. A modified **coelom** is usually recognizable in the adult as the pericardial cavity and the cavities of the reproductive organs.

Mollusks eat both vegetable and animal food. **Jaws** are present in most gastropods and all cephalopods. A rasping organ, the

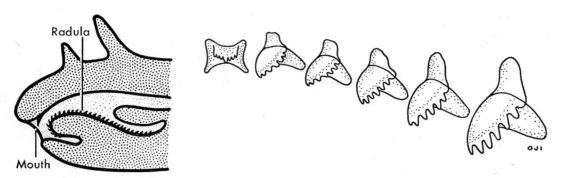

FIGURE 178. *Radula of a gastropod. Left,* diagram of longitudinal section through anterior end of a snail. *Right,* dorsal view of a few teeth from radula of a snail; the one on extreme left is a central tooth. The radula is pressed against food and moved rapidly back and forth, rasping off small particles.

radula (Fig. 178), exists usually in the mouth cavity or pharynx of all mollusks, except the bivalves; it consists of rows of chitinous teeth which tear up the food by being drawn across it. **Respiration** takes place primarily in the gills and in the mantle. Most fresh-water and land snails (pulmonate gastropods) take air into the vascularized mantle cavity, which thus serves the purpose of a lung; or, they breathe cutaneously.

The **sexes** are usually separate, though certain groups are hermaphroditic. The number of **eggs** that develop in some mollusks is very great; for example, nearly 500 million in the oyster in a single season. In all such cases, the eggs when laid are subjected to the dangers of the ocean currents and numerous enemies. They also pass through a metamorphosis after hatching. Other mollusks lay very few eggs, for example, *Lymnaea*, 20 to 100 and *Mesodon*, 40 to 100.

The **development** of the eggs of most mollusks includes a **trochophore larval stage** (Fig. 179), which later develops into a **veliger larva**, so called because of the presence of a band of cilia, the **velum**, in front of the mouth. The velum is an organ of locomotion and is somewhat responsible for the dispersion of the species. However, the major factor in the dispersal of most marine bivalves is oceanic currents. Con-

siderable importance is attached to the presence of a trochophore in the developmental history of certain mollusks, and many embryologists are inclined to consider this stage an indication of the ancestral condition. According to this view, the mollusks and annelids, which pass through a trochophore stage in their ontogeny, have been derived from a common ancestor.

A newly found, primitive, deep-sea mollusk

The Danish "Galatheae Expedition" dredging off the west coast of Costa Rica (9°23′N., 89°32′W.) found among the many animals collected some extraordinary unidentified deep-sea mollusks. The 10 living specimens were dredged up from a depth of about 11,778 feet, or a little over two miles. This new limpet-like mollusk was reported by H. Lemche in February, 1957. Many zoologists regard the finding of *Neopilina galatheae* as a far more important discovery than that of the living coelacanth, found a few years ago off the coast of Africa.

Neopilina is a living representative of the class Monoplacophora. The class name was originally proposed to cover a group of extinct primitive paleozoic mollusks. Now it includes a living mollusk, which is radically different from all other mollusks in that it

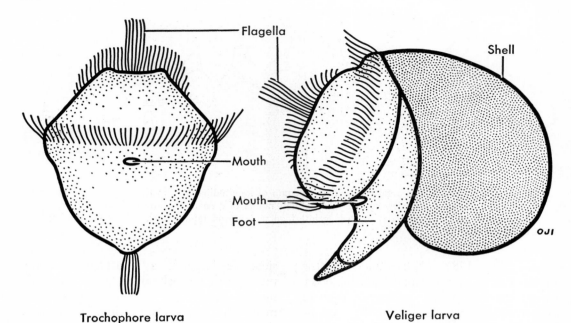

Trochophore larva   **Veliger larva**

FIGURE 179. Two stages in the development of a mollusk; both are free-swimming larvae. Both annelids and mollusks have a trochophore larval stage, and many zoologists interpret this to mean that both groups of animals have developed from a common ancestor (Fig. 107).

is internally segmented and not quite bilaterally symmetrical. The segmentation violates one of the general criteria by which mollusks are most readily known, that of an unsegmented body plan. *Neopilina* (no common name) is the generic name of this new mollusk.

The new mollusk has a single shell, and several pairs of internal organs, such as auricles, excretory organs, and nephridia— all evidences of internal segmentation. There may still be other internal organs which are segmented, but further study of the internal anatomy will be necessary to determine this. There are 5 pairs of strong double muscles on the inner surface of the shell, and the animal has 5 pairs of gills (Fig. 180). It possesses a well-developed radula.

Neopilina apparently belongs to a very ancient stock. Its early fossil ancestors are already known, and further study should throw additional light on our knowledge of molluscan evolution.

Chitons

The **coat-of-mail shells** (Fig. 170) are protected by a shell of 8 transverse plates, which are arched above and overlapping like shingles on a roof. These plates are not evidence of metamerism. When detached from the rocks to which they cling, chitons roll up like an armadillo, with the soft parts practically covered by the hard shell. They live on rocky seashores mostly in water less than 25 fathoms in depth and cling tightly to the rocks by means of the suction of the foot.

Gastropods

Gastropods (Figs. 181 and 182) live in fresh or salt water and on land. A few are parasitic on other animals. Land snails must protect themselves from drying at certain seasons; they retire into their shell as far as possible and secrete a parchmentlike wall (epiphragm) across the opening, which pre-

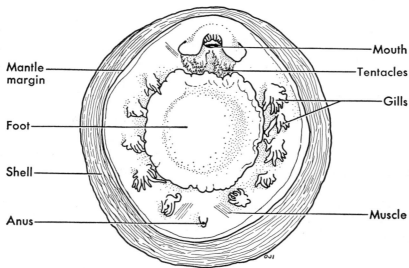

FIGURE 180. *Top,* photograph of a segmented mollusk, *Neopilina galatheae,* a newly found primitive mollusk which represents a class that probably existed about 450,000,000 years ago; it is truly a "living fossil." The largest specimen collected measured about 37 mm. in length, 33 mm. in width, and 14 mm. in height. (Photo courtesy of Henning Lemche, Zoological Museum, University of Copenhagen, who published the first report on Neopilina.) *Bottom,* drawing from a sketch by Henning Lemche of the most primitive mollusk.

vents evaporation. **Locomotion** in snails is very interesting. **A slime gland** at the forward end of the foot deposits a film of mucus on which the snail moves by means of wavelike contractions of the foot muscles. It thus lays its own pavement ahead of itself, which is always the same, whether the path is rough or smooth, uphill or downhill. Progress is therefore always about the same; it may be two inches per minute, 10 feet per hour, and 240 feet per day, provided the animal keeps going continuously.

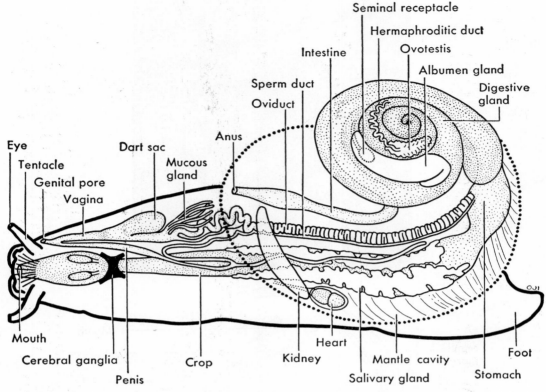

FIGURE 181.   Internal structure of a snail; dorsal view.

Fresh-water snails are numerous in creeks and pools. Snail shells may coil in two directions—clockwise or counterclockwise. These are distinguished by the terms **dextral** and **sinistral**. The type of coiling can be determined by holding the shell with the aperture toward the observer: if the opening is on the right as in *Busycon canaliculatum* (Fig. 182), then it is dextral, but if on the left, then it is sinistral. The difference is the same as that between a "right-handed" and a "left-handed" screw. Some fresh-water snails possess **gills** with which they breathe under water, others are pulmonates and have a **lung cavity** so that they must come to the surface from time to time for air when the water is warm, otherwise cutaneous respiration may be adequate. Many gastropods—land, fresh-water, and marine—serve as intermediate hosts for blood and liver flukes.

Land slugs (pulmonates) are closely related to the land snails, but are completely naked. To keep from drying up, slugs must live in a moist place such as is afforded under boards and stones and in holes in the ground. At night they feed on vegetation. Some **sea slugs** (nudibranchs) live among seaweeds, which they may resemble so closely that it is practically impossible to see them, while others are quite conspicuous.

Whelks and **periwinkles** are among the commonest of the smaller marine snails. The largest marine snail in America is the **queen conch** which lives in the Atlantic, being especially common along the shores of the Florida Keys and the West Indies. The shell may be a foot long and weigh 5 pounds. Also called a conch is the **channel shell** which hermit crabs find very satisfactory as a place in which to live. The spiral characteristic of the snail shell is absent

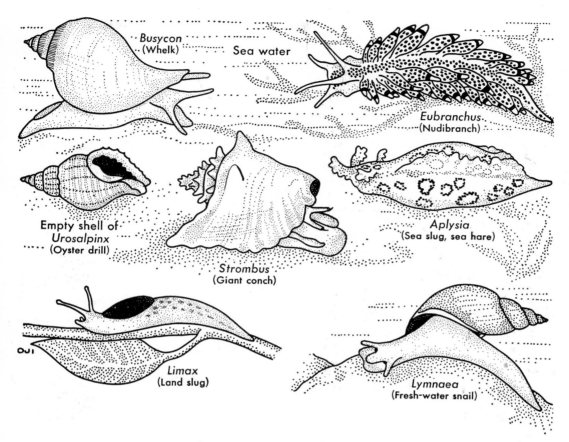

Busycon
(Whelk)

Sea water

Eubranchus.
(Nudibranch)

Empty shell of
Urosalpinx
(Oyster drill)

Aplysia
(Sea slug, sea hare)

Strombus
(Giant conch)

Limax
(Land slug)

Lymnaea
(Fresh-water snail)

FIGURE 182. Representative gastropods.

from that of the **limpet,** and what is left is a rather high-arched disk. Limpets cling tenaciously to rocks. The sea butterflies or wing-footed mollusks (**pteropods**) spend their lives near the surface of the open sea. They live in vast schools, sometimes covering the sea for many miles. Whales feed on them to such an extent that they are known as "whale food."

Squids, octopuses, and other cephalopods

The cephalopods are the most highly developed class of mollusks.

A common squid along the eastern coast of North America from Maine to South Carolina is known as *Loligo pealii* (Fig. 183). The **foot** of this species consists of

10 **arms** bearing suckers, and a **funnel** (**siphon**). The arms are used for capturing prey. The funnel is the principal steering and locomotor organ; if it is directed forward, the jets of water forced through it propel the animal backward; if directed backward, the animal is propelled forward. Thus the jet propulsion principle was old in nature before it was applied to the powering of airplanes. The mantle in the posterior region is extended into triangular **fins** which may propel the squid slowly forward or backward by undulatory movements.

The **pen (shell)** of this squid is a feather-shaped plate concealed beneath the skin of the back (anterior surface). The true **head** is the short region between the arms and the **mantle collar**; it contains two large eyes. The **digestive system** includes a muscular

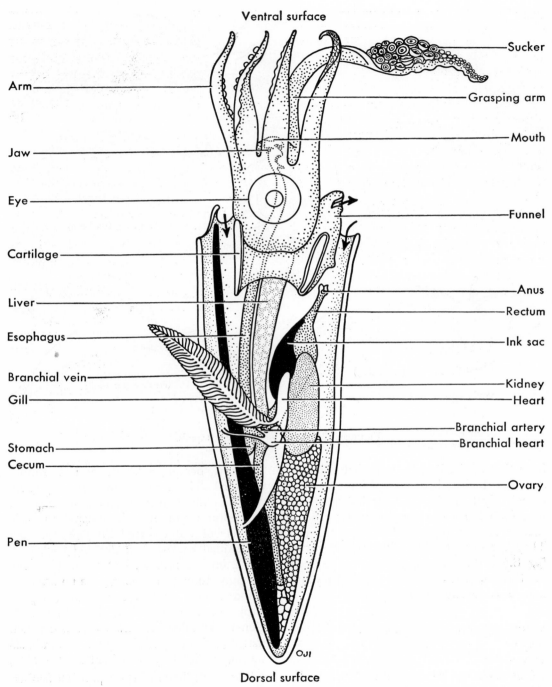

Ventral surface

Arm

Jaw

Eye

Cartilage

Liver

Esophagus

Branchial vein

Gill

Stomach

Cecum

Pen

Sucker

Grasping arm

Mouth

Funnel

Anus

Rectum

Ink sac

Kidney

Heart

Branchial artery

Branchial heart

Ovary

Dorsal surface

FIGURE 183. Internal structure of a squid as seen with body wall and arms removed from right side.

pharynx (buccal mass), **esophagus, salivary glands, stomach, cecum, intestine, rectum, liver,** and a small "**pancreas.**" There are two powerful horny **jaws** in the pharynx, and a **radula** is also present. Above the rectum is the **ink sac,** with a duct which opens near the anus; this is a protective adaptation. When the squid is attacked, it emits a cloud of inky fluid through the funnel to provide what had been thought to be a "smoke screen" for its escape. However, recent studies show that the squid does not eject a large cloud cover of ink as has been supposed; it discharges just enough ink to color a volume of water its own size. An enemy in pursuit often mistakes the ink for the squid; meanwhile the squid escapes.

The blood of the squid is contained in a double, closed, vascular system. Two **gills** and two **nephridia** are present. The **nervous system** consists of a number of ganglia, mostly in the head. The **sensory organs** are two very highly developed **eyes,** two **statocysts,** and probably two **olfactory organs.** The eyes are large, and, superficially, somewhat similar to those of vertebrates (Figs. 184 and 397).

In squids the sexes are separate.

Squids are especially famous for their color changes. Pigment cells filled with blue, purple, red, and yellow color are present in the skin; and when these become larger or smaller, the color changes rapidly as though the animal were blushing. These chameleon-like changes in color harmonize with the color of the background, resulting in partial concealment of the animal.

Near the coast of Newfoundland, **giant**

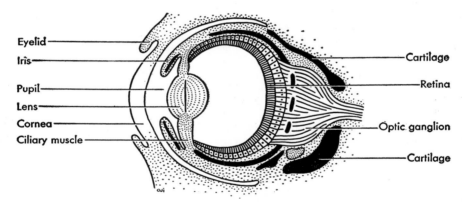

Eyelid — Iris — Pupil — Lens — Cornea — Ciliary muscle — Cartilage — Retina — Optic ganglion — Cartilage

FIGURE 184. Diagram of a section through the eye of a squid. This eye is constructed on the same principle as a camera, which consists of a dark chamber to which light is admitted only through an opening (pupil) in the diaphragm (iris). Behind this opening is a lens which focuses the light on the retina. It can form real images, as does the eye of the vertebrate, but differs from the vertebrate eye in that light is received directly on the visual part of the retina without having to traverse nerves and cell bodies before it strikes the light receptors as in the vertebrate eye.

squids are occasionally encountered. These may be 50 feet or more in total length, with arms as large as a man's legs, and suckers as big as teacups. Probably certain sea serpent stories are founded on the sudden and unexpected appearance of these monsters. The giant squid is the largest living invertebrate animal known.

The **cuttlefish** has a short oval body bordered by fins that are usually united behind and possesses arms, two of which are much longer than the others. Its internal calcareous shell is the cuttlebone used as a bill sharpener for caged birds. Its ink has provided the sepia pigment used by artists for hundreds of years.

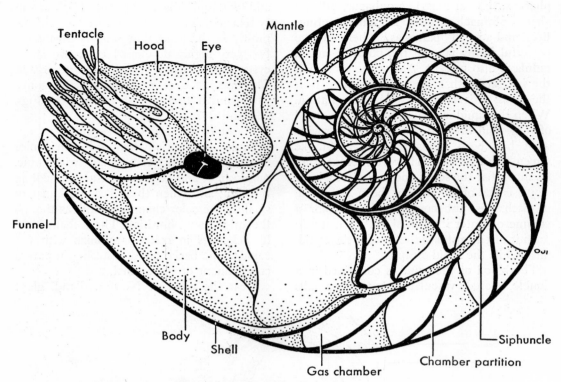

Tentacle   Hood   Eye   Mantle

Funnel

Body   Shell   Gas chamber   Chamber partition   Siphuncle

FIGURE 185. Chambered (pearly) nautilus with shell cut away to the midline to show the animal and the many gas-filled chambers in which it lived at successive stages in its growth. The siphuncle is a limy tube that encloses a cord of living tissue which extends from the last chamber to the first one formed. It lives in the south Pacific Ocean. Natural size up to 10 inches in diameter.

The **chambered nautilus** (Fig. 185) was immortalized by Oliver Wendell Holmes in his great poem, "The Chambered Nautilus," in which he called it "the ship of pearl." It has a shell that is coiled like a watch spring and is divided by cross walls into a series of compartments. A new and larger chamber is built when the old compartment is outgrown, and a new wall is secreted behind it. The head bears 60 to 90 tentacles without suckers.

Octopuses (devilfishes) (Fig. 186) live in dark crevices and in coral reefs. Most of them are not large enough to harm a human being, but the **giant octopus** of the Pacific reaches a diameter of about 30 feet and can be dangerous. These are feared by pearl divers.

Bivalve mollusks

Bivalves (Fig. 172) may live in fresh water or in the sea. More than 500 species of **fresh-water clams** live in the United States and many species of **oysters** have also been described. Adult oysters are unable to move about, being attached by the left valve to some solid object. Oysters feed in much the way fresh-water clams do. A single oyster may deposit approximately a half billion eggs in one season; these develop in

FIGURE 186. The common octopus is a cephalopod without a shell. It pulls itself over the rocks with its arms or it can move by expelling water from its funnel. The sucker-bearing arms are used to seize the animals on which it feeds. (Courtesy of D.P. Wilson, Plymouth, England.)

the oyster's gills into little ciliated spheres, called **spat.**

Pearls are sometimes found in our edible oysters, but these are not nacreous, and therefore of little value. The most valuable pearls come from pearl oysters, which are not closely related to the edible oyster. The pearl is the result of an injury to the mollusk caused by either an organism or a foreign particle which embeds itself in the fleshy part of the bivalve and causes an irritation. The irritation stimulates the animal to deposit layer upon layer of nacre around the intruding body to form the pearl; the amount of deposition is in direct proportion to the degree of irritation. The Japanese produce artificial pearls by inserting a foreign body into the mantle of the bivalves which are kept in cages until pearls are produced. The mollusk requires from 3 to 4 years to form a pearl of considerable size and 7 years to

form a large one. Because the inner layer of the shell is composed of the same nacreous substance as the pearl, it is called mother-of-pearl.

ORIGIN AND RELATIONS OF THE MOLLUSCA

The Monoplacophora appear to be the most primitive class of mollusks and have changed the least from the ancestral condition. The gastropods have changed to a short creeping type, with a spiral visceral hump revolved through an angle of 180°. The pelecypods separated from the rest of the phylum at an early date; they became flattened laterally and developed a large bilobed mantle that secretes a shell of two valves, a large mantle cavity containing gills, a burrowing foot in place of the creeping

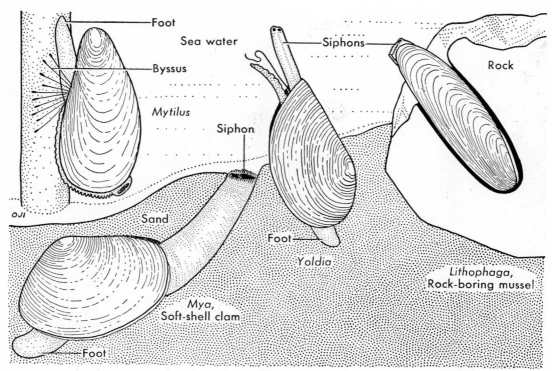

FIGURE 187. Some marine bivalves showing adaptations. *Mytilus*, the edible mussel, attached by byssal threads to a wooden pier. *Mya*, the mud clam, a burrowing form with a long siphon. Contrary to a general misconception, the "head" end of a clam is the end opposite the siphons. The walrus is said to feed almost entirely on this clam. *Yoldia* is capable of leaping through the water; note the united retractible siphons. *Lithophaga*, the rock-boring mussel, is said to secrete an acid to dissolve the rock into which it burrows.

type, and no true head. The cephalopods have become free-swimming animals with the foot modified into prehensile tentacles and with the brain and sense organs highly developed. The dominant view of the relation of the mollusks to other phyla is based on the presence of the trochophore larvae among both mollusks and annelids, which indicates that these may have been derived from the same ancestral type. Some of the fossil relatives of *Neopilina* may well have been the connecting link between the mollusks and the segmented annelid worms and arthropods.

RELATIONS OF THE MOLLUSKS TO MAN

Most of the mollusks may be considered beneficial to man; some are not. Slugs are sometimes injurious in greenhouses and gardens; shipworms (*Teredo*, Fig. 188) burrow into the bottom of wooden vessels, wharfs, and piles, weakening and destroying them. Some of the larger octopuses (Fig. 186) have the reputation of killing human beings, but are probably not as black as they are painted. Octopuses are very good food; many people prefer them to oysters. They are clean animals; but, because of prejudices, Americans do not use them for food as much as do other peoples, with the exception of one species found along the southern coast of California, which is much sought after for food.

The value of mollusks as scavengers is little appreciated. The fresh-water clams, for example, are continually ingesting organic particles and thus purifying the water in which they live. Mollusks, however, are

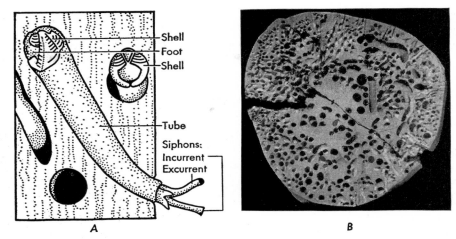

FIGURE 188. A, shipworms (*Teredo*) exposed in their burrows in a piece of wood that has been split open. *Teredo* is a bivalve, but the two shells which are used for boring enclose only a very small part of the anterior end of the body. The shipworm feeds on wood particles and minute organisms. B, damage done to a wharf pile section, driven March, 1944, and removed August, 1945. Every year these mollusks do millions of dollars worth of damage to wooden wharf pilings and to ships. (B courtesy of William F. Clapp Laboratories.)

most favorably known as food, especially the bivalves. Aborigines of our own shores used oysters in great quantities long before the white settlers came to America. Proof of

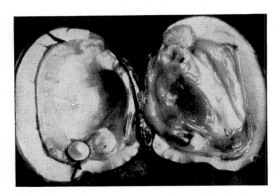

FIGURE 189. A pearl in a fresh-water clam; arrow points to pearl. A fresh-water pearl has sold for as much as $10,000. Pearls are protective secretions, made of the same substance (nacre) that lines the bivalve shell. (Courtesy of F.L. Clark.)

the popularity of the oyster with the Indian is found in the many piles of shells, that have been found around onetime camping grounds. Some of these piles contain tens of thousands of bushels of shells, which in

recent years have been mined for use in road building and for manufacture of lime. Oysters exceed in value any other kind of marine animals used as food by man. About 30 million bushels are gathered annually in the United States. Oyster culture is being carried on with success. The soft-shell or long-neck clam, *Mya arenaria*, and the hard-shell clam, *Mercenaria mercenaria*, are both widely used marine bivalves. The edible clam is used for the famous Cape Cod chowder. The edible mussel *Mytilus edulis* (see colored frontispiece at beginning of text) is eaten extensively in Europe but not very much in this country. Only the large adductor muscles of scallops (Pecten, Fig. 170) are eaten. In certain parts of Europe snails are considered a delicacy; and one type of gastropod, the abalone, is a common article of food on our western coast. Squids (Fig. 183), cuttlefishes, and octopuses are esteemed by palates in the south of Europe and in the Orient. In the United States, it is only because of prejudice that people make less use of these clean animals for food than do people of other countries. But squids are used by the ton for fish bait in America.

The giant clam (*Tridacna*) of the tropics may reach a length of three feet and weigh 500 pounds. The large shells are used as cradles for babies by some natives of the East Indies.

Among the products of value derived from mollusks are pearls and pearl buttons. Pearls are found especially in pearl oysters (*Pinctada*) in Ceylon, India, Japan, and north Australia. They also occur in the common oyster and in clams, but these are never of high value. The shells of fresh-water mussels are used for the manufacture of pearl buttons and many tons are collected annually in the United States, mainly from the Mississippi and Ohio rivers and their tributaries. Overfishing of mussels for buttons has seriously depleted them. The U.S. Fish and Wildlife Service has conducted many experiments in an effort to improve mussel fishing.

CLASSIFICATION OF THE MOLLUSCA *

(For reference purposes only)

Mollusks are unsegmented invertebrates (except the class Monoplacophora), and without jointed appendages. They usually possess a shell which is secreted by a mantle. A muscular foot of some sort is generally present. The classification of the more than 90,000 species is based on the characteristics of the foot, mantle, shell, radula, and respiratory organs. Six classes, three subclasses, and eight orders are described here as follows:

Class 1. **Monoplacophora** (bearing one flat shell). This name was originally proposed to cover a group of extinct paleozoic mollusks, but now contains a remarkable living form *Neopilina* (Fig. 180). A small disklike foot, a single shell, but the body is divided into segments with pairs of muscle scars on the inner surface of the shell,

* This classification is according to W.J. Clench and R.D. Turner, Museum of Comparative Zoology, Harvard University.

and paired auricles, nephridia, and breathing organs. This is the only class of segmented mollusks.

Order 1. **Tryblidiacea.** Shell is spoon- or cap-shaped. The animal has a head region and 5 well-developed metameres which have paired auricles, nephridia, and comblike gills (ctenida). The extraordinary deep-sea form, *Neopilina galatheae*, first reported in 1957, is the only known, living, segmented mollusk.

Class 2. **Amphineura** (Gr. *amphi*, both; *neuron*, nerve). Chitons (Fig. 170). Marine; elongate body; head reduced; shell of 8 plates or none; no tentacles; and bilateral symmetry obvious.

Order 1. **Polyplacophora.** Chitons. Elliptical body; large flat foot; shell a middorsal row of 8 plates, surrounded by a fleshy girdle; 6 to 80 pairs of gills in groove around foot. Sexes separate. Exs. *Tonicella* and *Chiton*.

Order 2. **Aplacophora.** Wormlike forms; integument thick; lacks any evidence of shell, except tiny limy spicules in the mantle; and rudimentary foot. Ex. *Neomenia*.

Class 3. **Scaphopoda** (Gr. *skaphe*, boat; *pous*, foot). Tooth shells or tusk shells (Fig. 170). Marine; body enclosed in tubular shell, open at both ends, no gills, delicate tentacles, and dioecious. Ex. *Dentalium entale*; from Cape Cod northward.

Class 4. **Pelecypoda** (Gr. *pelekys*, hatchet; *pous*, foot). (Lamellibranchiata). The pelecypods are familiar forms to most people because of their economic importance. Bivalve mollusks, clams, mussels, oysters, scallops, nut clams, cockles, shipworms, etc. (Figs. 170, 174, 187, 188). Marine or in fresh water; mantle secretes shell, usually two valves; head, eyes, tentacles; radula absent; foot usually wedge-shaped and adapted for ploughing; usually two gills on either side of the mantle cavity. Entirely aquatic.

Order 1. **Taxodonta.** The mantle margins are united ventrally and posteriorly with openings for siphon and foot; gills usually absent, and hinges reduced or absent. Shells with many similar teeth on hinge margin; usually two equal adductor muscles. Entirely marine. Ex. *Yoldia limatula* in deep water from Connecticut northward.

Order 2. **Anisomyaria.** The mantle margins are usually separate, ventrally and posteriorly; and the siphons are lacking, or only slightly developed. Teeth various; anterior adductor muscle small or none; posterior adductor, a large powerful muscle. *Ostrea*, edible oysters; *Mytilus*, sea mussel; *Pecten*, frequently called scallop; *Pinctada* (formerly *Margaritana*) are marine forms, and sometimes called pearl oysters.

Order 3. **Eulamellibranchia.** The mantle more or less connected ventrally and behind; siphons generally well developed. Hinge teeth usually small in number and unlike in form; adductor muscles equal, or anterior muscle smaller. Marine, brackish, and fresh water. Exs. *Mercenaria* (formerly *Venus*), quahog or hard-shell clam; *Ensis*, razor clams; *Mya aenaria*, sand clam; *Teredo*, shipworm; *Pisidium*, free-living in fresh water; and *Unio*, *Anodonta*, *Lampsilis*, fresh-water clams, shells used for buttons.

Class 5. **Gastropoda** (Gr. *gastro*, belly; *pous*, foot). Snails, slugs, whelks, etc. (Figs. 170, 181, and 182). Foot flat for creeping, head distinct, with eyes and tentacles; shell if present of one piece (one valve); shell usually spiral but uncoiled, reduced, or absent in some; radula present in all but a few parasitic species; trochophore and usually veliger larvae.

Subclass 1. **Prosobranchia.** Mostly marine snails, but fresh-water and land forms are represented (Fig. 170). Respiration usually by gills which are situated in the mantle cavity anterior to the heart. If gills are absent then respiration may be by means of mantle, or pulmonary chamber. Exs. *Strombus gigas*, giant conch; *Helicina orbiculata*, a terrestrial southern species which is frequently arboreal; *Fissurella*, keyhole limpets, abalones, oyster drills; and *Crepidula*, slipper or boat shells.

Subclass 2. **Opisthobranchia.** Strictly marine (Figs. 170 and 182). Small shell or none; gills, if present, are situated posterior to the heart. Hermaphroditic. Exs. *Clione*, pteropods or sea butterflies, the foot may be expanded into two fins used in swimming; the sea hare and nudibranchs (snails without shells).

Subclass 3. **Pulmonata** (Fig. 170) (Gr. *pulmones*, lungs). Mostly freshwater and land snails. No gills; mantle cavity serves as a pulmonary sac (lung); shell usually present, sometimes rudimentary or absent; one or two pairs of tentacles; mostly terrestrial, many in fresh water, a few marine; mostly vegetarian, a few carnivorous. Exs. *Lymnaea stagnalis*, fresh-water species; *Helix*, European garden snails, introduced into America; *Arion*, slugs with no shell; *Limax*, with rudimentary shell in mantle; and *Testacella haliotidea*, a slug that lives in greenhouses and preys on earthworms.

Class 6. **Cephalopoda** (Gr. *kephale*, head; *pous*, foot). Squids, cuttlefish, octopuses, and nautili (Fig. 170). All marine; head large; eyes large and often complex (Fig. 184); radula present; the foot is modified into 8 or 10 prehensile arms in the octopuses and squids, but many tentacles in the nautili; muscular funnel (siphon); shell external, internal, or none; and dioecious.

Order 1. Tetrabranchia. Calcareous shell, closely coiled, tentacles numerous and without suckers; eyes without lens; no chromatophores; no ink sac; two pairs of gills and two pairs of nephridia. Ex. *Nautilus pompilius*, the pearly or chambered nautilus (Fig. 185).

Order 2. Dibranchia. Shell absent or reduced, and internal, calcareous, or horny, not coiled; body cylindrical or globose; one pair of gills, one pair of nephridia; tentacles 8 to 10, with suckers or hooks; eyes with lens; chromatophores and ink sac present. Ex. *Loligo pealii*, squid (Fig. 183).

SELECTED COLLATERAL READINGS

Abbott, R.T., *American Sea Shells*. Van Nostrand, New York, 1954.

Clench, W.J., Turner, R.D., *et al. Johnsonia Monographs of the Marine Mollusks of the Western Atlantic, 1941 to date*. Department of Mollusks, M.C.Z., Harvard Univ., Cambridge.

Coker, R.T., and Clark, A.F. "Natural History and Propagation of Fresh Water Mussels." *Bull. U.S. Bur. Fisheries*, 37:77–181, 1921.

Grave, B.H. "Natural History of the Shipworm, *Teredo navalis*, at Woods Hole, Mass." *Biol. Bull.*, 55:260–282, 1928.

MacGinitie, G.E., and MacGinitie, N. *Natural History of Marine Animals*. McGraw-Hill, New York, 1949.

Pilsbry, Henry A. "Land Mollusca of North America (North of Mexico)." *Acad. Nat. Sci. Phila. Monograph* 3, Vol. **1**, Parts 1 and and 2, 1939 and 1940; Vol. **2**, Parts 1 and 2, 1946 and 1948.

Pratt, H.S. *A Manual of the Common Invertebrate Animals*. Blakiston, Philadelphia, 1932.

Prosser, C.L., *et al. Comparative Animal Physiology*. Saunders, Philadelphia, 1950.

Robson, G.C. *A Monograph of the Recent Cephalopoda*. British Museum, London, 1932.

Shrock, R.R., and Twenhofel, W.H. *Principles of Invertebrate Paleontology*. McGraw-Hill, New York, 1953.

Stiles, Karl A., and Stiles, Nettie R. "The Pearl, A Biological Gem." *Bios*, 14:3–16, 1943.

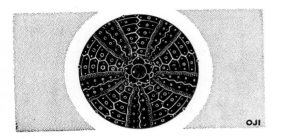

CHAPTER 21

Phylum Echinodermata. Starfishes, Sea Urchins, Sea Cucumbers, Sea Lilies, and Others

THE echinoderms, which are spiny-skinned, consist of the starfishes, brittle stars, sea urchins, sea cucumbers, and sea lilies (Fig. 190). They are all marine animals and constitute a considerable proportion of the animal life of the seashore. The starfish is the best-known type, but the sea urchin and sea cucumber are also quite well known to the seashore visitor.

The echinoderms are of particular interest because: (1) they change from a bilaterally symmetrical larva to a radially symmetrical adult; (2) they have remarkable powers of autotomy (self-mutilation) and regeneration of lost parts; (3) the eggs are especially suitable for extensive experimentation on artificial parthenogenesis; (4) they have a **water-vascular system** which includes organs known as tube feet, and (5) they have internal skeletons of calcareous plates. There are 5 classes of living echinoderms.

ASTERIAS—A STARFISH

Structure

The starfish does not resemble a fish, and a more appropriate name would be "sea-star" because of its habitat and shape; but the name "starfish" is the one by which this animal is best known. On the upper or aboral surface are many spines of various sizes, pedicellariae at the base of the spines, a madreporite which is the entrance to the water-vascular system, and the anal opening. On the oral surface are a mouth centrally situated in the membranous peristome and 5 grooves (ambulacral), 1 in each ray, from which 2 or 4 rows of tube feet extend.

The **skeleton** is made up of **calcareous plates** or **ossicles** (Fig. 193), bound together by muscle and connective tissue fibers. The **spines** are short and blunt and covered by **epidermis.** Around their bases are many whitish modified spines called **pedicellariae.** These are little jaws; they look like tiny scissor-blades mounted on a stalk, which,

303

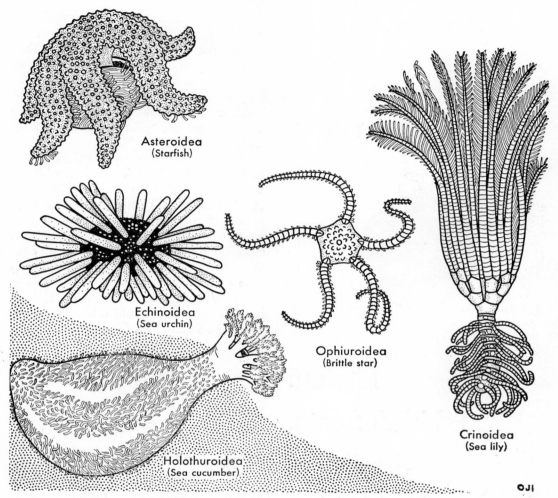

Figure 190. Representatives of the living classes of echinoderms. The figures are not drawn to scale.

when irritated, may be opened and closed by several sets of muscles. Their function is to protect the **dermal branchiae**, to prevent debris and small organisms from collecting on the surface, and to capture food. The **rays** may be flexed slowly by a few muscle fibers in the body wall. The **tube feet** are also supplied with muscle fibers.

Water-vascular system

The water-vascular system (Fig. 191) is a division of the coelom, peculiar to echino-

derms. Beginning with the **madreporite**, the following structures are encountered: the **stone canal** running downward enters the **ring canal**, which encircles the mouth; from this canal 5 **radial canals**, 1 in each ray, pass outward just above the **ambulacral grooves**. The radial canals give off side branches from which arise the **tube feet** and **ampullae** (Fig. 193). There are 9 small spherical swellings on the inner wall of the ring canal which open into its lumen; these are called **Tiedemann's bodies**. No function is known for these bodies.

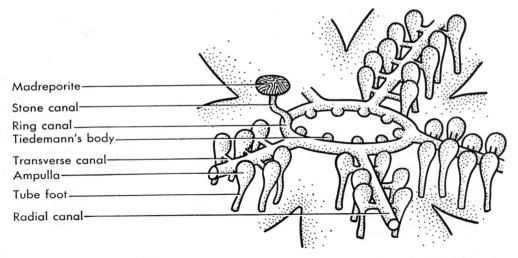

Madreporite

Stone canal

Ring canal

Tiedemann's body

Transverse canal

Ampulla

Tube foot

Radial canal

FIGURE 191. Starfish. Diagram of a part of the water-vascular system; one of the radial canals is cut off at the base and the other four near the base.

The water-vascular system provides an hydraulic pressure mechanism for locomotion. The starfish walks by means of its tube feet. Extension of the foot is brought about by contraction of the bulblike ampulla, forcing fluid into the cavity of the foot. Contraction of the foot muscles causes the fluid to run back into the ampulla.

The action of the tube foot is usually that of stepping forward. The foot, from a contracted position, points forward; it then elongates as the muscles of the ampulla contract, thus forcing fluid into the tube foot; and the bottom of the foot, the sucker, becomes pressed against the substrate. The action of certain muscles in the foot provides a forward thrust of the animal's body; thus the total effect of the forward thrusts of the many tube feet produces the movement of the starfish. After the forward thrust, the sucker is detached from the substrate and the foot contracts and points forward again to start the process over. All the tube feet act in a coordinated way by extending in the same direction, but not at the same time. The starfish advances slowly, only about six inches in a minute.

The tube feet are not only used for loco-motion, but for clinging to rocks and for capturing and handling food.

Digestive system

The digestive tract (Fig. 193) is short and greatly modified. The mouth opens into a very short **esophagus** which leads into a thin-walled sac, the **stomach.** The stomach consists of two parts—a larger oral portion and a small aboral or **pyloric** portion. From the pyloric portion, a tube passes into each ray, then divides into two branches, each of which possesses a large number of lateral pouches; these branches are called **pyloric** or **hepatic ceca.** They are green in color. Above the stomach is the slender **intestine,** which opens to the outside through the **anus.** Two branched pouches, brown in color, arise from the intestine and are known as **intestinal ceca.**

The **food** of the starfish consists of fish, oysters, mussels, barnacles, clams, snails, worms, crustaceans, etc. Digestion is chiefly extracellular. The stomach and pyloric ceca secrete several digestive enzymes. Undigested matter is ejected through the mouth. The intestinal ceca secrete a brownish material of unknown function, possibly excretory. The fluid in the coelom is kept in motion by **cilia** and carries the absorbed food to all parts of the body.

Excretion

Excretion is accomplished by the **amoebocytes** in the coelomic fluid, which pass to the outside of the body through the walls of the dermal branchiae.

Respiration

Respiration is carried on by means of the **dermal branchiae (papulae)**, which look like a soft furry substance, on the aboral surface of the rays. This appearance is caused by the outpouchings of the thin lining of the body cavity through minute openings in the skeleton. These dermal branchiae are covered with cilia on both the inside and outside. The external cilia keep a cur-

FIGURE 192. A starfish opening a clam. The starfish attaches its tube feet to the two shells of the clam and, by a continuous pull, virtually at right angles to the surface of each shell, eventually opens it. Then the stomach of the starfish is everted through the mouth and brought in contact with the soft parts of the clam (Fig. 190), and the bivalve is actually digested in its own shell. Note that this starfish has lost one ray. (Courtesy of George G. Lower.)

rent of oxygenated water passing over the branchiae on the outside, and the internal cilia cause the body fluid to flow out into the branchiae. While the body fluid is in the branchiae, an exchange of oxygen and carbon dioxide takes place exactly as it does in our own lungs when the blood flows past the tiny air sacs in them.

Nervous system and sense organs

Besides many nerve cells which lie among the epidermal cells, there are ridges of nerv-

ous tissue, the **radial nerve cords** (Fig. 193), running along the ambulacral grooves, and uniting with an **oral nerve (circumoral) ring** encircling the mouth. In each ray there is (1) a radial nerve cord, (2) a pair of nerves that are aboral to the radial nerve cord, and (3) a nerve cord in the aboral peritoneum. The **tube feet** are the principal sense organs. They receive fibers from the radial nerves. At the end of each ray is a small, soft, tactile tentacle and a light-sensitive eye spot. The dermal branchiae are probably sensory also.

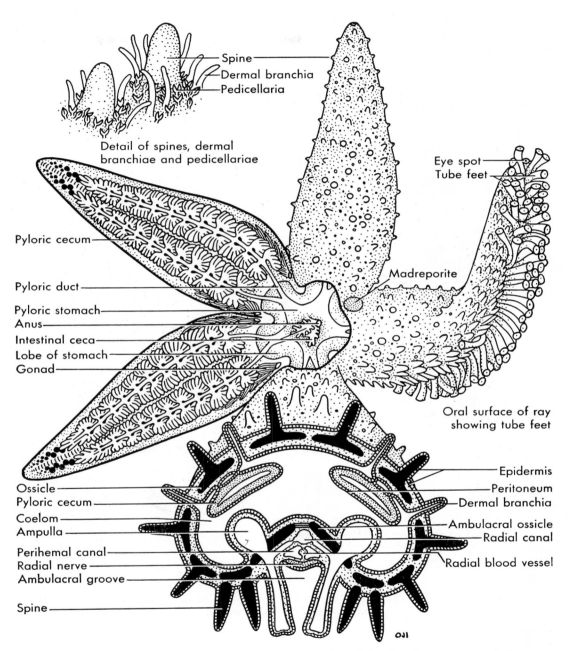

Spine
Dermal branchia
Pedicellaria

Detail of spines, dermal
branchiae and pedicellariae

Eye spot
Tube feet

Pyloric cecum

Pyloric duct

Pyloric stomach
Anus

Intestinal ceca
Lobe of stomach
Gonad

Madreporite

Oral surface of ray
showing tube feet

Ossicle
Pyloric cecum

Coelom
Ampulla

Perihemal canal
Radial nerve
Ambulacral groove

Spine

Epidermis
Peritoneum
Dermal branchia

Ambulacral ossicle
Radial canal

Radial blood vessel

FIGURE 193. General structure of the starfish. The disk and aboral surface are removed from two rays. *Below,* one ray is shown in cross section, without gonads.

Reproduction

The sexes of starfishes are separate. The reproductive organs are branched structures, two in the base of each arm (Fig. 193). The female has been known to release as many as 2½ million eggs in two hours, and 200 million eggs may be liberated in a season. A male produces many times that number of sperms. The eggs of many starfishes are fertilized in the water and develop into a type of larva called a **bipinnaria** (Fig. 194) that has bilateral symmetry before it attains the radial symmetry of an adult.

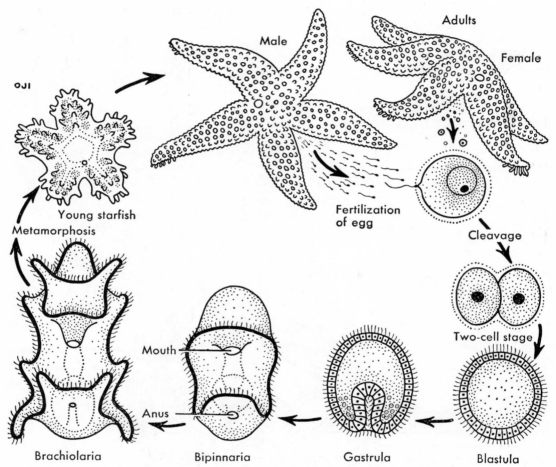

FIGURE 194. The life cycle of the common starfish. Note that in the later larval stages the starfish has bilateral symmetry before it attains radial symmetry.

Regeneration

The starfish has remarkable powers of regeneration. A single arm with part of the disk will regenerate an entire body. In all species tested, arms cut off at any level are regenerated, although at a slow rate. If an arm is injured, it is usually cast off near the base at the fourth or fifth ambulacral ossicle. This is **autotomy.**

OTHER ECHINODERMATA

Starfishes

The principal characteristics of echinoderms have been described in our account of the starfish. Three orders and about 20 families of starfishes are recognized. About 1200 species are known. Usually 5 or multiples of 5 rays are present. These rays may be long or short, sometimes so short that the body resembles a 5-sided pad. Starfishes are common marine animals all over the world and may be found in both shallow and deep water.

Brittle stars and basket stars

Brittle stars (Fig. 190) and basket stars have slender or branched flexible rays; the tube feet have largely lost their locomotor function and serve as sensory and respiratory organs. Food consists of minute organisms and decaying organic matter lying on the sea bottom. Locomotion is comparatively rapid. The rays bend like a whip and enable animals belonging to certain species to "run," cling, and probably swim. The term "brittle star" is derived from the fact that these animals break off their arms when they become injured.

Sea urchins

A common type of sea urchin (Fig. 190) is *Arbacia punctulata*, a purple-colored species that lives in both shallow and deep water from Cape Cod to southern Mexico. It is somewhat globular in shape. The **test** (shell) (see head piece, p. 303) is made up of calcareous plates which bear movable spines about 25 mm. long. There is a **system of plates** in the ray, 5 pairs of columns of **ambulacral plates,** so called because they are penetrated by tube feet and 5 pairs of columns of **interambulacral plates** (see headpiece). These correspond to the same regions on the starfish, assuming that the rays are folded back on its aboral surface. Most of the skeletal plates bear spines which are attached by muscles and move freely on little knoblike elevations called **tubercles.** The food consists of plant and animal matter which falls to the sea bottom and is ingested by means of a complicated structure known as **Aristotle's lantern** (Fig. 195).

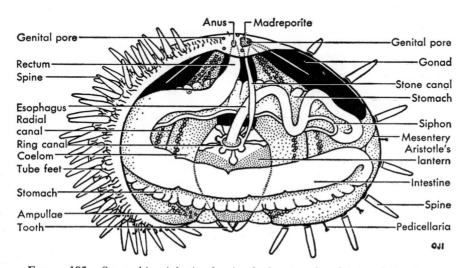

FIGURE 195. Sea urchin, *Arbacia*, showing both external and internal structure.

The **water-vascular system** consists of a madreporite, a stone canal, a ring canal, and 5 radial canals which extend meridionally, connecting with the tube feet (Fig. 195). Transverse canals leading to the tube feet and ampullae are given off by the radial canals. **Respiration** takes place in most echinoids through 10 branched pouches situated on the area surrounding the mouth.

Echinocardium is a heart-shaped urchin, and *Echinarachnius* resembles a silver dollar. Sea urchins are variously colored; they may be white, purple, green, yellowish green, gray, black, etc. Some species possess very long poisonous spines, such as *Diadema* of Florida and the West Indies.

Sea cucumbers

The sea cucumber differs from other echinoderms in that it has an elongated body, and lies on its side. One type of sea cucumber (Fig. 190) sometimes used for study is *Cucumaria frondosa*. This species is abundant on the coast of Maine. Sea cucumbers live sluggishly on the sea bottom or burrow in the surface mud or sand with only the ends exposed. Instead of a test or skeleton of spine-bearing plates, *Cucumaria* has a muscular body wall containing very small calcareous plates. The **digestive tract** (Fig. 196) consists of a mouth, a short esophagus, a small muscular stomach, and a

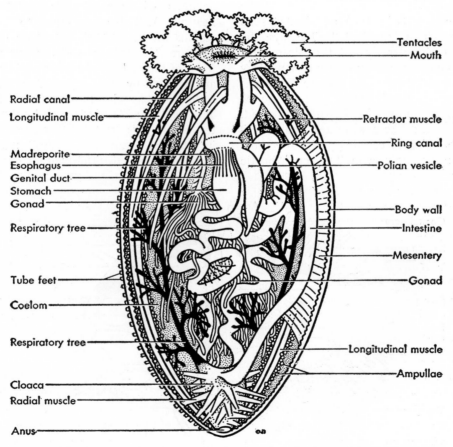

FIGURE 196. Sea cucumber, *Cucumaria,* showing the tube feet and internal structure.

long looped intestine, the posterior end of which is a muscular enlargement called the **cloaca** ending at the posterior anus. The **food** of most sea cucumbers consists of organic particles extracted from the sand or mud which is taken into the digestive tract. From 10 to 30 of the tube feet surrounding the mouth are modified as tentacles for procuring food. **Respiration** is carried on through the cloaca. Connected to the cloaca are two long-branched tubes, **respiratory trees.** The muscular cloaca pumps water in and out of the tree, which serves both as a respiratory and excretory organ. The cloaca and respiratory trees also function as excretory organs.

Some sea cucumbers are long, slender, and wormlike. Their colors are varied—brown, yellowish, reddish, whitish, black, pink, purplish, etc. One Puget Sound species, *Psolus chitinoides,* has an orange-colored body and crimson-colored neck and tentacles.

Sea lilies or feather stars

These (Fig. 190) are called crinoids. In some species they are attached to the sea bottom by a long jointed **stalk.** Their rays, 5 or 10 in number, are often branched near the base and bear smaller branches called **pinnules** along their sides, giving them a feathery appearance. About 630 living species of crinoids are known. They live in both shallow and deep water. Fossil remains of crinoids are very abundant in some limestone formations.

Autotomy

Both starfishes and sea cucumbers practice autotomy. Starfishes break off injured arms at a particular point; and the sea cucumbers, *Thyone,* when irritated, may, by violent contractions, cast out through the cloacal opening most of the viscera; only the ends are left inside to regenerate. In both cases, the lost parts are soon regenerated. One investigator found that of 150 eviscerated sea cucumbers (*Thyone*), all but 5 lived and replaced the parts successfully. Starfishes with regenerating arms as shown in Fig. 197 are often encountered in nature.

Artificial parthenogenesis

The eggs of echinoderms have been used extensively for the study of artificial parthenogenesis, that is, the activation of development in eggs by artificial means instead of by the penetration of spermatozoa. Loeb succeeded in obtaining actively swimming embryos from sea-urchin eggs by changing the chemical constitution of the sea water. Later it was found that the eggs of various species of animals, particularly those of starfishes, sea urchins, and frogs, could be induced to develop when subjected to a number of agents including heat, acids, and potassium and sodium chloride. Electrifying, shaking, and pricking some eggs with a needle also stimulate development. The efficacy of the agent differs for different types of eggs, each type responding to one agent more readily than to others. Artificially stimulated eggs may give rise to embryos and larvae; and in some cases, such as the starfishes, sea urchins, and frogs, they may produce adult animals. Even fatherless rabbits have been obtained by stimulating unfertilized rabbits' eggs to develop, and then replacing them in female rabbits. Thus eggs that normally require union with spermatozoa to initiate development may give rise to mature animals just as do parthenogenetic eggs.

ORIGIN AND RELATIONS OF THE ECHINODERMATA

Echinoderms and coelenterates, because of their radial symmetry, were at one time placed together in a group called Radiata.

FIGURE 197. Four-rayed starfish is regenerating one new ray which appears as a small bud growing from the disk. (Courtesy of N.Y. Zoological Society.)

The anatomy of the adult and the structure of the larvae, however, show that these phyla really occupy widely separated positions in the animal kingdom. The adult echinoderms cannot be compared with any other group of animals, and we must look to the larvae for signs of relationship. The bilateral larva is either a modification for a free-swimming life or an indication of the condition of its ancestors. The latter view is accepted by most zoologists. The ancestors of echinoderms were doubtless bilateral, wormlike animals which became radial and took up sessile habits secondarily, and present-day free-living echinoderms are probably derived from a fixed ancestor whose symmetry they still retain.

RELATIONS OF ECHINODERMATA TO MAN

The value of echinoderms in their relations to other lower animals is problematic. Apparently, however, they are of considerable importance to man. In the Orient, sea cucumbers are dried in the sun and sold as bêche-de-mer or trepang for use especially in soup. The gonads of the sea urchin and the eggs of the starfish are also eaten in certain tropical regions.

The dried skeletons of echinoderms have been crushed and used as a fertilizer because of the high calcium and nitrogenous content.

Starfish are very destructive in oyster beds since they succeed in pulling open the shells and eating large numbers of these bivalves (Fig. 192). A starfish has been observed to eat 10 oysters or clams in a day. Two control measures are in general use at the present time: (1) in some regions a moplike tangle of threads (Fig. 198) is dragged across the oyster beds and the starfish that grab onto these with their pedicellariae are removed from the water and destroyed; and (2) the most efficacious method of killing starfish is to spread quicklime over the oyster beds in a strength that is harmless to the oysters but is death to the starfish.

FIGURE 198. Starfish collected by dragging a mop of threads behind a boat. (Courtesy of General Biological Supply House, Inc.)

CLASSIFICATION OF THE ECHINODERMATA

(For reference purposes only)

Echinoderms are radially symmetrical as adults but bilaterally symmetrical as larvae; no segmentation; the body wall usually contains calcareous plates that form an endoskeleton; nervous system with oral nerve ring and radial nerves; sexes usually separate; a water-vascular system, including tube feet, is usually present. The 6000 known species are placed in 5 classes as follows:

Class 1. **Crinoidea** (Gr. *krinon*, lily). Sea lilies (Fig. 190). Adults usually with 5 branched rays and with pinnules; cuplike calyx; tube feet suckerless; aboral pole sometimes with cirri, but only about 60 out of 630 existing species possess a stalk for temporary or permanent attachment; few modern species but many fossils. Ex. *Antedon tenella*, sea lily.

Class 2. **Asteroidea** (Gr. *aster*, star). Starfishes (Fig. 190). Adults typically with 5 rays; rays usually not sharply marked off from disk; ambulacral grooves open with tube feet; madreporite aboral; respiration by dermal branchiae. Ex. *Asterias forbesi*, starfish.

Class 3. **Ophiuroidea** (Gr. *ophis*, snake). Brittle stars (Fig. 190). Typically 5 rays; rays sharply marked off from distinct disk; flexible rays; no ambulacral grooves; no pedicellariae; madreporite oral. Ex. *Ophioderma brevispinum*, brittle star.

Class 4. **Echinoidea** (Gr. *echinos*, spiny). Sea urchins (Fig. 190). Body hemispherical, egg-shaped, or disk-shaped; no free rays; skeleton of calcareous plates forming a test, bearing movable spines; usually three-jawed pedicellariae; tube feet with suckers. Ex. *Echinarachnius parma*, sand dollar.

Class 5. **Holothurioidea** (Gr. *holothourion*, sea cucumber). Sea cucumber (Fig. 190). Adult body long, ovoid, and soft, with muscular wall; retractile tentacles around mouth; body wall usually contains calcareous plates; no rays; no spines nor pedicellariae; tube feet usually present; cloaca usually with respiratory tree. Ex. *Thyone briareus*, common sea cucumber.

SELECTED COLLATERAL READINGS

Clark, A.H. "Sea Lilies and Feather Stars." *Smithsonian Misc. Collections*, **72**, No. 7, 1921.

Coe, W.R., "Echinoderms of Connecticut." *Connecticut State Geological and Natural History Survey, Bull. 19*, 1912.

Harvey, E.B. *The American Arbacia and Other Sea Urchins*. Univ. Press, Princeton, 1956.

Hyman, L.H. *The Invertebrates: Echinodermata*. McGraw-Hill, New York, 1955.

Jennings, H.S. "Behavior of the Starfish *Asterias forreri* DeLoriol." *Univ. Calif. Pub. Zool.*, **4**:53–185. 1907.

Johnson, M.E., and Snook, H.J. *Seashore Animals of the Pacific Coast*. Macmillan, New York, 1927.

MacGinitie, G.E., and MacGinitie, Nettie. *Natural History of Marine Animals*. McGraw-Hill, New York, 1949.

Mead, A.D. "Natural History of the Starfish." *Bull. U.S. Fish Commission*, 19, 203–224, 1900.

Mortensen, Theodore. *Handbook of the Echinoderms of the British Isles*. Oxford Univ. Press, Oxford, 1927.

CHAPTER 22

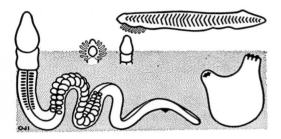

Phylum Chordata. Amphioxus, Tunicates, Vertebrates, and Others

THE phylum Chordata includes the vertebrate animals such as the mammals, birds, reptiles, amphibians, fishes, elasmobranchs, cyclostomes, and a number of marine forms that are less well known. All of these animals are characterized by:

1. A skeletal axis, the **notochord** at some stage in the life cycle (Fig. 207).
2. Paired **gill slits** connecting the pharynx with the exterior at some stage in the life cycle. All chordates up to and including the fishes carry on respiration by means of gills throughout life. In the higher vertebrates, gill slits or traces of them are usually present only in embryonic or larval stages. In mammals the gill slits never open.
3. A **central nerve cord** which contains a cavity or system of cavities; it is dorsal to the digestive tract.

These chordate characters all appear at some stage in development, and they may persist, change, or disappear in the adult.

Figure 199 shows some of the fundamental differences in the body plan of an achordate and a chordate.

DIVISION OF THE CHORDATA INTO SUBPHYLA

In many respects the chordates differ widely from one another, and it is customary to separate them into 4 subphyla:

1. Hemichordata.* Two classes of wormlike animals:
   a. Enteropneusta. Acorn (tongue) worm, wormlike with many gill slits.
   b. Pterobranchia. Very small chordates with one pair of gills or none.

* Some zoologists question the presence of a true notochord in the hemichordates, and they would remove them from the Chordata and place them in an independent invertebrate phylum, but embryology is the crucial thing and can be interpreted differently depending on what are regarded as the really defining features of a notochord. Because the experts do not agree, classification of the hemichordates must be considered controversial.

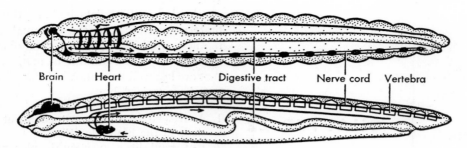

Figure 199. Diagram showing some of the fundamental differences in the body plan of (*top*) an achordate or invertebrate (annelid) and (*bottom*) a chordate (snake) in the location of the digestive system, heart, and nervous system. The arrows indicate the direction of the flow of blood.

2. Urochordata (Tunicata). Tunicates (sea squirts) and a number of other marine forms.
3. Cephalochordata. Two families of fishlike animals called lancelets.
4. Vertebrata. Animals with backbones.

The subphylum Vertebrata includes most of the chordates (Fig. 200), but the other three subphyla, often called protochordates, are of considerable interest since they are more primitive and hence give us some idea of the character of the animals from which the vertebrates probably developed. The primitive chordate most frequently studied in general zoology laboratories is the amphioxus of the subphylum Cephalochordata. The amphioxus exhibits chordate characteristics (notochord, gill slits, and a dorsal tubular nerve cord) so clearly that it illustrates well the basic chordate characteristics. In the next chapter a detailed description of the frog is presented as an introduction to the subphylum Vertebrata.

AMPHIOXUS—A PRIMITIVE CHORDATE

The Cephalochordata comprise about 30 species of marine animals of which *Branchiostoma lanceolatus*, commonly known as the amphioxus, lives in the waters of tropical and temperate seacoasts (Fig. 201). The amphioxus is of special interest, since it exhibits the characteristics of the chordates in a simple condition. Furthermore, it may be similar to some ancient ancestor of the vertebrates.

The amphioxus is about two inches long. The semitransparent body is pointed at both ends and laterally compressed. It is found near the shore, where it burrows in the clean sand with its head or tail, and conceals all but the anterior end (see headpiece, p. 315). It sometimes leaves its burrow at night and swims about by means of rapid lateral movements of the body. When it ceases to move, it falls on its side.

External anatomy

The amphioxus (Fig. 201) is shaped like a fish but has no lateral fins and no distinct head. Along the middorsal line is a low **dorsal fin** which extends the entire length of the body and widens at the posterior end into a **caudal fin**. The caudal fin extends forward on the ventral surface to form the short **ventral fin**. Both dorsal and ventral fins are strengthened by rods of connective tissue called **fin rays**. In front of the ventral fin, the lower surface of the body is flattened, and on each side is an expansion of the integument called the **metapleural fold** (Fig. 202).

The **body wall** is divided into V-shaped muscle segments, the **myotomes**; these are separated from one another by septa of

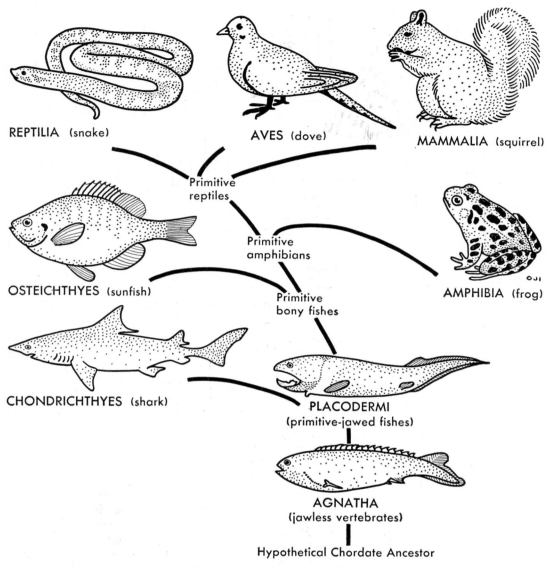

REPTILIA (snake)

AVES (dove)

MAMMALIA (squirrel)

Primitive reptiles

OSTEICHTHYES (sunfish)

Primitive amphibians

AMPHIBIA (frog)

Primitive bony fishes

CHONDRICHTHYES (shark)

PLACODERMI
(primitive-jawed fishes)

AGNATHA
(jawless vertebrates)

Hypothetical Chordate Ancestor

FIGURE 200. A simplified family tree of the vertebrates. The ancestor to the most primitive jawless vertebrates (class Agnatha), which are fossil ostracoderms, is unknown. The primitive jawed placoderm is also a fossil form. (The ostracoderm and placoderm after A.S. Romer.)

connective tissue. The myotomes on one side of the body alternate with those on the other side. The muscle fibers contained in them are longitudinal; and since they are attached to the connective tissue partitions, they are able to produce the lateral movements of the body used in swimming.

The **mouth** proper is an opening in a membrane posterior in the oral hood. The **anus** is situated on the left side of the body near the base of the caudal fin. The **atriopore** is just anterior to the ventral fin; it is a ventral opening through which water used in respiration passes to the outside.

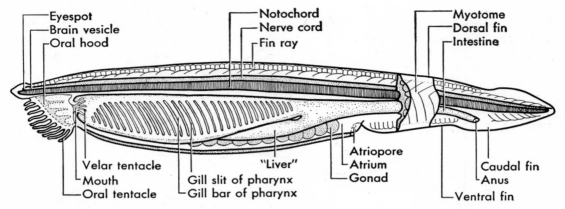

FIGURE 201. Amphioxus, an animal that illustrates the three fundamental chordate characteristics. An adult with part of body wall removed from the left side to show the general structure. Natural size about two inches long.

Internal anatomy and physiology

Skeleton

The amphioxus has a well-developed **notochord** (Figs. 201 and 202), which is the main support of the body. This is a rod of connective tissue lying near the dorsal surface and extending almost the entire length of the body. The notochord is composed of vacuolated cells which are made turgid by their fluid contents, and are therefore rigid. Other skeletal structures are the connective tissue rods which form the fin rays, and similar structures that support the **oral tentacles** (cirri) of the **oral hood** and gill bars.

Digestive system

The food of the amphioxus consists of minute organisms which are carried into the mouth with the current of water produced by cilia on the gills. The **mouth** is an opening in a membrane, the **velum**, and may be closed by circular muscle fibers which surround it. Twelve sensory-oral or **velar tentacles** protect the mouth, and when folded across it, act as a strainer, thus preventing entrance of coarse solid objects. The funnel-shaped **vestibule** is the cavity

of the **oral hood.** The 22 ciliated tentacles which project from the edge of the oral hood are provided with **sensory cells.** The inner wall of the oral hood bears a number of ciliated lobes and is known as the **wheel organ** because, during life, its cilia appear to produce a rotatory movement. Water is drawn into the mouth chiefly by the action of the gill cilia.

The mouth opens into a large, laterally compressed **pharynx.** A ciliated middorsal groove in the pharynx is called the **hyperbranchial groove.** A ventral groove, the **hypobranchial groove** (endostyle), is also present. The endostyle consists of a median ciliated region with a glandular portion on both sides. The glands secrete strings of mucus in which food particles become entangled as the mucus passes up the gills. The cilia drive this mucus forward and upward, by way of the gills and two **peripharyngeal grooves,** into the **hyperbranchial groove.** From here it is carried by the hyperbranchial cilia into the **intestine.** Other food particles are caught by mucus produced in the hyperbranchial groove and then carried posteriorly by the action of cilia to the intestine. A ventral finger-shaped outpocketing of the intestine is known as the "**liver,**" but it might better be called the midgut cecum, since it is an outgrowth of the midgut. Although it secretes digestive enzymes, it is not known to function as the vertebrate liver. The intestine leads directly to the **anus.**

Respiratory system

The **pharynx** (Fig. 202) is attached dorsally and hangs down into a cavity called the **atrium.** The atrium is not the coelom,

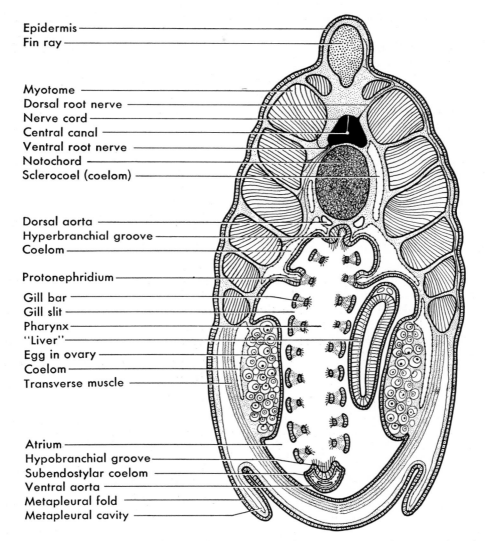

Epidermis
Fin ray

Myotome
Dorsal root nerve
Nerve cord
Central canal
Ventral root nerve
Notochord
Sclerocoel (coelom)

Dorsal aorta
Hyperbranchial groove
Coelom

Protonephridium

Gill bar
Gill slit
Pharynx
"Liver"
Egg in ovary
Coelom
Transverse muscle

Atrium
Hypobranchial groove
Subendostylar coelom
Ventral aorta
Metapleural fold
Metapleural cavity

FIGURE 202. A cross section of the amphioxus in the pharyngeal region, showing various internal structures, including some of the coelomic cavities.

but it is lined with an ectodermal epithelium and is really external to the body, as has been proved by the study of its development. Water, which is carried into the pharynx by way of the mouth, passes through the **gill slits** into the atrium and out of the atriopore. The gill slits are separated by **gill bars;** these are ciliated and supported by rods of connective tissue. **Respiration** takes place as the water, driven by the cilia, flows through the gill slits; the pharyngeal mechanism and gill slits are probably of equal importance in the function of food catching.

Circulatory system

The circulatory system is similar to that in a higher chordate such as the fish, but lacks a heart. Besides the definite blood vessels, there are tissue spaces into which the colorless blood escapes. The **subintestinal vein** collects blood loaded with nutriment from the intestine and carries it forward into the **hepatic portal vein,** and thence to the liver. The **hepatic vein** leads from the liver to the **ventral aorta.** Blood is forced by the rhythmic contractions of the ventral aorta into the **afferent branchial arteries,** which are situated in the gill bars, and then through the **efferent branchial arteries** into the paired **dorsal aortae.** It passes back into the median dorsal aorta, and finally by way of **intestinal capillaries** into the **subintestinal vein.** The blood is oxygenated during its passage through the gill slits. The direction of the blood flow, backward in the dorsal and forward in the ventral vessel, is the same as that of the vertebrates, but the reverse of that in invertebrates such as annelids.

Coelom

The reduced coelom is represented in the adult by cavities around the digestive tract. The position of the coelomic cavities is shown in the pharyngeal region in Fig. 202.

Excretory system

The excretory organs, although often described as ciliated, are actually flagellated nephridia (**protonephridia**) situated near the dorsal region of the pharynx. Each nephridium bears several clusters of solenocytes, which are flagellated cells extending out of a tube in which the flagella play. About 100 pairs of protonephridia connect the dorsal coelom with the atrial cavity. These protonephridia are not homologous to the tubules of the vertebrate kidney.

Nervous system

The amphioxus possesses a central **nerve cord** (Fig. 202) lying entirely above the digestive tract in contrast to the ventral nerve cords of annelids and arthropods. It rests on the notochord and is almost as long. A minute **central canal** traverses its entire length and widens at the anterior end to form a **brain vesicle,** which is the only trace of a brain present. An **olfactory pit** opens into this vesicle in young specimens. At the anterior end of the nerve cord is a black pigmented spot called an "eye spot," although it is not sensitive to light. The "eyes" consist of numerous single light-sensory cells, each with a pigment cup in the ventral wall of the nerve cord. Two pairs of sensory nerves arise from the cerebral vesicle and supply the anterior region of the body. The rest of the nerve cord gives off nerves on opposite sides, but alternating with one another. These nerves are of two kinds: (1) **dorsal nerves** with a sensory function which pass to the skin and (2) **ventral nerves** with a motor function which enter the myotomes. The sense organs include the olfactory pit, sensory cells in the epidermis on the oral and velar tentacles, "eyes," and possibly the "eye spot."

Reproduction

In the amphioxus the sexes are separate. The paired gonads (Fig. 201) project into the atrium. Eggs and sperms are discharged into the atrial cavity and reach the exterior through the atriopore. Fertilization takes place externally in the water. The cleavage is holoblastic as in the starfish.

OTHER CHORDATA

Subphylum Hemichordata

The hemichordates, traditionally, have been considered the lowest chordates, but some recent authorities do not regard them as chordates at all. They say the so-called "notochord" is not a true notochord, but is what they call a stomocord. However, as explained in the footnote (p. 315), this is still an open question.

The acorn or tongue worms are the common names by which the hemichordates are known. They are soft-bodied animals and most of them live in shallow water along the seashore. Some species have persistent and unpleasant odors. The external features of one are shown in Fig. 203.

Three regions may be distinguished: a

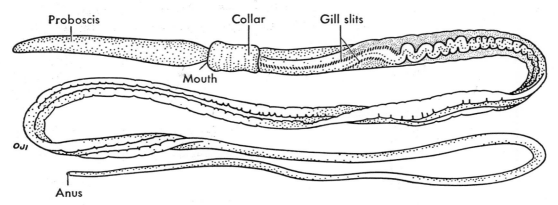

FIGURE 203. An acorn worm, *Saccoglossus (Dolichoglossus) kowalevskii*, a species that lives on sand flats from Massachusetts Bay to Beaufort, N.C. Natural size about 7 inches long.

proboscis, a **collar**, and a **trunk**, which make up most of the body. Paired lateral gill slits are present in the anterior part of the trunk. Figure 204 shows diagrammatically the principal internal structures of another species. The mud or sand in which the animals live is taken into the mouth and forced slowly through the digestive tract, where nutriment is extracted from the organic matter contained in it—a process similar to digestion in the earthworm. Respiratory, circulatory, and nervous systems are present. The sexes are separate. In some species each egg develops into a free-swimming larva called a tornaria. The resemblance of the tornaria to the larvae of echinoderms is quite striking and has led to one hypothesis of the origin of the vertebrates (Chap. 36).

Subphylum Urochordata

The tunicates all live in the sea. They are either free-swimming or attached; they are widely distributed and occur at all levels from near the surface to a depth of over three miles. They range in size from about $\frac{1}{100}$ inch to over a foot in diameter. Some are brilliantly colored. The adult in some species (Fig. 205) is saclike and has received the common name "sea squirt" because when irritated it may eject water through two openings in the unattached end. The term Tunicata was formerly applied to members of the group on account of a cuticular outer covering known as a **tunic** or **test.**

The chordate characteristics of tunicates were not recognized until the development of the egg and metamorphosis of the larva were fully investigated. It was then discovered that the typical larva (Fig. 206), which is about ¼ inch long and resembles a frog tadpole, possesses (1) a distinct **notochord,** (2) a dorsal **neural tube** in the tail enlarging in the trunk and ending in a vesicle, which is considered the forerunner of the brain of the vertebrates, and (3) a **pharyngeal sac** which opens to the exterior by innumerable ciliated **gill slits.** The tail propels the larva forward by lateral strokes.

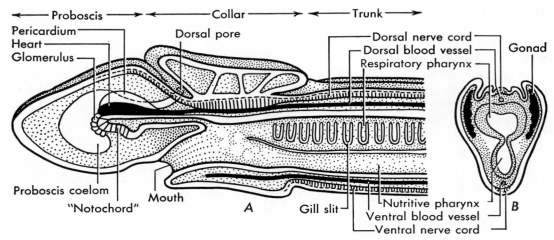

FIGURE 204. Acorn worm (*Glossobalanus*). A, longitudinal section through the middle line. Some zoologists call the short anterior structure, which has long been called a notochord, a "stomochord," but this new name does not rule out the possibility of its being homologous with the notochord of the vertebrates. B, cross section through the trunk region. (A modified from Bullock; B after Bullock.)

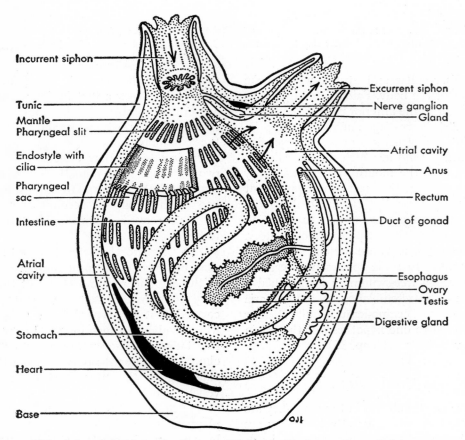

FIGURE 205. Internal structure of a tunicate (*Molgula*). Tunic, mantle, and pharynx removed from left side. Arrows indicate flow of water currents through the animal.

After a short existence as a free-swimming organism, the larva becomes attached to some object by three projections on the anterior end, which secrete a sticky fluid. It then undergoes a **retrogressive metamorphosis**, during which the tail with the notochord disappears, and the nervous system is reduced to a ganglion.

The typical adult tunicate (Fig. 205) is attached by a **base** or stalk and surrounded by a thick, tough, elastic membrane, the **tunic.** This is composed of a celluloselike substance, a material rarely found in animals but common in plants. The tunic is lined by a membranous **mantle** which contains muscle fibers and blood vessels. At the distal end are two external openings: one is the "mouth" or **incurrent siphon** (branchial opening), into which a current of water passes; the other is the **excurrent siphon** (atrial opening) through which the water escapes to the outside. This current of water brings food into the digestive tract, furnishes oxygen for respiration, and carries away gametes and excretory substances. Within the test and mantle is the **atrial cavity** which contains the internal organs. At the base of the incurrent siphon is a **velum**, forming a sensory sieve, through which incoming water and food must pass. Below the velum is a **pharyngeal sac**; on the ventral side of this is the endostyle, a pharyngeal

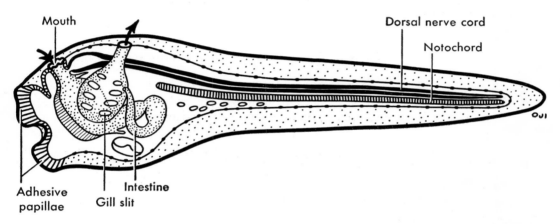

Mouth

Dorsal nerve cord

Notochord

Adhesive papillae   Gill slit   Intestine

FIGURE 206. The free-swimming larva of a tunicate, showing all three chordate characteristics: notochord, dorsal nerve cord, and gill slits.

groove, lined with mucous and ciliated cells. Microscopic plants and animals are entangled in mucus secreted by the **endostyle** and move downward into the **esophagus.** This leads to the **stomach** which connects with the **intestine.** The **digestive tube** is bent upon itself and opens into the **atrial cavity** through the **anus.** A **digestive gland** connects by a duct to the stomach. A single **nerve ganglion** lies between the two siphons, with nerves to various structures. Located near this is a **neural gland** which may have an endocrine function.

The **circulatory system** consists of a tubular **heart,** to each end of which is connected a large vessel, and each of the vessels gives off branches to various structures. One unusual feature of the circulation in these forms is that the direction of blood flow is reversed at short intervals.

Tunicates are hermaphroditic, but they are usually self-sterile so that sexual reproduction requires two animals. Some species also reproduce asexually by budding.

Subphylum Vertebrata

The Vertebrata are chordates having a segmental backbone or vertebral column. They also possess an axial notochord at some time in their lives. Although this notochord persists in some of the lower vertebrates, it becomes modified by an investment of cartilage (Fig. 207) which becomes segmented and constitutes the vertebral column. In the higher vertebrates the vertebral column is made up of a series of bodies called vertebrae, and the notochord disappears before the adult stage is reached. Seven classes of vertebrates are recognized.

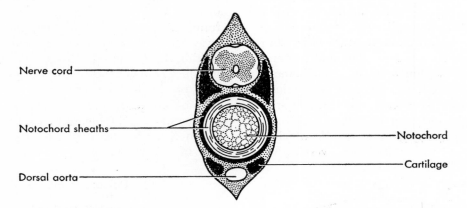

FIGURE 207.   Notochord of a young dogfish. Cross section shows nerve cord and sheaths of notochord.

Plan of structure

The vertebrates resemble the other chordates in their **metamerism** and **bilateral symmetry**, in the possession of a **coelom**, a **notochord**, and **gill slits** at some stage in their existence, and a **dorsal nerve tube.** They differ from other chordates and resemble one another in the possession of cartilaginous or bony **vertebrae,** usually two pairs of **appendages,** an internal and jointed **skeleton,** a **ventrally situated heart** with at least two chambers, and **red corpuscles** in the blood.

The body of a vertebrate may be divided into a **head,** usually a **neck,** and a **trunk.** In many species there is a posterior extension, the **tail.** Two pairs of **lateral appendages** are generally present, the thoracic (pectoral fins, forelimbs, wings, or arms) and the pelvic (pelvic fins, hindlimbs). The limbs support the body, serve in locomotion, and usually have other special functions.

The plan of structure of a vertebrate can be presented most clearly with diagrams showing longitudinal and cross sections through the body (Figs. 208 and 213). As in the amphioxus, the nerve cord is dorsal but extends in front of the end of the notochord and enlarges into a **brain.** The **notochord** becomes invested by the vertebrae. The **coelom** is large. The **digestive canal** forms a more or less convoluted tube which lies in the body cavity. The **liver, pancreas,** and **spleen** are situated near the digestive canal. In the anterior trunk region are the **lungs** and **heart.** The **kidneys** and **gonads** lie above the digestive canal.

Classes of Vertebrata

The principal classes of vertebrates having living representatives are:

Class 1. **Agnatha** (*L. a,* without; Gr. *gnathos,* jaws). Lampreys and hags (Fig. 240). Cold-blooded (poikilothermous), fishlike vertebrates without scales, jaws, or lateral fins.

Class 2. **Chondrichthyes** (**Elasmobranchii**) (Gr. *chondros,* cartilage; *ichthys,* fish). Sharks, rays, skates, and chi-

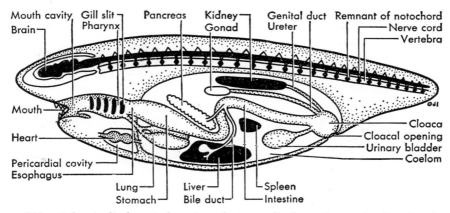

Mouth cavity · Gill slit · Pharynx · Pancreas · Kidney · Gonad · Genital duct · Ureter · Remnant of notochord · Nerve cord · Vertebra · Brain · Mouth · Heart · Pericardial cavity · Esophagus · Lung · Stomach · Liver · Bile duct · Spleen · Intestine · Cloaca · Cloacal opening · Urinary bladder · Coelom

FIGURE 208. A longitudinal vertical section of a generalized vertebrate, showing the plan of structure.

maeras. Cold-blooded vertebrates with jaws, a cartilaginous skeleton, 5 to 7 pairs of gills in separate clefts, a persistent notochord, placoid scales, and paired fins.

Class 3. **Osteichthyes** (Gr. *osteon*, bone; *ichthys*, fish). Fishes (Fig. 200). Cold-blooded vertebrates with jaws, bony skeleton, 4 pairs of gills in common cavity under opercula, skin usually with cycloid or ctenoid scales, usually with paired fins.

Class 4. **Amphibia** (Gr. *amphi*, both; *bios*, life). Frogs, toads, and salamanders (Fig. 200). Cold-blooded vertebrates, skin moist, no external scales, mostly with pentadactyl (5-fingered) limbs; young usually aquatic and breathe by gills; adults usually lose the gills and breathe by means of lungs.

Class 5. **Reptilia** (L. *repere*, to crawl). Turtles, sphenodon, lizards, snakes, and crocodiles (Fig. 200). Cold-blooded vertebrates breathing by means of lungs and usually having a dry scaly skin; respiration always by lungs.

Class 6. **Aves** (L. *avis*, bird). Birds (Fig. 200). Warm-blooded vertebrates with the forelimbs modified into wings and the body covered with feathers.

Class 7. **Mammalia** (L. *mamma*, breast). Hairy quadrupeds, whales, squirrels, bats, monkeys, and man (Fig. 200). Warm-blooded vertebrates with a hairy covering at some stage in their existence; the young nourished after birth by the secretion of the mammary glands of the mother.

SELECTED COLLATERAL READINGS

Berrill, N.J. *The Origin of Vertebrates*. Clarendon Press, Oxford, 1955.

Bullock, T.H. "The Anatomical Organization of the Nervous System of Enteropneusta." *Quar. J. Microscop. Sci.*, 86:55–111, 1945.

Carson, R.L. *The Sea Around Us*. Oxford Univ. Press, New York, 1951.

Morgan, T.H. "The Development of Balanoglossus." *J. Morphol. and Physiol.*, 9:1–86, 1894.

Ritter, W.E., and Davis, B.M. "Studies on the Ecology, Morphology and Speciology of the Young of Some Enteropneusta of Western North America." *Univ. Calif. Pub. Zool.*, 1:171–210, 1904.

Willey, A. *Amphioxus and the Ancestry of the Vertebrates*. Columbia Univ. Press, New York, 1894.

CHAPTER 23

A Representative Vertebrate. Frog

THE frog is used for laboratory study more often than any other animal as a vertebrate type. A knowledge of its structures and physiologic processes helps in understanding the vertebrates in general and gives a background for the study of more complex forms, including man. The following account of the structure, physiology, and development of the frog applies to any common species such as the leopard frog, *Rana pipiens*, or the bullfrog, *Rana catesbeiana*. The principal subjects considered are the external features, histology and physiology of the skin, structure of the systems of organs, processes of digestion, respiration, internal transport by blood and lymph, disposal of wastes, mechanical support and movement by bones and muscles, control of the body exercised by nerves and sense organs, ecology, behavior, reproduction, and embryonic development.

Many structural and physiologic characteristics of the frog are similar to those of man, hence it is suggested that comparisons be made from time to time. Chapters 31 to 34, which contain general considerations of nutrition, skeletal structures and movement, coordination and behavior, and reproduction and development, might profitably be included with the study of the frog.

The leopard frog lives in or near fresh-water lakes, ponds, and streams, and is distributed over the North American continent except on the Pacific slope. The frog **leaps** on land and **swims** in water. The **hind-limbs** are large and powerful; when the frog is on land they are folded up, but to propel the body through the air they are suddenly extended. Likewise in swimming, the hind-limbs are alternately folded up and extended; and during their backward stroke, the toes are spread apart, increasing the webbed surface so as to offer more resistance to the water. Frequently frogs float on the surface with just the tip of the nose exposed and with the hindlegs hanging down. When disturbed in this position, the frog dives under water, the hindlimbs are flexed, a movement which withdraws the body, and the forelimbs direct the animal downward; then the hindlimbs are extended again, completing the dive.

Frogs **croak** mostly during the breeding season, but also at other times of the year, especially in the evening or when the atmosphere becomes damp. Croaking may take place either in air or under water. In the latter case, the air is forced from the lungs, past the vocal cords, into the mouth cavity, and back again.

The principal **enemies** of frogs are snakes, turtles, cranes, herons, other amphibians, and man. The excellence of frog legs for the table has resulted in their widespread destruction, and this has been augmented by the capture of great numbers for use in

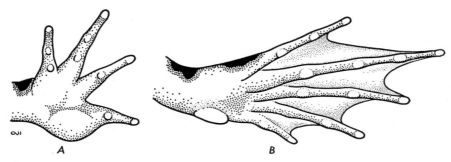

FIGURE 209. Feet of a male frog, *Rana pipiens*. A, forefoot showing enlarged first digit (thumb), which is most developed during the breeding season. B, hindfoot showing web.

scientific investigations. Tadpoles fall prey to aquatic insects, fish, and waterfowl, and relatively few of them reach maturity.

External anatomy

The body of the frog may be divided into the head and trunk (Fig. 217); there is no neck region. The **eyes** usually protrude from the head, but are drawn into their orbits when the frog closes its eyelids. Behind each eye there is a flat **eardrum** (**tympanic membrane**). A pair of **nostrils** (**external nares**) is situated on the dorsal surface near the end of the snout. In the dorsal midline, just in front of the eyes in some specimens, is a light area called the **brow spot**, which, in the embryo, was connected with the brain. The **mouth** of the frog extends from one side of the head to the other. The **cloacal opening**, or what is sometimes called the anus, is situated at the posterior end of the body.

The **forelimbs** are short and serve to hold up the anterior part of the body. The **hands** possess 4 digits and the rudiment of a fifth,

the thumb. In the male, the inner digit is thicker than the corresponding digit of the female, especially during the breeding season (Fig. 209). The **hindlimbs** are folded together when the frog is at rest. The 5 toes are connected by a **web**, making the foot an efficient swimming organ.

Body covering

The **skin** is smooth and loosely attached to the body. Along either side of the body, behind the eyes, is a ridge formed by a thickening of the skin; this is called the **dorsolateral fold** (**dermal plica**). The skin is colored by scattered **pigment granules** in the epidermis and pigment cells known as chromatophores in the dermis. The chromatophores are of several different kinds, the most important being those which contain black or yellow pigment. There are also interference cells that contain whitish crystals. There is no green pigment in the frog's skin. Frogs are usually **protectively colored** by resembling their surroundings. The color of

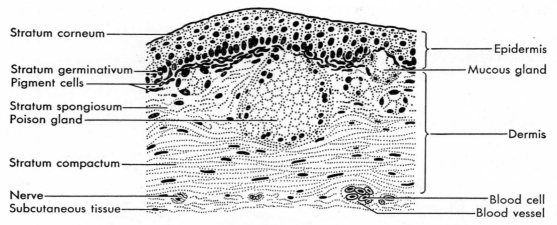

FIGURE 210. Section of frog skin showing microscopic structure (histology). Vertical section. (After *Laboratory Explorations in General Zoology*, by Karl A. Stiles. Third edition. Copyright 1955 by The Macmillan Company.)

the dorsal and lateral surfaces is darker than the ventral surface, which is whitish. Changes in color may occur as described on page 398.

Histologically, the skin consists of two layers as in other vertebrates (Fig. 210), an outer epidermis and an inner dermis. There are several layers of cells in the **epidermis** (stratified epithelium, Fig. 43). That on the outside, the **stratum corneum,** is horny and consists of broad, thin cells, the **squamous epithelium.** Beneath this lies a transitional zone of polygonal cells, which in turn rest upon the basal columnar cells of the **stratum germinativum.** During molting the stratum corneum is shed. New cells are being continually formed by those of the columnar layer, and the outward pressure of these cells brings about the flattening of the surface layers.

The **dermis** consists of two layers, a loose outer layer, the **stratum spongiosum,** which contains the dermal glands and pigment cells (**chromatophores**), and a dense inner layer of connective tissue, the **stratum compactum,** which contains white and yellow fibers, a few smooth muscle cells, blood vessels, and nerves. Beneath the dermis is a subcutaneous layer of loose connective tissue, which is divided into two layers by

lymph spaces and serves to attach the skin to the body wall by septa.

The skin is richly provided with glands. These are of two principal types: **mucous glands,** which are more numerous and small, and **poison glands,** which are larger and less common. These glands open to the outside by means of ducts. The mucus-covered surface of the frog makes him slippery, which often helps him to escape the grasp of enemies. Each gland consists of an epithelial layer of secreting cells, outside of which are muscle fibers and connective tissue. The mucous glands may be present in great numbers, as many as 60 to each square millimeter of surface. Mucus is formed in the secreting epithelium, discharged into the lumen of the gland, and forced through the duct to the surface of the skin by the muscle cells. The poison glands secrete a whitish fluid with a burning taste, which serves as a means of protection against enemies. The expulsion of this secretion may be stimulated by rough handling or chloroforming a frog.

The skin in man and other vertebrates

The skin in vertebrates, in general, is chiefly protective and sensory, but it may also carry on respiration, secretion, and excretion. Secretion and excretion take place by means of glands, which may be simple as the **mucous glands** of amphibians and fishes, or complex as the **sweat, oil,** and **mammary glands.** The skin often produces outgrowths such as hair, feathers, nails, hoofs, claws, scales, teeth, and bony plates.

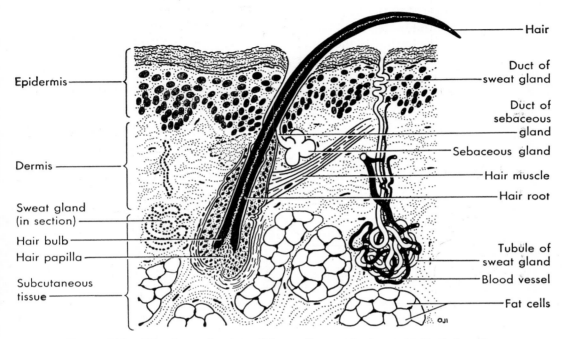

FIGURE 211. Skin of man showing cell layers, fibers, and other parts. Vertical section.

In **man** the skin (Fig. 211) protects the deeper tissues from drying, from injury, and from the invasion of bacteria and other organisms. It contains the end organs of many sensory nerves. The balance between heat production and heat dissipation is effected largely by the skin, since skin offers a large surface for radiation and evaporation of sweat, and it contains a large amount of blood. About 87.5 per cent of the body heat passes out through the skin as compared with 10.7 per cent through the lungs, and 1.8 per cent in the urine and feces. **Sebaceous glands** occur everywhere except on the palms of the hands and soles of the feet. They are compound alveolar glands with ducts that usually open into a hair follicle. Their secretion, **sebum,** is a fatty, oily substance that keeps the skin and hair flexible and covers the skin with a layer that prevents too rapid evaporation of water. **Sweat glands** are distributed over the surface of the skin, with the exception of the margins of the lips, the skin under the nails, and the glans penis. They are tubular, with the inner portion coiled into a ball. The average amount of sweat secreted in 24 hours is about 16 to 20 fluid ounces. Sweat contains some waste substances, but it is particularly important because of the heat that is necessary to evaporate it.

General internal anatomy

If the body wall of the frog is split open in the ventral midline, from the posterior end of the body to the angle of the jaw, the organs in the body cavity or **coelom** will be exposed (Fig. 212). The **heart** lies within the saclike **pericardium;** it is partially surrounded by the three lobes of the reddish-brown **liver.** The two **lungs** lie, one on either side, near the anterior end of the abdominal cavity. Coiled about within the body cavity are the **stomach** and **intestine.** The **kidneys** are flat reddish bodies attached to the dorsal body wall; they lie outside the coelom, just behind a thin membrane, the peritoneum. The two **testes** of the male are small ovoid organs suspended by membranes and lying at the sides of the digestive tract. The **ovaries** and **oviducts** of the female occupy a large part of the body cavity during the breeding season. The **coelom** is lined with a membrane of mesodermal origin, the **peritoneum.** The reproductive organs and digestive tract are suspended by double layers of peritoneum called **mesenteries** (Fig. 213).

In **man,** a **diaphragm** separates the tho-

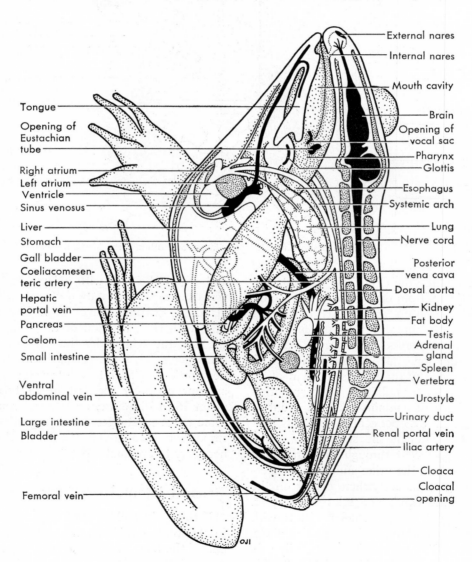

FIGURE 212.   Internal structure of a frog.

racic and abdominal cavities. The **thoracic cavity** contains the esophagus, trachea, lungs, heart, and blood vessels. The **abdominal cavity** contains the stomach, spleen, pancreas, liver, gall bladder, kidneys, and large and small intestines. The lower part of the abdominal cavity is called the **pelvic cavity**; this contains the bladder, rectum, and some of the reproductive organs.

Digestive system

The principal functions of the digestive system are to receive, digest, and absorb food and eliminate some wastes.

The **food** of the frog consists principally of living worms and insects. These are usually captured by the **extensile tongue**, which can be thrown forward as shown in the

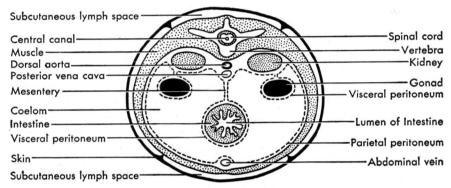

FIGURE 213. Diagram of a cross section of the body of a frog through the kidneys and gonads to show relation of the peritoneum (broken lines) to other organs.

illustration at the head of this chapter (headpiece). The object adheres to the tongue, which is covered with a sticky secretion, and is then drawn into the mouth. No attention is paid to objects that are not moving. Large insects are pushed into the mouth with the forefeet. In case the object swallowed proves undesirable, it can be ejected through the mouth.

The **mouth cavity** is large. The **tongue** lies on the floor of the cavity with its anterior end attached to the jaw and its forked

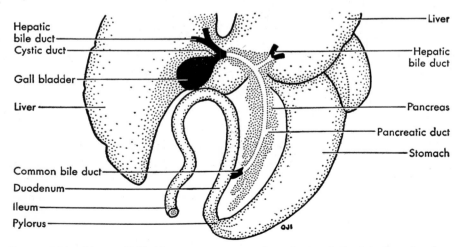

FIGURE 214. Liver, gall bladder, pancreas, stomach, and part of the intestine of a frog.

posterior end lying free. When a lymph space beneath the tongue is filled, the tongue is thrown forward for capturing insects. The **teeth** are conical in shape; they are borne by the upper jaw and two bones in the roof of the mouth called **vomers.** Teeth are used only for holding food and not for chewing it. New teeth replace those that may be lost.

The **esophagus** opens into the mouth cavity by a horizontal slit. Its inner surface bears longitudinal folds, which give it the remarkable powers of distension necessary for swallowing large animals for food. Histologically it resembles the stomach. The **stomach** is crescent-shaped and lies mostly on the left side of the body. The anterior or **cardiac** end is larger than the esophagus. It decreases in size toward the posterior or **pyloric** end, where it joins the small intestine. The stomach is held in place by a dorsal fold of the peritoneum, and a ventral fold of the peritoneum.

The walls of the stomach are thick, consisting of 4 layers: (1) the outer thin peritoneum, the **serosa** or serous membrane; (2)

a tough **muscular layer;** (3) a spongy layer, the **submucosa;** and (4) an inner folded mucous layer, the **mucosa.** The mucosa or mucous membrane is an inner lining, with many glands, both one-celled and many-celled. These glands are tubular in shape and sometimes branched. They are formed by the invagination of the epithelium of the stomach lining. Those near the cardiac end of the stomach are longer and differ histologically from those near the pyloric end.

The two largest **digestive glands** are the pancreas and liver (Fig. 214). The **pancreas** lies between the duodenum and the stomach. It is a much branched tubular gland, which secretes an alkaline digestive fluid and empties it into the common bile duct. The **liver** is a large, three-lobed, reddish gland, which secretes an alkaline digestive fluid called bile. This fluid is stored in the **gall bladder** until food enters the intestine, then it passes into the duodenum through the common **bile duct.**

The anterior portion of the small intestine is known as the **duodenum;** this leads to the much coiled **ileum,** which widens abruptly

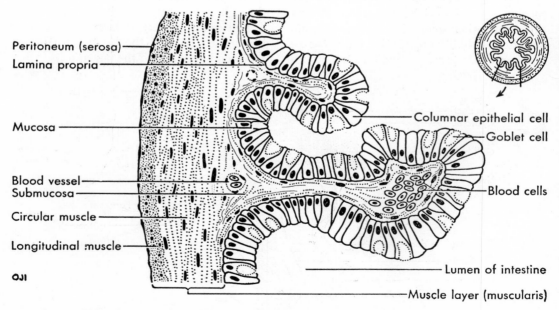

Peritoneum (serosa)
Lamina propria

Mucosa

Blood vessel
Submucosa
Circular muscle
Longitudinal muscle
OJI

Columnar epithelial cell
Goblet cell

Blood cells

Lumen of intestine
Muscle layer (muscularis)

FIGURE 215. Diagram of a small portion of a cross section of the frog intestine showing its histology. (After *Laboratory Explorations in General Zoology,* by Karl A. Stiles. Third edition. Copyright 1955 by The Macmillan Company.)

into the **large intestine.** The digestive canal, the urinary bladder, and the reproductive ducts open into an enlarged cavity called the **cloaca.** Waste products and reproductive cells pass from the cloaca to the outside through the **cloacal opening.** In the frog the cloacal opening is often, but incorrectly, called the anus. An anus is the posterior opening of only the digestive system. The cloacal opening is the common posterior aperture through which the products of the intestine, kidneys, and reproductive organs pass to the outside of the body. The intestine is held in place by a dorsal fold of the peritoneum. The layers of cells that make up the intestinal wall (Fig. 215) consist first of a very thin outer coat of **peritoneum.** Beneath this is a layer of **longitudinal muscle fibers,** then a thicker layer of **circular muscle fibers;** next comes a connective tissue layer, the **submucosa,** containing numerous blood vessels, separated more or less from the innermost layer, the **mucosa,** by a thin layer of fibrous connective tissue, the **lamina (tunica) propria.** The mucosal epithelium consists of two types of cylindrical cells forming a single layer: (1) **absorptive cells,** which

are narrow, and (2) **goblet cells,** which produce a slippery mucus. The mucosa is thrown into many folds but no true villi nor definite glands and crypts are present as in higher vertebrates.

Digestion in vertebrates is fully treated in Chapter 32.

Respiratory system and respiration

The primary functions of the respiratory system are to provide oxygen to the tissues and to get rid of excess carbon dioxide.

Two kinds of respiration may be recognized: (1) **external respiration,** whereby oxygen in the air enters the body and is transported to the cells, and carbon dioxide is carried away from the cells to the outside of the body. There are two successive phases to this process: (a) breathing, which brings oxygen and blood together in the lungs, and (b) transportation of oxygen and carbon dioxide between the lungs and cells. (2) **Internal respiration,** during which the blood supplies oxygen to, and takes carbon dioxide from the cells of the body. Oxygen in the

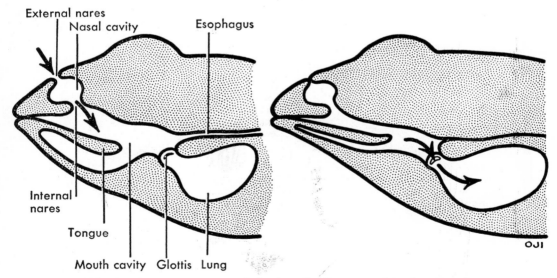

FIGURE 216. Respiratory movements of the frog. In diagram at *left*, the external nares are open and air enters the mouth cavity. In diagram at *right*, the external nares are closed, the floor of the mouth cavity is raised, and air is forced into the lungs. Labels have been omitted from the very short larynx and bronchus. Arrows show pathway of air to lungs.

lungs unites readily with the hemoglobin in the red corpuscles. The hemoglobin combines with the oxygen to form a compound which is then transported by the blood from the respiratory organs to the capillaries, where it breaks up, the oxygen being absorbed by the tissues. Carbon dioxide from the tissues is carried to the lungs and discharged to the outside.

External respiration is carried on by **gills** in most aquatic vertebrates and by **lungs** in terrestrial vertebrates. **Respiration** in the frog, as just described, is carried on largely by the **lungs**, but takes place also, to a considerable extent, through the skin. As shown in Fig. 216, air passes through the nostrils or **external nares** into the **nasal cavity** and then through the **internal** or **posterior nares** into the **mouth cavity.** The external nares are then closed, the floor of the mouth is raised, and the air is forced through the glottis into a short tube, the larynx, then into a very short tube, the **bronchus,** and thence into the lungs. Air is expelled from the lungs into the mouth cavity by the contraction of the muscles of the body wall. In addition to the skin and lungs, some gaseous exchange takes place through the mucous membrane lining the mouth.

The air in the mouth cavity is changed

FIGURE 217. The leopard frog (*Rana pipiens*) is one of the most common amphibians in North America. Note the expanded vocal sacs between ear and shoulder; these are found only in the male. (Courtesy of American Museum of Natural History.)

by throat movements. The **glottis** remains closed, while the floor of the mouth is alternately raised and lowered. Air is thus drawn in and expelled through the nares.

The **lungs** (Fig. 218) are ovoid sacs with thin elastic walls. The inner surface of the lungs is divided by a network of partitions into many minute chambers called alveoli. Blood capillaries are numerous in the walls

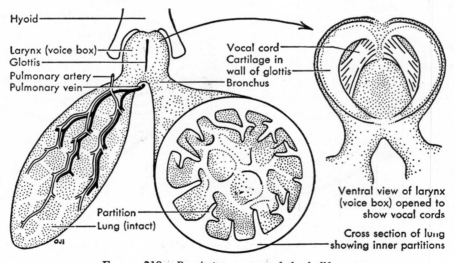

FIGURE 218. Respiratory organs of the bullfrog.

of these alveoli, where oxygen diffuses into the blood and carbon dioxide is released into the lung.

The **larynx** (voice box) is strengthened by cartilages. Across it are stretched two elastic bands, the vocal cords (Fig. 218). The croaking of the frog is produced by the vibrations of the free edges of the vocal cords, due to expulsion of air from the lungs. The laryngeal muscles regulate the tension of the cords, and hence the pitch of the sound. Many male frogs have a pair of **vocal sacs** which open into the mouth cavity. (Fig. 217); they serve as resonators to increase the volume of sound.

The subject of respiration in vertebrates is treated more fully in Chapter 32.

Circulatory system and internal transport

The chief function of the circulatory system is to distribute body fluids to all the cells, maintaining the tissue fluid which bathes them in about the same state at all times.

The circulatory system of the frog consists of a heart, arteries, veins, and lymph spaces. The liquid portion of the blood, which is known as plasma, contains three kinds of corpuscles: red corpuscles (erythrocytes), white corpuscles (leucocytes), and spindle cells (thrombocytes). The **blood plasma** carries food and waste matter in solution. It **coagulates** under certain conditions, forming a **clot** of fibrin and corpuscles, and a liquid called **serum.** The power of coagulation is an adaptation of great importance,

since the clot soon closes a wound and thus prevents bleeding to death.

The **red corpuscles (erythrocytes)** are elliptical, flattened cells (Fig. 219) containing a respiratory pigment called **hemoglobin.** Hemoglobin combines with oxygen in the capillaries of the respiratory organs and gives it out to the tissues of the body. The **white corpuscles (leucocytes)** are of several types (Fig. 219); they vary in size, and most are capable of independent amoeboid movement. Certain kinds (phagocytes) are of great value to the animal since they engulf small bodies such as bacteria, frequently preventing the multiplication of pathogenic organisms and helping to overcome infectious diseases. White corpuscles also aid in the removal of broken-down tissue. The thrombocytes are usually spindle-shaped. They are unstable; and when brought in contact with foreign substances, they break down, releasing an enzyme, **thrombin,** which changes fibrinogen into the insoluble **fibrin** so necessary for blood clotting. Blood corpuscles arise principally in the marrow of the bones. They also increase in numbers by division while in the blood vessels. Some white corpuscles are probably formed in the spleen, a gland in which worn-out red corpuscles are destroyed.

The **heart** (Fig. 220) is the central pumping station of the circulatory system. It is composed of a conical, muscular **ventricle;** two thin-walled **atria,*** one on the right, the

* Auricles, according to the old terminology. In human anatomy, only the ear-shaped lobe of the atrium is called the auricle. The plural of atrium is atria.

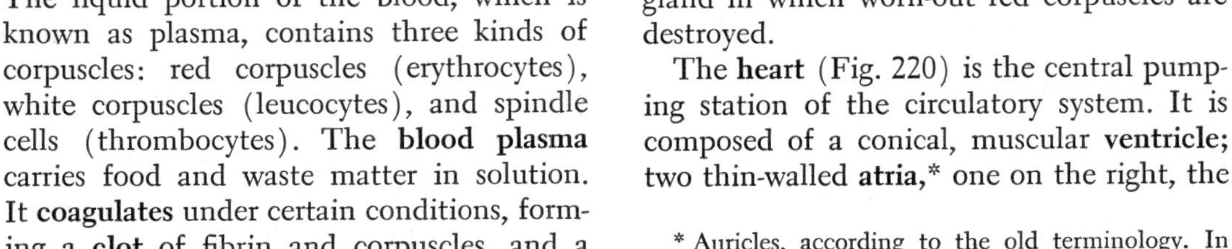

Erythrocyte   Lymphocyte   Eosinophil   Basophil   Neutrophil   Thrombocyte

FIGURE 219. Types of blood cells of the frog.

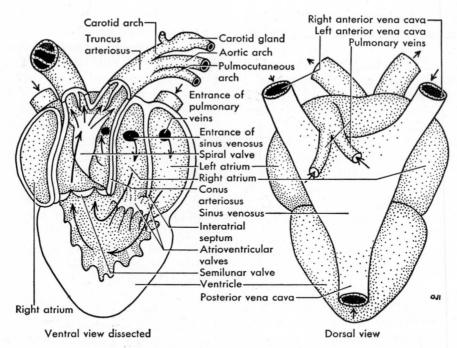

FIGURE 220. Heart of the frog. The arrows indicate the direction in which the blood flows. In ventral view, unlabeled opening is to pulmocutaneous arch.

other on the left; a thick-walled tube, the **conus arteriosus**, which arises from the base of the ventricle; and a thin-walled triangular sac, the **sinus venosus**, on the dorsal side.

The **arteries** (Fig. 221) carry blood away from the heart. The conus arteriosus divides near the anterior border of the atria into two vessels as shown in Fig. 220. Each branch is called a **truncus arteriosus**, and each gives rise to the following three arteries: 1. The **common carotid** divides into the **external carotid** (lingual), which supplies the tongue and neighboring parts, and the **internal carotid**, which gives off the **palatine artery** to the roof of the mouth, the **cerebral carotid** to the brain, and the **ophthalmic artery** to the eye. Where the common carotid branches is a swelling called the **carotid gland**; this body serves to equalize the blood flow, especially in the internal carotid artery.

2. The **pulmocutaneous artery** branches, forming the **pulmonary artery**, which passes

to the lungs and the **cutaneous artery**. The latter gives off the **auricularis**, which is distributed to the lower jaw and neighboring parts, the **dorsalis**, which supplies the skin of the back, and the **lateralis**, which supplies the skin of the sides. Most of these branches carry blood to the respiratory organs—lungs, skin, and mouth.

3. The **aortic** (systemic) **arches**, after passing outward and around the digestive tract, unite to form the **dorsal aorta**. Before the union of the two aortic arches, several branches are given off, two of which are: (a) the **occipitovertebral** artery, which gives off branches dorsally that supply the backbone and posterior part of the skull; (b) the **subclavian artery**, located just posterior to the occipitovertebral, arising at about the level of the shoulder and extending into the forelimbs as the **brachial artery**. The dorsal aorta gives off the **coeliacomesenteric artery**; this divides, forming the **coeliac**, which supplies the stomach, pancreas, and

liver; and the **anterior mesenteric**, which is distributed to the intestine, spleen, and cloaca. Posterior to the origin of the coeliacomesenteric, the dorsal aorta gives off several renal arteries which supply the kidneys. A small **posterior mesenteric artery** arises near the posterior end of the dorsal aorta and passes to the large intestine; and in the female, to the uterus. The dorsal aorta finally divides into two **common iliac arteries**, which are distributed to the ventral body wall, the rectum, bladder, the anterior part of the thigh (**femoral artery**), and other parts of the hindlimbs (**sciatic artery**).

The **veins** (Fig. 221) return blood to the heart. The blood from the lungs is collected in the **pulmonary veins** and poured into the left atrium. Venous blood is carried to the **sinus venosus** by three large trunks: the two **anterior venae cavae** and the **posterior vena cava**. The anterior vanae cavae receive blood from the (1) **external jugulars**, which collect blood from the tongue, thyroid, and neighboring parts; (2) the **innominates**, which collect blood from the head by means of the **internal jugulars** and from the shoulder by means of the **subscapulars**; and (3) the **subclavians**, which collect blood from the forelimbs by means of the **brachial**, and from the side of the body and head by means of the **musculocutaneous veins**. The posterior vena cava receives blood from the kidneys by means of 4 to 6 pairs of **renal veins**; from the reproductive organs by means of **spermatic** or **ovarian veins**; and from the liver by means of two **hepatic veins**.

The veins which carry blood to the kidneys constitute the **renal portal system**. The renal portal vein receives the blood from the hindlimbs by means of the **sciatic** and **femoral veins**, and from the body wall by means of the **dorsolumbar vein**. While it is true that the blood systems of the various vertebrates are built on the same general plan, there is no renal portal system in man.

The liver receives blood from the **hepatic portal system**. The **femoral veins** from the hindlimbs divide, and their ventral branches unite to form the **ventral abdominal vein**. The ventral abdominal vein collects blood from the bladder, ventral body wall, and heart. The **hepatic portal vein** carries blood into the liver from the stomach, intestine, spleen, and pancreas. This passage of the venous blood from the intestinal tract through the liver before entering the main circulation makes it possible for the liver to add or remove substances from the blood as physiologic needs may require.

Circulation in the frog takes place in the following manner: the sinus venosis contracts, forcing the nonoxygenated venous blood into the right atrium (Fig. 220). Oxygenated blood from the lungs passes into the left atrium. Then both atria contract and force their contents into the ventricle. Formerly, it was thought that when the ventricle contracted, the spiral valve deflected nonoxygenated blood from the right side into the pulmocutaneous arch and oxygenated blood from the left side into the carotid and aortic arches. But experiments have proved that the two blood streams mix. Therefore, it must be assumed that mixed blood is pumped to all parts of the frog's body. The blood is prevented from flowing back into the heart by means of **valves** (Figs. 220 and 384). Respiration through the skin of the frog, both in water and on land, is thought to compensate, at least in part, for failure of all nonoxygenated blood to be pumped to the lungs.

The blood that is thus forced through the arteries makes its way into tubular blood vessels that become smaller and smaller until the extremely narrow **capillaries** are reached (Fig. 383, p. 529). Here food and oxygen are delivered to the tissues, and waste products are taken up from the tissues. The renal portal system carries blood to the kidneys, where urea and similar impurities are taken out. The hepatic portal system carries blood to the liver, where bile and glycogen are formed. The blood brought to

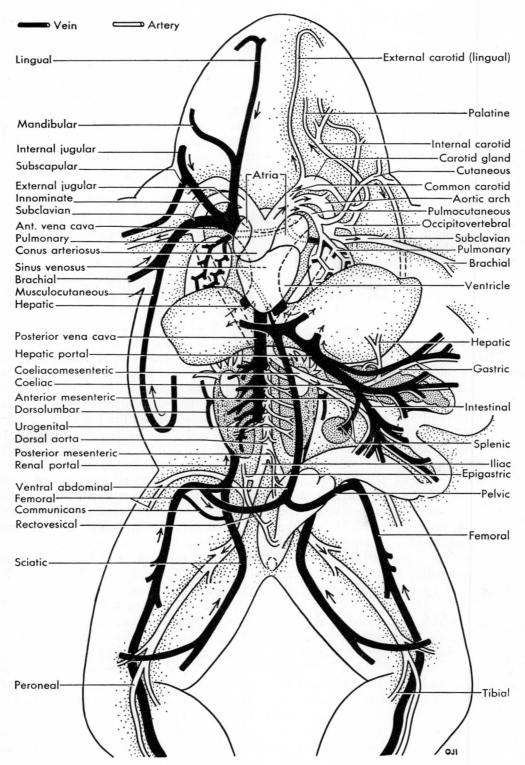

Vein ▬▬▬○ **Artery** ▭▭▷

Lingual

External carotid (lingual)

Palatine

Mandibular

Internal carotid
Carotid gland
Cutaneous

Internal jugular
Subscapular

External jugular
Innominate
Subclavian

Common carotid
Aortic arch
Pulmocutaneous
Occipitovertebral
Subclavian
Pulmonary
Brachial

Ant. vena cava
Pulmonary
Conus arteriosus

Atria

Sinus venosus
Brachial
Musculocutaneous
Hepatic

Ventricle

Posterior vena cava
Hepatic portal

Hepatic

Gastric

Coeliacomesenteric
Coeliac

Anterior mesenteric
Dorsolumbar

Intestinal

Urogenital
Dorsal aorta

Posterior mesenteric
Renal portal

Splenic

Iliac
Epigastric

Ventral abdominal
Femoral
Communicans

Pelvic

Rectovesical

Femoral

Sciatic

Peroneal

Tibial

FIGURE 221. Circulatory system of the bullfrog in ventral view, showing the larger arteries and veins in relation to the internal organs. The arrows indicate the direction in which the blood flows.

the lungs and skin is oxygenated and then carried back to the heart. The passage of blood through the capillaries can easily be observed in the web of the frog's foot or in the tail of the tadpole.

The **lymphatic system** of the frog includes many lymph vessels of various sizes that form networks co-extensive with blood vessels but are difficult to see. The frogs and toads, unlike other vertebrates, have several lymph spaces between the skin and the body. Four **lymph hearts,** two near the third vertebra and two near the end of the vertebral column, force the lymph by pulsations into the internal jugular and a branch of the renal portal veins. The watery lymph which is colorless contains leucocytes and various constituents of blood plasma.

Relations of the hearts of vertebrates to respiration

In the fish (Fig. 222) the heart consists of a single muscular ventricle and a single thin-walled atrium. Blood enters the atrium from the body and, when the atrium contracts, passes into the ventricle; it is prevented by valves from returning to the atrium. The ventricle forces it into arteries leading to the gills; here it is oxygenated and carried directly to the body tissues before again returning to the atrium. Valves prevent it from flowing back into the ventricle.

In Amphibia (Fig. 220) there are two atria. Nonoxygenated venous blood from the body enters the right atrium and oxygenated blood from the lungs flows into the left atrium. Both atria contract and force their contents into the single ventricle. The ventricle forces the blood through the conus and truncus arteriosus, into the carotid, aortic (systemic), and pulmocutaneous arches.

In most reptiles there are two atria, and the ventricle is partly divided into two chambers (Fig. 222). Nonoxygenated venous blood from the body entering the right atrium is thus kept more or less separated

from the oxygenated blood that flows into the left ventricle from the lungs. When the ventricle contracts, the nonoxygenated blood is forced through the pulmonary arteries to the lungs, and through the left aorta into the dorsal aorta; and the oxygenated blood is forced through the right aortic arch which merges into the dorsal aorta. Thus the dorsal aorta contains a mixture of both nonoxygenated and oxygenated blood.

In birds and mammals (Fig. 222), the ventricle is completely separated into two chambers, forming a four-chambered heart; and thus the nonoxygenated and oxygenated blood are kept entirely separate, hence providing an efficient pulmonary circulation.

Excretory system and disposal of wastes

A certain amount of substance resulting from the breaking down of living matter is excreted by the skin, lungs, liver, and intestinal walls; but most of it is taken from the blood in the kidney. From the kidney, it passes through the urinary * (mesonephric) duct, and then into the **cloaca.** It may be voided at once through the cloacal opening or stored in the **bladder** temporarily (Figs. 223 and 224). The **kidneys** lie dorsal to the peritoneum in the subvertebral lymph space. They are composed of connective tissue containing a large number of **uriniferous tubules,** each of which begins in a **renal corpuscle.** The renal corpuscle consists of a coiled mass of thin-walled blood vessels, the **glomerulus,** and an enclosing, thin, double-walled cup called **Bowman's capsule.** It acts as a selective filter which removes organic wastes (especially urea), excess inorganic salts, and water from the body. The liquid waste collected in the kidney is called urine. It is carried by the uriniferous tubules to a **collecting tubule** and thence into the urinary duct. Ciliated funnels called **nephrostomes** occur in the ventral portion; these

---

* Sometimes incorrectly called a ureter. The true ureter is found only in the reptiles, birds, and mammals.

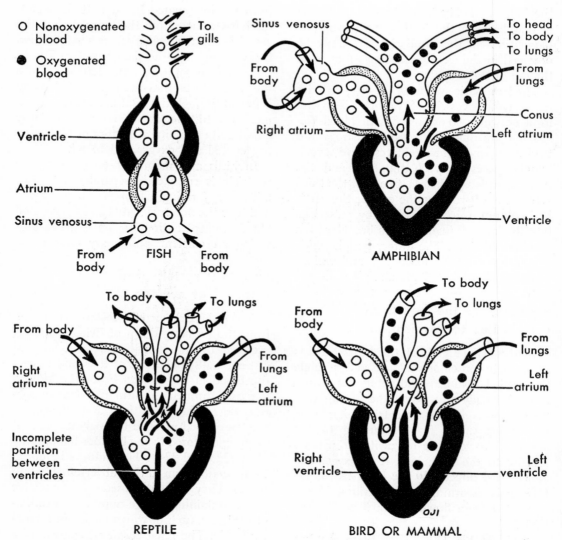

FIGURE 222. Diagrams showing the comparative structure and evolution of the heart among different types of vertebrates; valves omitted. The arrows indicate the direction in which the blood flows.

drain wastes from the coelom. The nephrostomes in tadpoles are connected with the uriniferous tubules, but they open into branches of the renal vein in the adult. The nephrostome mechanism for removal of wastes probably represents a stage in the evolution of the kidney. Urogenital arteries and the renal portal vein (Fig. 221) bring blood into the kidney. Blood leaves the kidney by way of the renal veins.

Reproductive system

The function of the reproductive system is the maintenance of the species from one generation to the next. In the frog the sexes are separate. The male can be distinguished from the female by the greater thickness of the first digit of his forelimbs (Fig. 209). The **sperms** of the male arise in the **testes** (Fig. 224), pass into the kidneys through the **vasa efferentia**, then to the **urinary duct** by a route that differs in different species. The urinary duct is dilated at the posterior end in some species to form the **seminal vesicle.** The sperms then pass from the urinary duct or seminal vesicle, as the case may be, to the outside through the **cloacal opening.**

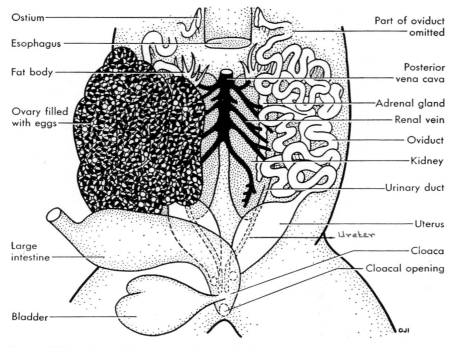

Ostium
Esophagus
Fat body
Ovary filled with eggs
Large intestine
Bladder

Part of oviduct omitted
Posterior vena cava
Adrenal gland
Renal vein
Oviduct
Kidney
Urinary duct
Uterus
Ureter
Cloaca
Cloacal opening

FIGURE 223. Urogenital system of the female frog in ventral view; left ovary removed.

The **eggs** arise in the **ovaries** of the female (Fig. 223); and during the breeding season, they break through the ovarian walls into the body cavity. There they are moved anteriorly by the beating of cilia which cover the peritoneum. The cilia at the entrance to the oviduct, the **ostium**, create currents which draw the eggs into the convoluted **oviduct;** they are carried down the oviduct into the thin-walled distensible **uterus** by action of the cilia in the oviduct. The glandular wall of the oviduct secretes the gelatinous coats of the eggs. The fertilization and development of the eggs will be described later.

Just in front of each reproductive organ is a yellowish, glove-shaped **fat body** which probably constitutes reserve supplies of food that serve the animal during its period of hibernation.

Reproductive organs of man

The reproductive organs of **human beings** (Fig. 225) resemble those of the frog rather closely. **In the male,** the two testes produce sperms and internal secretions. Within the testes are **seminiferous tubules** which unite to form the **epididymis,** a much coiled tubule about 20 feet long. The epididymis leads into the sperm duct (**vas deferens**); this duct joins the duct of a **seminal vesicle** to form an **ejaculatory duct.** The ejaculatory ducts open into the **urethra.** Near this point is situated a gland about the size of a chestnut, the **prostate gland.** On either side of the gland is a body about the size of a pea, the **bulbourethral (Cowper's) gland.** Sperms are formed in the testes and pass down the vasa deferentia. Secretions are supplied by

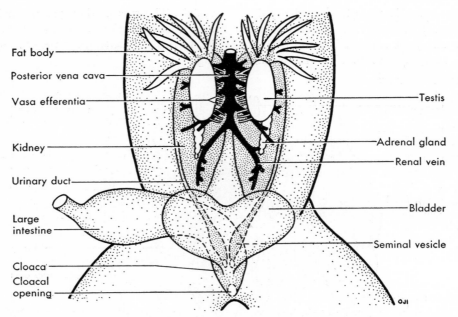

FIGURE 224. Urogenital system of the male frog in ventral view. The seminal vesicle is poorly developed in the leopard frog.

the seminal vesicles, Cowper's glands, and the prostate gland; these are ultimately added to the sperms and constitute the **seminal fluid (semen).** The semen flows through the ejaculatory ducts into the urethra and thence out of the body through the **penis.**

In the **female,** there are two ovaries

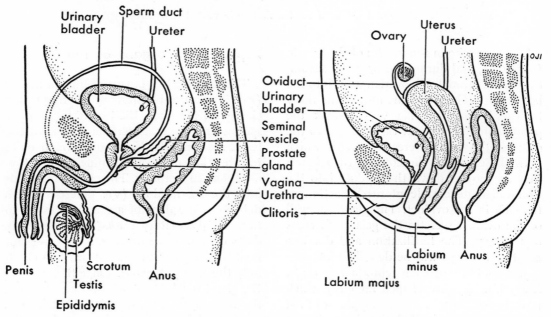

FIGURE 225. Diagram of a median section of the human male and female reproductive organs showing their relation to the urinary bladder and urethra.

which produce eggs and internal secretions, two **oviducts** or **Fallopian tubes** about 4 inches long, a **uterus**, a **vagina**, and the **external genitalia**. The ovaries are almond-shaped and weigh from 2 to 3½ grams. They contain at birth about 70,000 developing egg cells, most of which later disappear. The ova discharged from the ovary into the coelomic cavity then enter the oviduct and are carried to the uterus; here, if an egg is fertilized, it remains during embryonic development.

A general account of reproduction and development is contained in Chapter 34.

Skeletal system

The principal functions of the skeleton are mechanical support, motion, and protection. The internal supporting framework of the frog's body is an **endoskeleton** consisting largely of cartilage and bone. **Cartilage** (gristle) is a tissue in which the cells are embedded in a matrix that they secrete; it is firm, tough, and elastic (Fig. 43). Bone tissue is a connective tissue impregnated with mineral salts. About 58 per cent of bone is calcium phosphate, 7 per cent calcium carbonate, and 33 per cent organic matter such as cells and gelatinous substances. The endoskeleton supports the soft parts of the body, furnishes points of attachment for the muscles, and protects some of the delicate organs such as the brain, spinal cord, and eyes.

A study of the skeleton reveals an interesting story of the relation of structure to function. The ridges, lines, depressions, and protuberances on a bone all have some functional significance and are, therefore, mean-

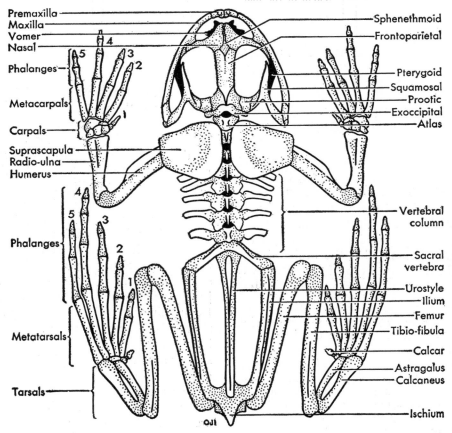

FIGURE 226. Skeleton of the frog.

ingful to the student of gross anatomy.

There are two main subdivisions of the skeleton: (1) the **axial** and (2) the **appendicular skeleton.**

The **axial skeleton** comprises the skull, vertebral column, and sternum.* The **appendicular skeleton** consists of the pectoral and pelvic girdles, and the bones of the limbs which they support.

The cartilage and bones of the skull may be grouped into two main divisions: (1) the brain case, and auditory and olfactory capsules, which constitute the **cranium;** and (2) the **visceral skeleton** (Fig. 228).

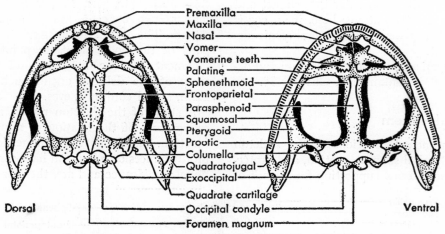

Premaxilla
Maxilla
Nasal
Vomer
Vomerine teeth
Palatine
Sphenethmoid
Frontoparietal
Parasphenoid
Squamosal
Pterygoid
Prootic
Columella
Quadratojugal
Exoccipital
Quadrate cartilage
Occipital condyle
Foramen magnum

Dorsal   Ventral

FIGURE 227.   Skull of the bullfrog in dorsal and ventral views.

Cranium

A large part of the cranium consists of cartilage. The bones are either ossifications of the cartilage, the **cartilage bones,** or have developed into connective tissue without passing through a cartilage stage, the **membrane bones.** The spinal cord passes through a large opening, the **foramen magnum,** in the posterior end of the cranium. On either side of this opening is a convexity of the exoccipital bones called the **occipital condyle,** which articulates in life in a concavity of the first vertebra and enables the frog to move its head.

The cranial bones of the dorsal side are the **prootics,** which enclose the inner ears; the **frontoparietals,** which form most of the

roof of the cranium; the **sphenethmoid,** which forms the posterior wall of the nasal cavity; and the **nasals,** which lie above the nasal capsules. The ventral surface of the cranium discloses the central, dagger-shaped **parasphenoid** and the **vomers,** which bear the vomerine teeth (Fig. 227).

Visceral skeleton

The jaws, hyoid, and cartilages of the larynx, which constitute the visceral skeleton, are preformed in cartilage and then strengthened by ossifications. The upper jaw (**maxilla**) consists of a pair of **premaxillae,** a pair of **maxillae,** and a pair of **quadratojugals.** The maxillae and premaxillae bear teeth. The lower jaw (**mandible**) consists of a pair of **angulosplenials** and a pair of **dentary bones** which overlap the angulosplenials and extend forward to meet a pair of **mentomecklian** bones. The **visceral arches** are represented in the adult by the hyoid and its processes (Fig. 228).

---

* The sternum may be regarded as a part of the appendicular skeleton because it supposedly originated in the early history of the land vertebrates from the pectoral girdle. However, it may be considered a part of the axial skeleton because of its medial (central) location.

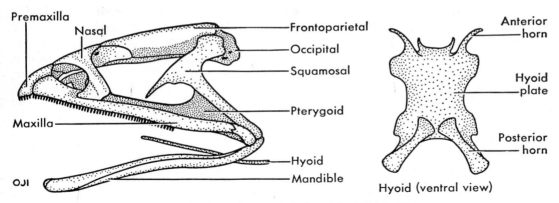

FIGURE 228.   Lateral view of skull and hyoid of bullfrog.

Vertebral column

The vertebral column (Fig. 226) or backbone consists of 9 **vertebrae** and a bladelike posterior extension, the **urostyle**. Each vertebra consists of a basal **centrum**, which is concave in front and convex behind, and a **neural arch** through which the spinal cord passes. The neural arch possesses a short **neural spine**, a **transverse process** on each side (except on the first vertebra), and a pair of articular processes called **zygapophyses** at each end. The vertebrae are held together by ligaments and move on one another by means of the centra and zygapophyses. The

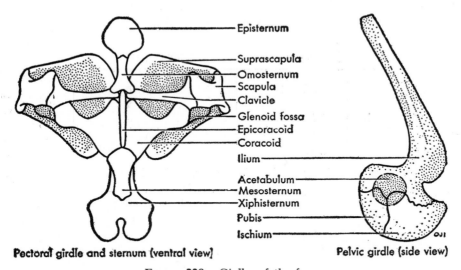

FIGURE 229.   Girdles of the frog.

vertebral column thus serves as a firm axial support which also allows bending of the body. A frog has no ribs.

* Although in this text the sternum is regarded as a part of the axial skeleton, it is described with the pectoral girdle because of the functional relationship of the two structures.

Appendicular skeleton

The **pectoral girdle** and sternum * (Fig. 229) support the forelimbs, serve as attachments for the muscles that move the forelimbs, and protect the organs lying within the anterior portion of the trunk. They are composed partly of bone and partly of cartilage. The suprascapulae lie above the vertebral column, and the rest of the girdle passes downward on either side and unites with the sternum in the ventral middle line. The principal parts of the pectoral girdle are: the **suprascapulae, scapulae, clavicles, coracoids,** and **epicoracoids;** of the sternum: the **episternum, omosternum, mesosternum,** and **xiphisternum.** The end of the long bone of the forelimb (**humerus**) lies in a concavity in the scapula and coracoid called the **glenoid fossa.**

The **pelvic girdle** supports the hindlimbs. It consists of two sets of three parts each: the **ilium,** the **ischium,** and the **pubis.** The pubis is cartilaginous. The anterior end of each ilium is attached to one of the transverse processes of the ninth vertebra. Where the parts of each half of the pelvic girdle unite, there is a concavity called the **acetabulum,** in which the head of the long leg bone (femur) lies.

The **forelimb** consists of a **humerus** which articulates with the glenoid fossa of the pectoral girdle at its proximal end and with the **radioulna** at its distal end. The bone of the forearm (radioulna) consists of the radius and ulna fused. The **wrist** contains 6 bones arranged in two rows, each consisting of three small bones (**carpals**). The palm of the **hand** is supported by 4 proximal **metacarpal** bones, followed by digits 2 and 3 which consist of 2 **phalanges** each, and by digits 4 and 5 which consist of 3 phalanges each, and the rudimentary thumb is represented by the first metacarpal.

The **hindlimb** consists of (1) a **femur** (thighbone), (2) a **tibiofibula** (the tibia and fibula fused) or lower leg bone, (3) four **tarsal** bones, the **astragalus,** the **calcaneum,** and 2 smaller bones, (4) the 5 **metatarsals** of the sole of the foot, (5) the phalanges of the digits, and (6) the **prehallux** (**calcar**) of the accessory digit. The two pairs of limbs differ in size but have similar component bones. This is easily seen in the accompanying table.

FORELIMB (ARM)	NO. OF BONES	HINDLIMB (LEG)	NO. OF BONES
Humerus (upper arm)	1	Femur (thighbone)	1
Radioulna (forearm)	2 fused	Tibiofibula (lower leg bone or shank)	2 fused
Carpals (wrist)	6	Tarsals (ankle)	4
Metacarpals (palm of hand)	5	Metatarsals (sole of foot)	5
Phalanges (fingers)	10	Phalanges (toes)	14 + prehallux

The skeletons of animals in general and of man in particular are described in Chapter 31.

Muscular system, motion, and locomotion

The main function of the muscular system is to cause movement by contraction. Muscles (Figs. 230 and 231) are of three principal types—**smooth, cardiac,** and **striated,** which is of a skeletal type; these differ in their microscopic structure and function. Smooth muscle is **involuntary muscle.** Cardiac muscle is "involuntary" striated muscle that occurs in the vertebrate heart only. Striated muscle of the skeletal type—that is, the muscles of the external muscular system—is **voluntary muscle.**

Muscle fibers may be 4 or 5 cm. long and, when bound together by connective tissue, form the larger bundles known as muscle. Skeletal muscles are usually attached by one or both ends to bones either directly or by means of a **tendon,** which is an inelastic band of connective tissue (Fig. 43). The two ends of a muscle are designated by different terms: the **origin** is the end attached to a relatively immovable part; the **insertion** is the movable end. Usually the origin is near the spinal axis of the body, while the insertion is peripheral. A muscle which bends one

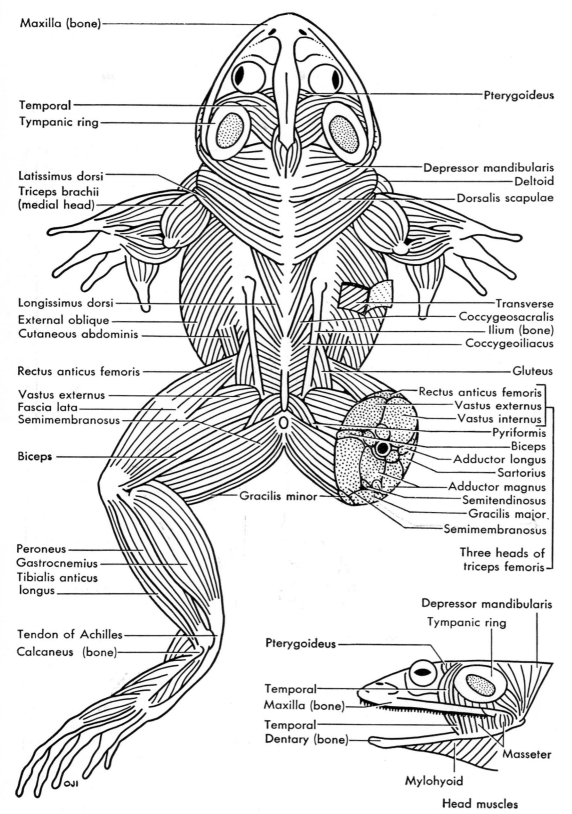

Maxilla (bone)

Temporal
Tympanic ring

Latissimus dorsi
Triceps brachii
(medial head)

Longissimus dorsi
External oblique
Cutaneous abdominis

Rectus anticus femoris

Vastus externus
Fascia lata
Semimembranosus

Biceps

Peroneus
Gastrocnemius
Tibialis anticus
longus

Tendon of Achilles
Calcaneus (bone)

Pterygoideus

Depressor mandibularis
Deltoid
Dorsalis scapulae

Transverse
Coccygeosacralis
Ilium (bone)
Coccygeoiliacus

Gluteus

Rectus anticus femoris
Vastus externus
Vastus internus
Pyriformis
Biceps
Adductor longus
Sartorius
Adductor magnus
Semitendinosus
Gracilis major
Semimembranosus

Three heads of
triceps femoris

Gracilis minor

Depressor mandibularis
Tympanic ring

Pterygoideus

Temporal
Maxilla (bone)

Temporal
Dentary (bone)

Masseter

Mylohyoid

Head muscles

FIGURE 230. The muscles of the bullfrog, dorsal view.

347

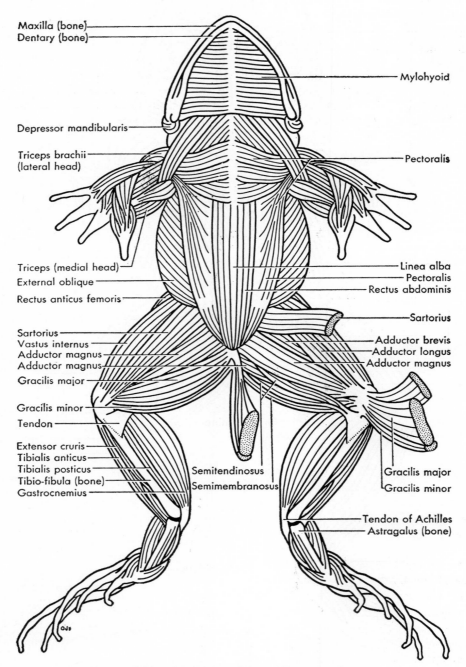

Maxilla (bone)
Dentary (bone)

Mylohyoid

Depressor mandibularis

Triceps brachii
(lateral head)

Pectoralis

Triceps (medial head)
External oblique
Rectus anticus femoris

Linea alba
Pectoralis
Rectus abdominis

Sartorius

Sartorius
Vastus internus
Adductor magnus
Adductor magnus
Gracilis major

Adductor brevis
Adductor longus
Adductor magnus

Gracilis minor
Tendon

Extensor cruris
Tibialis anticus
Tibialis posticus
Tibio-fibula (bone)
Gastrocnemius

Semitendinosus
Semimembranosus

Gracilis major
Gracilis minor

Tendon of Achilles
Astragalus (bone)

FIGURE 231. The muscles of the bullfrog, ventral view.

part upon another, as the leg upon the thigh, is a **flexor;** one that straightens out a part, as the extending of the foot, is an **extensor;** one that draws a part toward the midline of the body is an **adductor;** one that moves a part away from the midline of the body is an **abductor;** one that lowers a part is a **depressor;** one that raises a part is a **levator;** and one that rotates one part on another is a **rotator.** The movements of an organ depend on the origin and insertion of the muscles and the nature of the articulations of its bones with each other and with other parts of the body (Fig. 232).

The muscles of the hindlimb of the frog are usually selected for study to illustrate the methods of action of muscles in general. The accompanying table gives the name,

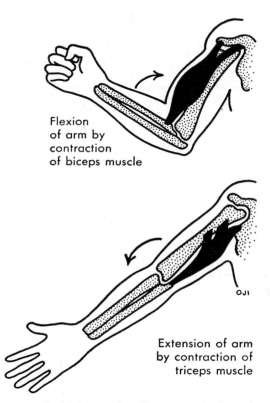

Flexion of arm by contraction of biceps muscle

Extension of arm by contraction of triceps muscle

FIGURE 232. Movements produced by muscles. Contraction is the only action produced by a muscle. Note the two opposing muscles in the arm and bones to which they are attached.

origin, insertion, and action of some of the muscles of the hindlimb. Figure 230 shows that the triceps femoris arises from three distinct heads; namely, vastus internus, rectus anticus femoris, and vastus externus.

The following are a few of the muscles of the other parts of the body: the **rectus abdominis** extends longitudinally along the ventral side of the trunk; the **external oblique** covers most of the sides of the trunk; the **transverse** lies beneath the external oblique and serves to contract the body cavity; the **pectoralis major** moves the forelimbs; and the **mylohyoid** raises the floor of the mouth cavity during respiration.

The muscles of animals in general and of man in particular are described in Chapter 31.

THE NAME, ORIGIN, INSERTION, AND ACTION OF SOME OF THE MUSCLES OF THE HINDLIMB OF THE FROG

NAME	ORIGIN	INSERTION	ACTION
Sartorius	Ilium, just in front of pubis	Just below head of tibia	Flexes leg; and adducts thigh
Adductor magnus	Ischium and pubis	Distal end of femur	Adducts thigh and leg
Adductor longus	Ventral part of ilium	Joins adductor magnus to attach on femur	Adducts thigh and leg
Triceps femoris	From three heads, one acetabulum, and two heads from ilium	Upper end of tibiofibula	Abducts thigh and extends leg
Gracilis major	Posterior margin of ischium	Proximal end of tibio-fibula	Adducts thigh; flexes leg
Gracilis minor	Tendon behind ischium	Joins tendon of gracilis major and tibiofibula	Adducts thigh; flexes leg
Semimembranosus	Dorsal half of ischium	Proximal end of tibiofibula	Adducts thigh; flexes leg
Biceps (iliofibularis)	Dorsal side of ilium	Tibiofibula	Adducts thigh; flexes leg
Gastrocnemius	Distal end of femur; tendon of triceps	Tendon of Achilles	Flexes leg, extends foot
Tibialis posticus	Posterior side of tibio-fibula	Proximal end of astragalus	When foot is flexed, acts as an extensor
Tibialis anticus longus	Distal end of femur	Proximal end of astragalus and calcaneus (ankle bones)	Extends leg; flexes foot
Peroneus	Distal end of femur	Distal end of tibiofibula; head of calcaneus	Extends leg
Extensor cruris	Distal end of femur	Anterior surface of tibio-fibula	Extends leg

Nervous system

The principal function of the nervous system is coordination of parts of the body that are widely separated.

The nervous system of vertebrates is more complex than that of any other animals. It is composed of two main subdivisions: (1) a **central nervous system** consisting of the **brain** and **spinal cord** and (2) a **peripheral nervous system** includes the **cerebral** and **spinal nerves** together with the **automatic system**. The brain is protected by the cranium of the skull. The brain consists of 6 main parts when viewed dorsally (Fig. 234): (1) two **olfactory lobes** with nerves to the nostrils; (2) two **cerebral hemispheres**; (3) **diencephalon** (between-brain) which has a dorsal **pineal body** (epiphysis); (4) two **optic lobes**; (5) **cerebellum**, a narrow transverse portion of the brain; and (6) **medulla** (medulla oblongata) which joins the spinal cord.

On the ventral side of the diencephalon the **optic nerves** cross each other to form the **optic chiasma.** Just posterior to the optic chiasma is the **infundibulum,** a large median projection. The **pituitary gland** (**hypophysis**) is the flattened ventral end of the infundibulum.

The **cavities** within the brain are shown in Fig. 234. The cavities of both the brain

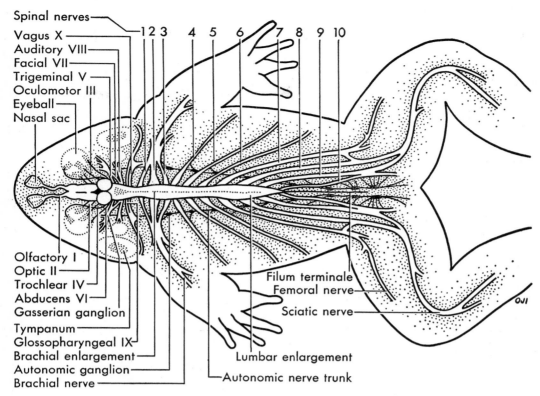

Spinal nerves

Vagus X
Auditory VIII
Facial VII
Trigeminal V
Oculomotor III
Eyeball
Nasal sac

1 2 3   4   5   6   7 8   9 10

Olfactory I
Optic II
Trochlear IV
Abducens VI
Gasserian ganglion
Tympanum
Glossopharyngeal IX
Brachial enlargement
Autonomic ganglion
Brachial nerve

Filum terminale
Femoral nerve
Sciatic nerve

Lumbar enlargement
Autonomic nerve trunk

FIGURE 233. Nervous system of the bullfrog, dorsal view.

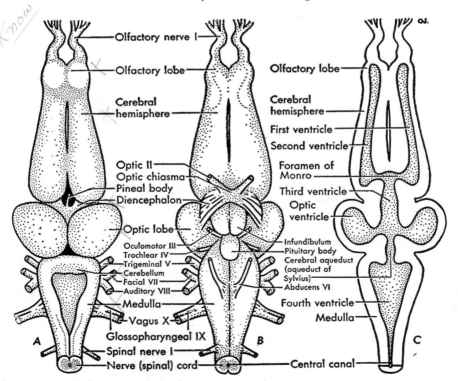

Olfactory nerve I
Olfactory lobe
Cerebral hemisphere

Olfactory lobe
Cerebral hemisphere
First ventricle
Second ventricle

Optic II
Optic chiasma
Pineal body
Diencephalon

Foramen of Monro
Third ventricle
Optic ventricle

Optic lobe

Oculomotor III
Trochlear IV
Trigeminal V
Cerebellum
Facial VII
Auditory VIII
Medulla
Vagus X
Glossopharyngeal IX

Infundibulum
Pituitary body
Cerebral aqueduct (aqueduct of Sylvius)
Abducens VI

Fourth ventricle
Medulla

Spinal nerve I
Nerve (spinal) cord

Central canal

A   B   C

FIGURE 234. Brain of the frog. A, dorsal view. B, ventral view. C, ventricles (cavities) in dorsal view.

351

and spinal cord are filled with a fluid appropriately called the **cerebrospinal fluid.** Although this fluid looks somewhat like lymph, the two are not identical in composition.

The **peripheral nervous system** (Fig. 233) includes 11 pairs of **cranial nerves** in the frog and a number of pairs of **spinal nerves.** Older textbooks give only 10 pairs of cranial nerves, but the discovery of the **terminal nerve** (**nervus terminalis**) makes it necessary to revise the former figure. The terminal nerve is found in many vertebrates, representing every class except the Agnatha and

birds. Little is known about it, but it appears to be sensory in function. The origin, distribution, and function of the cranial nerves are indicated in the accompanying table.

The **spinal cord** is a thick tube connected directly with the brain; it passes through the neural arches of the vertebral column. The **spinal nerves** arise from the spinal cord in pairs, one on either side in each body segment, and pass out between the vertebrae. Each nerve has two roots (Fig. 235), a **dorsal root** (sensory), and a **ventral root** (motor). The dorsal root possesses a ganglion containing nerve cells. Its fibers carry

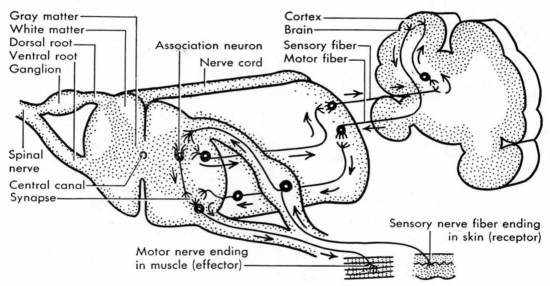

FIGURE 235. Paths of sensory and motor nerve fibers. Arrows indicate direction of nerve impulses. A reflex arc from sensory nerve ending by way of the spinal cord to muscles is shown at *lower right*; also connections to and from the brain.

impulses toward the spinal cord from various parts of the body and are therefore sensory. The fibers of the ventral root carry impulses from the spinal cord to the tissues and are therefore motor. The structure of the nerve cells (**neurons,** Fig. 236) is similar to that of the earthworm. The direction of the nervous impulses is indicated by arrows in Fig. 235.

On each side of the spinal cord is a chain of ganglia which is connected at various places with the central nervous system. This

is known as the **autonomic nervous system,** once called the sympathetic nervous system, but now that term is reserved for one subdivision of the autonomic system. These ganglia send nerves chiefly to the digestive tract, circulatory system, and glandular organs.

Visceral and other activities of which we are not ordinarily conscious are regulated and controlled by the autonomic system; these include movements of the stomach and intestine, glandular activities, and the

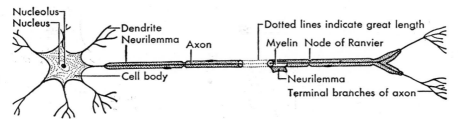

FIGURE 236.   A motor neuron from the spinal cord of man.

beating of the heart. The autonomic nervous system is composed of two main subdivisions, termed (1) **parasympathetic (craniosacral)** and (2) **sympathetic (thoracolumbar)**, but the details of these divisions are beyond the scope of this book.

It will be sufficient in this place to point out certain selected points concerning the nervous system of the frog, since general accounts of nervous tissue, nervous activity, and the nervous system of vertebrates are presented elsewhere.

THE NUMBER, NAME, ORIGIN, DISTRIBUTION, AND FUNCTION OF THE CRANIAL NERVES OF VERTEBRATES

NUM-BER	NAME	ORIGIN	DISTRIBUTION	FUNCTION
0	Terminal	Forebrain *	Lining of nose	Probably sensory
I	Olfactory	Olfactory lobe	Lining of nasal cavities	Sensory
II	Optic	Diencephalon	Retina of eye	Sensory
III	Oculomotor	Ventral side of midbrain	Four muscles of eye	Motor
IV	Trochlear	Dorsal side of midbrain	Superior oblique muscle of eye	Motor
V	Trigeminal	Side of medulla	Skin of face, mouth, and tongue, and muscles of jaws	Sensory and motor, mostly sensory
VI	Abducens	Ventral side of medulla	External rectus muscle of eye	Motor
VII	Facial	Side of medulla	Chiefly to muscles of face	Motor and sensory, mostly motor
VIII	Auditory	Side of medulla	Inner ear	Sensory
IX	Glossopharyngeal	Side of medulla	Muscles and membranes of pharynx, and tongue	Sensory and motor
X	Vagus	Side of medulla	Larynx, lungs, heart, esophagus, stomach, and intestines	Sensory and motor
XI	Spinal accessory (not present in frog)	Side of medulla	Chiefly muscles of shoulder	Sensory and motor
XII	Hypoglossal (not present in frog)	Ventral side of medulla	Muscles of tongue and neck	Motor

* According to Herrick, it originates from both telencephalon and diencephalon in most species.

Brain

The brain (Fig. 234) has two large **olfactory lobes** which are fused together, two large **cerebral hemispheres, diencephalon,** two large **optic lobes,** a very small **cerebellum,** and a **medulla** (medulla oblongata), which is produced by the broadening of the spinal cord.

The **functions** of the different parts of the frog's brain have been partially determined by experiments in which the parts were removed and the effects upon the animals observed. There is evidence that the cerebral hemispheres are involved in associate memory, but the frog has a very low "I.Q." The cerebrum is the seat of intelligence and voluntary control in higher animals. When the diencephalon is removed with the cerebral hemispheres, the frog loses the power of spontaneous movement. When the optic lobes are removed, the spinal cord becomes more irritable; this shows that these lobes have an inhibiting influence on the reflex activity of the spinal cord. In man the cerebellum is a center of coordination, but experiments on the frog cerebellum have produced conflicting results. Many activities are still possible when everything but the medulla is removed. The animal breathes normally, snaps at and swallows food, leaps and swims regularly, and is able to right itself when thrown on its back. Extirpation of the posterior region of the medulla results in early death of the frog. The brain as a whole controls the actions effected by the nerve centers of the spinal cord. "The higher centers of the brain are comparable to the captain of a steamer, who issues orders to the man running the engine, when to start and when to stop, and who has his hand on the wheel so as to guide the course of the vessel" (Holmes).

Spinal cord

The spinal cord (Fig. 233) extends backward from the medulla and ends in the urostyle. It is surrounded by two membranes, an outer **dura mater** and an inner **pia mater.** The cord is composed of a central mass of gray matter (Fig. 235) consisting mainly of **nerve cells,** and an outer mass of **white matter** made up chiefly of nerve fibers. A median **fissure** occurs both in the dorsal and in the ventral side of the cord, and a **central canal** lies in the gray matter and communicates anteriorly with the cavities of the brain.

Spinal nerves

The relation of the spinal nerves to the spinal cord and the paths taken by nervous impulses are indicated in Fig. 235. There are 10 pairs of spinal nerves in the frog (Fig. 233). Each arises by a **dorsal** and a **ventral root,** which arise from the gray matter of the cord. The two roots unite to form a trunk, which passes out between the arches of adjacent vertebrae. The two largest nerves are (1) the **brachials,** each of which is composed of the second pair of spinal nerves and branches from the first and third pairs—these are distributed to the forelimbs and shoulders; and (2) the **sciatics,** which arise from plexuses composed of the seventh, eighth, and ninth spinal nerves, and are distributed to the hindlimbs.

Autonomic system

This system (Fig. 233) consists of two principal trunks, which begin at the cranium and extend posteriorly, one on each side of the vertebral column. Each trunk is provided with 10 ganglionic enlargements at the points where branches from the spinal nerves unite with it. The nerves of the autonomic system are distributed to internal organs and regulate many functions that are not under the control of conscious or voluntary action, such as heart beat, secretions, movements of the digestive tract, and respiratory, urogenital, reproductive systems, and others.

Sense organs

The principal sense organs are the **eyes, ears,** and **olfactory organs.** There are many smaller structures on the surface of the tongue, and on the floor and roof of the mouth, which probably function as organs of **taste**. In the skin are also many sensory nerve endings which receive contact, chemical, temperature, and light stimuli.

Olfactory organs

The olfactory nerves (Fig. 234) extend from the olfactory lobe of the brain to the nasal cavities, where they are distributed to the epithelial lining. The importance of the sense of smell in the life of the frog is not known.

Ear

The **inner ear** of the frog lies within the **auditory capsule** and is protected by the prootic (Fig. 227) and exoccipital bones. It is supplied by branches of the auditory nerve. There is no external ear in the frog. The **middle ear** is a cavity which communicates with the mouth cavity through the Eustachian tube and is closed externally by the **eardrum** (**tympanic membrane**).

A rod, the **columella**, extends across the cavity of the middle ear from the eardrum to the inner ear. The vibrations of the eardrum produced by sound waves are transmitted to the inner ear through the columella. The sensory end organs of the auditory nerve are stimulated by the vibrations, and the impulses carried to the brain give rise to the sensation of sound. The inner ears serve also as organs of **equilibrium**. Frogs, from which they are removed, cannot maintain an upright position.

Eye

The eyes of the frog resemble those of man in general structure and function, but differ in certain details. The **eyeballs** lie in cavities (orbits) in the sides of the head. They may be rotated by 6 muscles and also pulled into the orbit. The **upper eyelid** does not move independently. The **lower eyelid** consists of the lower eyelid proper, fused with the transparent third eyelid or **nictitating membrane**. The **lens** is large and almost spherical. It cannot be changed in form or in position, and is therefore fitted for viewing objects distinctly at a certain definite distance. Movements are noted much oftener than form. The amount of light that enters the eye can be regulated by the contraction of the **pupil**. The **retina** of the eye is stimulated by the rays of light which pass through the pupil; and the impulses, which are carried through the optic nerve to the brain, give rise to sensations of sight.

Endocrine glands

The frog body, like that of other vertebrates, is influenced tremendously by hormones which are produced by the endocrine (ductless) glands. These internal secretions pass directly into the blood. Some of the endocrines influence other glands, the rate of growth, even the whole organism, with its behavior and physiologic and structural characteristics. The endocrine glands of vertebrates are discussed in Chapter 33.

Behavior

The activities of the frog are such as to enable it to exist within the confines of its habitat. The ordinary movements are those employed in leaping, diving, crawling, burrowing, and maintaining an upright position. These and most of its other activities may be resolved into a series of inborn reflexes; they are commonly said to be "instinctive." Inborn reflexes result in the faculty to act in such a way as to produce certain ends, without foresight of the ends, and without previous education in the performance.

Some of the movements of the frog are due to internal causes, but many are responses to external stimuli. Frogs are sensitive to light, and recent experiments have shown that skin responses to light come by the way of the eyes and pituitary gland. The reaction to light causes the animal to orient its body so that it faces the source and is in line with the direction of the rays. Nevertheless, frogs tend to congregate in shady places. Frogs also seem to be stimulated by contact as shown by their tendency to crawl under stones and into crevices. Other factors probably have some influence upon this reaction. Temperature and other stimuli modify the responses both to light and to contact.

Investigators who have studied the behavior of frogs have come to the conclusion that they are very stupid animals, but it is possible to teach them certain things, and habits once formed are not easily changed. For example, Yerkes found that a frog could learn to follow a path in a labyrinth after about 100 trials. If we consider the power to learn by individual experience as evidence of intelligence, we must attribute a primitive sort of intelligence to the frog.

Life cycle of the frog

Frogs lay their eggs in water in the early spring. The male clasps the female firmly with his forelegs just behind her forelegs. This is one of the strongest seasonal inborn reflexes (instincts) of the male frog; he will even clasp one's finger when caught during this time of the year. After the male has been carried about by the female for several days, the eggs pass from the uterus out of the cloaca. As the eggs are extruded by the female, they are fertilized by the sperms which the male discharges over them. The male then releases his grip on the female and leaves her. Each female lays several hundred or more eggs, but some of these fail to develop, and others are eaten by enemies.

The jelly which surrounds and protects the eggs soon swells up through absorption of water. The frog egg is well adapted to hatch in the cold pond water of early spring. The upper black surface of the egg absorbs the sun's heat like a black coat. The transparent jelly covering holds heat like the glass of a greenhouse.

Cleavage takes place as indicated in Fig. 237. Some of the cells, called **macromeres**, are large because of a bountiful supply of yolk; others, the **micromeres**, are smaller. A **blastula** is formed by the development of a cavity, the **blastocoel**, near the center of the egg. **Gastrulation** is modified in the frog's egg because of the amount of yolk present. The dark side of the egg gradually grows over the lighter portion until only a circular area called the **yolk plug** is visible. The gastrula contains two germ layers, an outer **ectoderm** and an inner **endoderm**. A third layer, the **mesoderm**, soon appears between the other two and splits into two, an inner **splanchnic layer**, which forms the supporting tissue and musculature of the digestive canal, and an outer **parietal layer**, which forms the connective tissue, muscle, and peritoneum of the body wall. The cavity between these two mesodermal layers is the **coelom**.

Soon after gastrulation, the **neural groove** appears, on either side of which is a **neural fold**. The neural folds grow together at the top, forming a tube which later develops into the brain and spinal cord of the embryo. The neural groove lies along the median dorsal line, and the embryo now lengthens in this direction. The region where the yolk plug was situated lies at the posterior end. On either side near the anterior end two **gill arches** appear; and in front of each of these a depression arises which unites with its fellow and moves to the ventral surface, becoming the **ventral sucker**. An invagination soon appears just above the ventral sucker; this is an oval pit which develops into the mouth.

The invagination, which becomes the cloacal opening (anus) appears beneath the tail at the posterior end. On either side above the mouth, a thickening of the ectoderm represents the beginning of the **eye**, and just above the gills appear the invaginations which form the vesicles of the inner ears. The markings of the muscle segments show through the skin along the sides of the body and tail.

The embryo moves about within the egg membranes partly by means of cilia, but these soon disappear after hatching (Fig.

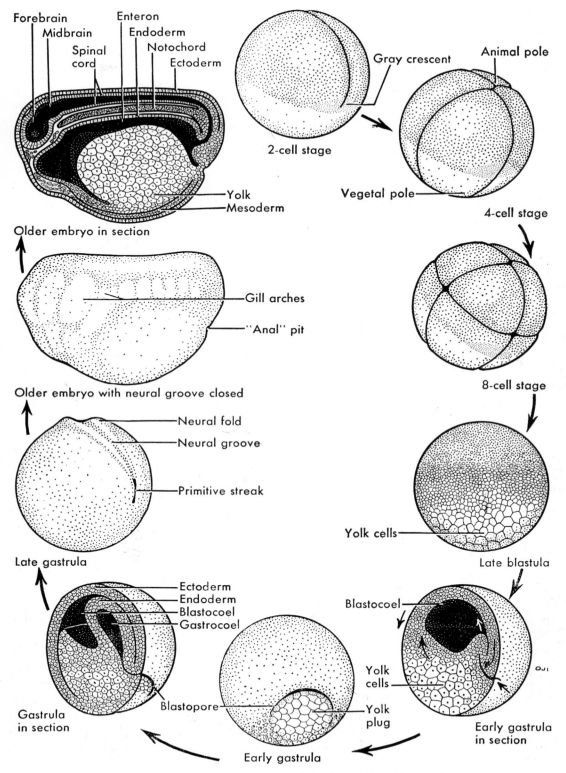

Forebrain
Midbrain
Spinal cord
Enteron
Endoderm
Notochord
Ectoderm
Yolk
Mesoderm

Older embryo in section

Gill arches
"Anal" pit

Older embryo with neural groove closed

Neural fold
Neural groove
Primitive streak

Late gastrula

Ectoderm
Endoderm
Blastocoel
Gastrocoel

Gastrula in section

Blastopore

Yolk plug

Early gastrula

Gray crescent

Animal pole

2-cell stage

Vegetal pole

4-cell stage

8-cell stage

Yolk cells

Late blastula

Blastocoel

Yolk cells

Early gastrula in section

FIGURE 237. Early development of the frog. (After Huettner.)

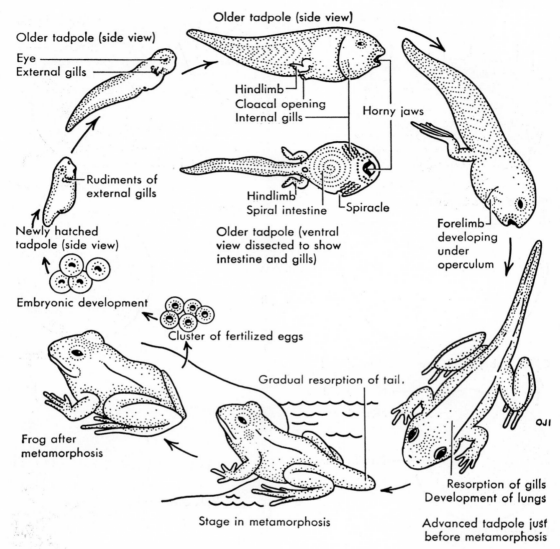

Older tadpole (side view)

Older tadpole (side view)
Eye
External gills

Hindlimb
Cloacal opening
Internal gills
Horny jaws

Rudiments of
external gills

Hindlimb
Spiral intestine
Spiracle

Newly hatched
tadpole (side view)

Older tadpole (ventral
view dissected to show
intestine and gills)

Forelimb
developing
under
operculum

Embryonic development

Cluster of fertilized eggs

Gradual resorption of tail.

Frog after
metamorphosis

Resorption of gills
Development of lungs

Stage in metamorphosis

Advanced tadpole just
before metamorphosis

FIGURE 238.   Life cycle of the frog from egg to adult.

238). The tadpole breaks out of the membranes, lives for a few days on the yolk in the digestive tract, and then feeds on algae and other vegetable matter. The **external gills** grow out into long branching tufts. A skin fold or **operculum** grows over the external gills, which then degenerate, and are replaced by **internal gills**; water enters the mouth, passes through the gill slits, and out of an opening on the left side of the body, the **spiracle**.

The hindlimbs appear first; later the forelimbs break out. The tail decreases in size because it is gradually reabsorbed as the end of the larval period approaches. The gills are reabsorbed, and the lungs develop to take their place. Finally the form resembling that of the adult frog is acquired (Fig. 238).

SELECTED COLLATERAL READINGS

(See Chapter 27 for additional collateral readings)

Carroll, P.L., and Horner, W.F. *An Atlas of the Frog.* Mosby, St. Louis, 1940.

Gaupp, E.A. *Ecker und R. Wiedersheim's Anatomie des Frosches.* Vieweg, Brunswick, Germany, 1896–1904.

Holmes, S.J. *The Biology of the Frog.* Macmillan, New York, 1927.

Marshall, A.M. *The Frog: An Introduction to Anatomy, Histology and Embryology.* Macmillan, London, 1928.

Pope, C.H. *Amphibians and Reptiles of the Chicago Area.* Chicago Natural History Museum, Chicago, 1947.

Stuart, Richard R. *The Anatomy of the Bull Frog.* Denoyer-Geppert, Chicago, 1940.

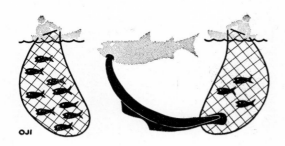

CHAPTER 24

Class Agnatha (Jawless Vertebrates). Lampreys and Hagfishes

THE animals in the order Cyclostomata (Fig. 240) represent a primitive level of vertebrate development. The name means round mouth. These eel-shaped vertebrates, without jaws or paired fins, and with only one olfactory pit, are commonly known as lampreys, hagfishes, and slime eels.

The suborder Myxinoidea, or hagfishes, are all marine; and the suborder Petromyzontia, or lampreys, occur in both salt water and fresh water. The cyclostomes usually feed on the blood and tissue fluid of fishes which they attack with their rasping mouth (Fig. 239). The cyclostomes are not only interesting chordates, but some are of great economic importance.

SEA LAMPREY

Petromyzon marinus, the sea lamprey (Fig. 240), a rather unpleasant animal, is a modified survivor of some of the first vertebrates that lived on the earth. It inhabits the waters along the Atlantic Coast of North America, Great Lakes, the coasts of Europe, and the west coast of Africa. It swims about near the bottom by undulations of its body, or, when in a strong current, progresses by darting suddenly forward and attaching itself to a rock by means of its suctorial mouth. In the spring adult lampreys ascend the rivers to spawn.

External anatomy

The marine lamprey reaches a length of about three feet. Land-locked populations such as those in the Great Lakes attain a maximum size of only two feet. The body of the lamprey is nearly cylindrical, except at the posterior end where it is laterally compressed. There is no exoskeleton. The skin is soft and slimy, made so by secretions from **epidermal glands.** It is a mottled greenish-brown in color. A row of segmental sense pits, the **lateral line,** is located on each side of the body and on the head. The

FIGURE 239. A lake trout showing a typical lamprey scar; arrow points to scar. This fish has been the backbone of the Great Lakes fishing industry. (Courtesy of U.S. Fish and Wildlife Service.)

mouth (Fig. 241) lies at the bottom of a suctorial disk, the **oral (buccal) funnel**, and is held open by a ring of cartilage. Around the oral funnel are a number of **papillae** and **horny "teeth."** At the apex of the oral funnel is the **mouth**, through which the pistonlike tongue protrudes; it bears horny teeth. On each side of the head is an **eye**,

FIGURE 240. Female sea lamprey; a jawless vertebrate, 20¾ inches long, showing the characteristically mottled back of a sexually mature adult. Note the laterally placed eye, behind which are the gill slits. The sea lamprey is an eel-like parasite that preys on fish. (Courtesy of Institute for Fisheries Research, Michigan Department of Conservation.)

and posterior to the eye, 7 **gill slits**. Between the eyes on the dorsal surface is a single opening, the **nasal opening** (Fig. 242). The **anus** opens on the ventral surface near the posterior end; just behind it is the **urogenital opening** in the end of a small papilla. There are two **dorsal fins** and one **caudal fin** (Fig. 240).

Skeletal system

The **notochord** of *Petromyzon* persists as a well-developed structure in the adult (Fig. 242). In the trunk region it is supplemented by small cartilaginous neural arches. Cartilaginous **rays** hold the fins upright. The organs in the head are supported by a cartilaginous cranium and a cartilaginous branchial basket.

Muscular system

The muscles in the walls of the trunk and tail are segmental, in a $<$-shaped arrangement, similar to the fishes. The tongue is moved by large retractor and smaller protractor muscles. The buccal funnel is operated by a number of radiating muscles.

Digestive system

The adult *Petromyzon* lives chiefly on the blood of fishes. The expansion of the oral funnel (Fig. 241) causes the mouth to act like a sucker and enables the animal to cling to stones or to fasten itself to fishes such as shad, sturgeon, cod, and mackerel in the ocean, and lake trout, whitefish, yellow pike-perch, and carp in the Great Lakes. With its rasplike tongue, it files a hole through the scales and flesh of its victim and sucks out the blood.

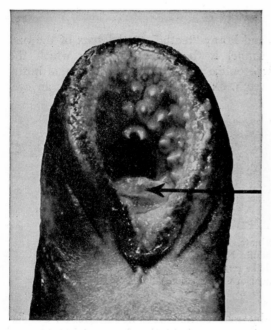

FIGURE 241. The head of a sea lamprey showing the oral funnel which serves as a suction cup by which it attaches itself to its prey. It is by means of the sharply pointed horny teeth inside the oral funnel and the rasplike tongue that it can penetrate through the scales and flesh of its victim. Arrow points to pistonlike tongue. (Courtesy of Institute for Fisheries Research, Michigan Department of Conservation.)

The **mouth** cavity opens at its posterior end into two tubes (Fig. 242), an upper one, the **esophagus**, and the ventral one, the pharynx. A fold, the **velum**, at the anterior end of the **pharynx** prevents the passage of food into the respiratory system.

There is no distinct stomach. The posterior end of the esophagus is separated from the straight **intestine** only by a valve. A fold in the intestine called the **typhlosole** forms a sort of **spiral valve**. The digestive tract ends at the small **anus**. A **liver** is present, but there is usually no bile duct in the adult; it is not definitely known whether or not there is a pancreas.

Circulatory system

Petromyzon possesses a heart, a number of veins and arteries, and many lymphatic sinuses. The **heart** (Fig. 242) lies in the pericardial cavity, and consists of a **ventricle** which forces the blood into the arteries and an **atrium** which receives the blood from the veins. A **renal portal system** is absent.

Respiratory system

Respiration is carried on by means of 7 pairs of **gill pouches**, which open to the outside by the **gill slits** and internally to the **pharynx**. Each gill pouch contains numerous gill filaments that contain many capillaries in which the blood is oxygenated by the water in the pouch. In the adult lamprey, water is taken into the gill pouches through the external gill slits and is discharged through the same openings (Fig. 242). This method, which is unlike that in the true fishes, is necessary because the lamprey, when attached to its food by its oral funnel, cannot take water through the mouth. However, in a larval lamprey, the water used in respiration passes in through the mouth and out the gill slits as in fishes.

Nervous system

The **brain** (Fig. 242) of the adult lamprey is very primitive. The forebrain consists of a large pair of **olfactory lobes**; behind these are the small **cerebral hemispheres** attached

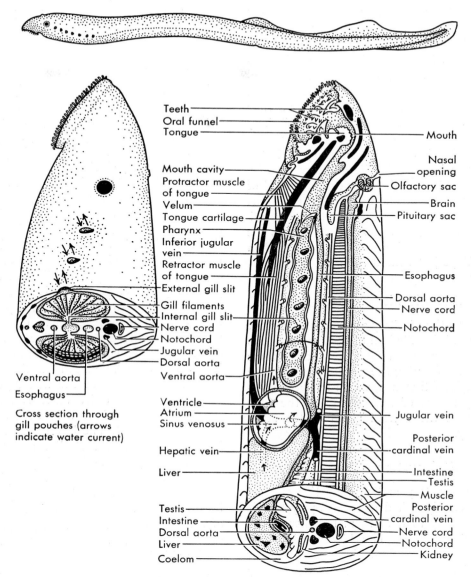

FIGURE 242. *Petromyzon*, an adult lamprey. Shown in cross section and with left side of body removed to demonstrate the structure.

to the **diencephalon;** ventral to the latter is a broad **infundibulum,** and above it a **pineal structure.** On the midbrain is a pair of large **optic lobes.** In the hindbrain, the rudimentary **cerebellum** is a small, dorsal, transverse band, but the ventral **medulla oblongata (medulla)** is fairly well developed. There are only 10 pairs of cranial nerves as the terminal nerve is absent. The **nerve cord** is flat and lies on the floor of the neural canal. There are no sympathetic ganglia, and the autonomic system consists only of an intestinal plexus linked with the brain.

Sense organs

Organs of taste, smell, equilibrium, and sight are present in the lamprey. The end organs of **taste** are situated between the gill pouches on the pharyngeal wall. The organ of smell is an **olfactory sac** (Fig. 242) which lies in the **nasal capsule**; this communicates with the outside by a nasal opening on the dorsal surface between the eyes. The olfactory sac gives off ventrally a tube of unknown function, called the **pituitary sac.**

The "ears" (balancing organs) of *Petromyzon*, which lie in the **auditory capsule**, have only two semicircular canals instead of the usual three. The hagfish has only one. The **eyes** of the adult lamprey, though primitive, are excellent visual organs. Besides the paired eyes there is a well-developed median **pineal eye** just behind the nasal opening.

Endocrine glands

Where the pituitary sac comes in contact with the infundibulum of the brain, it gives off numerous small follicles which become separated, forming the **pituitary gland**. The endostyle of the larva, which has been studied by means of radio-iodine, is the forerunner of the thyroid gland of the adult lamprey.

Urogenital system

The excretory and reproductive systems are so closely united in the lamprey that it is customary to treat them together as the urogenital system. The **kidneys** lie along the dorsal wall of the body cavity, and each pours its secretions by means of the **urinary duct** into the **urogenital sinus**, and thence to the outside through the **urogenital opening**. The sexes are separate in the adult; however, the immature gonad is hermaphroditic, but later becomes male or female for an individual. The single **gonad** fills most of the abdominal cavity at the time of sexual maturity. There is no genital duct; eggs or sperms break out into the coelom, make their way through two **genital pores** into the urogenital sinus, and then pass out

through the urogenital opening into the water, where fertilization occurs.

Reproduction

The sea lampreys become sexually mature in May or early June; then both sexes migrate into streams, sometimes "hitchhiking" on a passing boat. They seek a gravelly bottom under moderately fast-flowing water; and, by means of the oral hood, move stones on the bottom of the stream to form a shallow rounded depression called a nest. The female then fastens to a stone in the nest and the male attaches to the female by the use of their oral funnels. Partly entwined, they move back and forth as sperms and eggs are discharged, fertilization taking place in the water. Each female sea lamprey produces 24,000 to 107,000 eggs, depending on her size. The average female lays 62,500 eggs and dies after spawning. The eggs hatch out into larvae, known as "ammocoetes," in 20 to 21 days. The blind harmless larvae make their way out of the nest and drift downstream until quiet water is reached. Here they dive and burrow into the bottom if it is mud or silt. The larval period spent in burrows is, recent studies indicate, at least 7 to 8 years, and possibly longer in duration. Inspiration of water for respiratory purposes appears to be largely responsible for drawing of food organisms in the mouth of the larvae. Thereafter, food particles are carried forward to the esophagus by action of the cilia in certain areas of the pharynx. An endostyle on the floor of the pharynx secretes mucus which entangles the food, as in the amphioxus.

The ammocoetes lies buried in mud and sand and probably keeps its skin free from bacteria, fungi, and other parasitic growths by means of an integumentary secretion. In the winter of the seventh or eighth year, the larval lamprey undergoes a metamorphosis, after which it migrates to the sea, or, if it is in the Great Lakes region, to one of the lakes, where growth to sexual maturity takes

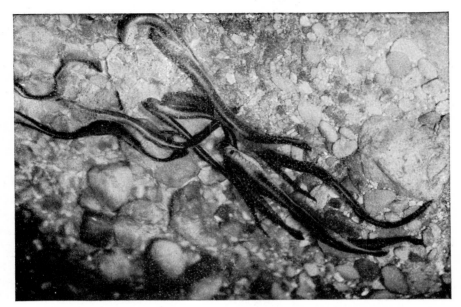

FIGURE 243. American brook lampreys spawning. (Courtesy of Institute for Fisheries Research, Michigan Department of Conservation.)

place. It is at this stage that the parasitic species begins to feed on fish.

BROOK LAMPREY

The nonparasitic **brook lampreys** of North America, *Entosphenus lamottenii*, breed in the spring. They move stones by means of their oral hoods until a space is cleared on the bottom where a number of them may congregate. A male clings to the head of a female for a moment, winds his tail about her body, and discharges spermatozoa over the eggs when they are extruded. There is a long larval stage in development. After spawning the adults probably take no food and soon die; they are therefore not injurious to fishes.

HAGFISHES

Hagfishes live in the mud of the sea bottom, down to a depth of nearly 350 fathoms. They are very destructive to fishes, especially those caught on lines or in nets; they bore their way into the body and eat out the soft parts. Cod and flounders are the fish usually attacked.

In the hagfishes the same individual produces first sperms and then later eggs. Growth to the adult is direct, that is, without a larval stage.

RELATIONS OF THE CYCLOSTOMATA TO OTHER GROUPS

The chordate characters of the cyclostomes are obvious. Some, such as a continuous notochord and many gill slits, are similar to the primitive characters of the amphioxus. Others are of a more advanced nature, such as a distinct head, cranium, better-developed brain, and cartilaginous neural arches. Cyclostomes are less advanced than fishes as indicated by the absence of hinged jaws, paired limbs, true teeth, and complete vertebrae.

RELATIONS OF THE CYCLOSTOMATA TO MAN

The flesh of the lamprey, in many parts of Europe, has been a popular food for centuries. Work has been done in the United States to make lampreys palatable as food, or to find other commercial use for them, but so far these efforts have met with little or no success. Larval lampreys sometimes serve as bait for both commercial and sport fishermen. Some adult lampreys are serious enemies of valuable food and game fishes. The Atlantic lamprey (*Petromyzon marinus*) is found in all the Great Lakes and now threatens their important commercial fish resources. It passed the Niagara Falls barrier by way of the Welland Canal. Lake Huron and Lake Michigan's trout fishing has been practically destroyed by the lamprey, and Lake Superior's potentiality is 30 per cent below that of former years. In 1946, commercial fishermen took a catch of lake trout from Lake Michigan of about 5,500,000 pounds but the catch in 1953 was only 482 pounds. The lampreys not only kill many fish by feeding on their blood, but they inflict injuries on many leaving scars (Fig. 239) and impairing their commercial value. Some large fish show several scars.

States adjoining the Great Lakes and the United States and Canadian governments are trying to work out methods to control the sea lamprey. At present the electric barriers (weirs) are the most dependable devices in use for sea lamprey control. However, recent experiments with a chemical compound have been reported unconditionally successful. Electric weirs, chemical treatment, and other control measures should eventually make the sea lamprey problem less serious. But it is doubtful that this pest will ever be completely removed from the Great Lakes. The St. Lawrence Seaway probably means that the lamprey will always be a troublemaker in the Great Lakes, for it doubtless will be brought in from the oceans in increased numbers, attached to the bottoms of big ships.

The migration of the sea lamprey into the Great Lakes is acting as a great disturber of the balance in nature, as is demonstrated by the important influence on the large commercial fisheries of these extremely productive waters.

CLASSIFICATION OF THE LIVING AGNATHA

(For reference purposes only)

Class Agnatha includes the orders which constitute the ostracoderms of the Silurian and Devonian geological periods. The ostracoderms are known only from their fossil remains.

Order 1. Cyclostomata (the living cyclostomes). Hagfishes and lampreys. Eel-shaped; skin smooth, without scales; no lateral fins, functional jaws, or genital ducts; mouth suctorial, with horny teeth; 1 olfactory pit; 7 or more pairs of gill clefts.

The cyclostomes are the most primitive of all living vertebrates. Two suborders are recognized as follows:

Suborder 1. Petromyzontia (Gr. *petra*, rock; *myzon*, sucker). Lampreys. One family; nasal opening in front of eyes; mouth suctorial; 7 pairs of gill slits. Exs. *Petromyzon marinus*, sea lamprey (Fig. 240), Atlantic Coast from Chesapeake Bay northward, and, in Europe, landlocked in the Finger Lakes; *Entosphenus tridentatus*, Pacific Coast, southern California to Alaska; *Ichthyomyzon*, brook lampreys, central North America, including the Great Lakes; *Entosphenus lamottenii*, nonparasitic lampreys, eastern and midwestern states.

Suborder 2. Myxinoidia (Gr. *myxa*, slime). Slime eels and hagfishes.

One family; three genera; nasal opening terminal; four tentacles on either side of mouth; oral funnel absent. Exs. *Myxine limosa*, slime eel, Atlantic Coast; *Polistotrema*, southern California to Alaska; and *Bdellostoma (Eptatretus)*, Chile.

SELECTED COLLATERAL READINGS

Applegate, V.C. *Natural History of the Sea Lamprey, Petromyzon marinus in Michigan.* Special Scientific Report, Fisheries No. 55, U.S. Fish and Wildlife Service, 1950.

———, and Moffett, J.W. "The Sea Lamprey." *Scientific American*, 192:36–41, 1955.

Gage, S.H. *The Lake and Brook Lampreys of New York. Wilder Quarterly Century Book.* Comstock, Ithaca, N.Y., 1893.

Hubbs, C.L. "The Life-Cycle and Growth of Lampreys." *Papers Mich. Acad. Sci.*, 4:587–603, 1924.

Lennon, R.E. *Feeding Mechanism of the Sea Lamprey and Its Effects on Host Fishes.* U.S. Fish and Wildlife Service. Fish. Bull., 56:245–293, 1954.

Reynolds, T.E. "Hydrostatics of the Suctorial Mouth of the Lamprey." *Univ. Calif. Pub. Zool.*, 37:15–34, 1931.

CHAPTER 25

Class Chondrichthyes. Cartilaginous Fishes

T<small>HE</small> Chondrichthyes (cartilage fishes), also called elasmobranchs, are the sharks, rays, and skates. They are the most generalized of the living vertebrates that have complete vertebrae, movable jaws, and paired appendages.

SQUALUS ACANTHIAS— A DOGFISH SHARK

The common dogfish shark, known since Aristotle's time as being ovoviparous, is abundant in the waters off the coasts of New England and northern Europe. It is of special biologic interest because many of the basic vertebrate features are present in this shark in simple form, and this helps one to understand the more complex systems of higher vertebrates. This is an ancient group of fishes and is represented by many fossil remains.

External anatomy

The body is spindle-shaped and about 2½ feet long. There are two **dorsal fins,** one behind the other, each with a **spine** at the anterior end, two **pectoral fins,** and two **pelvic fins.** The pelvic fins in the male possess cartilaginous appendages known as **claspers.** The tail (caudal fin) is **heterocercal** (Fig. 260). The **mouth** is a transverse slit on the ventral surface of the head. On either side, above the mouth is an **eye,** and each **nostril** on the ventral side of the head opens into a blind pouch, the **olfactory sac.** Anterior to each pectoral fin are 6 **gill slits,** the first of which is situated back of the eye and modified as a **spiracle.** Between the pelvic fins is the **cloacal opening,** sometimes called an anus.

The gray-colored skin is covered with **placoid scales** (Fig. 245). For a dorsal view

F<small>IGURE</small> 244. *Facing page,* the internal organs of the spiny dogfish. The veins are in solid black, the arteries in outline.

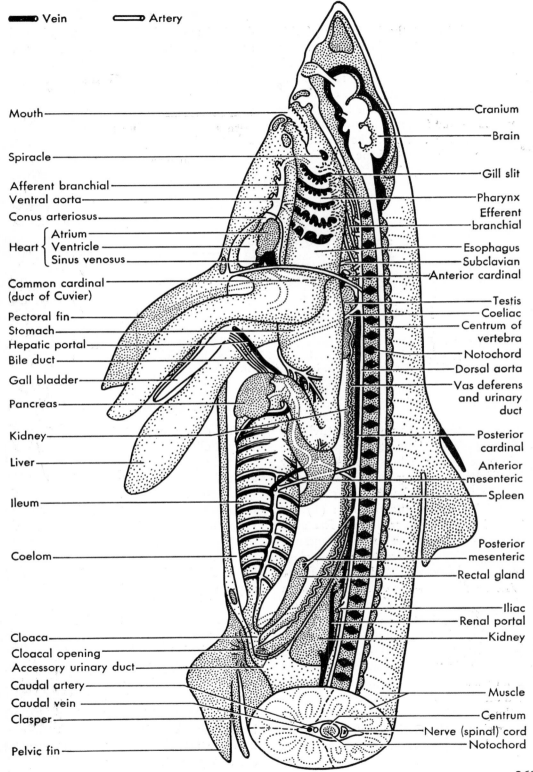

Vein   Artery

Mouth

Spiracle

Afferent branchial
Ventral aorta
Conus arteriosus

Heart { Atrium
        Ventricle
        Sinus venosus

Common cardinal
(duct of Cuvier)

Pectoral fin
Stomach
Hepatic portal
Bile duct

Gall bladder

Pancreas

Kidney

Liver

Ileum

Coelom

Cloaca
Cloacal opening
Accessory urinary duct
Caudal artery
Caudal vein
Clasper

Pelvic fin

Cranium

Brain

Gill slit

Pharynx
Efferent
branchial

Esophagus
Subclavian
Anterior cardinal

Testis
Coeliac
Centrum of
vertebra
Notochord
Dorsal aorta
Vas deferens
and urinary
duct

Posterior
cardinal

Anterior
mesenteric

Spleen

Posterior
mesenteric

Rectal gland

Iliac
Renal portal
Kidney

Muscle

Centrum
Nerve (spinal) cord
Notochord

369

see the headpiece at the beginning of this chapter. Over the jaws the placoid scales are modified as teeth with their points directed backward and are used for holding and tearing prey. A placoid scale consists of a bony basal plate, with a spine in the center composed of **dentine,** and is covered with a hard enamel-like dentine. The method of embryonic development of the scale and its

dentinal nature indicate that placoid scales are homologous with vertebrate teeth. Although the best evidence denies the presence of enamel on the surface of the placoid scale, the enamel-forming organ is present as in developing teeth. The homology of the teeth and scales is due to the fact that the mouth lining is inturned skin and hence possesses skin structures.

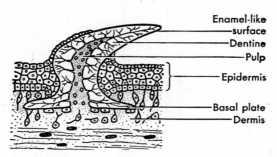

Enamel-like surface
Dentine
Pulp
Epidermis
Basal plate
Dermis

FIGURE 245. Detail of a placoid scale (dermal denticle) as seen in section. Because of the pointed scales, the skin is rasplike in texture. Thus, if a shark brushes against a man in the water, it could inflict a severe wound in his skin. (After Kerr.)

Skeletal system

The skeleton is composed entirely of **cartilage** (gristle). The cartilaginous skeleton in the elasmobranchs is in all probability a degenerate and not a primitive characteristic as was formerly believed. There are two main subdivisions of the skeleton: (1) the **axial** and (2) the **appendicular.** The axial skeleton consists of the vertebral column and the skull. The **vertebrae** are hour-glass-shaped (amphicoelous), and the **notochord** persists in the lens-shaped spaces between them. The **skull** is much more highly developed than that of the cyclostomes. It is composed of (1) the **cranium** or brain case; (2) two large anterior **nasal capsules** and two posterior **auditory capsules;** and (3) the visceral skeleton, made up of the **jaws,** the **hyoid arch,** and 5 **branchial arches** supporting the gill region. The **appendicular skeleton** consists of the cartilages of the fins and those of the **pectoral** and **pelvic girdles** which support them.

Digestive system

The **digestive tract** is longer than the body. Following the **mouth** (Fig. 244) is a large **pharynx** into which open the **spiracles** and **gill slits.** The pharynx leads into the short wide **esophagus** which opens into the U-shaped **stomach.** The posterior end of the stomach ends at a circular sphincter muscle, the **pyloric valve.** The **intestine** follows and terminates in the **cloaca** and **cloacal opening.** A slender, fingerlike **rectal gland,** which apparently secretes mucus, attaches dorsally at the junction near the point where the small and large intestines join. Within the intestine is a spiral fold of mucous membrane called the **spiral valve** (Fig. 246), which prevents a too rapid passage of food and thus allows increased absorption. The **liver** is large and consists of two long lobes; its secretion, the bile, is stored up in a **gall bladder** and empties through the bile duct into the intestine. A **pancreas** and **spleen** are also present.

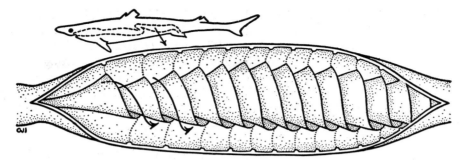

FIGURE 246. Intestine of a dogfish shark cut open to show the structure of the spiral valve. The arrows inside valve show the direction of movement of food.

Circulatory system

As in the cyclostomes and most of the true fishes, the heart contains venous blood only (Fig. 244). It is pumped through the **ventral aorta** and thence into the **afferent branchial arteries,** becoming oxygenated in the capillaries of the gills. It then passes into the **efferent branchial arteries,** which carry it to the **dorsal aorta.** The dorsal aorta supplies the various parts of the body. Veins carry the blood back to the heart, opening into the **sinus venosus.** Other veins, called the **hepatic portal system,** transport the blood from the digestive canal, pancreas, and spleen to the liver from which hepatic sinuses return it to the sinus venosus. A third system, the **renal portal system,** conveys the blood from the posterior part of the body to the kidneys. Blood leaves the kidneys by way of several **renal veins,** emptying into the **posterior cardinal sinuses** which return it to the sinus venosus.

Respiratory system

Respiration is carried on by means of gills (Fig. 247). These are folds of mucous mem-

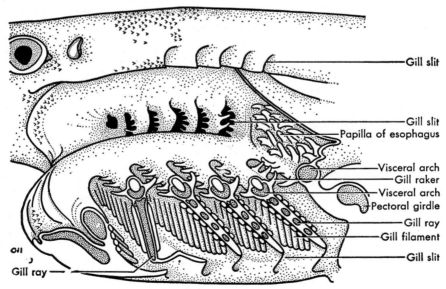

FIGURE 247. Respiratory structures in the dogfish shark. The left side of the pharynx is cut lengthwise and laid open to show the gills and other structures.

brane well supplied with capillaries and borne by the hyoid arch and first 4 branchial arches. They are supported by these arches and by gill rays. Water entering the mouth passes between the branchial arches and out through the gill slits and spiracles, thus bathing the gills and supplying oxygen to the branchial blood vessels.

Nervous system

The brain (Figs. 248 and 249) is more highly developed than that of the cyclostomes. It possesses two remarkably large **olfactory lobes**, a **cerebrum** of two hemispheres, a pair of **optic lobes**, and a **cerebellum** which projects backward over the medulla oblongata. There are 11 pairs of **cranial nerves** if the terminal is included. The **nerve (spinal) cord** is a dorsoventrally flattened tube with a narrow central canal; it is protected by the vertebral column. **Spinal nerves** arise from its sides in pairs.

Sense organs

The two **olfactory sacs** are characteristically large in elasmobranchs. The ears are membranous sacs, each with three semicircular canals; they lie within the auditory capsules. The **eyes** are well developed. Along each side of the head and body is a longitudinal groove called the **lateral line**; it contains a canal with numerous openings

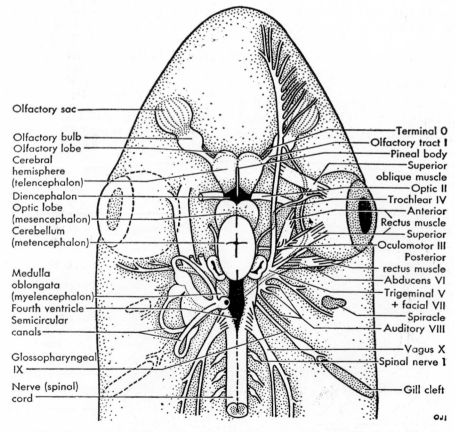

FIGURE 248. Dorsal view of the brain and cranial nerves of the dogfish shark. The Roman numerals are used to identify the cranial nerves.

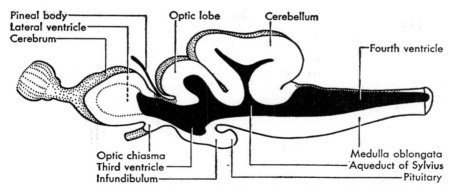

Pineal body
Lateral ventricle
Cerebrum
Optic lobe
Cerebellum
Fourth ventricle
Optic chiasma
Third ventricle
Infundibulum
Medulla oblongata
Aqueduct of Sylvius
Pituitary

FIGURE 249. Longitudinal section between the first and second ventricles of the brain of the dogfish shark showing its structure.

to the surface. Inside the canal are sensory hair cells connected to a branch of the tenth cranial nerve. On the surface of the head are also **sensory canals,** which open into pores containing **pit organs** with sensory hairs.

Urogenital system

The dogfish shark possesses two ribbon-like **kidneys** (Fig. 250), one on either side of the dorsal aorta. Their secretion is carried by small ducts into a larger one, the **urinary (mesonephric) duct** which empties into a **urogenital sinus;** it then passes out of the body through the **cloacal opening.** A series of yellowish bodies called **adrenals** are located on the medial border of the kidney.

The sexes are separate. The sperms of the male arise in two **testes** and are carried by the **vasa efferentia** to the much convoluted **vasa deferentia** which empty into the urogenital sinus. During **copulation** the sperms are transferred to the oviducts of the female with the aid of the **claspers.**

The eggs of the female arise in the paired **ovaries,** which are attached to the dorsal wall of the abdominal cavity. They break out into this cavity and enter the funnel-like opening, the **ostium,** common to both oviducts. An expanded anterior portion of

each oviduct is called a **shell gland,** and a posterior part is enlarged in the dogfish to form a "uterus" in which the young develop (Fig. 250). The oviducts have separate openings into the cloaca.

OTHER CHONDRICHTHYES

The cartilaginous fishes now living are all that remain of a type that once dominated the ancient seas. Most of them occur in the warm waters of the tropics. The sharks are the largest of all fishes; they are to fishes what elephants are to land animals. The whale shark (*Rhineodon typicus*) is from 40 to 50 feet long. The sharks are the largest living vertebrates with the exception of the whales. Among the interesting species is the great white shark, *Carcharodon carcharias,* which reaches a length of 36½ feet and has earned the name of man-eater by occasionally devouring a human being. One of the most peculiar sharks is the hammerhead (Fig. 251); its head is shaped like the head of a mallet, with an eye on each side. The sawfish (Fig. 251) is abundant in the Gulf of Mexico and reaches a length of from 10 to 20 feet. The saw is about 5 feet long; it is used for the capture of its prey; it swings the "saw" back and forth in a school of fishes to injure some of them sufficiently

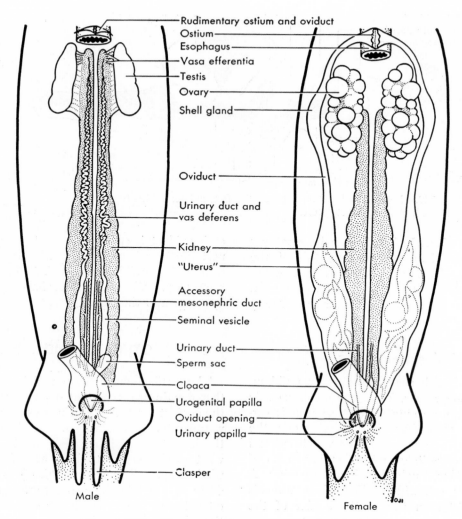

Rudimentary ostium and oviduct
Ostium
Esophagus
Vasa efferentia
Testis
Ovary
Shell gland

Oviduct

Urinary duct and
vas deferens

Kidney
"Uterus"

Accessory
mesonephric duct
Seminal vesicle

Urinary duct
Sperm sac

Cloaca
Urogenital papilla
Oviduct opening
Urinary papilla

Clasper

Male

Female

FIGURE 250. The urogenital systems of the dogfish shark.

for capture; it is also used as a weapon of defense.

The sting ray, *Dasyatis* (Fig. 251), lives half buried in the sand along the seacoast. Its whiplike tail bears a barbed spine, which is provided with a poison gland; it makes a painful wound when driven into the hand or even through the side of a shoe into the foot.

The electric eel, *Electrophorus electricus*, is an eel-shaped fish of the Amazon and Orinoca basins. It is an extreme example of specialization for the greater part of the

dorsal half of the body behind the head is occupied by the electric organ. This huge mass of electric tissue is made up of about 70 columns of electroplates, each containing no fewer than 6000 cells in a series. In water an electric eel four feet long can produce up to 600 volts in potential. The maximum power output is about 1000 watts. The discharge of the electric organ may occur a second or more apart and continue for more than an hour without fatigue to the animal. It is sufficient to disable a fairly large animal; thus it may serve as an effective weapon for

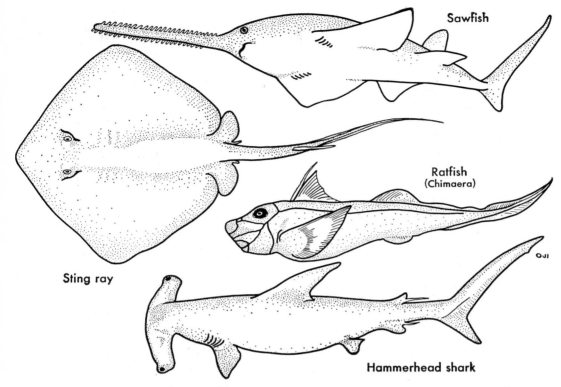

FIGURE 251. Some cartilaginous fishes showing extreme variation in form. The sting ray has pectoral fins so oversized that when the ray is swimming, the fins look like the wings of a bird in flight.

securing food or for offense and defense. A horse wading through a shallow river where the electric eel lives has received enough shock to cause it to throw its rider.

RELATIONS OF CHONDRICHTHYES TO OTHER GROUPS

The cartilaginous fishes exhibit a number of structural advances over the cyclostomes; they possess paired fins, a lower jaw, gill arches, and placoid scales. Among the peculiarities which separate the cartilaginous fishes from the bony fishes (Osteichthyes) are the absence of lungs, bones, air bladder, true scales, and the presence of skeletal characteristics which are not found in bony fishes.

RELATIONS OF THE CARTILAGINOUS FISHES TO MAN

Sharks feed chiefly on crustaceans, squids, fish, other aquatic animals, and not on human beings as one might infer from some newspaper accounts. However, there are reliable reports of shark attacks on swimmers in all warm seas, but only an occasional attack in temperate waters. Most of these attacks have occurred near beaches or reefs, and a few in Lake Nicaragua by fresh-water sharks living in this lake. In recent years, an ever increasing number of sports enthusiasts, equipped with swimfins, snorkels, and aqualungs, have moved out to new underwater frontiers. Some of those who have been too venturesome have been killed by sharks.

Sharks injure the nets of fishermen and destroy large numbers of lobsters, crabs, and food fishes. In certain parts of the world, especially the Orient, the smaller sharks and some skates are used for food—fresh, salted, and dried. In America, much prejudice exists against use of shark meat for food. However, in California they are being sold fresh as "grayfish." Also, dogfish are now being canned in the United States under a trade name and may become an important addition to our list of fish foods. The fins of sharks and rays are considered a delicacy in certain Oriental countries. Sharkskin leather is of some commercial importance in the manufacture of shoes and handbags. Sharkskin, tanned with the scales on, is called shagren, and has been used as an abrasive. It is also used for binding books and as a covering for jewel boxes. The extraction of shark-liver oil is also being carried on. The cub shark, for example, possesses a liver that constitutes about 16 per cent of the total weight of the animal and yields a considerable quantity of oil. This oil has been used principally in the tanning industry for leather. However, during World War II, the liver of the dogfish shark was America's chief source of vitamin A, and many shark livers are still used for this purpose. The pituitary gland provides an extract for medical use. The sting ray is often a nuisance to bathers, and an occasional death results from the injury inflicted by its spines.

CLASSIFICATION OF THE CHONDRICHTHYES *

(For reference purposes only)

Class 1. Chondrichthyes (Elasmobranchii). The chief characteristics of this class

are the presence of a cartilaginous skeleton; persistent notochord; placoid scales; spiral valve in intestine; two-chambered heart; claspers in male; no gill cover, pyloric ceca, or air bladder; mouth, a transverse opening on ventral side of head; tail heterocercal. Approximately 600 species according to Schultz.

Superorder 1. Selachiica (Gr. *selachos,* shark). Sharks, slender and cylindrical, with gill slits on the side.

Order 1. Heterodontia. Ex. Bullhead sharks.

Order 2. Hexanchida. Exs. Frilled and cow sharks.

Order 3. Lamnida. Exs. Carpet, whale, mackerel, thresher, basking, cat, gray, and hammerhead sharks.

Order 4. Squalida. Mostly under 8 feet long; carnivorous; voracious; but seldom attack man. Exs. *Squalus acanthias,* dogfish shark; bramble, saw, and angle sharks.

Superorder 2. Hypotrematica.

Order 1. Rajida. Rays and skates (Fig. 251). Flattened dorsoventrally, with gill slits beneath. These are highly specialized sharks, adapted for life on the bottom of the seas. The rays are ovoviviparous; they have a long whiplike tail, usually without a trace of a caudal fin, and near the midlength of the tail is a long sharp-pointed barbed spine, connected with poison glands. The skates are oviparous; they have a short thick "tail" without the poison spine, and the caudal fin is represented by a low dermal fold. Ex. *Dasyatis sabina,* sting ray.

Class 2. Holocephali (Gr. *holos,* whole; *kephale,* head). Elephant fishes and

---

* This classification is according to Leonard P. Schultz, Curator of Fishes, United States National Museum, Smithsonian Institution. The endings for superorders, orders, and suborders for the cartila-

ginous and bony fishes are those accepted by a unanimous vote of the ichthyologists at the meetings of the American Society of Ichthyologists and Herpetologists in Salt Lake City, June, 1950.

chimaeras. The latter (Fig. 251) are grotesque-looking creatures named after the fire-breathing monster of Greek mythology. One olfactory sac; gills covered by operculum; no spiracles or cloaca; adults nearly scaleless. Ex. *Chimaera* (Fig. 251).

SELECTED COLLATERAL READINGS

(See also Chapter 26)

Daniel, J.F. *The Elasmobranch Fishes*. Univ. of Cal. Press, Berkeley, 1934.

CHAPTER 26

ابي

Class Osteichthyes.
Bony Fishes

T_{HE} Osteichthyes (bony fishes) are the true fishes. They range from the ordinary fish, such as the yellow perch, to the unusual lungfish. They are aquatic animals; one adaptation to their habitat is the gills which serve as respiratory organs. They are found in all the waters of the world, from the surfaces to great ocean depths. Usually, they have an exoskeleton of scales or bony plates which furnishes protective covering for their bodies. They swim by means of fins. Their bodies are usually streamlined, but some are grotesque in shape; and others possess amazing luminescent organs.

PERCA FLAVESCENS— A BONY FISH

External anatomy

The yellow perch, *Perca flavescens* (Fig. 253), inhabits the fresh-water streams and lakes of the northeastern United States and ranges west to the Mississippi Valley. Its body is about a foot long and is divisible into **head, trunk,** and **tail.** There are two **dorsal fins, a caudal fin,** a single median **anal fin** just posterior to the anus, two **lateral pelvic fins,** and two **lateral pectoral fins.** On each side of the body is a **lateral line.** The head bears a **mouth** with well-developed **jaws** armed with **teeth,** a pair of lateral **eyes,** a pair of **external nares** in front of each eye, and gill covers (**opercula**), beneath which are the **gills.** The **skin** is provided with a number of **scales,** which are arranged like the shingles on the roof of a house, and protect the fish from mechanical injury. Mucous glands are abundant in the skin, and they produce the "slime" (mucus) which makes the fish slippery.

FIGURE 252. *Facing page,* representatives of the bony fishes. The lines suggest possible relationships. The figures are not drawn to scale. (Based on a diagram by Leonard P. Schultz, Curator of Fishes, United States National Museum, Smithsonian Institution, and made expressly for this book.)

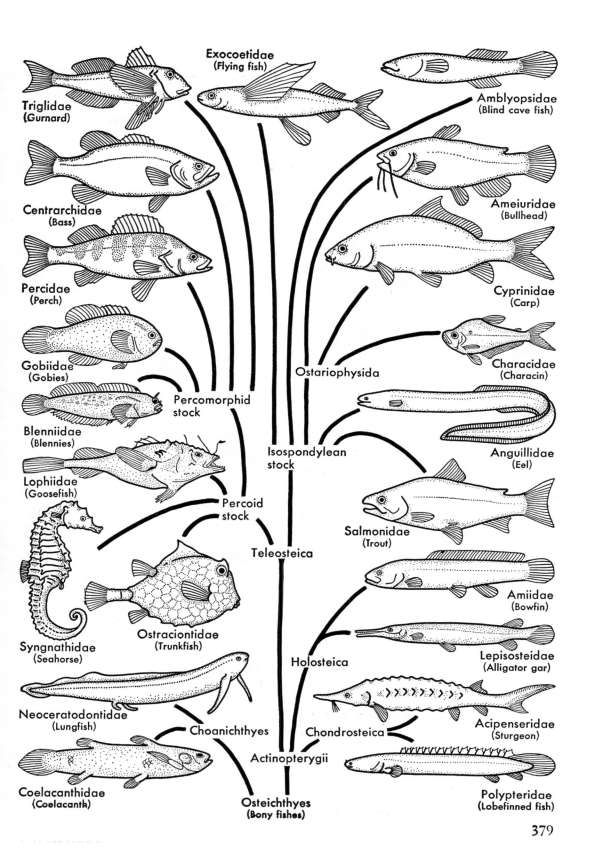

Exocoetidae
(Flying fish)

Triglidae
(Gurnard)

Amblyopsidae
(Blind cave fish)

Centrarchidae
(Bass)

Ameiuridae
(Bullhead)

Percidae
(Perch)

Cyprinidae
(Carp)

Gobiidae
(Gobies)

Percomorphid
stock

Characidae
(Characin)

Ostariophysida

Blenniidae
(Blennies)

Isospondylean
stock

Anguillidae
(Eel)

Lophiidae
(Goosefish)

Percoid
stock

Salmonidae
(Trout)

Teleosteica

Syngnathidae
(Seahorse)

Amiidae
(Bowfin)

Ostraciontidae
(Trunkfish)

Holosteica

Lepisosteidae
(Alligator gar)

Acipenseridae
(Sturgeon)

Neoceratodontidae
(Lungfish)

Choanichthyes

Chondrosteica

Actinopterygii

Coelacanthidae
(Coelacanth)

Osteichthyes
(Bony fishes)

Polypteridae
(Lobefinned fish)

379

Locomotor organs

The body of the perch and of most other fishes is streamlined and offers little resistance to the water through which the animal swims. By means of an air bladder, it is kept at the same weight as that of the water it displaces. The fish is thus able to remain stationary without much muscular exertion. The principal locomotor organ is the **tail**. By alternating contractions of the muscular bands on the sides of the trunk and tail, the tail with its caudal fin is lashed from one side to the other, thus enabling the fish to swim. Similar movements are employed in sculling a boat, when one oar at the stern is moved from side to side.

The **fins** are integumentary expansions supported by bony or cartilaginous rays. The paired lateral fins (pectoral and pelvic) are used as oars in swimming when the fish is moving slowly. They also aid the caudal fin in steering. Movement up or down results from holding the lateral fins in certain positions—obliquely backward with the anterior edge higher for the ascent, and obliquely forward for the descent.

Fishes must maintain their **equilibrium**

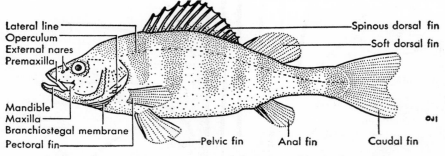

Lateral line
Operculum
External nares
Premaxilla
Mandible
Maxilla
Branchiostegal membrane
Pectoral fin
Spinous dorsal fin
Soft dorsal fin
Pelvic fin
Anal fin
Caudal fin

FIGURE 253. External features of a typical bony fish, the yellow perch.

in some way, since the back is the heaviest part of the body and tends to turn them over. The dorsal, anal, and caudal fins increase the vertical surface of the body, and, like the keel of a boat, assist the animal in maintaining an upright position. The paired lateral fins are also organs of equilibrium, acting as balancers. However, experimentation shows that if one or two of the paired fins are removed, the fish soon learns to compensate for their loss.

Skeletal system

The **exoskeleton** of the perch includes scales and fin rays. The **scales** develop in pouches in the dermis. They are arranged in oblique rows and overlap like the shingles on the roof of a house, thus forming an efficient protective covering. The posterior edge of each scale which extends out from under the preceding scale is toothed and therefore rough to the touch. Scales of this kind are called **ctenoid** scales (Fig. 261). The **fin rays** support the fins. Those of the spinous dorsal fin (Fig. 254) and of the anterior edge of the anal and pelvic fins are unjointed and unbranched **spines**. The caudal, pectoral, pelvic, soft dorsal, and anal fins are supplied with jointed, and, usually branched, **soft fin rays**.

The bones of the **endoskeleton** are shown in Fig. 254. They include the skull, vertebral column, ribs, pectoral girdle, and the interspinous bones which aid in supporting the unpaired fins. The body of the fish is, to a considerable extent, supported by the surrounding water; consequently, the bones do not need to be so strong as those of land animals, like birds and mammals, which support the entire weight of the body.

The **vertebrae** are simple and compara-

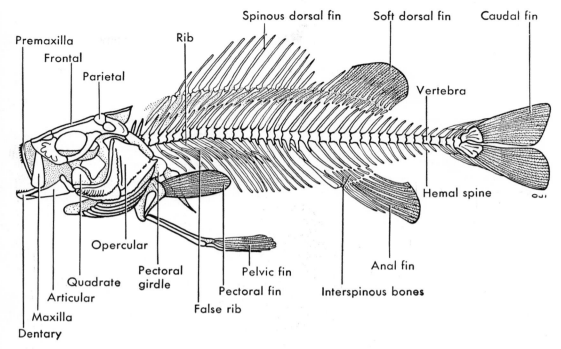

FIGURE 254. The skeleton of a fish (yellow perch). Note that the skeleton centers about the vertebral column and skull.

tively uniform in structure. **Ribs** are attached by ligaments to the abdominal vertebrae and serve as a protecting framework for the body cavity and its contents. There is no sternum. The **skull** consists of a large number of parts—some bone, others cartilage. The **visceral skeleton** is composed of 7 **paired arches** more or less modified. The first or **mandibular arch** forms the jaws. The second or **hyoid arch** is modified as a support for the gill covers. Arches 3 to 7 support the gills and are known as **gill arches.** The first 4 bear spinelike ossifications, the **gill rakers,** which act as a sieve to intercept solid particles and keep them away from the gills.

The **appendicular skeleton** is represented in the perch by **pectoral** and **pelvic girdles** and fins associated with them; and median fins (Fig. 254). The pelvic girdle is not very typical in form, being degenerate or possibly primitive.

Muscular system

The principal muscles are those used in locomotion, respiration, and in obtaining food. The movements of the body employed in swimming are produced by 4 longitudinal bands of muscles, one heavy band on each side along the back, and a thinner band on each side of both trunk and tail. These are arranged in zigzag **myotomes.** Weaker muscles move the gill arches, operculum, hyoid, and jaws.

Digestive system

The aquatic insects, mollusks, and small fishes that constitute a large part of the food of the perch are captured by the jaws and held by the many conical teeth. **Teeth** are borne on the mandibles and premaxillae, and on the roof of the mouth. They are not used for chewing food, but only for holding it. A rudimentary **tongue** projects from the

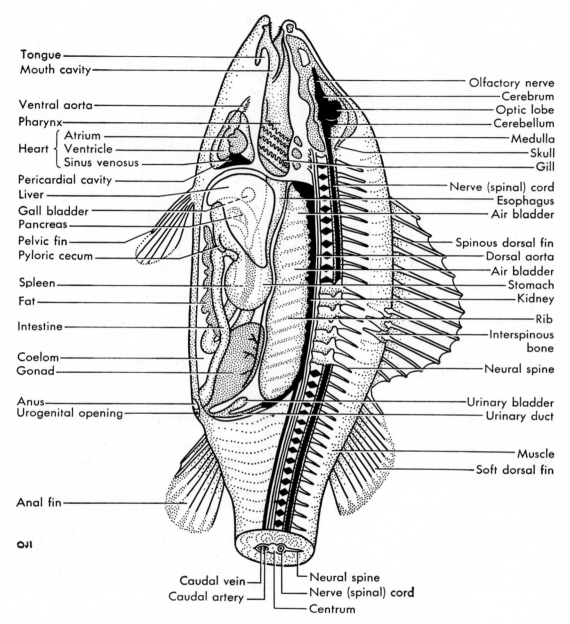

Tongue
Mouth cavity

Ventral aorta
Pharynx
Heart { Atrium
         Ventricle
         Sinus venosus
Pericardial cavity
Liver
Gall bladder
Pancreas
Pelvic fin
Pyloric cecum

Spleen
Fat

Intestine

Coelom
Gonad

Anus
Urogenital opening

Anal fin

Olfactory nerve
Cerebrum
Optic lobe
Cerebellum
Medulla
Skull
Gill

Nerve (spinal) cord
Esophagus
Air bladder

Spinous dorsal fin
Dorsal aorta
Air bladder
Stomach
Kidney

Rib
Interspinous bone

Neural spine

Urinary bladder
Urinary duct

Muscle
Soft dorsal fin

Caudal vein
Caudal artery
Neural spine
Nerve (spinal) cord
Centrum

FIGURE 255. General structure of a yellow perch.

floor of the mouth cavity; it is not capable of independent movement, but functions as a **tactile organ.** The **mouth cavity** is followed by the **pharynx,** on either side of which are 4 **gill slits.** Food passes directly to the stomach through a short **esophagus.**

The **stomach, intestine, liver, gall bladder, pyloric ceca,** and **anus** are shown in Fig. 255. The **pancreas** is located in the first loop of the intestine; however, it is so diffuse that it is not usually seen in gross dissection.

Circulatory system

The blood of the perch contains oval nucleated **red corpuscles** and amoeboid **white corpuscles.** The **heart** lies in a portion of the coelom, the **pericardial cavity,** beneath the pharynx. **Circulation** in the perch, which is similar to that in the dogfish shark, is shown through the heart and gills in Fig. 256. Circulation is much slower in fishes than it is in the higher vertebrates.

Respiratory system

The perch breathes with 4 pairs of **gills** supported by the first 4 gill arches. Each gill bears a double row of **gill filaments,** which are abundantly supplied with capillaries. The **afferent branchial artery** (Fig. 256) brings the blood from the heart to the gill filaments; here an exchange of gases takes place. The carbon dioxide, with which the blood is loaded, passes out the gill, and a

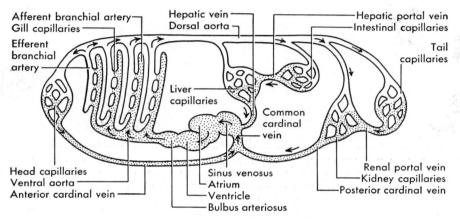

FIGURE 256. Diagram of the main blood vessels of a fish (yellow perch) as seen in lateral view. The unstippled parts represent oxygenated blood and the stippled, nonoxygenated blood.

supply of oxygen is taken in from the continuous stream of water, which enters the pharynx through the mouth and bathes the gills on its way out through the **gill slits.**

The oxygenated blood is collected into the **efferent branchial artery** and is carried about the body. The gills are protected from external injury by the gill covering or **operculum** (Fig. 253), and from solid particles which enter the mouth by the **gill rakers.** Because oxygen is taken up by the capillaries of the gill filaments, a constant supply of fresh water is necessary for the life of the fish. If it is deprived of water entirely, respiration is prevented, and the fish dies of suffocation.

The **air bladder** is a comparatively large, thin-walled sac lying in the dorsal part of the body cavity. It is filled with gas and is a

hydrostatic organ or "float"; in certain fishes, but not in perch, it may also aid in respiration. The gas contained in it is a mixture of oxygen, nitrogen, and carbon dioxide, and is derived from the blood vessels in its walls. The air bladder decreases the specific gravity, making the body of the fish equal in weight to the amount of water it displaces. The fish, therefore, is able to maintain a stationary position without muscular effort. The amount of gas within the air bladder depends upon the pressure of the surrounding water; and, in some way, it is regulated by the fish according to depth. If a fish is suddenly brought to the surface from a great depth, the air bladder which was under considerable pressure is suddenly relieved, and therefore expands, often forcing the stomach out of the mouth. In some

FIGURE 257. Winterkill of fish due to suffocation. This is a scene in spring on the shore of a northern lake. The first complete freezing over of a lake seals the water away from further contact with the air, an important source of oxygen. Then when the snow on top of the ice becomes deep enough to cut off the light necessary for photosynthesis in plants, an additional source of oxygen is eliminated. The fish, robbed of their life-sustaining oxygen, die, as is shown in this photograph. (Photo by Ouradnik. Courtesy of Institute for Fisheries Research, Michigan Department of Conservation.)

fishes the air bladder may serve in sound production. It is lunglike in the lungfishes.

Excretory system

The **kidneys** lie just beneath the backbone in the abdominal cavity. They extract urea and other waste products from the blood. Two thin tubes, the **urinary (mesonephric) ducts** or "**ureters**," carry the excretory matter into a **urinary bladder** (Fig. 255), where it is stored for a time and then expelled through the **urogenital opening**, which is located just posterior to the anus.

Nervous system

The brain of the perch (Figs. 255 and 392) is more highly developed than that of the cyclostome or shark. The 4 chief divi-sions are well marked: the **cerebrum, optic lobes, cerebellum,** and the **medulla.** The brain gives off **cranial nerves** to the sense organs and other parts of the anterior portion of the body. The **nerve (spinal) cord** lies above the centra of the vertebral column and passes through the neural arches of the vertebrae. **Spinal nerves** arise from the sides of the spinal cord.

Sense organs

The principal sense organs are: (1) cutaneous sense organs, (2) olfactory sacs, (3) ears, and (4) eyes. The integument, especially that of the lips, serves as an organ of touch. Dermal barbels on some fishes such as the catfishes also function as sensory organs for locating food. The **lateral line** contains sensory cells which serve to detect

CLASS OSTEICHTHYES. BONY FISHES

vibrations in water and pressure stimuli. There are also numerous other cutaneous sense organs.

The two **olfactory sacs** lie in the anterior part of the skull and communicate to the outside by a pair of openings in front of each eye. They are not connected with the mouth cavity and take no part in respiration. The inner surface is thrown up into folds which contain many sense cells. Ability to detect odors lies in the olfactory sacs.

The **ear** consists of the membranous labyrinth only. As in the cyclostome and shark, the sound waves are transmitted by the bones of the skull to the fluid within the labyrinth. Three semicircular canals (Fig. 396) are present, and the sacculus contains concretions of calcium carbonate called ear stones or **otoliths**. Experiments indicate that goldfishes can hear. The ear serves both as an organ of hearing and an organ of equilibrium.

The **eye** of the perch differs in several respects from that of the terrestrial vertebrates. The **eyelids** are absent in bony fishes since the water keeps the eyeball moist and free from foreign objects. The **cornea** is flattened and of about the same refractive power as the water. The **lens** is almost spherical. The **pupil** is usually larger than that of other vertebrates and allows the entrance of more light rays; this is necessary, since semidarkness prevails at moderate depths. When at rest the eye focuses clearly at about 15 inches, but it can detect the movement of objects much farther away. To focus on distant objects the lens is pulled backward. Many fishes are nearsighted. However, the sharks that pursue rapidly moving prey have lenses that are set for distant vision. Recent evidence makes it appear that fishes can distinguish colors; therefore, it is possible that gaudy colors on hook lures are an aid to success in fishing.

Reproductive system

The sexes are separate. The single ovary is probably the result of a fusion of two ovaries in the embryo. The **ovary** or **testes** lie in the body cavity. The germ cells pass through the reproductive ducts and out of the urogenital opening. Perch migrate in the spring from the deep waters of lakes and ponds, where they have spent the winter, to the shallow waters near shore. The female lays many thousands of eggs in a long ribbonlike mass. The male fertilizes the eggs by depositing sperm (milt) over them. Very few eggs develop because of the numerous animals such as other fishes and aquatic birds which feed on them.

Development

The embryogeny of the goldfish is substituted here for the perch because it is better known, yet the development of the perch is similar. The young goldfish hatches from the egg in about 3 to 14 days, depending upon the temperature of the water. The egg passes through the stages shown in Fig. 258. A large part of the egg consists of yolk. A protoplasmic accumulation which forms a slight projection at one end is called the **germinal disk (blastodisk)**. **Cleavage** of the germinal disk takes place, and the **blastoderm** produced gradually grows around the yolk. The **embryo** appears as a thickening of the edge of the blastoderm; this grows in size at the expense of the yolk. After a time the head and tail become free from the yolk, and the young fish breaks out of the egg membranes. The young fish lives at first upon the yolk in the yolk sac, but it is soon able to obtain food from the water.

OTHER FISHES

External features

Form of the body

The bodies of the majority of fishes are spindle-shaped and laterally compressed as in the perch—a form that offers slight resistance to progress through the water. Varia-

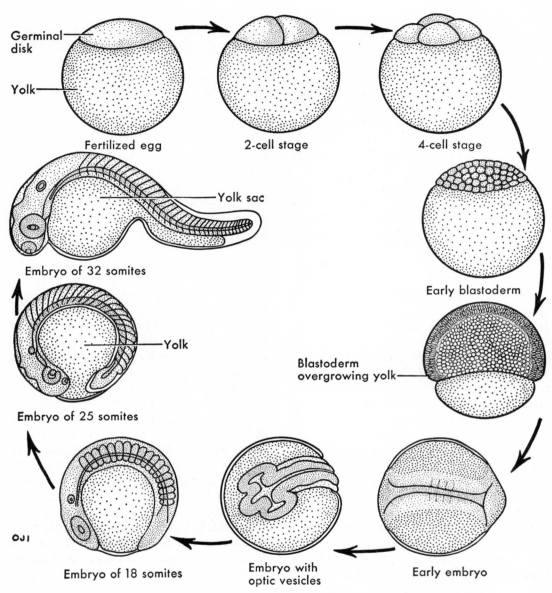

Germinal disk

Yolk

Fertilized egg

2-cell stage

4-cell stage

Early blastoderm

Blastoderm overgrowing yolk

Yolk sac

Embryo of 32 somites

Yolk

Embryo of 25 somites

OJI

Embryo of 18 somites

Embryo with optic vesicles

Early embryo

FIGURE 258. Early embryology of a bony fish, the goldfish. (After Helen I. Battle, *Ohio J. Sci.* 40:85, 1940.)

tions in form are correlated with the habits of the fish. For example, flounders (Fig. 262) have flat bodies and are adapted for life on the sea bottom; and eels (Fig. 252) have long cylindrical bodies which enable them to enter holes and crevices.

Fins and tail

Fins, according to some zoologists, arise in the embryo as median and lateral folds of the integument (Fig. 259), which are at first continuous. Later, parts of the folds disappear and the isolated **dorsal, caudal, anal,**

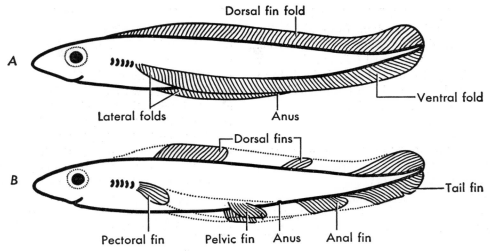

FIGURE 259. Diagrams illustrating the finfold theory of the origin of fins. A, the continuous folds of the paired and unpaired fins in the embryo. B, parts of the continuous folds disappear to form the permanent fins. (After Wiedersheim.)

pelvic, and **pectoral fins** persist. The pelvic fins vary considerably in position. In the perch (Fig. 253) they are situated beneath the pectoral fins; in the fresh-water catfish, they are just in front of the anus and are called abdominal; and in certain other species they are in the throat region.

The shape of the **caudal fin** and the terminal portion of the tail differs in the main groups of fishes and is therefore of importance in classification (Fig. 260).

The three main types of caudal or tail fins found in fishes are: heterocercal, diphycercal, and homocercal. The **heterocercal** tail is found in modern sharks; it is two-lobed, with the vertebral column extending into the larger dorsal lobe. The stroke of the asym-

metrical heterocercal tail forces the anterior part of the body downward. This type is therefore of advantage to and characteristic of those fishes that have ventrally situated mouths and feed on the bottom.

In the **diphycercal type** the vertebral column extends straight back to the tip of the body, with the tail fin developed symmetrically above and below it; the living lungfishes have tail fins of this type. The **homocercal fin** is externally symmetrical, but the internal structure shows that the backbone extends into the dorsal lobe. The stroke of the homocercal tail forces the fish straight forward. It is characteristic of those fishes with a terminal mouth and is the type possessed by most bony fishes.

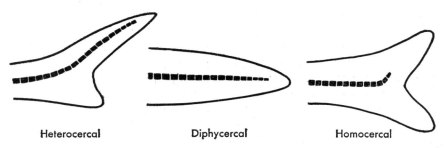

FIGURE 260. Types of tails in fishes.

The diphycercal tail has long been considered the primitive type from which the others were derived, but this is not true. In most cases diphycercal tails are shown by fossil history to have been derived from heterocercal ones, and the homocercal type is also of heterocercal origin.

Scales

The scales of fishes form a protecting exoskeleton. They are of three principal types: (1) ganoid, (2) cycloid, and (3) ctenoid (Fig. 261). **Ganoid scales** are usually rhomboid- or diamond-shaped. They have layers of ganoin deposited on a layer of bone. Ganoid scales occur in gars, pikes, sturgeons, and their allies; these are often called ganoid fishes. Cycloid and ctenoid scales are arranged in overlapping rows as described for the perch. **Cycloid scales** are nearly circular with concentric rings about a central point; they are characteristic of the more primitive teleosts. **Ctenoid scales** are similar to cycloid scales, but the part which extends out from under the neighboring scales bears small spines; these are generally found in the higher teleosts. In many fishes the scales develop into large spines or fuse to form bony plates which are protective. Some fishes such as the catfishes are scaleless.

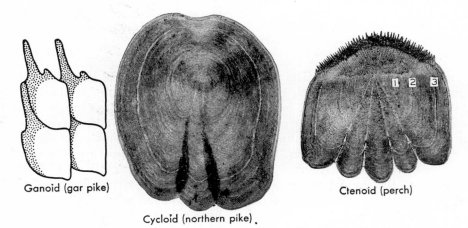

Ganoid (gar pike)

Cycloid (northern pike).

Ctenoid (perch)

FIGURE 261. The different types of scales on bony fishes. Ctenoid scale shows winter growth rings (numbered), which are used to determine age in years. The winter rings show slower growth periods which result from low food supply. (Photomicrographs of cycloid and ctenoid scales courtesy of Institute for Fisheries Research, Michigan Department of Conservation.)

Color

The general impression is that fishes are not brightly colored, but many, especially those in tropical waters, are exceedingly brilliant. The colors are due to pigments within special dermal cells called chromatophores or to reflection and iridescence resulting from the physical structure of the scales which contain crystals of guanine. The pigments are red, orange, yellow, or black, but other colors may be produced by a combination of chromatophores; for example, yellow and black when blended give brown. Usually the colors are arranged in a definite pattern consisting of transverse or longitudinal stripes and spots of various sizes. Coral-reef fishes have long been famous for their brilliant colors, and many fresh-water fishes of the temperate zone exhibit bright hues distributed so as to form striking and intricate patterns (e.g., the rainbow darter).

The dispersion or concentration of the pigment in the chromatophores of certain fishes results in changes in coloration. These changes are due to incident light reflected from surrounding surfaces and act through the eye and nervous system on the differ-

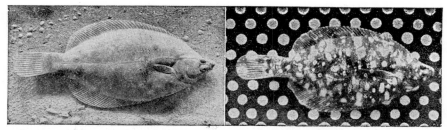

FIGURE 262. Protective resemblance in the flounder. The flounder changes in pattern and color to blend with its surroundings by dispersion or concentration of pigment bodies. Even when placed on such an unnatural background as that on the right, the resemblance is striking. (Courtesy of A.M. Winchester.)

ently colored chromatophores. The changes are therefore dependent upon the color of the fish's environment and are often protective because they help to conceal the animal. The change in color is slow in some fishes, but usually it only takes a few minutes, as in the case of the flounders (Fig. 262), which respond to pattern of background as well as simple illumination. In this respect flatfishes probably exceed even the famed chameleon. Male fishes are often more brightly colored than the females, especially during spawning activities.

Sound production in fishes

A surprisingly large number of fishes can produce sounds audible to man; these noises are used either to bring the sexes together or to warn or startle enemies. Fishes make various sounds in various ways.

Certain sculpins vibrate their gill covers against the sides of their heads to produce a humming note. The hogfish grunts by gnashing its pharyngeal teeth. The sea robin produces a grunt by means of special muscles in the air bladder. In open water, the croaker probably makes more noise than any other kind of fish, it can be heard 30 feet down. The sounds are produced by the action of special muscles on the air bladder. Croakers are edible fish found along our southern Atlantic Coast.

Naval men during World War II had more than an academic interest in undersea sounds; at first, some of the noises made by fishes and other sea animals threw submarine detection by radar into confusion.

Fishes of ancient lineage

Among the ancient fishes were those known as the lobefins, because of the thick, lobe-shaped, paired fins. The lobefins contain skeletal structures that correspond with similar bony structures in the appendages of true land forms. Descendants of the ancient stocks from which these fishes were derived migrated onto land at a later time to give rise to land vertebrates. Lobefinned fishes were long considered extinct until one was caught off the coast of Africa in 1938. This was a coelacanth (*Latimeria*), and about a dozen more have been collected since then (Fig. 263). The chances look good for more coelacanths to be hooked in the future, so that eventually we will have a more detailed knowledge of them. As a matter of fact, their internal structure is being carefully studied by Professor Millot of Paris, and we should soon know more about the anatomy of these most interesting creatures.

The coelacanth is the only surviving member of the ancient crossopterygian fishes which gave rise to the amphibians. Here we have a valuable link with the past that gives us an understanding of an important group of vertebrates, previously known only from fossils.

Many of the ancient fishes were covered with ganoid scales. The sturgeons (Fig. 252) and garpikes are protected in this way. Only

FIGURE 263. An ancient fish (*Latimeria*), first caught off the coast of Africa in 1938; supposedly extinct for millions of years. It is a "living fossil," estimated to have lived in the Devonian period. Length about 5 feet. Note the thick lobe-shaped fins. (Courtesy of Sport and General Press Agency, Ltd., London.)

two species of paddlefishes are now known: *Polyodon* lives in the Mississippi Valley, and *Psephurus* in China. The fresh-water dogfish, *Amia calva*, is the only existing species of the family *Amiidae*.

Fishes that live in caves

Six species of cave fishes live in the subterranean streams of the cave region of Indiana, Kentucky, and Missouri. They are small, but of special interest because the eyes of some are rudimentary and covered with a thick skin. Cavefish (*Amblyopsis*) (Fig. 252) is common in the River Styx of Mammoth Cave. Did the sightless cave dwellers lose their eyes after they took up cave life, or were they blind fishes before they began their life underground? The answer is, we do not know.

Flying fish

Sixty-five or more species of flying fish live in warm seas (Fig. 252). Some are able to leave the water and, rising in the air a few yards, "fly" a distance of from a few rods to more than ⅛ mile. Contrary to a popular belief, the pectoral fins do not force the fish

forward, but simply sustain the body in the air. It is the tail fin only that is used for forward propulsion when the fish skims the water surface during the "take-off."

Eels

The true eels (Fig. 252) should not be confused with the so-called lamprey eels which are cyclostomes. The single species of North American fresh-water eel, *Anguilla rostrata* occurs in the streams of the Atlantic Coast. It is long and slender, and its scales are inconspicuous. The dorsal, caudal, and anal fins are continuous. Eels enter the sea in the autumn to spawn, after which they die. The eggs are laid in deep water off the Bermuda shore. The young develop in the sea and then migrate up the rivers.

Sticklebacks

The famous nest-building stickleback (Fig. 266), has 5 large spines on its back. The nest is built of sticks fastened together with threads secreted by a gland in the male. The female lays eggs in the nest; the male then enters the nest and fertilizes them, after which he guards them from intruders.

Seahorses

Seahorses (Fig. 252) are small and do not look much like fish, the head resembling that of a horse. They swim by means of the dorsal and pectoral fins, holding themselves in a vertical position; they move at a snail's pace. Often they cling to objects with their prehensile tail. The eggs are carried in a brood pouch of the male until they hatch. The sea dragon of Australia (Fig. 264) is

FIGURE 264. Australian sea dragon, *Phyllopteryx*, the most bizarre of all seahorses. The postures and antics of these fishes are as distinctive and grotesque as their appearance. The leaflike extentions from the body tend to conceal the fish among seaweed. Natural size up to 12 inches long. (Courtesy of the American Museum of Natural History.)

provided with leaflike appendages of skin which have a remarkable resemblance to seaweed among which they live. These fishes represent a more specialized stage in evolution than the streamlined fishes.

Porcupine fishes

These inhabitants of tropical seas are covered with movable spines, hence their name. They live on the bottom among seaweeds and corals, and, when disturbed, inflate their bodies by swallowing water or air (Fig. 266), in which condition they are not easily injured by their enemies.

Anglers

Living on the bottom of the Atlantic, Indian, and Pacific oceans are about a dozen genera of extremely large-mouthed fishes known as anglers (Fig. 265). *Lophius*, the fishing frog or goosefish, occurs along the Atlantic Coast of North America. Its long dorsal ray is inserted on the snout and serves as a fishing rod with "bait." The latter consists of dermal tentacles. Their wormlike appearance attracts other fishes, which are engulfed into the big mouth cavity as the

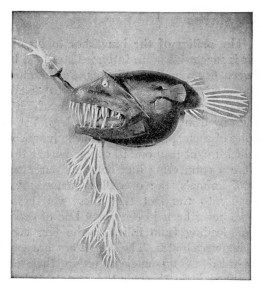

FIGURE 265. An anglerfish from the deep sea; a fish that fishes. Note large mouth with sharp teeth and luminous dermal tentacles projecting from the upper and lower jaws. The one on top of the snout is called a rod with a luminous "bait" at the tip. (Courtesy of the American Museum of Natural History.)

jaws are quickly opened. This fish reaches a length of over three feet and has a mouth more than a foot wide.

Deep-sea fishes

Many families of fishes contain deep-sea species (Fig. 265) which are often curiously modified. Some have very large eyes, which enable them to catch as many rays of light as possible; these eyes probably serve in connection with luminescent organs. Others have small or rudimentary eyes and are blind; they depend upon organs of touch instead of eyes. Many have large mouths with long sharp teeth and enormous stomachs. The luminescent organs are variously distributed over the body. One type consists of a cup of secretory cells covered by a cellular lens. The secretion is luminous, and in certain cases acts as a lure; in others, it probably enables the fish to see in the dark abyss of the ocean.

Lungfishes

The ability of the lungfishes to breathe air is suggestive of an intermediate stage between fishes and amphibians. Furthermore, the Australian lungfish is able to "walk" along the bottom of the rivers in which it lives by using its paired fins as legs. Yet in spite of such specializations in the lungfishes which might lead one to conclude that they were a connecting link between water and land animals, the over-all evidence points clearly to the fact that these vertebrates have never been in the direct line of evolution leading from fishes to the first land-living vertebrates. The lungfishes are now regarded as an ancient group that has changed little through the recent geologic ages.

The lungfish has an opening between the nasal sac and the mouth cavity, a persistent unconstricted notochord, and an air bladder which opens into the pharynx and functions as a lung. The Australian lungfish *Neocera-*todus (Fig. 252) lies on the bottom of stagnant pools and feeds on small animals; occasionally it comes to the surface in order to change the air in its single lung. Because of this lung it can exist in water unfit for fishes that breathe entirely with gills.

The African lungfishes, *Protopterus*, live in the marshes of central Africa. During the dry summer season they burrow about 18 inches into the mud, where a cocoon of slime is secreted; here they remain inactive, breathing with lungs and living on fat stored in the kidneys and gonads until the rainy season comes again. The South American lungfish *Lepidosiren* also hibernates in the mud during the dry season.

Fossil fishes

A large number of species of fish are known only from their fossil remains. The earliest fish remains consist of spines and scales from the lower Silurian or Ordovician strata of the earth's crust, which were laid down probably over 300 million years ago. The Devonian age is called the "Age of Fishes" because of the predominance of fishes over the other animals that lived at that time. A considerable portion of the Osteichthyes are fossils: 4 of the 7 families of the Neoceratodida (Dipnoi); 6 of the 7 families of the Crossopterygiida; 41 of the 43 families of Chondrosteica; 9 of the 11 families of Holosteica; and but 28 of the 402 families of Teleosteica. The study of fossil fishes is very important because of the light these prehistoric forms shed upon the affinities of modern species.

RELATIONS OF BONY FISHES TO MAN

Although a few fishes are injurious because they destroy valuable food fishes and other useful aquatic animals, many are of use to man, serving either as food or as a means of recreation. Among the fresh-water

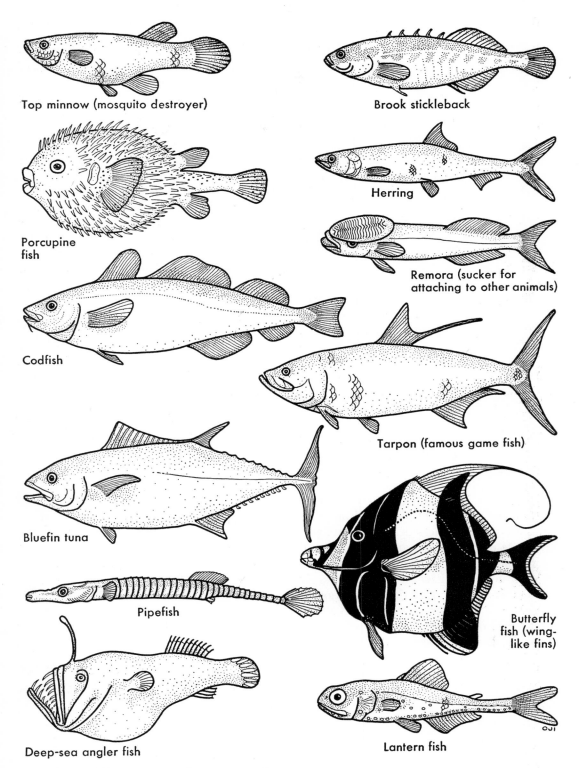

Top minnow (mosquito destroyer)

Brook stickleback

Porcupine fish

Herring

Remora (sucker for attaching to other animals)

Codfish

Tarpon (famous game fish)

Bluefin tuna

Pipefish

Butterfly fish (wing-like fins)

Deep-sea angler fish

Lantern fish

Figure 266.   Some bony fishes to show the great variety of forms in the modern fish group. The codfish, herring, and tuna are of great economic importance.

393

game fishes are the yellow perch, various species of trout, pikes, muskellunge, and bass (Fig. 252). Marine game fish include the tarpon (Fig. 266), sea bass, and tuna.

Marine food fish are of great value. Herring (Fig. 266), in vast quantities, are smoked, salted, pickled, and packed as sardines. Mackerel are caught in enormous numbers. The flounder family (Fig. 262) contains halibuts, soles, plaice, and turbots. Codfish (Fig. 266) is especially valuable, together with other members of its family such as pollacks, haddocks, and hakes. The average annual catch of codfish is over two billion pounds. Cod-liver oil is also the principal source of vitamin A and vitamin D. Rivaling the codfish in value are the salmon of the Pacific Coast, which are caught and canned in large quantities. In fresh water, live whitefish, lake trout, catfish and perch—all important food fishes. The eggs of sturgeons and certain other fishes are made into caviar, especially in Russia. The use of fish meal has become important in the fertilizer and pet-food industries.

Fishing is becoming increasingly popular as a recreation for millions of people. In one midwest state alone over a million fishing licenses are sold each year. The money spent by fishermen in pursuing their sport runs into many millions of dollars. Enormous sums are spent by the federal and state governments in rearing fish and in stream and lake improvement work.

Many food fish have decreased markedly in numbers due to overfishing, pollution of streams and lakes by sewage and chemical wastes, and other causes. For this reason the federal and state governments have placed certain restrictions on fishing and have also undertaken to propagate certain species artificially. These include fresh-water species such as whitefish, lake trout, pike perch, and bass, and marine species such as codfish, haddock, salmon, flounders, and sardines of the Pacific Coast.

Among the fish of benefit to man should be mentioned the top minnows (*Gambusia*,

Fig. 266) which feed voraciously on mosquito larvae. These are placed in bodies of fresh water to prevent the breeding of mosquitoes that transmit malaria and yellow fever.

The scales of the garpike are used for jewelry and novelties.

In recent years, considerable use has been made of fishes for experimental animals, especially in the fields of genetics, embryology, animal behavior, and pharmacology.

There has been a tremendous growth of interest in tropical fishes; many of them are popular for the home aquarium. Pet shops now stock many kinds of fishes for both scientists and hobbyists.

A BRIEF CLASSIFICATION OF LIVING OSTEICHTHYES *

(For reference purposes only)

About 40,000 living species of fishes are known from the entire world according to Schultz; of these, about 168 families and about 3300 species occur in North America. The families shown in Fig. 252 are some of the better known representatives of the orders listed below:

Class 1. Osteichthyes (bony fishes).
  Subclass 1. Choanichthyes.
    Order 1. Neoceratodida. Ex. lungfishes (Fig. 252).
    Order 2. Crossopterygiida. Ex. lobe-finned fishes.
      Suborder 1. Coelacanthiina. Ex. *Latimeria* (Fig. 263).
  Subclass 2. Actinopterygii. Ex. rayed fins.
    Superorder 1. Chondrosteica (cartilage and bone).
    Order 1. Polypterida. Ex. lobefinned fishes (Fig. 252).
    Order 2. Acipenserida. Ex. sturgeons (Fig. 252).
    Superorder 2. Holosteica (bone and cartilage).

* This classification is according to Leonard P. Schultz, Curator of Fishes, United States National Museum, Smithsonian Institution.

Order 1. **Lepisosteida.** Ex. gars.

Order 2. **Amiida.** Ex. bowfin (Fig. 252).

Superorder 3. **Teleosteica** (perfected bone).

Order 1. **Isospondylida. Exs. herring, salmon, deep-sea fishes, tarpon, shad, whitefish, and lake herring.

Order 2. **Bathyclupeida.** Ex. deep-sea herrings.

Order 3. **Mormyrida.**

Order 4. **Ateleopida.**

Order 5. **Giganturida.**

Order 6. **Lyomerida.**

Order 7. **Ostariophysida. Exs. catfishes, minnows, characins (Fig. 252), suckers, carp, buffalo.

Order 8. **Anguillida.** Ex. eels (Fig. 252).

Order 9. **Heteromida.** Ex. spiny eels.

Order 10. **Synbranchiida.** Ex. mud eels.

Order 11. **Cyprinodontida.** Exs. toothed carps, top minnows.

Order 12. **Salmopercida.** Ex. trout perches.

Order 13. **Berycomorphida.** Ex. Berycoid fishes.

Order 14. **Zeomorphida.** Ex. John dories.

Order 15. **Anacanthida. Exs. codfishes, haddock, pollack, burbot.

Order 16. **Thoracosteida.** Ex. sticklebacks.

Order 17. **Solenichthyida.** Exs. trumpet and pipefishes, sea horses.

Order 18. **Allotriognathida.** Exs. moonfishes, ribbonfishes.

Order 19. **Percomorphida. Exs. perches, basses, gobies, blennies (Fig. 252), snappers, parrot fishes, and butterfly fishes.

Order 20. **Scleropareida.** Exs. scorpion and rockfishes.

Order 21. **Cephalacanthida.** Ex. gurnards (Fig. 252).

Order 22. **Pleuronectida. Exs. flatfishes, soles, flounders, halibut.

Order 23. **Icosteida.** Ex. ragfishes.

Order 24. **Chaudhurida.**

Order 25. **Discocephalida.** Exs. Shark suckers, remoras.

Order 26. **Plectognathida.** Exs. puffers, filefishes, trunkfishes (Fig. 252).

Order 27. **Gobiesocida.** Ex. clingfishes.

Order 28. **Batrachoidida.** Ex. toadfishes.

Order 29. **Pediculatida.** Exs. anglers, goosefish (Fig. 252).

SELECTED COLLATERAL READINGS

Axelrod, H.R., and Schultz, L.P. *Handbook of Tropical Aquarium Fishes.* McGraw-Hill, New York, 1955.

Berg, L.S. *Classification of Fishes Both Recent and Fossil.* Edwards, Ann Arbor, Mich., 1940.

Brown, M.E. *The Physiology of Fishes.* Vols. 1 and 2. Academic Press, New York, 1957.

Curtis, B. *The Life Story of the Fish: His Morals and Manners.* Harcourt, Brace, New York, 1949.

Hubbs, C.L., and Lagler, K.F. *Fishes of the Great Lakes Region.* Cranbrook Institute of Science, Bloomfield Hills, Mich., 1947.

Jordan, D.S. *A Guide to the Study of Fishes.* Holt, New York, 1905.

Lagler, K.F. *Freshwater Fishery Biology,* W.C. Brown, Dubuque, Iowa, 1956.

LaGorce, J.O. *The Book of Fishes.* National Geographic Society, Washington, 1939.

Norman, J.R. *A History of Fishes.* Bern, London, 1931.

Schultz, L.P., with Stern, Edith. *The Ways of Fishes.* Van Nostrand, New York, 1948.

Treassler, D.K. *Marine Products of Commerce.* Chemical Catalogue Co., New York, 1923.

Walton, Izaak. *The Compleat Angler.* Luck Company, London, 1653.

** Orders of special economic importance.

CHAPTER 27

OJI

Class Amphibia.
Frogs, Toads,
Salamanders,
and Others

$\mathbf{T}_{\text{HE}}$ common amphibians are the frogs, toads, and salamanders (Fig. 267). They spend part or all of their existence in the water or in damp places. Most lay their eggs in the water; and the larvae, which breathe with gills, are known as tadpoles or pollywogs. Some amphibians are often confused with reptiles, especially the lizards, because of their similarity of form, but almost all reptiles possess scales and are not slimy, whereas amphibians usually have a smooth slimy skin without scales except in a few rare species.

Introduction

There are 10 orders of extinct Amphibia, and three orders of living forms, which are as follows:

1. The Apoda (Gymnophiona), which are commonly called caecilians, are wormlike amphibians inhabiting tropical and subtropical regions.
2. The Caudata are amphibians with tails; they include the mud puppies, sirens, and salamanders.
3. The Salientia are frogs and toads, which are tailless in the adult stage.

The United States is a paradise for the student of Amphibia because it contains large numbers of species and individuals. Since all amphibians require moisture, they should be looked for in or near bodies of fresh water and in moist places such as under logs and stones in damp woods. Among the most interesting features of amphibians are their ability to change color, their powers of regeneration, their varied and often curious breeding habits, their methods of spending the winter, and their poisonous secretions. As is the case with birds, more amphibians are heard than seen; hence it is advisable to become acquainted with the call notes of the various species. Many of these can be easily learned from the field recordings made and narrated by Charles M. Bogert in 1958.

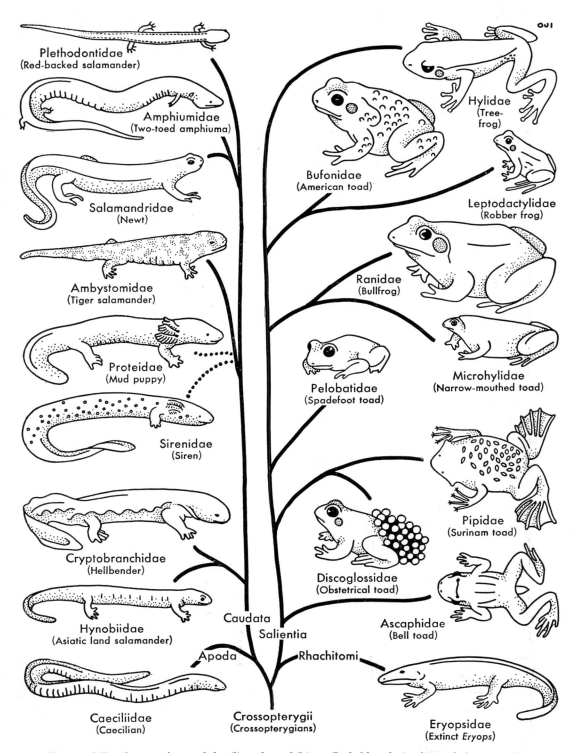

Plethodontidae
(Red-backed salamander)

Amphiumidae
(Two-toed amphiuma)

Salamandridae
(Newt)

Ambystomidae
(Tiger salamander)

Proteidae
(Mud puppy)

Sirenidae
(Siren)

Cryptobranchidae
(Hellbender)

Hynobiidae
(Asiatic land salamander)

Caeciliidae
(Caecilian)

Hylidae
(Tree-frog)

Bufonidae
(American toad)

Leptodactylidae
(Robber frog)

Ranidae
(Bullfrog)

Microhylidae
(Narrow-mouthed toad)

Pelobatidae
(Spadefoot toad)

Pipidae
(Surinam toad)

Discoglossidae
(Obstetrical toad)

Ascaphidae
(Bell toad)

Caudata

Salientia

Apoda

Rhachitomi

Crossopterygii
(Crossopterygians)

Eryopsidae
(Extinct *Eryops*)

FIGURE 267. Some orders and families of amphibians. Probable relationships of the more important living families are indicated by lines; the lines are broken where greatest doubt exists. (Based on diagram by Charles M. Bogert, Curator of Amphibians and Reptiles, American Museum of Natural History; made expressly for this text.)

Color and color changes

The colors in the skin of amphibians are due to scattered pigment granules in the epidermis and to pigment cells in the dermis. The latter are usually brown, black, yellow, or red and are contained in cells called chromatophores. The power of changing color is possessed by most amphibians, and especially by frogs. The common leopard frogs are supplied with black pigment cells called melanophores and with interference cells that contain whitish crystals, golden pigment cells, and sometimes red pigment cells.

The black melanophores are branching

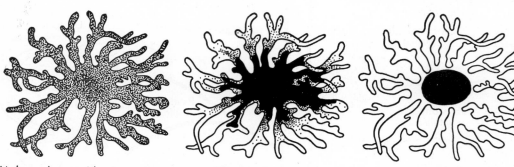

Melanophore with pigment dispersed throughout cell

Pigment beginning to concentrate

Pigment concentrated in body of cell

FIGURE 268. Stages in the changes of pigment-bearing cells (melanophores) in the skin of the frog. The color variation from the fully expanded to the completely contracted melanophore is black to gray.

cells as shown in Fig. 268. When the pigment is dispersed, it covers a larger area and consequently gives the skin a darker color. When the pigment is concentrated the skin becomes lighter. These changes in the color of the skin are shown in Fig. 269. The yellow pigment is contained in spherical golden cells. There is no green pigment; the green color results from a combined effect of light reflected from the granules of the interference cells and the yellow pigment through which the light passes. Most of the color changes are due to changes in the concentration of the black and yellow pigments.

Color changes are brought about primarily by a hormone called **intermedin,*** which is secreted by the **intermediate lobe** of the **pituitary gland.** Intermedin causes a dispersion of pigment granules. Light is the chief stimulus; it acts through the eye. Experimentally blinded frogs show a reduced capacity to change color. In a bright light the skin of the frog becomes light in color, whereas in the dark it changes to a darker hue.

Changes in color are due to both external and internal conditions; temperature is an important external factor. When the temperature is raised, the pigment becomes more concentrated, and the skin changes to a lighter color. When the temperature is lowered, the pigment becomes expanded, and a darker color results. It is evident that changes in the skin color of the frog are in part due to a hormone (intermedin) and in part to the nervous system. Usually the color changes are such as to cause the frog to resemble more closely its surroundings; thus it becomes less conspicuous and is protectively colored.

* Intermedin causes dispersion of pigment in the melanophores of fishes, amphibians, and reptiles, but appears to have no effect on the pigmentation of warm-blooded birds and mammals.

FIGURE 269. Leopard frogs. Dark color phase on the *left*, and light color phase on the *right*. When the animal is in darkness, the hormone intermedin is secreted into the blood stream; the pigment is then dispersed, causing the dark color phase. But when the retina of the eye is stimulated by light, nerve impulses pass to the intermediate lobe of the pituitary gland, causing the production of intermedin to be suppressed, which results in the light color phase. (Photo courtesy of Douglas Eastwood.)

Regeneration

The power of regenerating lost parts is remarkably well developed in many Amphibia. For example, the foot of a two-year-old axolotl was cut off, and in 12 weeks a complete foot was regenerated in its place. The newt (Fig. 270 A) has been observed to regenerate both limbs and tail. The tailless amphibians are apparently unable to regenerate lost parts to any considerable extent, except in the early stages. As a general rule, the younger tadpoles regenerate limbs or a tail more readily than older specimens. There is a distinct advantage in this possession of the power of regeneration, since amphibians often escape from their enemies with mutilated limbs or tails; but they are not permanently inconvenienced by the loss, since new parts rapidly grow out.

Breeding habits

Most Amphibia are oviparous; and their eggs, as in the leopard frog, are fertilized by the male after extrusion. In some of the tailed forms, however, the eggs are fertilized before they are laid. A few species bring forth their young alive; for example, the alpine salamander, *Salamandra*.

Several curious breeding habits are exhibited by certain species. The male obstetrical toad (Fig. 267), carries the egg strings with him, wound about his hindlimbs; and when the tadpoles are ready to emerge, he takes to the water and allows them to escape.

The eggs of the Surinam toad (Fig. 267) are placed on the back of the female during copulation, are held there by a sticky secretion, and are gradually enveloped by the skin. Within these epidermal pouches, the eggs develop and the tadpole stage is passed; then the young toads escape as air-breathing aquatic animals.

The American bell toad (Fig. 267) found in California is unique in that fertilization is internal. The male grasps the female around the pelvis, and by use of an external taillike copulatory organ the sperms are deposited in the cloaca of the female.

The brooding or marsupial tree frogs of Venezuela, *Gastrotheca*, have a pouch with an opening in the posterior part of the trunk in which the eggs are placed and the young are reared. The female of another species of tree frog carries her eggs in a depression on her back until they are almost ready for metamorphosis.

Hibernation

Many amphibians bury themselves in the mud at the bottom of ponds in the autumn and remain there in a dormant condition until the following spring. During this period of hibernation, the vital processes are reduced; no air is taken into the lungs, since all necessary respiration occurs through the skin; no food is eaten, but the physiologic activities are carried on by the use of nutriment stored in the body; and the temperature of the animal is only slightly above that of the surrounding medium. The body temperature of all cold-blooded vertebrates—cyclostomes, elasmobranchs, fishes, amphibians, and reptiles—varies with the surrounding medium. Frogs cannot be entirely frozen, as is often reported, since death ensues if the heart is frozen. In warm countries many amphibians seek a moist place of concealment; they pass the hotter part of the year in a quiet, torpid condition; they aestivate.

Poisonous amphibians

The poison glands of the leopard frog have already been mentioned. Certain salamanders and newts are also provided with poison glands. As a means of defense the poison is very effective, since an animal that has once felt the effects of an encounter with a poisonous amphibian will not soon repeat the experiment. Some of the most poisonous species, for example *Salamandra salamandra*, are said to be warningly colored. Dogs and cats that catch and bite *Bufo marinus* often die from the toxic effects of their secretions.

Fossil amphibians

From fossils, it has been determined that amphibians first appeared during the Age of Fishes in the Devonian period (p. 617). From that time on they increased so rapidly in numbers that the Late Paleozoic or Carboniferous period is spoken of as the Age of Amphibians. The Paleozoic amphibians are known as Stegocephali, a term that refers to the covered or mailed head, roofed over by dermal bones. Stegocephali were salamander-like animals that probably lived in fresh water or on land. Some of them are called labyrinthodonts because the dentine of their teeth is much folded. Primitive reptiles (cotylosaurs) and perhaps mammals stem-

med directly from stegocephalians, and the stegocephalians themselves came from crossopterygian ancestors.

OTHER AMPHIBIA

Legless amphibians

The family Caeciliidae includes over 50 species of wormlike or snakelike legless Amphibia (Fig. 266). They inhabit the tropical regions of the Americas, Africa, and Asia. They burrow in moist ground with their strong heads and possess eyes that are small and concealed. A sensory tentacle, which can be protruded from between the eyes and the nose, aids the animal in crawling about.

Giant salamanders

The family Cryptobranchidae contains two genera of giant salamanders. The American hellbender, *Cryptobranchus alleganiensis* (Fig. 267), occurs only in the streams of the eastern United States; it reaches a length of from 18 to 27 inches. The giant salamander of Japan is the largest living amphibian, reaching a length of over 5 feet.

Axolotl

The tiger salamander, *Ambystoma tigrinum*, occurs from New York to California and south to central Mexico and reaches a length of from 6 to 10 inches. In some parts of its geographic range, it fails to metamorphose and reproduces while it is in a larval state. Such a larval form is called an axolotl; it was long considered a separate species because the external gills persisted into the adult. However, if an axolotl is fed beef thyroid, even one or two meals, it develops into a land animal; it loses its gills and becomes an air-breathing salamander. This is not now thought to be a case of retarded evolution, but a secondary specialization for arid regions. Nonmetamorphosing forms

A

B

FIGURE 270. A, eastern newt, *Diemictylus viridescens* (3½ inches long). B, the "congo eel," *Amphiuma means* (32 inches long) is a semilarval type of amphibian. (Courtesy of N.Y. Zoological Society.)

arose in all probability from stocks that did undergo metamorphosis. Feeding the hormone (thyroxin) reverses this specialization.

Salamanders

The newts belong to the salamander family. The crimson-spotted newt, *Diemictylus viridescens*, lives in the water as a larva; but when it is about one inch long it loses its gills and usually lives on land for about one or two years. During its terrestrial life it is a bright coral red in color and is known as the red eft. It then returns to the water and changes to the adult coloration of yellowish green with black spots on the under surface and a row of black-bordered crimson spots on both sides. The cold slimy skin of

the salamanders gave rise to the belief in medieval times that the salamanders could live in fire and not be injured by it. The skin of the fire salamander of Europe secretes a particularly poisonous substance. This species is black with bright yellow spots and therefore very conspicuous; its colors are supposed to warn other animals that it is dangerous.

Toads

The family Bufonidae includes over 100 species of toads, most of which belong to the genus *Bufo*. About 15 species of this genus have been reported from the United States. The common toad of the northeastern United States, *Bufo terrestris* (formerly

FIGURE 271. *Necturus,* commonly called mud-puppy. An aquatic species about 1½ feet long. (New York Zoological Society Photo.)

americanus) (Fig. 272), possesses a rough, warty skin, but it does not cause appearance of warts upon the hands of those who handle it, as is often supposed. Toads secrete a milky poisonous fluid by means of glands in the skin, which protects them from many animals that would otherwise be important enemies. During the day they remain concealed in some dark damp place, but at night they hop about, feeding upon worms, snails,

and especially insects, which they capture with their sticky tongues as frogs do.

Tree frogs

Tree frogs are usually arboreal amphibians with adhesive disks on their toes and fingers that usually enable them to climb trees. They are provided with large vocal sacs and have a correspondingly loud voice; see headpiece at beginning of this chapter for illustration of vocal sacs distended with air. Of the more than 180 species, 21 occur in the United States and about 130 in Central and South America. The common tree frog, *Hyla versicolor* (Fig. 267), is about two inches long. Other common tree frogs are the spring peeper, *Hyla crucifer*, and the cricket frog, *Acris gryllus*.

True frogs

The family Ranidae contains the true frogs. These occur in all parts of the globe except Australia, New Zealand, and southern South America. Only one genus, *Rana*, and about 16 species live in the United States. Of these, the leopard frog (Fig. 217) is the most common. The bullfrog *Rana catesbeiana* (Fig. 267) is the largest of the family in this country, often reaching a body length of 6 or 8 inches. Bullfrogs usually remain in or near water. They possess a deep bass voice like that of a bull. The tadpoles do not become frogs the first year, as do those of the leopard frog, but transform during the second or even the third year. Other true frogs include the green frog *Rana clamitans*, the eastern wood frog *Rana sylvatica*, and the pickerel frog *Rana palustris*.

RELATIONS OF AMPHIBIA TO MAN

Amphibians are virtually all beneficial to man. Many are so rare as to be of little value, but the frogs and toads are of considerable importance. Frogs have been and are now

FIGURE 272. The common American toad. Note warty skin, bright markings, and jewel-like eye. Natural size 3½ inches long. (Courtesy of the American Museum of Natural History.)

FIGURE 273. *Hyla andersonii*, a tree frog. (Courtesy of N.Y. Zoological Society.)

used extensively for laboratory dissections, physiologic experiments, human pregnancy tests, pharmacology, and for fish bait. Mud puppies (*Necturus*) also serve as teaching material; one firm in Chicago sells 2500 or more per year for this purpose. The skins of frogs are used for glue and book bindings. Frog legs are eagerly sought as an article of food; more than three million pounds are eaten every year in the United States. Mud puppies are also edible. In Japan, the giant salamander is much esteemed as an article of food.

Hellbenders are considered poisonous by many people, but they are not dangerous to man. Many superstitious beliefs are held about amphibians, such as: salamanders are not injured by fire, a croaking frog predicts rain, and the toad has a jewel in its head. In China, the skin of the toad is used as a medicine; its use may have some therapeutic value, since certain glands contain a digitalis-like secretion which increases the blood pressure when injected into human beings.

Frogs and toads are widely recognized as enemies of injurious insects. The toads are of special value, since they live in gardens where insects are most injurious. In France the gardeners even buy toads to aid them in keeping obnoxious insects under control. *Bufo marinus* has been introduced in the tropics, especially where sugar cane is grown, to control insects.

Frog farming has been promoted for pleasure and profit, but it has generally proved a great disappointment to those who engaged in the enterprise. Many so-called "farms" are only favorable marshes where natural reproduction is encouraged. Artificial rearing of frogs is not practicable because it is difficult to find a satisfactory supply of food; unless the frogs of different sizes are separated, the large ones eat the smaller individuals; losses from predators and disease may be high where there is a great concentration of frogs; and the selling price has been inadequate to make the business profitable. Most of the money in frog farming has been made by unscrupulous promoters who sold breeding stock and books on frog raising at exorbitant prices.

A BRIEF CLASSIFICATION OF LIVING AMPHIBIA

(For reference purposes only)

Class Amphibia. About 2500 different species of living Amphibia are known, a number very much smaller than that of the other principal classes of vertebrates. Approximately 60 belong to the order Apoda (Gymnophiona), about 200 to the Caudata, and approximately 1740 to the Salientia.

Order 1. Apoda (Gr. *a,* not; *podos,* foot) or Gymnophiona (Gr. *gymnos,* naked). Caecilians (Fig. 267). Wormlike; no limbs or limb girdles; sometimes with small scales embedded in skin; tail short or absent.

Family 1. Caeciliidae. Ex. *Ichthyophis glutinosa,* blindworm.

Order 2. Caudata (L. *cauda,* tail). Tailed Amphibia. With a tail; without scales; usually two pairs of limbs.

Family 1. Cryptobranchidae. Hellbenders. Ex. *Cryptobranchus alleganiensis,* American hellbender (Fig. 267).

Family 2. Ambystomidae. Ex. *Ambystoma tigrinum,* tiger salamander (Fig. 267).

Family 3. Salamandridae. Salamanders and newts. Ex. *Diemictylus viridescens,* eastern newt (Fig. 270).

Family 4. Amphiumidae. Ex. *Amphiuma means,* congo eel (Fig. 267).

Family 5. Plethodontidae. Lungless salamanders. Ex. *Plethodon cinereus,* red-backed salamander (Fig. 267).

Family 6. Proteidae. Ex. *Necturus maculosus,* mud puppy (Fig. 271).

Family 7. Sirenidae. Ex. *Siren lacertina,* greater siren (Fig. 267). Eel-shaped amphibians having small forelimbs, but lacking hindlimbs and pelvis and having permanent external gills as well as lungs.

Order 3. Salientia (L. *salio,* leap). Tailless Amphibia. Without a tail; without scales; two pairs of limbs; without external gills or gill openings in adult.

Family 1. Pelobatidae. Ex. *Scaphiopus holbrookii,* spadefoot toad.

Family 2. Bufonidae. Ex. *Bufo terrestris,* toad (Fig. 272).

Family 3. Hylidae. Ex. *Hyla versicolor,* tree frog (Fig. 267).

Family 4. Ranidae. Ex. *Rana pipiens,* leopard frog (Fig. 217).

SELECTED COLLATERAL READINGS

(See also Chapter 23)

Barbour, T. *Reptiles and Amphibians, Their Habits and Adaptations.* Houghton Mifflin, Boston, 1934.

Bishop, S.C. *Handbook of Salamanders. The Salamanders of the United States, of Canada, and Lower California.* Comstock, Ithaca, N.Y., 1943.

Noble, G. Kingsley. *Biology of the Amphibia.* McGraw-Hill, New York, 1931. Reprinted, Dover Publications, 1955.

Oliver, J.A. *The Natural History of North American Amphibians and Reptiles.* Van Nostrand, New York, 1955.

Stebbins, R.C. *Amphibians and Reptiles of Western North America.* McGraw-Hill, New York, 1954.

Wright, A.H., and Wright, A.A. *Handbook of Frogs and Toads: Of the United States and Canada.* Comstock, Ithaca, N.Y., 1949.

CHAPTER 28

Class Reptilia.
Turtles, Lizards,
Snakes, Crocodiles,
and Others

THE reptiles constitute one of the most interesting, and, in general, one of the least-known classes of the vertebrates. They are cold-blooded; usually covered with scales, and, frequently, with bony plates; and they always breathe by lungs. The popular notion that reptiles are slimy is erroneous. Contrary also to general belief, very few reptiles, at least those in the United States, are dangerous to man; the majority are harmless, and many are even beneficial. The reptiles living today are but a fraction of the vast hordes that inhabited the earth's surface in prehistoric times. In fact, of the approximately 16 orders of reptiles now recognized by herpetologists, only 4 possess living representatives, and one of these includes a nearly exterminated species confined to New Zealand. The 4 orders of living reptiles are as follows:

Order 1. Chelonia (Testudinata). Turtles and tortoises.
Order 2. Rhynchocephalia. *Sphenodon*, a lizardlike reptile confined to New Zealand.
Order 3. Squamata. Lizards, and snakes.
Order 4. Crocodilia. Crocodiles, alligators, gavials, and caimans.

The reptiles are better adapted for living on land than amphibians. Some of the advances shown by reptiles over amphibians are: (1) a dry scaly skin which is an adaptation for a complete existence on land, (2) limbs better suited for rapid locomotion, (3) partial or complete separation of the ventricle resulting in further separation of the oxygenated and nonoxygenated blood in the heart, (4) well-ossified skeleton, (5) some form of copulatory organ which is necessary for internal fertilization, (6) eggs with shells suited for development on land and protective embryonic membranes to prevent drying, another adaption for life on land.

Reptiles are most abundant in the warmer regions of the world; very few live in the colder parts of the temperate zone, and none in the Arctic or Antarctic regions. Nevertheless, the United States is well supplied with

405

both species and individuals. About 243 species of all the reptiles that have been described are known to occur in this country. Reptiles occupy an important place in the vertebrate series because their anatomy is intermediate between that of a typical amphibian on the one hand and that of a typical bird on the other. Comparison of the structure and physiology of reptiles with those of amphibians and birds is well worth while. The poisonous nature of certain reptiles, the enormous size of some of the prehistoric species, and the relations of reptiles to man are among the most interesting general features of the class.

TURTLE

The turtle has been selected as a representative reptile. The body is so constructed that it is adapted to live either in the water or on land. Although it is slow-moving on land, it can swim quite rapidly.

External features

The turtle is distinguished from all other animals by the **shell** which is broad and flattened and protects the vital organs (Fig. 275). Even the head, limbs, and tail can be more or less completely withdrawn into the shell. The **neck** is long and very flexible; the **head** is flattened dorsoventrally. The **mouth** is large, but instead of teeth, horny plates form the margin of the jaws; they are used to crush their food. The **external nares** (nostrils) are placed together, near the anterior end of the snout. The **eyes**, situated one on each side of the head, are each guarded by three **eyelids:** (1) a short, thick, opaque upper lid; (2) a longer, thin lower lid; and (3) a transparent nictitating membrane, which moves over the eyeball from the anterior corner of the eye. Just behind the angle of the jaw on either side is a thin **tympanic membrane.** The **limbs** usually possess 5 **digits** each; most of the digits are armed with large horny claws that are useful

in crawling, climbing, or digging. The **skin** is thin and smooth on the head, but thick, tough, scaly, and much wrinkled over the exposed parts of the body.

Skeleton

Since the life of the turtle is influenced so strongly by the skeleton, this system will be briefly described first.

The shell (Fig. 275) consists of a convex dorsal armor, the **carapace,** and a flattened ventral armor, the **plastron;** these are strongly bound together on each side by bony bridges varying in width with the species. Both carapace and plastron are usually covered by a number of symmetrically arranged horny plates, called **scutes** (shields); the scutes do not correspond either in number or arrangement to the bony plates beneath them. The number and shape of the scutes vary according to the species but are usually constant in individuals of the same species. The horny scutes of the hawksbill turtle furnish the tortoise shell of commerce. Beneath the scutes are a number of **bony plates** formed by the dermis and closely united by sutures.

The vertebrae and ribs are usually consolidated with the bony carapace; no sternum is found in these forms. Soft-shelled turtles (Fig. 280) have a leathery shell which is not divided into scutes, and it contains little bony substance.

Digestive system

Turtles feed on both plants and animals; some are entirely vegetarian. The animals preyed upon are waterfowl, small mammals, and many kinds of invertebrates. The flexible neck enables the turtle to rest on the bottom and reach out in all directions for food. The jaws of large snapping turtles are powerful enough to amputate a finger, or even a hand.

The **digestive organs** are simple. The broad soft **tongue** is attached to the floor of the mouth cavity; it is not protrusible. The

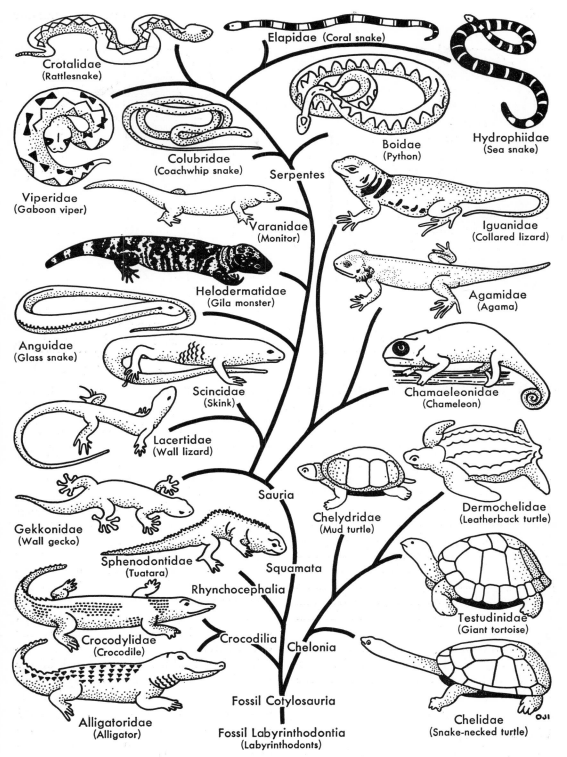

Figure 274. Some orders and families of reptiles. The lines indicate probable relationships. (Based on a diagram by Charles M. Bogert, Curator of Amphibians and Reptiles, American Museum of Natural History; made expressly for this book.)

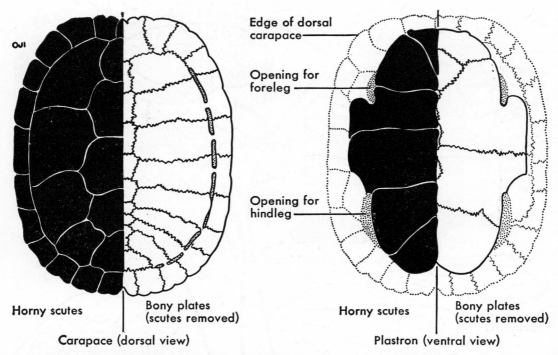

FIGURE 275. Turtle shell showing the external horny scutes and the bony plates beneath. The living epidermis, which covers the bony plates, produces the horny scutes.

two **posterior nares** are situated in the anterior part of the roof of the mouth. At the base of the tongue is a longitudinal slit, the **glottis,** and a short distance back of the angle of the jaw are the openings of the Eustachian tubes. The **pharynx** is thin-walled and very distensible; it leads into the more slender and thick-walled **esophagus.** The **stomach** opens by a **pyloric valve** into the **small intestine;** this is separated from the **large intestine** by the **ileocecal valve.** The terminal portion of the digestive canal is the **rectum;** it opens into the **cloaca.** There is no intestinal cecum.

The **liver** discharges bile into the intestine through the bile duct. Several pancreatic ducts lead from the **pancreas** to the intestine.

Circulatory system

The reptilian heart (Fig. 222), except in the case of the Crocodilia, consists of two **atria** and a single **ventricle** which is divided into two by an incomplete septum. In the crocodilians the longitudinal septum in the ventricle is complete, forming a 4-chambered heart. The venous blood from the body (Fig. 276) is carried by the posterior vena cava and the two anterior venae cavae into the sinus venosus and thence into the right atrium. From here it passes into the right side of the ventricle, and when the latter contracts, it is forced out through the pulmonary artery which sends a branch to each lung and through the left aorta which conveys blood to the viscera, and into the dorsal aorta.

The blood which is oxygenated in the lungs is returned by the pulmonary veins to the left atrium and thence into the left side of the ventricle. This blood is pumped out through the right aortic arch, which merges into the dorsal aorta. Because the septum dividing the ventricle into two is incomplete, the blood that enters the right aortic arch is

Vein ▭ Artery

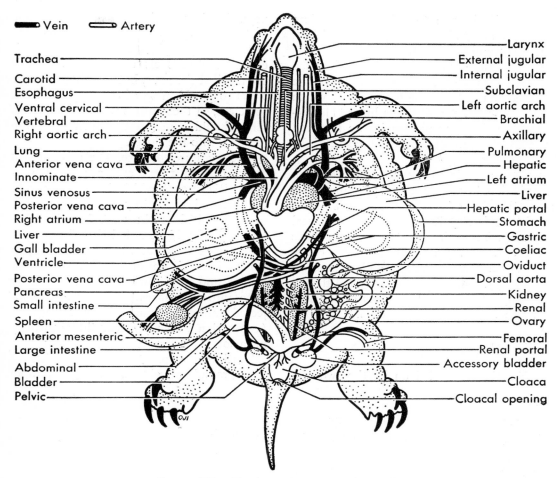

Trachea

Carotid

Esophagus

Ventral cervical

Vertebral

Right aortic arch

Lung

Anterior vena cava

Innominate

Sinus venosus

Posterior vena cava

Right atrium

Liver

Gall bladder

Ventricle

Posterior vena cava

Pancreas

Small intestine

Spleen

Anterior mesenteric

Large intestine

Abdominal

Bladder

Pelvic

Larynx

External jugular

Internal jugular

Subclavian

Left aortic arch

Brachial

Axillary

Pulmonary

Hepatic

Left atrium

Liver

Hepatic portal

Stomach

Gastric

Coeliac

Oviduct

Dorsal aorta

Kidney

Renal

Ovary

Femoral

Renal portal

Accessory bladder

Cloaca

Cloacal opening

FIGURE 276. The internal structure of a turtle.

a mixture of oxygenated blood from the left atrium and venous blood from the right atrium.

Certain species of turtles have a well-developed renal portal system; the **hepatic portal system** shows an advance in development over the condition as described in the frog.

Respiratory system

Turtles breathe by means of **lungs.** Air enters the mouth cavity by way of the nasal passages. The **glottis** opens into the **larynx,** through which the air passes into the **trachea** or windpipe. The trachea divides, sending one **bronchus** to each lung. The lungs are more complicated than those of the amphibians. The bronchi branch out a number of times, and the lung cavity is broken up into many spaces so that the respiratory surface is greatly increased.

The presence of a hard rigid shell, in turtles, makes general expansion and contraction of the body impossible. Turtle respiration, therefore, presents some unusual problems. It was formerly thought that it had a breathing mechanism similar to amphibians, but this is not the case; the turtle has its own unique method of breathing. Inspiration is accomplished by two flank muscles which serve the same function as the mammalian diaphragm: to enlarge the coelom and cause air to be "sucked" into the lungs. To accomplish expiration, the turtle uses paired expiratory muscles which enclose the viscera. Air is forced out of the lungs by the contraction of the expiratory muscles which press the viscera against the lungs. This action is assisted by pulling in the legs and neck, which further decreases the size of the body cavity.

Many aquatic turtles probably carry on respiration to some extent by taking water into the cloaca and the accessory bladders and then forcing it out through the cloacal opening. Thus these structures may serve as supplementary respiratory organs (compare with sea cucumber, and nymph of dragonfly). It has also been sugested that in the aquatic forms certain areas of the skin may be modified for respiration.

Urogenital system

Excretion is carried on by the two kid-neys. Their secretions pass through the **ureters** into the **cloaca** (Fig. 277), are stored in the **urinary bladder**, and then make their exit through the **cloacal opening**. This is often called the **anus**, but the anus properly refers to the opening of the digestive tract; therefore, in those forms with a cloaca, this term should apply to the opening of the intestine into the cloaca.

The sexes are separate. The **male organs** are a pair of **testes** and a pair of **vasa deferentia** through which the sperms pass to the grooved copulatory organ or erectile **penis** attached to the ventral wall of the cloaca. It should be noted that the reptiles are the first vertebrates in which there is a penis. The **female organs** are a pair of **ovaries** and a pair of **oviducts**; the latter open into the **cloaca**. The sperms are injected into the female by a sexual act (**copulation**), usually preceded by courtship behavior.

Turtles are **oviparous**. The eggs which are white, round or oval, and covered by a more

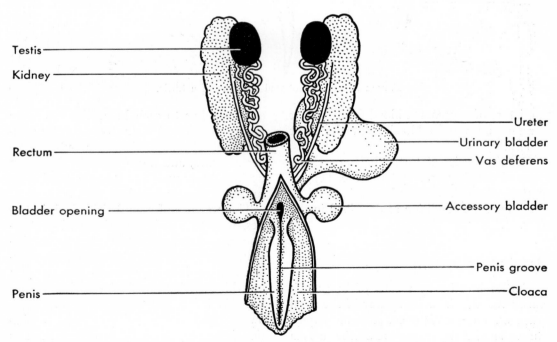

Testis
Kidney
Rectum
Bladder opening
Penis

Ureter
Urinary bladder
Vas deferens
Accessory bladder
Penis groove
Cloaca

Figure 277. Cloaca and urogenital organs of a turtle, ventral view. (After Gegenbaur.)

or less hardened shell, are laid in the holes dug by the female, in soil or decaying vegetation, in which heat aids in incubation.

Nervous system

The **brain** is more highly developed than in the amphibians. The **cerebral hemispheres** are larger, and a distinction can be made between the superficial gray layer and the central white medulla. The **cerebellum** is also larger, indicating an increase in the power of coordinating movements. There are 12 pairs of cranial nerves.

Sense organs

The **eye** is small. It has a round pupil and an iris which is usually dark in terrestrial forms, but often colored in aquatic turtles. The sense of **hearing** is not well developed, but the turtle responds readily to vibrations

through the skin, so it is easily frightened by noises. The sense of **smell** enables the turtle to distinguish between various kinds of food both in and out of the water. The skin over many parts of the body is very sensitive to touch.

OTHER REPTILIA

Turtles

Turtles live on land, in fresh water, or in the sea. The word **turtle** is often applied to semiaquatic species; **tortoise**, mainly or entirely, to land species; and **terrapin** to certain species that are edible and sold in markets. Most of the land and fresh-water turtles hibernate in the earth during the winter, but in warmer countries they "sleep" (estivate) during the hotter months.

Some of the more interesting types of tur-

Snapping turtle

Painted turtle

FIGURE 278. Common American turtles. The painted turtle is common in ponds. The snapping turtle is less protected by shell than some turtles; it is well named for it is said that it will snap as soon as hatched.

tles are as follows. The snapping turtle (Fig. 278) is famous for its strong jaws and vicious bite. The musk turtle *Sternotherus* emits a disagreeable odor when molested or captured. The painted turtle (Fig. 278) is brilliantly colored. The diamondback terrapin *Malaclemys* (Fig. 279) is famous as

food for man. The plastron of the box turtle (Fig. 281) is hinged transversely near the center so that the shell can be closed completely when the animal is in danger. The gopher tortoise *Gopherus* lives in burrows in dry sandy areas of the southeastern United States. Some of the giant tortoises,

FIGURE 279. *Malaclemys*, the diamondback terrapin. It derives its common name from the markings on its shell. One of the most famous of all turtles as food for man. (Courtesy of Shedd Aquarium, Chicago.)

Testudo (Fig. 274), which are found on the Galapagos Islands, have been known to weigh over 500 pounds and are probably over 200 years old.

Sea turtles inhabit tropical and semitropical seas and come to land only to lay their eggs on sandy beaches. Their limbs are modified as paddles for swimming. The leatherback turtle *Dermochelys* (Fig. 274) is the largest of all living turtles, sometimes attaining a weight well over 1500 pounds. It has a leathery covering over the shell instead of horny shields. Soft-shelled turtles (Fig. 280) also have shells that are leathery and without shields.

Sphenodon, a living fossil

Sphenodon is the sole surviving species (Fig. 283) of the order to which it belongs. Numerous skeletal characteristics are like

FIGURE 280. *Amyda*, the soft-shelled turtle. Length of shell of adult about one foot. According to Ditmars, a large specimen can amputate a man's finger. Note the leathery integument which is not divided into horny scutes. (Courtesy of N.Y. Zoological Society.)

those possessed by some of the oldest fossil reptiles, and the ancestors of living reptiles were apparently much like this queer relic of past ages. *Sphenodon* is now restricted to some small islands in the Bay of Plenty in New Zealand; and because it is now protected, it is thriving with an estimated 5000 on Stephen Island alone. It is about two feet long and resembles a lizard in form. It lives in burrows, is nocturnal, and feeds

FIGURE 281. The western box turtle *Terrapene*. The under part of the shell is hinged and encloses the animal as though it were in a box. This is a protective mechanism. The turtle is known to live to the ripe old age of 123 years. (Courtesy of American Museum of Natural History.)

on other live animals. One of its most striking peculiarities, shared with many lizards, is the presence of a parietal organ or **parietal eye** in the roof of the cranium—a structure

for example the glass snakes, have no limbs or only vestiges. The tail is generally long; it is easily broken off, but in many a new organ is soon regenerated which does not possess

FIGURE 282. The green turtle *Chelonia*. A marine species that has been so much hunted for food that it may be in danger of extinction. Its fat is green in color. The frontlimbs are flippers used for swimming, and its hindlimbs are used as a steering apparatus and as kickers. It weighs about 400 pounds. (Courtesy of American Museum of Natural History.)

with a retina and other characters resembling a true eye in juveniles, but it is vestigial in adults, and scarcely visible.

Lizards

The lizards usually have an elongated body and 4 well-developed limbs for running, clinging, climbing, or digging. Some,

FIGURE 283. Tuatara (*Sphenodon punctatus*) at the entrance of its burrow. It has characters of the early ancestral reptiles. A relic of a remote past ("a living fossil"), now found only on islands near New Zealand. Length about two feet. (Photo by Blanchard. (Courtesy of National Geographic Society.)

vertebrae. The fact that the tail breaks off easily is of survival value, for the predator is attracted to and eats the wiggling tail, while the animal escapes. The skin of the lizard is usually covered with small scales.

Geckos inhabit all the warmer parts of the globe; they are harmless and usually nocturnal. Many have specialized lamellae under the toes, which enable them to climb over trees, rocks, walls, and ceilings.

Figure 284. An interesting lizard, the coal skink *Eumeces*. It illustrates autotomy in the vertebrates; when the touched skink sheds its tail, the would-be captor stops to eat the tail while the skink escapes. (Photo courtesy of J.F. Nist and published by permission of *The American Biology Teacher*.)

The American chameleon is common in the southeastern United States and in Cuba. The common iguana, *Iguana*, reaches a length of 6 feet. It inhabits tropical America and is a favorite article of food. The horned "toads" (Fig. 286) occur in the western United States and in Mexico. They live in hot, dry regions, many of them inhabiting deserts. They are ovoviviparous or oviparous.

The flying dragon is a species whose sides are expanded into thin membranes supported by false ribs. These membranes enable the lizard to glide from tree to tree and are folded when not in use. A number of different kinds of lizards are called **chameleons**, but the 75 species of true chameleons all live in Africa, Madagascar, Arabia, and India. One of the features that have made the chameleons famous is the

power to change colors rapidly. **Worm lizards** are limbless, burrowing lizards resembling worms in appearance. Only one species, the Florida worm lizard, *Rhineura floridana*, occurs in the United States; it is restricted to the Florida peninsula. Somewhat similar lizards are the "glass snakes" (Fig. 274) in the United States and Mexico. These have no limbs and move as most snakes do by lateral undulations. They can be distinguished from true snakes by the presence of movable eyelids and ear openings. Their name is due to the extreme brittleness of the long tail. Another species called the "blindworm" (*Anguis*) inhabits Europe, western Asia, and Algeria. It looks like a large, brightly colored worm, but it is not blind since it has well-developed eyes.

Swifts and skinks are types of lizards that live in North America; many species of

FIGURE 285. The American chameleon or green anole (*Anolis*). Anoles have great power to change their color (green to dark brown) and they are often sold for pets. About 6 inches long. (Courtesy of N.Y. Zoological Society.)

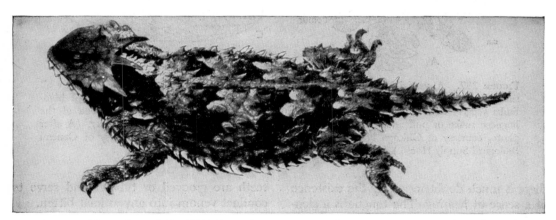

FIGURE 286. A horned "toad" (*Phrynosoma*), not a toad, but a common lizard in the arid western and southwestern states. Natural size, 6 inches long. (Courtesy of the American Museum of Natural History.)

lizards are known only from the Old World. The largest of all the lizards is the dragon lizard of Komodo (*Varanus*) which lives on some of the small islands in the Dutch East Indies. The natives of the island of Komodo claimed that dragons existed on the island; and, in 1914, these "dragons" were discovered to be the largest living lizards. They reach a length of 9 feet and a weight of over 250 pounds; they are ferocious reptiles able to capture wild pigs and other animals on which they feed. They readily lose their ferocity and become quite tame in captivity.

Snakes

Snakes resemble lizards in many of their anatomic features. They differ from them in at least 4 respects: (1) the right and left halves of the lower jaw are not firmly united, but are connected by an elastic ligament, (2) there is no pectoral girdle, (3) the urinary bladder is absent; and (4) the brain case is closed anteriorly.

Snakes are covered with scales; those on the head are usually so regular as to be of importance in classification (Fig. 287B,C). On the ventral surface in front of the cloacal opening is a single row of broad scales called abdominal scutes, to which the ends of the ribs are attached. The outer horny layer of the skin is shed a number of times during the year. Appendages are entirely absent except in a few species like the python, which possesses a pair of short spurlike projections, one on each side of the cloacal opening—vestiges of the hindlimbs (Fig. 287A). The eyelids are fused over the eyes, but there is a transparent portion which allows the animal to see. When the skin is being shed, the snake is partially blind.

There is no tympanic membrane, and

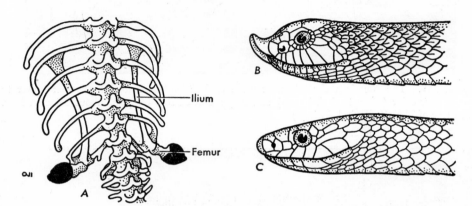

FIGURE 287. A, vestigial hindlimb and girdle bones of the python. The skeletons of nearly all snakes are without limbs but the pythons are among the exceptions. These remnants of hind-limbs suggest that the ancestors of snakes traveled on legs. B, scales on anterior end of the hognose snake or puff adder. C, scales on anterior end of black snake or blue racer. (A after photo, courtesy of Chicago Natural History Museum; B, C, after photo, courtesy of General Biological Supply House.)

there is much doubt regarding the existence of a sense of hearing. The tongue is a slender, deeply notched, protrusible structure that can be thrust out even when the mouth is closed because of the presence of grooves in the jaws. It serves as an auxiliary olfactory organ, carrying odorous particles to the paired organs of Jacobson in the roof of the mouth. The prevalent idea that the tongue can inflict an injury is erroneous. Furthermore, there appears to be no good evidence that the tongue is sensitive to vibrations. The teeth are sharp and curve inward (Fig. 288). They are adapted to prevent food from slipping forward, once swallowing has commenced. In the venomous snakes certain teeth are grooved or tubular and serve to conduct venom into any animal bitten.

Snakes do not chew their food but swallow it whole. They can eat animals much larger than their own bodies (Fig. 290). Some of the structural adaptations making this possible are: (1) the lower jaw joins with the skull very loosely, by means of two slender bones (quadrates); (2) furthermore, the lower jaw can spread at the anterior midpoint, allowing for lateral expansion; and (3) the bones of the palate are movable.

Movement on land is accompanied by several types of motion, but the two principal ones are: lateral undulations of the body and the shifting of the abdominal

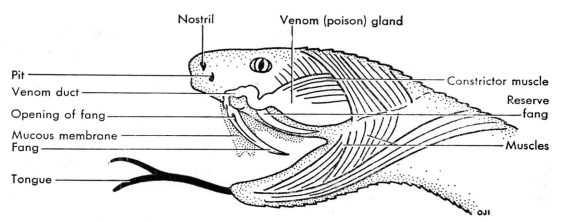

FIGURE 288. Rattlesnake drawing, showing the hollow teeth (fangs), venom gland, venom duct, and muscles used in forcing poison into the victim's flesh, as is done with a hypodermic needle. Note the pit between the nostril and eye, which is characteristic of pit vipers. (After drawing, courtesy of American Museum of Natural History.)

scutes forward in alternate sections of the body. The body is drawn forward in the latter method by pressing the rough posterior edges of the abdominal scutes against the substratum. Most snakes cannot move forward efficiently on a smooth surface. All species are able to swim, and this, of course, is the normal method of locomotion of the aquatic forms.

The majority of snakes are oviparous, but some are ovoviviparous, like the garter snake which brings forth its young alive. The idea that they swallow their young in order to protect them and then spew them out again when danger has passed is one of the common snake fallacies.

The tropics, perhaps, are more plentifully supplied with snakes than the temperate zones; and snakes are found in many places not inhabited by lizards. Madagascar seems to be the only large country in warm and temperate latitudes not inhabited by dangerous snakes. As in the other groups of vertebrates, the snakes are found in almost every kind of habitat; some species live in salt water, others in fresh water, some are arboreal, and many live underground.

Only 5 of the 10 families of Serpentes occur in North America. With a few exceptions those described below are found in the United States.

Blind snakes

Two species of these small burrowing reptiles (genus *Leptotyphlops*) occur in the United States. They burrow long tunnels in the earth and feed on worms and insect larvae.

Other snakes

Pythons (Fig. 291) and **boas** (Fig. 290) live almost exclusively upon birds and mammals which they squeeze to death in their coils. None of them is venomous and only a few are large enough to be dangerous to man. There is only one boa constrictor. It is a native of the tropical parts of the Americas and reaches a length of 18 feet. Boa constrictors are readily tamed in captivity and therefore preferred by snake "charmers."

The common **garter snake** (Fig. 292) of eastern North America is the most abundant of our harmless snakes. It feeds largely on frogs, toads, fishes, and earthworms. The young are born alive, usually in August. The common water snake *Natrix* is semiaquatic

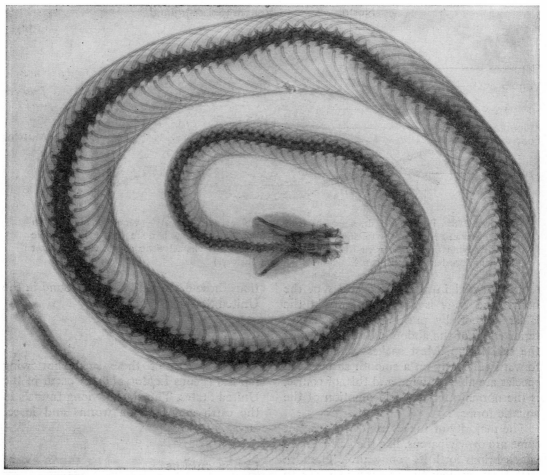

FIGURE 289.   Rattlesnake. A radiograph showing the absence of limbs, limb girdles, and sternum, but the numerous vertebrae and ribs are much alike in structure. Two rattles are visible at the posterior end of the body. (Courtesy of Armed Forces Institute of Pathology, Washington 25, D.C.)

but is not a water moccasin. The **black snake** (*Coluber*) is a slender long-tailed snake which reaches a length of 6 feet. West of the Mississippi it gives way to a subspecies called the **blue racer** and to another species, the red racer, in Texas. Contrary to popular belief, this reptile does not attack snakes larger than itself, has no power to squeeze its prey to death, and is unable to hypnotize birds and squirrels. **King snakes** (Fig. 293) are of various sizes; they are constrictors and have received their common name because they prey on other snakes. The scarlet or coral king snake resembles the venomous coral snake in color. King snakes are immune to pit viper venom, but not to coral snake venom; hence they do not hesitate to attack rattlesnakes, water moccasins, and copperheads. The **milk snake** derives its name from the erroneous supposition that it steals milk from cows. The **hog-nosed snakes**, *Heterodon* (Fig. 287B), are popularly known as puff adders, spreading vipers, or blowsnakes. They are nonvenomous, though they fiercely intimidate and also play possum.

FIGURE 290. Boa constrictor in action. As this picture proves, the snake really deserves its name. It captured the deer, which it squeezed to death in its coils. Arrow indicates the point on the deer to which it had been swallowed when the photographer started preparations for taking the picture. Fear of man caused the snake to disgorge as much of the deer as possible before the shutter clicked. This boa is a native of tropical America; it has a length of from 10 to 15 feet. (Courtesy of James M. Keller and Clark Zeek.)

Venomous (poisonous) reptiles will be considered in a later section.

Crocodilians

Crocodilians are lizardlike in form, but the jaws are extended into a long snout. The nostrils are at the end of the snout and the eyes protrude from the head so that the crocodilians can float at the surface with only these parts above water. The skin is thick and leathery, covered with horny epidermal scales, and with dorsal and sometimes ventral bony plates somewhat like

FIGURE 291. Indian python (*Python*) in its natural habitat. This is one of the world's largest snakes; it reaches a length of 25 feet. (Courtesy of N.Y. Zoological Society.)

those in the shell of the turtles. The nostrils and ears are provided with valves and are closed when the animal is under water.

The limbs are well developed. There are 5 digits on the forelimbs and 4 more or less webbed digits on the hindlimbs. The tail is a laterally compressed swimming organ. The "anus" is a longitudinal slit. Two pairs of musk glands are present—one on the throat and one in the cloaca.

Only 21 species of living crocodilians are

known. One belongs to the family Gavialidae, 13 are included in the family Crocodylidae, and 7 are placed in the Alligatoridae. The **American crocodile** (Fig. 294) is an inhabitant of Florida, Mexico, and Central and South America. The **African crocodile** is one of the few man-eating species. Formerly it was held sacred by the Egyptians, and many specimens were preserved as mummies. There are two species of the genus *Alligator*; the American alligator

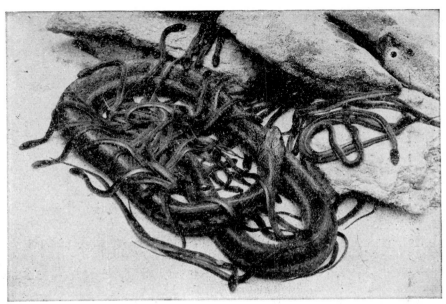

FIGURE 292. Common garter snake of eastern North America (*Thamnophis sirtalis*) with young; the latter are "born alive," as many as 30 at one time. Many have the erroneous idea that the young garter snakes remain with the parent. Length of adult about 3 feet. (Courtesy of N.Y. Zoological Society.)

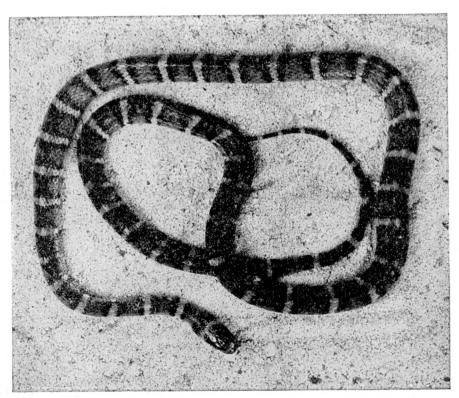

FIGURE 293. Arizona king snake (*Lampropeltis*), a constrictor. Called "king" because it captures and kills other snakes, including poisonous species. Color black with white or yellowish bands. (Courtesy of N.Y. Zoological Society.)

FIGURE 294. The American crocodile. Note pointed snout, laterally compressed tail, webbed hindfeet, 5 toes in front and 4 behind, and claws on 3 inner digits. This is the largest known crocodile, reaching a length of 23 feet. (Courtesy of N.Y. Zoological Society.)

FIGURE 295. The American alligator. Snout blunt, not pointed as in the crocodile. Natural size up to 16 feet long. (Courtesy of N.Y. Zoological Society.)

(Fig. 295) inhabits the southeastern part of the United States; and the Chinese alligator is found only in China.

Venomous (poisonous) reptiles

Very few reptiles are poisonous. All turtles are nonvenomous. Only one species of lizard and 19 species of poisonous snakes live in the United States.

Gila monsters

This poisonous "beaded" lizard (Fig. 296) inhabits parts of Arizona, Utah, Nevada, and New Mexico. It is black and conspicuously spotted with pink or orange. A large specimen measures about two feet. The bite is fatal to small animals and dangerous to man. The venom of the Gila monster is as strong a poison as that of some of the venomous snakes, but the mechanism for injecting it into the body of an animal is less efficient.

Venomous snakes

Among the venomous snakes that it seems desirable to mention, besides those that occur in the United States, are the sea snakes

FIGURE 296. Gila monster of the American southwest, the only poisonous lizard in the United States. It is shown feeding on eggs, a common food. It is beautifully colored with black and orange patches; it has poison glands in the lower jaw, and grooved teeth which carry venom into an animal that is bitten. (Courtesy of N.Y. Zoological Society.)

and the cobras. The sea snakes are true sea serpents (Fig. 274). They inhabit the Indian Ocean and the western tropical Pacific; and one species occurs along the western coast of tropical America. They reach a length of from 3 to 8 feet or more, and all are venomous. The tail and sometimes the body is laterally compressed—an adaptation for swimming. The venom of sea snakes is so deadly that their prey, which consists of fish, are quickly benumbed by it. Laboratory tests have indicated that one species of sea snakes has venom more potent than that of cobras.

The **cobra-de-capello,** *Naja naja,* of India, China, and the Malay Archipelago is very vicious; when disturbed it raises the anterior part of the body from the ground, spreads its hood with a hiss, and strikes. In India the bare-legged natives are killed in large numbers by cobras (Fig. 297) and other snakes; for example, each year 7,000 to 12,000 are reported killed by snake bites, most of them probably the bites of kraits, a species related to the cobra.

Only 19 species of dangerously poisonous snakes occur in the United States: the **harlequin snake,** the **Arizona coral snake,** the **copperhead,** the **water moccasin** or cot-

tonmouth, and 15 species of **rattlesnakes.**[*] If the pupil of the eye is round and the snake is ringed with red, black, and yellow, and if the red rings are bordered by yellow rings, the species may be a venomous **coral snake.** If the pupil is vertical and there is a pit between the eye and nostril on each side of the head, the snake is a poisonous rattlesnake, moccasin, or copperhead. All other snakes that live in the United States are harmless. Very few people in this country die as the result of a snake bite. According to the World Health Organization study, there are only about 300 to 400 deaths per year in North America from snake bite.

The harlequin or coral snake, *Micrurus fulvius* (Fig. 298), of the southeastern United States is dangerous, but man is rarely bitten by it.

The water moccasin (Fig. 299) occurs in the swamps of the Atlantic Coast south of North Carolina, and in the Mississippi Valley from southern Illinois and Indiana southward. The length of an average specimen is 4 feet.

The copperhead snake (Fig. 300) occurs from southern Massachusetts to northern

[*] There are also 14 subspecies of rattlesnakes.

FIGURE 297. The ringhals, a South African cobra (*Hemachatus haemachatus*), with its neck spread, ready to strike and inject venom which may cause death in a few minutes. (Courtesy of American Museum of Natural History.)

Florida and west to Texas. An average specimen measures about 2½ feet.

The **rattlesnake** (Fig. 301) is easily distinguished by the rattle at the end of the tail in the adult. This consists of a number or horny, bell-shaped segments loosely held together. Before striking, the rattlesnake often vibrates the end of the tail rapidly, producing a sort of buzzing noise, which to the wise serves as a warning. The venom is

secreted by a pair of glands on each side of the head above the jaws (Fig. 288). These glands open by venom ducts into the fangs. The poison fangs are pierced by a canal which opens near the end. The venom glands are surrounded by muscles that contract to squeeze the poison out of them through the fangs and into the animal bitten. There are several small fangs lying just behind the functional ones; these are

FIGURE 298. The coral snake, a very poisonous snake, which lives in southern United States and the tropical countries. It is the only representative of the cobra family in North America. It is about three feet long. (Courtesy of N.Y. Zoological Society.)

held in reserve to replace those that are lost in struggles with prey or are normally shed. Rattlesnakes are most abundant both in regard to the number of species and the number of individuals in the deserts of the southwestern United States, but almost every part of this country is inhabited by one or more species.

The rattlesnake is one of the so-called pit vipers because it has a **pit** between the eye and nostril on each side of the head. In this pit is located the **pit organ** which consists of highly vascular tissue and many nerve endings. Experiments prove that this is a heat-sensitive organ; a rattlesnake can detect the movement of a moderately warm body passing its head at a distance of several feet. Obviously this sense is very useful to an animal which lives to a considerable extent on warm-blooded rodents.

Rattlesnakes and other pit vipers usually strike from an **S**-shaped position of the body. Unless the venom is injected directly into a blood vessel, it usually travels slowly. The best first-aid measures to take in the case of a **snake bite** are: (1) apply a ligature or tourniquet a few inches above the bite—a rubber garter, handkerchief, cord, or even a shoestring will do; about every 15 minutes

FIGURE 299. Water moccasin (cotton-mouth) snake about to strike. Its bite is occasionally fatal to man. Note the thick body, slender neck, and whitish mouth; it has a pit in front of the eye. It lives in or near water. (Courtesy of N.Y. Zoological Society.)

FIGURE 300. The copperhead (*Agkistrodon*). Its common name comes from the fact that the top of the head is copper-colored. Natural size 33 inches long. (Courtesy of N.Y. Zoological Society.)

release for one minute, then retighten; (2) make a cross-cut incision, each cut ½ inch in length and ¼ inch in depth at each fang mark; (3) apply suction by mouth, suction cup, or other device; (4) have the patient lie down and keep quiet; (5) seek a physician and have him inject antivenom as soon as possible. A person suffering from snake bite should not run or get overheated, take whiskey, inject potassium permanganate into the wound, or cauterize the site of the bite with hot irons, strong acids, or anything of a similar nature.

Contrary to what many people think, fear of snakes is not inborn in children but is due entirely to conditioning by their elders.

Fossil reptiles

The reptiles now living are only a remnant of the great hordes that populated the earth during the Mesozoic Era. During this Age of Reptiles, a period of about 130 million years, enormous dinosaurs roamed the land, ichthyosaurs dominated the sea, and pterosaurs ruled the air. Today, comparatively puny representatives of only 4 of the 16 known orders of reptiles survive.

Dinosaur means terrible lizard. The dinosaurs probably lived in swamps and on the uplands; remains have been found in most continents. Some species measured over 85 feet in length. Both herbivorous and carnivorous forms existed. *Brontosaurus* (Fig. 302) was herbivorous and about 75 feet long; remains have been found in Wyoming and Colorado. *Stegosaurus* reached a length of about 28 feet and was also herbivorous. It possessed huge triangular plates along the back. Remains have been discovered in Wyoming and Colorado. *Protoceratops* (Fig. 303) was a small, hornless, herbivorous dinosaur only about 6 feet long; fossils were discovered in the deserts of Mongolia.

FIGURE 301. The timber or banded rattlesnake (*Crotalus horridus*). A dangerously poisonous species of the east and middle west; usually 3 or 4 feet long. (Courtesy of N.Y. Zoological Society.)

FIGURE 302. A dinosaur (*Brontosaurus*) with man drawn to the same scale. This giant reptile probably reached the maximum size possible for land animals; it is believed to have fed on soft lush vegetation. (After Mavor.)

Ichthyosaurs (Fig. 304) were fish-eating aquatic reptiles. Their bodies were admirably adapted for life in the water; they have been called the "whales" of the Mesozoic Era. The remains of ichthyosaurs occur in North America, Europe, Asia, Africa, and Australia. They showed a high degree of specialization for marine life.

Pterosaurs, flying reptiles, had forelimbs modified for flight. They resembled birds in certain skeletal characters, but differed from them in others. *Pteranodon* is the largest form known; it had a skull two feet long and a wing spread of more than 25 feet. Teeth were absent, and the tail was short.

RELATIONS OF REPTILIA TO MAN

The food of reptiles consists of both animals and plants. The animals eaten belong to just about all classes, including the Reptilia. Many of the snakes live almost entirely upon birds and mammals. Frogs and fish are favorite articles of food. Most of the smaller species of reptiles feed upon worms and insects. In general it may be stated that reptiles do very little damage by destroying animals and plants for food, but are often of considerable benefit since they kill large numbers of obnoxious insects and destruc-

FIGURE 303. *Protoceratops* (an armored dinosaur) with its eggs. The discovery of its eggs proved that some dinosaurs at least were hatched from eggs like turtles; furthermore, it is unusual in that all stages of growth from the egg to the adult are represented by fossils. (Courtesy of American Museum of Natural History.)

tive rodents. The U.S. Department of Agriculture estimates that the value of the larger snakes to the farmer is somewhere between $50 and $75.

The turtles and tortoises rank first as food for man. Especially worthy of mention are the green turtle, the diamondback terrapin, and the soft-shelled turtle. Certain lizards such as the iguana of tropical America form a valuable addition to the food supply in various localities. The flesh of the rattlesnake is said to have a distinctly agreeable flavor. There is a fair and growing market for canned rattlesnake meat.

Skins of the lizards, snakes, and crocodilians are used rather extensively for the manufacture of articles that need to combine beauty of surface with durability. The alligators in this country have decreased so rapidly because of the value of their hides that they will be of no great economic importance unless they are consistently protected or grown on farms. Tortoise shell,

especially that procured from the horny covering of the carapace of the hawksbill turtle and some others, is used for manufacture of combs and ornaments of various kinds.

As previously stated, the poisonous snakes of the United States are of very little danger to man. In tropical countries, especially India, venomous snakes cause a larger death rate than that due to any other group of animals. The Gila monster (Fig. 296), which is one of two poisonous lizards and the only one inhabiting the United States, attacks man only when handled carelessly and rarely inflicts a fatal wound.

A BRIEF CLASSIFICATION OF LIVING REPTILIA

(For reference purposes only)

Class Reptilia. Reptiles are cold-blooded vertebrates covered with horny scales or plates;

FIGURE 304. *Ichthyosaurus*, a fishlike reptile, and young. This fossil reptile had a fish-shaped body, porpoiselike snout, short neck, and dorsal and caudal fins. The limbs were modified into paddles, a remarkable adaptation for swimming. (Courtesy of American Museum of Natural History.)

their digits are usually provided with claws; the majority of them possess functional legs; and they breathe by lungs.

Bogert estimates that there are about 7000 or more species of living reptiles which may be grouped into 4 orders: (1) the Chelonia (Testudinata), containing about 275 species of turtles, terrapins, and tortoises; (2) the Rhynchocephalia, represented by a single New Zealand species; (3) The Squamata, containing about 6700 species of lizards and snakes; and (4) the Crocodilia, containing 25 species of crocodiles, gavials, alligators, and caimans.

Order 1. Chelonia (Testudinata). Turtles, terrapins, and tortoises. Body encased in bony capsule; jaws without teeth.

    Family 1. Chelydridae. Snapping turtles (Fig. 278). Exs. *Chely-*

dra serpentina, snapping turtle, and musk turtles, *Kinosternon*.

    Family 2. Testudinidae. Tortoises and most turtles. Ex. *Chrysemys picta*, painted turtle (Fig. 278).

    Family 3. Cheloniidae. Sea turtles. Ex. *Chelonia mydas*, green turtle (Fig. 282).

    Family 4. Dermochelidae. Leatherback turtle. Ex. *Dermochelys coriacea*, leatherback turtle (Fig. 274).

    Family 5. Trionychidae. Soft-shelled turtles. Ex. *Amyda spinifera*, soft-shelled turtle (Fig. 280).

Order 2. Rhynchocephalia. One genus of New Zealand lizardlike reptiles

Vertebrae biconcave, often containing remains of notochord; parietal organ present. Ex. *Sphenodon punctatus* (Fig. 283).

Order 3. **Squamata.** Lizards and snakes. Reptiles usually with horny epidermal scales; vertebrae usually procoelus; quadrate bones movable.

Suborder 1. **Sauria.** Lizards. Cloacal opening transverse; paired copulatory organs; usually well-developed limbs; rami of lower jaw united.

Family 1. **Gekkonidae.** Geckos (Fig. 274). Ex. *Tarentola maurentanica*, wall gecko.

Family 2. **Iguanidae.** New World lizards. Ex. *Anolis carolinensis*, American "chameleon" or green anole (Fig. 285).

Family 3. **Agamidae.** Old World lizards. Exs. *Draco volans*, "flying" lizard (dragon), and *Agama* (Fig. 274).

Family 4. **Chamaeleonidae.** Chameleons. Ex. *Chamaeleo chamaeleon*, true Chameleon (Fig. 274).

Family 5. **Lacertidae.** Typical Old World lizards. Ex. *Lacerta viridis*, green lizard.

Family 6. **Scincidae.** Skinks. Ex. *Eumeces antracinus* (Fig. 284).

Family 7. **Amphisbaenidae.** Worm lizards. Ex. *Rhineura floridana*, Florida worm lizard.

Family 8. **Helodermatidae.** Beaded lizards. Ex. *Heloderma suspectum*, Gila monster (Fig. 296).

Family 9. **Anguidae.** Old and New World lizards. Ex. *Ophisaurus ventralis*, "glass snake" (Fig. 274).

Suborder 2. **Serpentes.** Snakes. Elongated; no limbs; cloacal opening transverse; copulatory organs paired; without movable eyelids, tympanic cavity, urinary bladder, and pectoral arch; rami of lower jaw connected by ligament.

Family 1. **Leptotyphlopidae.** Blind snakes. Ex. *Leptotyphlops dulcis*, Texas blind snake.

Family 2. **Boidae.** Pythons and boas. Ex. *Boa constrictor*, boa constrictor (Fig. 290).

Family 3. **Colubridae.** Harmless snakes. Ex. *Thamnophis sirtalis*, garter snake (Fig. 292).

Family 4. **Crotalidae.** Pit vipers. Exs. *Crotalus horridus*, timber rattlesnake (Fig. 301), *Agkistrodon contortrix*, copperhead and *Agkistrodon piscivorus* water moccasin.

Order 4. **Crocodilia.** Crocodiles, alligators, gavials, and caimans. Vertebrae procoelous; nostrils paired, at end of snout; cloacal opening longitudinal.

Family 1. **Gavialidae.** Gavials. Ex. *Gavialis gangeticus*, Indian gavial.

Family 2. **Alligatoridae.** Alligators and caimans. Ex. *Alligator mississippiensis*, American alligator (Fig. 295).

Family 3. **Crocodylidae.** Crocodiles. Ex. *Crocodylus acutus* (Fig. 294).

SELECTED COLLATERAL READINGS

(See also Chapter 27)

Ashley, L.M. *Laboratory Anatomy of the Turtle.* W.C. Brown, Dubuque, Iowa, 1955.

Bogert, C.M., and del Campo, R.M. The Gila Monster and Its Allies. *Am. Mus. of Nat. Hist. Bull.* 109:1–238, 1956.

Carr, Archie. *Handbook of Turtles.* (Comstock) Cornell Univ. Press, Ithaca, N.Y., 1952.

Colbert, E.H. *The Dinosaur Book.* McGraw-Hill, New York, 1951.

Conant, Roger. *Reptile Study*. Boy Scouts of America, New York, 1944.

Ditmars, R.L. *Reptiles of the World*. Doubleday Doran, New York, 1928.

McIlhenny E.A. *The Alligator's Life History*. Christopher, Boston, 1935.

Pope, C.H. *The Reptile World*. Knopf, New York, 1955.

————, *The Poisonous Snakes of the New World*. New York Zoological Society, New York, 1944.

Romer, A.S. *Osteology of the Reptiles*. Univ. Chicago Press, Chicago, 1956.

Schmidt, K.P. *The Truth about Snake Stories*. Natural History Museum, Chicago, 1951.

Smith, H.M. *Handbook of Lizards of the United States and of Canada*. Comstock, Ithaca, N.Y. 1946.

Wright, A.H., and Wright, A.A. *Handbook of Snakes of the United States and Canada*. 2 vols. (Comstock) Cornell Univ. Press, Ithaca, N.Y., 1957.

CHAPTER 29

Class Aves. Birds

BIRDS are considered the most interesting of all animals. This is largely due to their beautiful and varied colors, their pleasing songs and call notes, their interesting behavior, their marvellous powers of flight, their mysterious migrations, and their many fascinating activities associated with their nests, eggs, and young. Bird clubs, which have arisen all over the country, and the large numbers of birds sold in pet shops are evidences of their popular appeal.

Because birds have reptilian origin, some have called them glorified reptiles. Birds have reptilian scales on their legs; and the earliest ones, which we know only from fossils, had reptilian teeth.

THE COMMON PIGEON

The common pigeons have been derived from the rock dove which ranges from Europe through the Mediterranean countries to central Asia and China. The pigeon is much used for studies of bird anatomy, not only because of its convenient size and availability, but also because it so well illustrates the many adaptations for life in the air, such as feathers, wings, hollow bones, and the rigid trunk skeleton.

External features

The body of the pigeon is spindle-shaped and therefore adapted for rapid movement through the air. Three regions may be recognized: head, neck, and trunk. The **head** is prolonged in front into a pointed horny bill, at the base of which is a patch of naked swollen skin, the **cere**. Between the bill and the cere are the two oblique, slitlike **nostrils** (Fig. 306). On either side is an **eye** which is provided with upper and lower **lids**, and with a well-developed third eyelid or **nictitating membrane** (Fig. 434). The third eyelid can be drawn across the eyeball from the anterior corner. Below and behind each eye is an external **ear opening** which leads to the tympanic cavity.

FIGURE 305. Representatives of selected orders of birds. The figures are not drawn to scale.

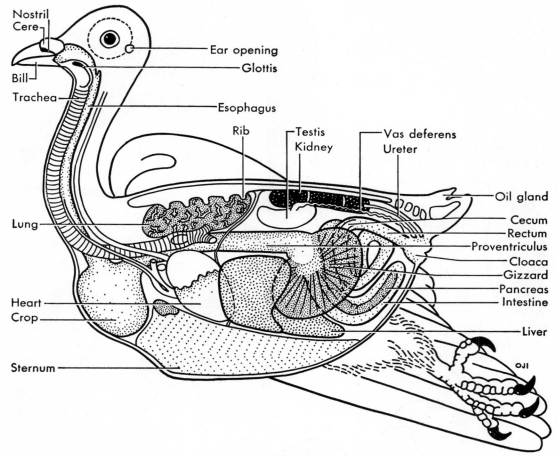

FIGURE 306. The internal structure of a pigeon.

The **neck** is long and flexible. At the posterior end of the trunk is a projection which bears the tail feathers. The two **wings** can be folded close to the body or extended in flight. The **feet** are covered with horny epidermal **scales**, and each digit is provided with a horny **claw**.

Feathers

Feathers are peculiar to birds. They arise, as do the scales of reptiles, from dermal papillae, with a covering of epidermis, and become enveloped in a pit, the feather follicle. A **typical feather** (Fig. 307) consists of a stiff axial rod, the **shaft**; the proximal portion is hollow and semitransparent and is called the **quill**; the flattish, distal portion is called the **vane**. The vane is composed of a series of parallel **barbs**, and each barb bears a fringe of small processes, the **barbules**, along either side. The barbules on one side of the barb bear **hooklets** which hold together the adjacent barbs. The whole structure is thus a pliable, but, nevertheless, a resistant organ, wonderfully adapted for use in flight.

The 3 principal kinds of feathers are:

1. The **contour feathers** are like that just described; these have a stiff shaft and vane; and since they appear on the surface, they determine to a large degree the contour of

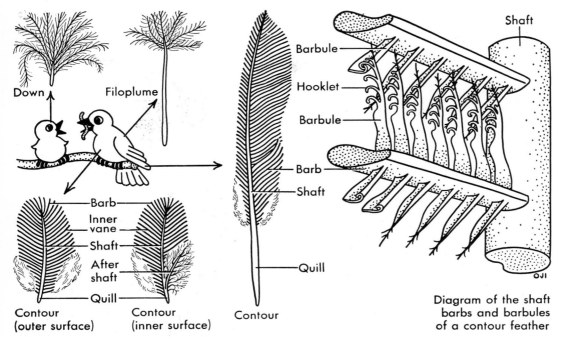

Contour
(outer surface)

Contour
(inner surface)

Contour

Diagram of the shaft
barbs and barbules
of a contour feather

FIGURE 307. *Left,* kinds of feathers. *Right,* microscopic detail of a contour feather to show the curved edge, along which the hooklets slide to make the feather flexible.

the body. These include the general body and wing (flight) and tail feathers.

2. The **down feathers** are without a shaft, the barbs arise as a fluffy tuft from the end of the quill; they provide the first plumage, natal down, of newly hatched birds and provide an insulating covering beneath the contour feathers in such birds as the waterfowl.

3. The **filoplumes** are hairlike feathers with a few barbs at the tip. These are the feathers singed off a chicken before it is cooked.

Only certain portions of the pigeon's body bear feathers; these feather **tracts** are termed **pterylae**, and the featherless areas, **apteria**. The feather tracts vary in different species of birds; those of the pigeon are shown in Fig. 308.

Birds shed their old feathers, that is, they **molt** usually in the late summer and acquire a complete new set of feathers, which are formed within the follicles and from the papillae of those that are cast off. There may be a partial or complete molt in the spring when the bird assumes its **breeding plum-**

age. At this time the plumage often changes color; this is usually due to wear or to the breaking off of the tips of the feathers, thus exposing new colors beneath.

Skeleton

The principal differences between the skeleton of a pigeon and that of a reptile are those made necessary by the methods of locomotion of the former. The hindlimbs and pelvic girdle of the pigeon are modified for **bipedal locomotion;** the forelimbs and pectoral girdle are modified for **flight;** the skeleton of the trunk is rigid; the **sternum** has a distinct median ridge, the **keel;** short projections, called **uncinate processes,** extend backward from some of the ribs, making the thoracic framework more firm; and most of the bones are very light, many containing **air cavities.** The skeleton of the common fowl (Fig. 309) is larger and more easily studied than that of the pigeon and is similar to the latter in most respects.

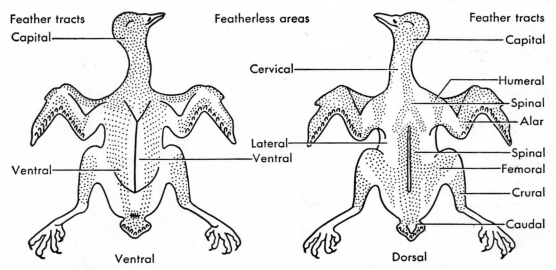

Feather tracts
Capital

Featherless areas
Cervical

Lateral
Ventral

Ventral

Ventral

Feather tracts
Capital

Humeral
Spinal
Alar

Spinal
Femoral

Crural

Caudal

Dorsal

FIGURE 308. Feather tracts of the pigeon, showing that feathers do not develop equally on all parts of the body as they do in some primitive birds such as the penguin. (After Nitzsch.)

The **skull** is very light, and most of the bones are so fused together that they can be distinguished only in the young bird. The **cranium** is rounded; the **orbits** are large; the **facial bones** extend forward into a bill; there is but a **single occipital condyle** for articulation with the first vertebra; and **no teeth** are present.

The **cervical vertebrae** are long and move freely upon one another by saddle-shaped articular surfaces, making the neck very flexible. This enables the bird to look in all directions and to use its bill for feeding, nest building, and many other purposes. The vertebrae of the trunk are almost completely fused together into a rigid skeletal axis which is necessary to support the body while in flight. There are 4 to 5 free caudal vertebrae, followed by a terminal pygostyle consisting of 5 to 6 fused vertebrae. The **pygostyle** supports the large tail feathers, and the free caudal vertebrae allow the movements of the tail for use as a rudder while flying and as a balancer while perching.

There are two **cervical ribs** and 4 to 5 **thoracic ribs** on each side. The second cervical and first 4 thoracic ribs each bear a **uncinate process** which arises from the posterior margin and overlaps the succeeding

rib, thus making a firmer framework. The thoracic ribs are connected with the breastbone (**sternum**). The sternum is united in front with the coracoid of the pectoral girdle and bears on its ventral surface a median ridge, the keel, to which are attached the large muscles that move the wings.

The **pectoral girdle** consists of a pair of long, narrow, bladelike **scapulae**, the shoulder blades, which lie above the ribs, one on each side of the vertebral column, in the thorax. The **coracoids** connect the sternum with the anterior ends of the scapulae at the shoulders. A concavity in these bones at their junction furnishes the articular surface for the long wing bone (humerus) and is called the **glenoid fossa**. The two **clavicles** connect proximally with the shoulder and fuse distally to form a V-shaped **furcula** or "wishbone." The clavicles are homologous to the collarbones of man and serve to brace the shoulders.

FIGURE 309. *Facing page,* skeleton of a bird (domestic fowl). Structurally the bird is adapted to flight and bipedal locomotion. The large keel provides a place for the attachment of the powerful wing muscles.

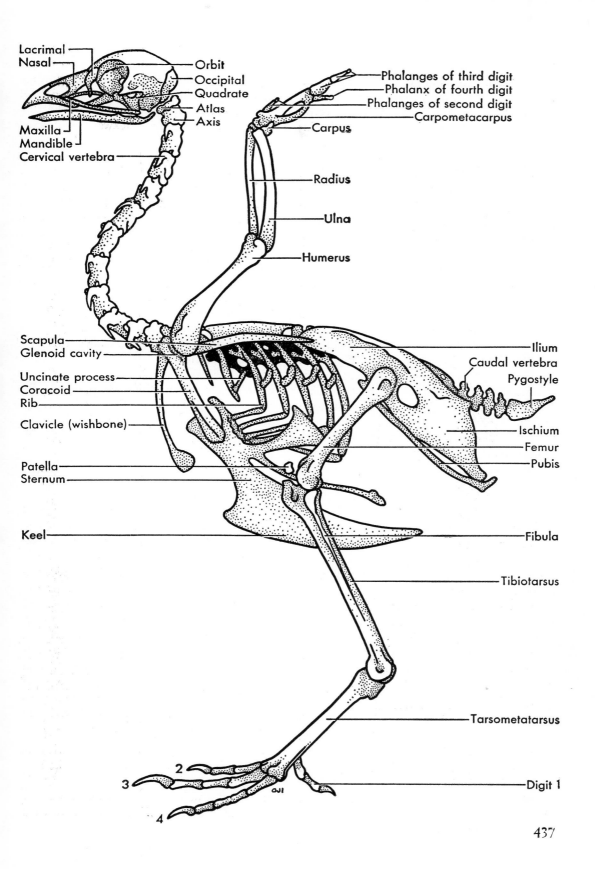

Lacrimal
Nasal
Orbit
Occipital
Quadrate
Atlas
Axis
Maxilla
Mandible
Cervical vertebra

Phalanges of third digit
Phalanx of fourth digit
Phalanges of second digit
Carpometacarpus
Carpus

Radius

Ulna

Humerus

Scapula
Glenoid cavity
Uncinate process
Coracoid
Rib
Clavicle (wishbone)

Ilium
Caudal vertebra
Pygostyle

Ischium
Femur
Pubis

Patella
Sternum

Keel

Fibula

Tibiotarsus

Tarsometatarsus

2
3
4
Digit 1

437

The forelimb or **wing** of the fowl is modified in many ways from that of the primitive vertebrate. For example, the primitive vertebrate had 5 digits numbered 1 to 5, beginning with the thumb, whereas, the fowl has but 3 digits (numbers 2, 3, and 4), and only the number 3 digit is well developed. The distal row of carpal bones and the 3 metacarpals are fused, forming a carpometacarpus; this adds to the rigidity of the wing. The arm, as in other vertebrates, contains a single bone, the **humerus**, with a convex head which lies in the glenoid fossa. The forearm possesses 2 bones, the **radius** and the **ulna**. The wrist contains 2 **carpal bones;** the other carpal bones are fused with the 3 **metacarpals**, forming the **carpometacarpus,** as stated above. Besides the carpometacarpus, the hand possesses a **second digit** of 2 small bones, which supports a small tuft of feathers and is known as the **bastard wing** (**alula**); a middle digit with 3 **phalanges;** and a **fourth digit** containing a single phalanx. The main flight feathers or **primaries** are supported by digits 3 and 4, the **secondaries** by the ulna, and the **tertiaries** by the humerus.

The **pelvic girdle** consists of a pair of **ilia**, the **ischia**, and the **pubes**, as in nearly all of the vertebrates above the fishes. These bones are firmly fused and united with the posterior part of the vertebral column.

The **hindlimbs** are used for bipedal locomotion. The thigh is concealed beneath the feathers. The **femur** is the short thick thighbone. In each leg there is a slender **fibula**, and a long, stout **tibiotarsus** (drumstick), the latter consists of the tibia fused with the proximal row of tarsal bones. The **ankle joint** is between the tibiotarsus and the **tarsometatarsus;** the latter represents the distal row of tarsal bones and the second, third, fourth, and fifth metatarsals fused. The **foot** possesses, besides the tarsometatarsus, 4 **digits;** the first is directed backward and is called the **hallux;** and the other 3 are directed forward. Each digit bears a terminal **claw.** The number of phalanges in each digit is one more than the digit number, hence digit 1 has 2 phalanges, and digit 4 has 5. The tarsometatarsus of the domestic fowl bears a backwardly directed spur.

Muscular system

The muscles of the neck, tail, wings, and legs are especially well developed. The muscle that produces the downward stroke of the wings, the **pectoralis major,** is the largest; it weighs about ⅕ as much as the entire body; it takes its origin from the sternal keel and inserts on the humerus; the **pectoralis minor** muscle raises the wing. These muscles constitute what is popularly known as the breast of the bird. Connected with the leg muscles is a perching mechanism which enables the bird to maintain itself upon a perch even while asleep. When the bird squats down for resting or sleeping, a pull is exerted on tendons which flexes all of the toes and holds the bird firmly to its perch.

Digestive system

Because of the high rate of metabolism in birds, they require large quantities of food, and digestion is rapid. Pigeons feed principally upon vegetable food such as seeds. The **mouth cavity** opens into the **esophagus** (Fig. 306), which enlarges into a **crop;** here the food is stored and moistened. Pigeons are noted for their ability to produce "pigeon milk," a cheesy secretion, which results from the degeneration of cells lining the crop, and is used for nourishing their young. The **stomach** consists of two parts, an anterior **proventriculus** with thick glandular walls which secrete the gastric juice, and a thick muscular **gizzard** (ventriculus), which grinds up the food with the aid of grit swallowed by the bird. The slender intestine with many coils leads to the **rectum** at a point where two blind pouches, the **ceca,** are given off. The digestive canal leads into the cloaca, into which the urinary and genital ducts also open. The cloaca opens to the outside by means of the **cloacal opening** or **vent**. In young birds a thick glandular pouch of lymphatic tissue, the **bursa Fabricii**, lies just above the cloaca.

The large **liver** is bilobed and has two **bile ducts**. There is no **gall bladder** in the common pigeon, though it is present in some birds and even in some species of pigeons. The **pancreas** pours its secretions into the duodenum through 3 ducts. A **spleen** and, in young pigeons, paired **thymus glands** are present. Lymph nodes are absent in birds except in waterfowl.

Circulatory system

The **heart** of a bird (Fig. 310) is comparatively large. It is composed of two entirely separated, muscular **ventricles** and two thin-walled **atria** (p. 340). The **right atrium** (Fig. 310) receives nonoxygenated venous blood from the **right anterior vena cava**, the **left anterior vena cava**, and the **posterior vena cava** veins. This blood passes from the right atrium into the **right ventricle** and is then pumped through the **pulmonary artery**, which divides into right and left pulmonary arteries, leading to the right and left lungs respectively.

The blood, after being oxygenated in the lungs, returns through 4 large **pulmonary veins** to the **left atrium**. It passes from the left atrium into the left ventricle and is then pumped through the **right aortic arch**, which gives off the **innominate arteries** and continues as the **dorsal aorta** (Fig. 310).

Circulation in birds is extremely rapid; the blood, which may reach the high temperature of 102° to 112° F. in some perching birds, is forced through the body by a heart that beats several hundred times per minute when at rest, and up to a thousand or more in the canary when under stress.

Contrasting the circulatory system of the pigeon with that of the turtle, it should be noted that the venous blood and arterial blood do not mingle in the heart of the pigeon. The **renal portal system** of the pigeon has almost completely disappeared, the blood being taken from the posterior part of the body directly to the heart, and not through the renal capillaries as in all lower vertebrates. The **jugular veins** of the pigeon are united just under the head by a cross vein; this special adaptation enables the blood to pass back to the heart from the head whenever the neck becomes momentarily twisted and one of the jugular veins is blocked.

Respiratory system

The two **lungs** in birds (Fig. 311) are assisted by a remarkable system of **air sacs**. During **inspiration**, relaxation of the thoracic and abdominal muscles allows elastic expansion of the thorax and abdomen. Air enters the mouth cavity through the **nostrils**, as in reptiles; it then passes through the **glottis** into the **trachea** or windpipe, which divides, sending a branch (**bronchus**) to each lung. Each bronchus as it enters into a lung breaks up into smaller tubes. To the smaller bronchial tubes are attached several large thin-walled **air sacs** (Fig. 311) that extend out between organs in the body to spaces in the neck region, and into cavities of the larger bones.

At **inspiration**, air rushes through the bronchial tubes into the air sacs; then, during expiration, the muscles of the thorax and abdomen contract, forcing the air from the air sacs through the lungs and trachea, and out through the nostrils. The bird has a high respiratory rate; for the pigeon it is 29 times per minute at rest as contrasted with 14 to 20 times per minute in man. This rapid flow of air through the respiratory system explains why the lungs of birds can be so small when they have the highest oxygen requirements of all animals because of their high metabolic rate.

The air sacs function principally as an accessory breathing organ; they may also

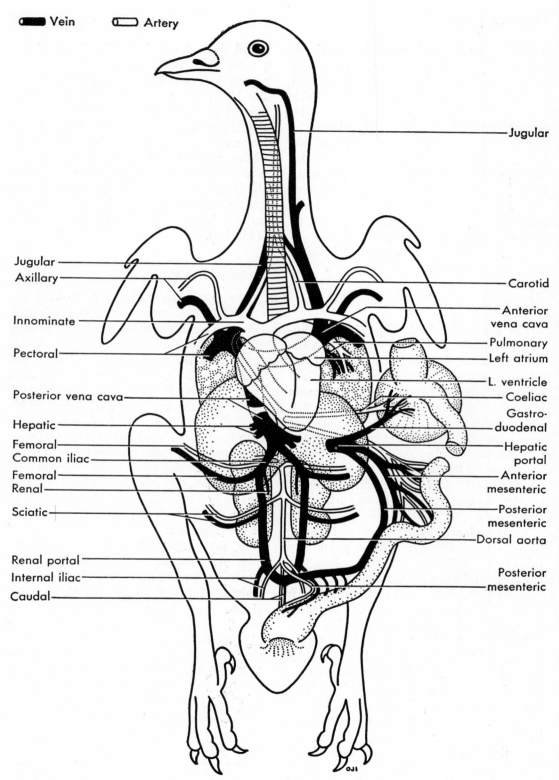

Vein   Artery

Jugular

Jugular
Axillary

Carotid

Innominate

Anterior
vena cava

Pectoral

Pulmonary
Left atrium

Posterior vena cava

L. ventricle
Coeliac
Gastro-
duodenal

Hepatic
Femoral
Common iliac
Femoral
Renal

Hepatic
portal

Anterior
mesenteric

Sciatic

Posterior
mesenteric
Dorsal aorta

Renal portal
Internal iliac
Caudal

Posterior
mesenteric

FIGURE 310.   Circulatory system of a pigeon.

440

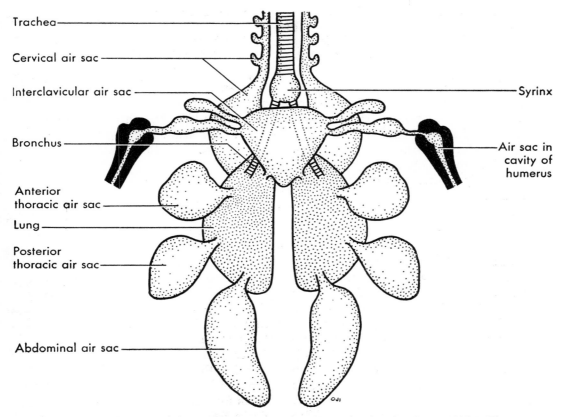

Trachea

Cervical air sac

Interclavicular air sac

Bronchus

Anterior
thoracic air sac

Lung

Posterior
thoracic air sac

Abdominal air sac

Syrinx

Air sac in
cavity of
humerus

FIGURE 311. Diagram of the respiratory organs of a pigeon, showing the air sacs. (After *Thomson's Outlines of Zoology* revised by James Ritchie. Ninth edition. Copyright 1944 by Oxford University Press.)

serve in temperature regulation by getting rid of excess body heat, since in birds there are no sweat glands. The air sacs do not reduce the specific gravity of the body as is commonly claimed.

The **trachea** is held open by partially calcified **cartilaginous rings.** Where the trachea at its lower end divides into the two bronchi, it enlarges to form the vocal organ or **syrinx,** a structure peculiar to birds. Extending forward from the angle of bifurcation of the trachea is a semilunar membrane which is vibrated like a reed when air is forcibly expelled from the lungs, thus helping to produce sound. The different songs and calls of birds are made possible by variations in the sound mechanism.

Because of the high rate of life processes

in the active bird, the demands for oxygen are exceedingly great, but they can adjust themselves remarkably well to varying environmental conditions with adaptations that enable them to conserve energy during cold weather, or when sleeping.

Excretory system

The **kidneys** are a pair of dark brown three-lobed bodies situated as shown in Fig. 306. Each discharges its semisolid nitrogenous waste (mostly urates) through a duct, the **ureter,** into the **cloaca.** There is no **urinary bladder,** but the semisolid "urine" passes directly out of the cloaca with the feces and appears as a whitish substance on the latter.

Nervous system

The **brain** of the pigeon (Fig. 392) is very short and broad. The **cerebrum** and **cerebellum** are comparatively large, as are also the **optic lobes,** showing that birds have well-developed powers of coordination and of sight. The **olfactory lobes,** on the other hand, are very small, indicating poorly developed olfactory organs. Contrary to popular belief vultures detect the presence of carrion largely by keenness of sight rather than smell.

Sense organs

The **bill** and **tongue** serve as **tactile organs.** Tactile nerves are also present at the base of the feathers, especially those of the wings and tail. Birds are usually unable to distinguish delicate odors; and on the whole their sense of **smell** is very poor. The sense of **taste** is also poorly developed, but it is nevertheless present as can easily be demonstrated if a bad-tasting morsel of food is presented to a bird.

The **cochlea** of the ear is more complex than that of reptiles. The **Eustachian tubes** open by a single aperture on the roof of the pharynx. Birds have acute and discriminating powers of **hearing**—a power correlated with their singing ability.

The **eyes** of birds are very large, and the sense of **sight** is remarkably keen. The visual acuity is 8 times that of man in some of the birds of prey. Birds also have a wide field of vision in all directions, and the night-hunting birds are adapted for vision in dim light; an owl's capacity for seeing in dim light is about 10 times that of man. The birds have extraordinary powers of eye **accommodation,** which explains why they can fly rapidly among the branches of a tree without striking a branch or swoop down to the ground from a great height in the air, changing from far-sighted to near-sighted vision in an instant. There is substantial evidence of good color vision in birds.

Endocrine glands

Birds have endocrine glands such as are characteristic of mammals. The pituitary gland is at the base of the brain, the thyroid in the neck, the islets of Langerhans in the pancreas, the adrenals on the ventral surface of the kidneys, and the endocrinal tissue in the gonads. The bird hormones most studied have been those associated with the gonads.

Reproductive system

The **male** has a pair of oval **testes** (Fig. 306). From each testis, a duct, the **vas deferens,** passes back and opens into the cloaca; often it is dilated at its distal end to form a **seminal vesicle.** The sperms pass through the vasa deferentia and are stored in the seminal vesicle. When **copulation** takes place, they are discharged into the cloaca and transferred by contact to the cloaca of the female. There is no **copulatory organ** in most birds; however, a curved penis arises from the ventral wall of the cloaca in ducks, geese, and swans.

The right **ovary** of the female usually disappears during development so that only the left ovary persists in the adult. The ova break out of the ovary and enter the **oviduct.** During their passage through the oviduct, the **albuminous substance** known as the "white" of the egg is secreted in the walls of the middle portion. The double parchmentlike **shell membrane** is then secreted about the egg, and finally the **shell** is added by the posterior part of the oviduct ("uterus") a short time before deposition.

Fertilization takes place in the upper oviduct about 41 hours before the eggs are laid. At the end of the **period of incubation,** about 14 days, the young have developed to such a stage that they can break through the shell, and **hatch.** They are at first covered with fine down, but they soon acquire a covering of contour feathers. During early life as nestlings, they are fed "pigeon's

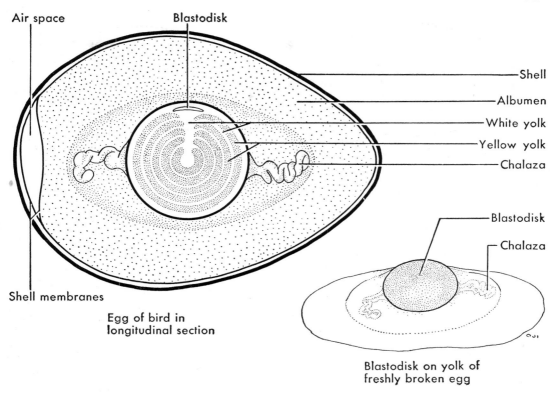

Air space   Blastodisk

Shell

Albumen

White yolk

Yellow yolk

Chalaza

Blastodisk

Chalaza

Shell membranes

Egg of bird in
longitudinal section

Blastodisk on yolk of
freshly broken egg

FIGURE 312.   Diagram of the structure of a bird's egg.

milk," a secretion which results from a degeneration of the cells which line the crop of the adult. The pigeon's milk is ejected from the crop of the parent into the mouth of the young nestling.

It has been demonstrated experimentally that injecting a pigeon with a lactogenic hormone (prolactin) will cause the secretion of pigeon's milk at any time of the year.

CHARACTERISTICS OF BIRDS IN GENERAL

Form and function

The bodies of birds have become adapted to various environments. This adaptation is best shown by the wings, tails, feet, and bills.

Fusiform shape

There are a few flightless birds, but the great majority fly. The adaptations that make flight possible are significant. One is the matter of body form. So much has been said about streamlining in recent years that nearly everyone knows about air resistance. It is relatively difficult to move a bulky and irregularly shaped body through the air; on the other hand, something that is fusiform in shape or tapering toward the ends will meet with less resistance in both air and water. The body of the average bird approaches this shape as do the bodies of most things that fly or swim (Fig. 313).

Wings

The wings of most birds are used as organs of flight, and several different types of flight are recognized. Some aerial birds, like the swallows, gulls, and albatrosses, have long pointed wings that enable them to remain in the air for many hours at a time; whereas terrestrial birds, such as the bob-

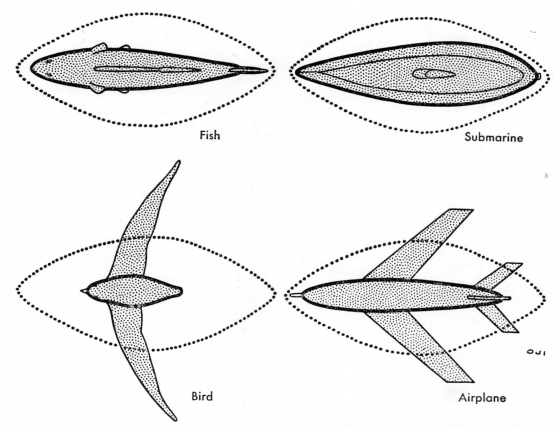

FIGURE 313. Diagrams of living and nonliving things that have a fusiform shape. This shape is characteristic of birds capable of rapid flight and fast-moving objects in air and water. The flightless fossil birds differed about as much in form from the fast-flying birds of today as the first airplanes differed in shape from a modern jet.

white and song sparrow, possess short rounded wings which enable them to fly rapidly for short distances. Many aquatic birds such as the penguins (Fig. 314), auks, and murres use their wings effectively for swimming and diving. Flightless birds such as the ostrich (Fig. 305), rhea (Fig. 322), emu (Fig. 321), and kiwi (Fig. 305) possess only the remnants of wings, but have very well-developed legs.

The primitive use of wings was probably for climbing in addition to gliding and flying. *Archaeornis* (Fig. 331) was provided with three strong claws on its forelimbs. Of living birds, the young of the hoatzin (Fig. 315), a peculiar bird inhabiting South Amer-

ica, is able to climb about before it can fly by the aid of two claws on each forelimb; small claws are found in numerous other species.

Wings may also serve as organs of offense and defense as in the large waterfowl, or as musical instruments for the "drumming" of the ruffed grouse.

Tails

During flight the tail acts as an aerial rudder; a long-tailed bird is able to fly in short curves or follow an erratic course without difficulty. The tail is also used as a brake. It is light and therefore easy to manage, and the tail feathers are firmly supported by the

FIGURE 314. King penguin. These antarctic birds are unable to fly. Their forelimbs are paddle-like flippers which are used like oars. When on land penguins usually assume an upright posture. They do not build a nest, but have a special brood pocket between their legs for keeping an egg warm. (Courtesy of N.Y. Zoological Society.)

FIGURE 315. Hoatzin of South America, unique in many ways. The young bird, as shown here, has claws on its wings and climbs about among the branches. It is regarded as a survivor of that ancient period when birds were distinctly reptilian in character. (Photo by Beebe.)

terminal bone of fused vertebrae, the pygostyle (Fig. 309). Movement of the tail is allowed by the freely movable vertebrae just preceding the pygostyle. While perching, the tail acts as a balancer. Birds that cling to the sides of trees, like the woodpeckers (Fig. 322), or to the sides of other objects, like the chimney swift, brace themselves by means of their stiff tails.

In many birds the tail of the male differs from that of the female; it is more beautiful in the former and serves as a secondary sexual character. Among the most famous of these dimorphic forms of birds are the lyrebird, peacock, and turkey.

Feet

Feet (Fig. 316) are used for locomotion, for obtaining food, for building nests, and for offensive and defensive purposes. Many ground birds have strong feet fitted for scratching; perching birds possess feet adapted for grasping a perch; most swimming birds have webbed feet; wading birds have long legs and long toes; and birds of prey such as the hawk possess very strong feet with long sharp claws for capturing other animals.

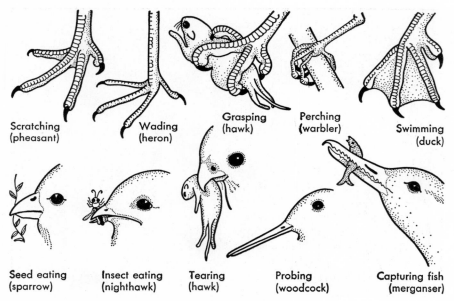

Scratching
(pheasant)

Wading
(heron)

Grasping
(hawk)

Perching
(warbler)

Swimming
(duck)

Seed eating
(sparrow)

Insect eating
(nighthawk)

Tearing
(hawk)

Probing
(woodcock)

Capturing fish
(merganser)

FIGURE 316. Some types of feet and bills of birds and their adaptations.

Bills

The bills of birds (Fig. 316) serve as hands, and their most important function is to procure food. Since bills are also used to construct nests, to preen feathers, and to perform other duties, their adaptations are such as to make them serve several purposes. In preening the feathers, a drop of oil is pressed from the oil gland at the base of the tail and appears to be spread on the feathers by means of the bill. At least in the waterfowl, the oil serves as a "dressing" that keeps the feathers in good condition. Another function of the oil is to prevent the covering of the bill from becoming brittle. There is also evidence that the oil gland has an antirachitic function. Experimental removal of the gland in some birds causes rickets.

Seed-eating birds possess strong short bills for crushing seeds (Fig. 316); some birds that eat insects have smaller and weaker bills; birds of prey are provided with strong curved beaks fitted for tearing flesh; and some birds have serrated bills for holding fish. Many other examples might be cited, which show the evolutionary possibilities of a simple organ.

Colors of birds

Birds are among the most beautifully colored of all animals. Some colors are due to pigments within the feather; these include pigment granules of brown, black, or dull yellow, and carotenoids either red or yellow. Green, blue, and iridescent markings as on some hummingbirds are due to the peculiar surface structure of their feathers. Absence of pigment causes partial or complete albinos. The juvenal plumage of birds gives way to the first winter plumage; this is usually worn throughout the first winter and is generally dull in color, often resembling the plumage of the adult female. Males and females frequently differ in color (sexual dimorphism), especially during the breeding season, when the male may acquire a brightly colored coat; the cardinal and scarlet tanager exhibit marked sexual dimorphism.

Color is often of protective value to the

bird. Colors and color patterns of many birds, as well as of other animals, conceal them in their surroundings. A striking example of protective coloration is the ptarmigan, which is white in winter when snow is on the ground, but a mottled brown in other seasons.

Bird songs

The songs of birds, as previously explained, are produced by the air passing through the **syrinx**. For one who wishes to study birds, a knowledge of bird songs is very helpful since one hears a great many more birds than he is able to see. Songs should be distinguished from call notes. The former are usually heard during the breeding season and are generally limited to the males. Call notes, on the other hand, are uttered throughout the year and correspond in meaning and effect to our conversation. The birds' songs and call notes serve (1) to warn of danger; (2) to bring together birds in a gregarious species; (3) for communication between parents and young; (4) to attract mates; and (5) to announce nesting territory.

Some birds, such as the pelican, are voiceless. The great power of mimicry among birds is interesting; among those possessing it are the catbird, mocking bird, and parrots. Do young birds sing instinctively the song of their species? It appears that calls and simple songs are instinctive, but the more elaborate songs require considerable practice by imitation before perfection is attained.

Bird flight

One of the most important functions of birds is that of flight. The bodies of flying birds are boat-shaped so that they offer little resistance to the air. The attachment of the wings high up on the trunk, the high position of such light organs as the lungs, the low position of the heavy muscles and digestive organs, the resulting low center of gravity, all tend to prevent the body from turning over.

Birds are able to glide or skim by spreading their wings and then moving forward by means of their acquired velocity. In soaring, birds do not depend entirely upon acquired velocity but rely upon favorable air currents.

The rates of speed at which birds fly vary considerably. The carrier pigeon in this country attains a maximum racing speed of about 60 miles per hour. Ninety miles per hour has been recorded for ducks, but the usual speed is 40 to 70. The duck hawk has been clocked flying 165 to 180 miles per hour in a nose dive. A speed of nearly 200 miles per hour has been reported for an Old World swift. Most passerine (perching) birds fly at a much slower speed.

Formerly, birds were supposed to hibernate during the winter in caves, hollow trees, or, in the case of swallows, in the mud at the bottom of lakes and ponds. We now know that most birds spend the winter in a more congenial southern climate, though a few, such as the poor-wills, possess the unusual ability of becoming torpid, and actually hibernate.

Bird migration

Birds are the most famous of all animals that migrate (Fig. 317). The world champion long-distance migrant is the arctic tern; the extremes of its nesting and wintering ranges are 11,000 miles apart. Since the routes taken are circuitous, these terns may fly 25,000 miles each year. In the autumn some birds gather in flocks and move southward, returning the following spring. Certain species migrate east and west. Birds that breed in the far north may spend the winter in parts of the temperate zone. Some birds do not migrate; for example, the great horned owl and bob-white. Certain other birds move southward only when the weather becomes very severe.

Most birds migrate on clear nights at an

FIGURE 317. A spectacular migration of snow geese, flying over the waters of Back Bay, Virginia. Picture shows only a small part of this majestic migration. (Photographed from a helicopter by Margaret Bourke-White. Courtesy of *Life* magazine.)

altitude of ½ mile or more, but there are some daytime migrants. Each species has a more or less definite time of migration, and one can predict with some degree of accuracy the date when it will arrive in a given locality. The speed of migration is as a rule rather slow, and a daily rate of 38 miles is about the average for the robin.

Many theories have been advanced to account for the migration of birds, such as the temperature, amount of light, condition of the food supply, and physiologic state of the gonads. Other theories attempt to explain how birds find their way during migration. A review of all available evidence makes it fairly clear that many problems raised by bird migration still remain unsolved; however, there seems no reason to believe that they are insoluble.

Nests, eggs, and young of birds

Some birds, like geese and eagles, usually mate for life, but the majority live together for a single season only. The nesting period varies according to the species.

As a rule birds conceal their nests or build them in places that are practically inaccessible. Some species do not build a nest, but lay their one or more eggs directly upon the ground (Fig. 318). A nest-building bird may construct a flimsy platform of twigs (mourning dove) or an intricate hanging basket (oriole), but most species build distinctive nests.

A few birds not only build no nests, but they neither incubate their eggs nor take care of their offspring. This is true of the

FIGURE 318. Eggs of whip-poor-will (*Caprimulgus*) laid on leaves in the woods. No attempt is made to build a nest. (Courtesy of the American Museum of Natural History.)

European cuckoo and the American cowbirds. Their eggs are usually laid in the nests of birds that are smaller than themselves (Fig. 319). The young birds are carefully reared by their foster parents and often starve or crowd out the rightful offspring.

The eggs of birds vary in shape, size, color, and number. The smallest eggs are those of certain hummingbirds, measuring less than ½ inch in length; the largest eggs are those of the extinct elephant bird of Madagascar, *Aepyornis* (Fig. 333).

FIGURE 319. Nest and eggs of the horned lark. The nest has thick well-built walls. The coarsely spotted eggs were laid in the nest by a cowbird. (Photo by Hegner.)

As a rule, eggs laid in dark places, such as those of woodpeckers, are white. Many eggs are colored or spotted; those of one species are in most cases distinguishable from those of another species.

FIGURE 320. *Top*, young chimney swifts are practically naked and blind at birth and are cared for in the nest for about three weeks (altricial). Note the nest of dried saliva and twigs. (Photo by Hegner.) *Bottom*, piping plovers, like the newly hatched ducks and pheasants, are covered with down and leave the nest soon after hatching (precocial). (Photo courtesy of Bertha Daubendiek.)

The number of eggs laid in a clutch (setting) varies in number from 1 to 20. The average period of incubation for the smaller passerine birds is about 12 to 14 days. The eggs of the ostrich hatch in about 45 days. Those of the royal albatross, a sea bird, have the longest period of incubation—about 80 days. In some cases, only the female incubates; in others, the male and female work in shifts; and with a few birds, such as some ostriches and shore birds, the male performs practically all of this duty.

Two general classes of young are recognized: (1) those that are able to run about soon after hatching, as young chickens do, are known as **precocial birds** (Fig. 320); and (2) those that remain in the nest for a greater or lesser period before they are able to take care of themselves are known as **altricial birds.**

OTHER BIRDS

Wingless and flightless birds

Five orders of living birds are flightless. These include ostriches, rheas, cassowaries, emus, penguins, and kiwis. **Ostriches** (Fig. 305) are the largest living birds, attaining a height of more than 8 feet and a weight of over 300 pounds. Although flight-

less, they can run at a speed of more than 50 miles per hour. They live in dry open regions of Africa and travel about in groups, but do not stick their heads in the sand and think themselves hidden, as commonly reported. The nest is a hollow in the sand, and several females lay their eggs in a single nest. The males uncover and incubate the eggs at night and cover them with warm sand by day.

Rheas (Fig. 322) are New World ostriches which inhabit the pampas of South America. They are smaller than the true ostriches, but their habits are quite similar. **Cassowaries** (Fig. 305) and emus are ostrich-like birds; the **emus** (Fig. 321) are confined to Australia, and the cassowaries, the world's third largest flightless bird, to New Guinea and neighboring islands. **Kiwis** (Fig. 305) are wingless birds that live in New Zealand. They are about the size of a common fowl; their wings are rudimentary, and they lack

FIGURE 321. An adult emu with chicks. The young emu is strikingly striped, a characteristic which disappears as the flightless bird becomes mature. (Courtesy of Victorian Railways.)

Loon

Peregrine falcon

Yellow-bellied sapsucker

Flamingo

Cooper's hawk

Rhea

FIGURE 322. Representatives of selected orders of birds. Some adaptations are shown.

tail feathers; they have a peculiar hairlike plumage throughout life and are credited with a keen sense of smell which is unique in birds.

Aquatic birds

Many birds spend a large part of their time in or near the water and are adapted for this type of life. They are generally known as swimmers, divers, shorebirds, and waterfowl. Perhaps the type most conspicuously adapted for an aquatic existence is the penguin (Fig. 314). The forelimbs are modified as paddles for swimming under water; the feet are webbed; the cold water can be shaken entirely from the feathers; and a layer of fat just beneath the skin serves to keep in the body heat. They feed on marine invertebrate animals. **Loons** (Fig. 322) are large birds that swim and dive with great agility. **Grebes** are smaller than loons and are also excellent swimmers and divers. **Albatrosses** (Fig. 305) possess exceptionally long and narrow wings. They are such strong fliers that they rarely come to land except for nesting.

The white **pelican** possesses a huge membranous pouch between the branches of the lower jaw, with which it scoops up small fish. Among the common **wading birds** are the **herons** (Fig. 324) and **bitterns**. They

Figure 323. California brown pelican. Note the pouch that hangs from the lower bill; this serves as a scoop net for capturing and storing fish. (Courtesy of N.Y. Zoological Society.)

possess long legs, broad wings, and short tails. Here also belong the **flamingos** (Fig. 322) that inhabit the tropics. They are

gregarious birds, congregating in thousands on mud flats, where they build their conical mud nests. Most species have rosy-white plumage with scarlet wing feathers. The **ducklike birds** (Fig. 305) are adapted for swimming, with short legs and fully webbed front toes. Their young are entirely covered with down and can swim or run about soon after hatching; they are precocial. In North America and other parts of the world are **swans, geese, river ducks, sea ducks,** and **mergansers.**

Figure 324. Great blue heron. Long neck, long legs, slender body, and a stilettolike bill are characteristics of this species; this bird is an expert fisherman. (Courtesy of N.Y. Zoological Society.)

The **marsh birds** are mostly of the wading type with incompletely webbed front toes. They include the **rails, gallinules, coots, cranes, limpkins,** and **trumpeters.** The order of **shorebirds** contains a varied assemblage of **plovers, sandpipers, gulls, terns, puffins, auks** (Fig. 305), etc., most of which frequent fresh or salt water. The **jacanas** are tropical shorebirds, with very long toes and claws enabling them to walk over lily pads without sinking. The **puffins, murres,** and **auks** spend a large part of their existence at sea. Most are excellent swimmers and divers, but very awkward on land.

The **great auk,** *Pinguinus impennis,* became extinct in 1844, when the last one appears to have been killed. Auks were destroyed for their feathers, and their eggs were used as food. All that remain today of the great auk are about 80 preserved specimens, 75 eggs, and some 25 skeletons.

Figure 325. Vulture showing naked head, and beak slightly hooked. (Photo by Gross. Courtesy of *Nature Magazine.*)

Birds of prey

The **falconlike** birds are busily engaged by day, and the owls by night, seeking whom they may devour. The **diurnal birds of prey** possess, in most cases, powerful wings, a stout hooked bill with a cere at the base, and strong toes armed with sharp claws. The **vultures** (Fig. 325) have weak feet and live on carrion (dead animals); they are especially valuable as scavengers, in warm countries, where they remove dead bodies before they become a health hazard. Some other species that live in the United States are the **swallow-tailed kite, osprey, bald eagle** (Fig. 328), **red-tailed hawk, Cooper's hawk** (Fig. 322), **sparrow hawk,** and **golden eagle.**

Owls (Fig. 305) are **nocturnal birds of prey.** They possess large rounded heads, strong legs, feet armed with sharp claws, strong bills with the upper mandible curved downward, large eyes directed forward and surrounded by a radiating disk of feathers,

and soft fluffy plumage which renders them noiseless during flight. Owls feed upon mice, rats, and other small mammals, as well as insects, birds, and fish. The indigestible parts of the food are cast out of the mouth in the form of pellets. Most species of owls are beneficial to man. Among the well-known North American species may be mentioned the **barn owl** (Fig. 305), **screech owl** (Fig. 327), **great horned owl** (Fig. 326), and **burrowing owl.**

Game birds

Many kinds of birds are hunted for sport. Among these are the **wild turkey, bob-white, pheasant** (Fig. 305), **ruffed grouse, prairie chicken,** etc. Game birds are as a rule terrestrial, but many roost or feed in trees. The members of one or more families often remain together as a covey, and in some species the coveys unite to form large flocks.

Cuckoos, road runners, hummingbirds, and others

Cuckoos are mostly tropical birds. The majority do not build a nest, but lay their eggs in the nests of other birds. This is not true, however, of the North American species. Their peculiar vocal powers have given them their common name. The **chimney swift** formerly made its nest in hollow trees, but now usually frequents chimneys (Fig. 320). When in the open air, it is always on the wing, catching insects or gathering twigs from the dead branches of trees for its nest. The twigs are glued together with saliva and firmly fastened to the inside of the chimney, forming a cup-shaped nest. Certain species of swifts inhabiting the East Indies make nests of a secretion from the salivary glands, producing the edible birds' nests relished by the Chinese.

The **road runner** is an inhabitant of deserts in the southwestern United States, where it lives among the cacti, sagebrush, and mesquite. It is a long, slender bird and

FIGURE 326. Great horned owl. There is evidence that the owls have a keen sense of hearing, which helps them in locating prey at night. The tufts of feathers around the large external ear openings of the great horned owl probably aid in collecting sounds. In captivity, great horned owls have lived for 68 years.

an excellent runner. Its main food is lizards and snakes.

The **hummingbirds** (Fig. 329), which are confined to the New World, have been appropriately called feathered gems, or according to Audubon, "glittering fragments of the rainbow." Six hundred eighty-eight species and subspecies are known.

The **belted kingfisher** lays its 5 to 8 white eggs at the end of a tunnel about 6 feet long

in the bank of a stream. The kingfisher captures small fish by hovering over a stream and then plunging into the water and securing the unsuspecting prey with its bill.

Woodpeckers use their chisel-shaped bills for excavating holes in trees, at the bottom of which their eggs are laid, or for digging out grubs from beneath the bark. Most of them are of great benefit because of the insects they destroy; but the **yellow-bellied**

FIGURE 327. Screech owl. This owl is one of the smallest of the birds of prey. These owls show two color phases, some being grayish, and the others rufous red. They are well known because of their weird nocturnal cries. (Courtesy of N.Y. Zoological Society.)

FIGURE 328. Bald eagle. The head and tail are white, the beak hooked, and the claws curved and sharp. This eagle is represented in the United States coat of arms and on certain coins. (Photo by Hegner.)

FIGURE 329. Ruby-throated hummingbird, the only hummingbird found east of the Mississippi. The nest is built on top of a limb; the outside of the nest is covered with lichens. Note the long slender bill adapted for collecting nectar and insects from flowers. (Courtesy of N.Y. Zoological Society.)

455

sapsucker (Fig. 322) is harmful, since it eats the cambium of trees and sucks sap, thus disfiguring and devitalizing fruit and ornamental trees, and reducing the market value of lumber.

Perching birds

More than half of all the living birds known (about 8600 species) belong to the order Passeriformes, the perching birds. The passerine or perching birds are usually small or of medium size, but they are the most highly organized of the birds. Their feet are four-toed and adapted for grasping. The first toe or hallux is directed backward and is on a level with the other three which are directed forward. The nonsinging birds have a syrinx which is poorly developed as a musical apparatus; the **tyrant flycatchers,** such as the **kingbird** (Fig. 330), **phoebe,** and **wood pewee,** are examples.

FIGURE 330. Kingbird on nest. Note crest and sharp beak. Length 8½ inches. (Photo by Merwin. Courtesy of *Nature Magazine.*)

Domesticated birds

The common hen was probably derived from the red jungle fowl, *Gallus gallus*, of northeastern and central India. The varieties of chickens that have been derived from this species are almost infinite. Many varieties of domesticated pigeons (**tumbler, fantail, pouter,** etc.) have all descended from the wild rock dove, *Columba livia*. Certain variations such as the fantail occur; the

breeder takes advantage of the opportunity afforded by nature, and pigeons with this type of tail are bred together until a new variety is established.

Geese are supposed to have been derived from the graylag goose, *Anser anser*; most of our domestic breeds of ducks have sprung from the mallard, *Anas platyrhynchos*. The common peacock, *Pavo cristatus*, of the Indian peninsula, Ceylon, and Assam, has been in domestication at least from the time of Solomon. The guinea fowl, *Numida meleagris*, is a native of West Africa; and our domestic turkeys are descendants of the Mexican wild turkey.

Fossil and extinct birds

The study of living birds is followed by many professional zoologists, and amateur bird students number many thousands. However, the study of fossil birds, although of great interest, is a very restricted field because so little of their fossil history is known.

It is customary to divide birds into two subclasses, the Archaeornithes or ancient birds, and the Neornithes or recent birds, containing all living birds and a number of orders of fossil forms because of their likeness to modern birds. A few of the more interesting fossil species are described in the following paragraphs.

Subclass Archaeornithes

The two genera *Archaeornis* (Fig. 331) and *Archaeopteryx* belonging to this subclass are known from two fairly complete skeletons that were found in the lithographic slates of Solenhofen, Bavaria, of the Upper Jurassic period. Each was about the size of a crow. They possessed teeth embedded in sockets, forelimbs with three-clawed digits and separate metacarpal bones, and a lizard-like tail with large feathers on both sides. Though reptilian features predominate in the skeleton, the presence of feathers, indicating warm blood, place these curious crea-

FIGURE 331. *Top,* Fossil remains of *Archaeornis* (ancient bird) showing claws on digits of forelimbs, and long tail. *Bottom,* restoration of *Archaeornis,* called by some *Archaeopteryx.* About 20 inches long. (Courtesy of the American Museum of Natural History.)

tures among the birds. These odd-feathered animals aid in showing the close relationship between the birds and the reptiles.

Order Hesperornithiformes

There are at least 7 species of fossil birds in this order. *Hesperornis* (Fig. 332), the best known, was over 5 feet in length. It possessed teeth set in a groove, strong hind-limbs with webbed feet which were used like oars, and a sternum without a keel. The entire anatomy indicates that *Hesperornis* was a flightless swimming and diving bird which lived upon aquatic animals. The remains of this and the other species probably belonging to this order were found in the Cretaceous deposits of Kansas, Montana, and Europe.

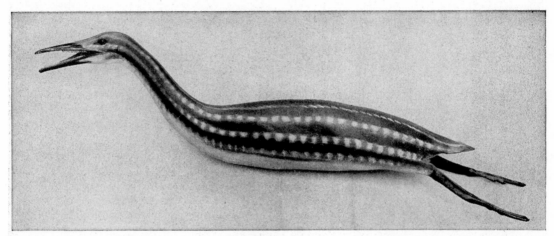

FIGURE 332. *Hesperornis*, a restoration, showing teeth, absence of wings, and laterally directed legs with lobed toes for swimming. Fossils of this bird have been found in the United States. (Courtesy of Chicago Natural History Museum.)

Order Ichthyornithiformes

Of the 8 species of fossil birds included in this order, *Ichthyornis* from the Cretaceous deposits of Kansas is the best known. This bird, which lived in the same period as *Hesperornis*, had a keeled sternum and well-developed wings. It was about the size of a pigeon, a strong flier, and probably fed upon aquatic animals.

Order Dinornithiformes. Moas

Members of this order have probably become extinct within the past 500 years. The remains of these peculiar birds have been found in great numbers in caves, refuse heaps, and old marsh beds of New Zealand, to which country they were confined. Twenty-eight species are known from the remains. They ranged from about the size of a turkey to nearly 10 feet high. They were flightless, but possessed enormous hind-limbs.

Order Aepyornithiformes. Elephant birds

The elephant birds (Fig. 333) have probably become extinct within the past 5 centuries. They inhabited Madagascar, were flightless, and possessed hindlimbs more enormous even than those of the moas. Many of their eggs have been found in the sand near the seashore. The elephant bird's egg is the largest known animal cell; it is more than 13 inches in length and 9 inches in width, and has a capacity of over two gallons, equivalent to 148 hen's eggs.

FIGURE 333. An elephant bird (*Aepyornis*), a restoration of this large, flightless, and strange bird, which once lived in Madagascar. (Courtesy of Chicago Natural History Museum.)

Order Diatrymiformes

These were large forms which could not fly because the wings were atrophied. They had three toes and a huge bill. They lived during the Eocene in western United States.

Other extinct birds

Passenger pigeons (Fig. 334), as well as great auks, dodos, Labrador ducks, heath hens, and various other birds, have become extinct in recent times. Alexander Wilson in 1808 saw a flock of passenger pigeons in Kentucky that contained over two billion birds, and Audubon writes of flocks that darkened the sky like the approach of a tornado. The last known passenger pigeon died of old age in the zoological park in Cincinnati in September, 1914. Probably the slaughter and persecution of this bird by man was an important factor in its becoming extinct. Every great food market from St. Louis to Boston received hundreds of barrels of pigeons every season until man realized too late that this bird needed protection.

FIGURE 334. The passenger pigeon, *Ectopistes migratorius*, which became extinct after incredible slaughter. Length 16 inches. (Courtesy of the American Museum of Natural History.)

RELATIONS OF BIRDS TO MAN

Birds are of great commercial value; they augment our food supply and furnish feathers for various purposes. Before the wearing of wild bird feathers was prohibited by law, vast numbers of birds were killed for their plumes. The American egrets (Fig. 336) were almost exterminated in order to secure the tuft of feathers or aigrettes that resemble spun glass. In certain regions, the excrement (guano) of sea birds exists in large quantities and is of great value as a fertilizer. The most valuable deposits are on small islands near the coast of Peru; these may amount to as much as 750 tons per acre per year. Cormorants (Fig. 335) are largely responsible for the production of guano. Game

FIGURE 335. The cormorant on nest. A fish eating bird of considerable economic importance. (Courtesy of *Nature Magazine.*)

birds are of considerable importance, and a constant effort is being made to maintain them for sport by intelligent game management.

One of the most evident services rendered by birds is destruction of weed seed. A very large proportion of the food of birds, however, consists of insects. Practically all the insects devoured by birds are injurious to plants or animals and consequently harmful to man. In Salt Lake City a monument has been erected to gulls. The crops of the Mormons in 1848–1849 were threatened by locusts, "Mormon crickets," but the gulls came, ate the locusts, and saved the crops. Another large element in the food of birds

FIGURE 336. American egret, *Casmerodius*, in a cypress swamp in the southern United States. The beautiful feathers, known as aigrettes, are carried only during the breeding season. Killing the parents for the plumes means starvation for the nestlings. Length 41 inches. (Courtesy of American Museum of Natural History.)

consists of small mammals such as field mice, ground squirrels, and rabbits. For many years, hawks, owls, and other birds of prey have been killed whenever possible because of the supposed destruction of poultry and game birds. However, the majority of the species are chiefly beneficial.

A BRIEF CLASSIFICATION OF LIVING BIRDS

(For reference purposes only)

Class Aves. The birds form a more homogeneous class of vertebrates than the reptiles and cannot be separated into a few well-defined groups. The structural differences that distinguish the orders, families, genera, and species are for the most part so slight as to make it impossible to state them in a brief and clear manner. There are more than 8600 species of birds. Their orders and phylogenetic arrangement follow Wetmore's, *A Revised Classification for Birds of the World.*

It will be noted that the subspecies names of birds in this text are omitted for it is now an approved practice of ornithologists to use only the species name except in a detailed taxonomic work.

Order 1. **Struthioniformes.** Ostriches. Ex. *Struthio camelus*, African ostrich (Fig. 305).

Order 2. **Rheiformes.** Rheas. Ex. *Rhea americana*, American ostrich (Fig. 322).

Order 3. **Casuariiformes.** Cassowaries and emus (Fig. 305). Ex. *Casuarius uniappendiculatus*, cassowary.

Order 4. **Apterygiformes.** Kiwis. Ex. *Apteryx australis*, kiwi (Fig. 305).

Order 5. **Tinamiformes.** Tinamous. Ex. *Rhynchotus rufescens*, great tinamou.

Order 6. **Sphenisciformes.** Penguins (Fig. 314). Ex. *Spheniscus demersus*, cape penguin.

Order 7. **Gaviiformes.** Loons. Ex. *Gavia immer*, loon (Fig. 322).

Order 8. **Podicipediformes.** Grebes. Ex. *Podilymbus podiceps*, pied-billed grebe.

Order 9. **Procellariiformes.** Albatrosses (Fig. 305), petrels, shearwaters and fulmars. Ex. *Diomedea nigripes*, black-footed albatross.

Order 10. **Pelecaniformes.** Tropic birds, pelicans (Fig. 323), cormorants, gannets, darters, boobies. Ex. *Pelecanus erythrorhynchos*, white pelican.

Order 11. **Ciconiiformes.** Long-legged waders: herons (Fig. 305), bitterns, storks, ibises, spoonbills, flamingos (Fig. 322). Ex. *Ardea herodias*, great blue heron.

Order 12. **Anseriformes.** Gooselike birds: screamers, swans, geese and ducks (Fig. 305). Ex. *Anas platyrhynchos*, mallard duck.

Order 13. **Falconiformes.** Falconlike birds of prey: vultures, secretary birds, falcons, kites, eagles, hawks, caracaras, condors, and buzzards. Ex. *Haliaeetus leucocephalus*, bald eagle (Fig. 328).

Order 14. **Galliformes.** Fowl-like birds: pheasants (Fig. 305), grouse, ptarmigan, partridge, quail, turkeys, hoatzin (Fig. 315). Ex. *Bonasa umbellus*, ruffed grouse.

Order 15. **Gruiformes.** Cranelike birds: limpkins, gallinules, coots, rails, and cranes. Ex. *Rallus elegans*, king rail.

Order 16. **Charadriiformes.** Shorebirds, etc. Great auk (Fig. 305), jacanas, oystercatchers, plovers, sandpipers, skuas, gulls, terns, skimmers, auks, murres, and puffins. Ex. *Charadrius vociferus*, killdeer.

Order 17. **Columbiformes.** Pigeons (Fig. 334) and doves. Ex. *Zenaidura macroura*, mourning dove.

Order 18. **Psittaciformes.** Parrots, parakeets, macaws, etc. Ex. *Conuropsis carolinensis*, Carolina paroquet.

Order 19. **Cuculiformes.** Cuckoos, anis, and road runners. Ex. *Coccyzus americanus*, yellow-billed cuckoo.

Order 20. **Strigiformes.** Owls. Ex. *Bubo virginianus*, great horned owl (Fig. 326).

Order 21. **Caprimulgiformes.** Goatsuckers: nighthawks, whip-poor-wills, oil

birds, etc. Ex. *Chordeiles minor,*
nighthawk.

Order 22. **Apodiformes.** Swifts, hummingbirds, etc. Ex. *Chaetura pelagica,*
chimney swift (Fig. 320).

Order 23. **Coliiformes.** Colies or mouse-
birds. Ex. *Colius.*

Order 24. **Trogoniformes.** Trogons (Fig.
305), quetzal. Ex. *Trogon ambi-
guus,* coppery-tailed trogon.

Order 25. **Coraciiformes.** Kingfishers, rollers, hornbills, motmots, bee eat-
ers, etc. Ex. *Megaceryle alcyon,*
belted kingfisher.

Order 26. **Piciformes.** Woodpeckers (Fig.
322), piculets, wrynecks, jaca-
mars, toucans, barbets, etc. Ex.
Colaptes auratus, southern flicker.

Order 27. **Passeriformes.** Perching birds.
Ex. *Tyrannus tyrannus,* king-
bird (Fig. 330).

PASSERIFORMES. FAMILIES IN NORTH AMERICA

FAMILY	COMMON NAME
1. Cotingidae	Chatterers
2. Tyrannidae	Flycatchers
3. Alaudidae	Larks
4. Hirundinidae	Swallows
5. Corvidae	Crows, jays, etc.
6. Paridae	Titmice
7. Sittidae	Nuthatches
8. Certhiidae	Creepers
9. Chamaeidae	Wren tits
10. Cinclidae	Dippers
11. Troglodytidae	Wrens
12. Mimidae	Thrashers, etc.
13. Turdidae	Thrushes, etc.
14. Sylviidae	Kinglets, etc.
15. Prunellidae	Accentors
16. Motacillidae	Wagtails
17. Bombycillidae	Waxwings
18. Ptilogonatidae	Silky flycatchers
19. Laniidae	Shrikes
20. Sturnidae	Starlings
21. Vireonidae	Vireos
22. Coerebidae	Honey creepers
23. Parulidae	Wood warblers
24. Ploceidae	Weaver finches
25. Icteridae	Blackbirds, etc.
26. Thraupidae	Tanagers
27. Fringillidae	Sparrows, etc.

SELECTED COLLATERAL READINGS

American Ornithologists' Union. *Check-list of
North American Birds.* American Ornithologists' Union, Lancaster, Pa., 1931.

Audubon, John James. *The Birds of America.*
Macmillan, New York, 1937.

Bent, A.C. *Life Histories of North American
Birds,* 19 vols. U.S. National Museum,
Washington, 1919–1953.

Bradley, O.C. *The Structure of the Fowl.*
Lippincott, Philadelphia, 1950.

Lincoln, F.C. *The Migration of American
Birds.* Doubleday, Doran, New York, 1952.

Peters, J.L. *Birds of the World.* 7 vols. Harvard Univ. Press, Cambridge, 1931, 1934,
1937, 1940, 1945, 1948, 1951.

Peterson, R.T. *A Field Guide to the Birds.*
Houghton Mifflin, Boston, 1947.

———. *Birds Over America.* Dodd, Mead,
New York, 1948.

Schorger, A.W. *The Passenger Pigeon.* Wisconsin Univ. Press, Madison, 1955.

Sturkie, P.D. *Avian Physiology.* Comstock,
Ithaca, N.Y., 1954.

The Auk. Quarterly journal published since
1884 by the American Ornithologists'
Union.

Wallace, G.J. *An Introduction to Ornithology.*
Macmillan, New York, 1955.

CHAPTER 30

Class Mammalia.
Mammals

Man is a mammal, a vertebrate with the most advanced brain and mental development. The name is derived from the fact that mammals possess mammary glands which secrete milk for the nourishment of their young. Mammals also possess coverings of hair at some time in their existence and are distinguished by this characteristic as certainly as birds are by their feathers. With few exceptions, adult mammals are provided with at least a small number of hairs, and all are warm-blooded. Parental care is generally most highly developed in this group and reaches its climax in humans.

The 5000 or more species of living mammals are found in all kinds of habitats from the tropics to the polar regions, and from the oceans to the driest deserts. Some are hunted for sport and others for their furs.

The majority of the mammals are viviparous, and their young are nourished before birth through placental tissue, which connects the mother with her offspring. The placenta is unique among all animals as an adaptation for the developing young. It makes possible the development of the young to a more advanced stage before birth.

Since detailed studies of mammals are ordinarily reserved for special courses in mammalian biology, only a brief account is presented here to furnish a general knowledge of the structure and physiology of a mammalian type. An idea of the variety of forms (Fig. 337) and activities exhibited by mammals is indicated in the section on other mammals. Some of the more interesting features of mammals are described here, such as integumentary structures (hair, teeth, nails, claws, cutaneous glands, and others), the development of the young from the egg, hibernation, migration, domestication of species, fossil forms, and the relations of mammals to man. The cat is so much like man in structure and function that a study of it is a good introduction to the human body. In Chapters 31 to 34, the morphology and physiology of man are considered.

Carnivora
(Hyena)

Artiodactyla
(Hippopotamus)

Perissodactyla
(Zebra)

Primates
(Baboon)

Cetacea
(Killer whale)

Sirenia
(Manatee)

Proboscidea
(Elephant)

Insectivora
(Shrew)

Tubulidentata
(Aardvark)

Pholidota
(Scaly anteater)

Chiroptera
(Brown bat)

Hyracoidea
(Hyrax)

Rodentia
(Porcupine)

Dermoptera
(Flying lemur)

Lagomorpha
(Rabbit)

Monotremata
(Spiny anteater)

Marsupialia
(Opossum)

Edentata
(Nine-banded
armadillo)

DOMESTIC CAT

The domestic cat is a carnivore; its scientific name is *Felis catus*, and it belongs to the same family as the lions, tigers, wildcats, and others. Often the lion is spoken of as a big cat, and he is in fact one kind of cat.

External features

The domestic cat is a 4-footed animal (quadruped), which illustrates well the characteristics of the higher mammals. It possesses an external covering of **hair** or **fur**, two **ears**, and separate genital and anal openings. The mouth is bounded by thin fleshy **lips**. At the end of the head are two narrow **nostrils**. The large **eyes**, one on either side of the head, are protected by an upper and a lower **eyelid** bordered by fine **eyelashes**, and a white, hairless, third eyelid or **nictitating membrane**, which may be drawn over the eyeball from the inner angle. Above and below the eyes and on the upper lip are long sensitive hairs, the **whiskers** (**vibrissae**).

The trunk may be separated into an anterior portion, the **thorax**, which is supported laterally by the ribs, and a posterior portion, the **abdomen**. The **tail** is long. Beneath its base is the **anus**, and just in front of this is the **urogenital opening**. In males the **scrotum** hangs beneath the anus. There are normally 4 pairs of small **teats** situated on the ventral surface of the thorax and abdomen. At the end of the teats open the ducts of the **mammary** or **milk glands**.

The **forelimbs** of the cat are used, as in the frog, for holding up the anterior part of the body. They each possess 5 **toes** with fleshy **pads** and retractile **claws**. The **hindlimbs** are stouter and more powerful than the forelimbs and serve as the principal power in locomotion. They are provided

with only 4 toes; the one corresponding to the great toe in man is absent. The cat walks on its toes and is, therefore, said to be **digitigrade**.

Skeleton

The skeleton of the cat (Fig. 338) contains bones that correspond closely to those in the skeleton of man. It consists principally of bone, but a small amount of cartilage is also present. As in the fishes, amphibians, reptiles, and birds, there are **cartilage bones** preformed in cartilage, and **membrane bones** arising by the transformation of connective tissue. A third type, called **sesamoid bones**, occurs in the tendons of some of the limb muscles, the action of which they modify; for example, the kneecap, or **patella**.

The **axial skeleton** consists, as in the **pigeon**, of a **skull**, ribs, sternum, and **vertebral column**. The skull (Fig. 339) is formed of both cartilage and membrane bones, and only a small amount of cartilage. The individual bones are immovably united to one another; their boundaries are in many cases obliterated in the adult and can be made out only in the embryo.

In humans, the incomplete ossification of the bones of the skull at the birth of a baby indicates an adaptive mechanism for childbirth. During labor the bones of the skull override each other, and the infant's skull, being reduced in size, accommodates itself to the size of the birth canal.

The **vertebral column** of the cat, as in other vertebrates, supports the body and protects the spinal cord. The **vertebrae** move upon one another; are separated by **intervertebral disks** of fibrocartilage, except in the sacrum; and are connected by **intervertebral ligaments**. The vertebrae of the neck or **cervical vertebrae** are 7 in number; those of the chest, the **thoracic vertebrae**, bear movably articulated ribs; those of the trunk region are called **lumbar vertebrae**; the 3 **sacral vertebrae** are fused together and support the pelvis; and the **caudal vertebrae**

FIGURE 337. *Facing page*, representatives of 18 different orders of mammals. These animals show the many adaptations characteristic of living organisms. The figures are not drawn to scale.

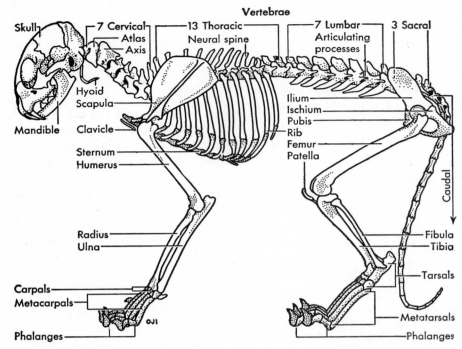

FIGURE 338. Skeleton of the domestic cat. Two ribs are hidden behind the scapula. This represents a highly specialized skeleton. Note how much more highly developed the appendicular skeleton is in comparison with that of the fish in Fig. 254.

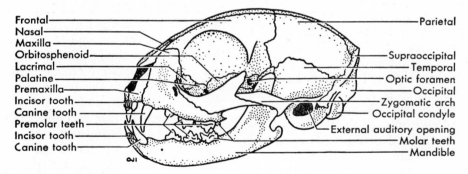

FIGURE 339. Skull of the domestic cat. Side view. Note that the bones are joined by dovetailed sutures. The skull protects some of the most important sense organs.

16 to 20 in number, form the skeletal axis of the tail.

The **ribs** and **sternum** constitute the framework of the thorax; they not only protect the vital organs in that region, but also play an important role in respiration. There are 13 pairs of ribs (Fig. 338). The first 9 pairs are attached separately to the sternum; the others do not reach the sternum. The **sternum** is a long, laterally compressed structure consisting mostly of bone. It is situated in the ventral wall of the thorax and is transversely divided into segments.

The **pectoral girdle** consists of 2 **scapulae**,

2 small **clavicles**, and 2 knoblike coracoid processes. The **forelimb** consists of the **humerus, radius, ulna,** 7 **carpal bones,** 5 **metacarpals,** and the **phalanges** of the toes. Each half of the **pelvic girdle** is called the hipbone or **innominate bone** and is made up of the **ilium, ischium,** and **pubis** fused together. The concavity in the innominate bone in which the head of the femur articulates is called the **acetabulum.**

The **hindlimb** is made up of the **femur, tibia, fibula,** 7 **tarsals** (ankle bones), 4 long **metatarsals** and a rudiment of the first (innermost), and the **phalanges.** The ankle joint of the cat lies between the tibia and fibula above, and the tarsal bones below. One of the **sesamoid bones** of the hind-

limb, which is situated on the front of the distal end of the femur, is called the knee-cap or **patella.**

Muscular system

Many of the muscles (Fig. 340) are more or less the same as in the lower vertebrates, but the mammals have a smaller amount of muscle on the vertebrae and ribs, and more highly developed muscles on the head, neck, and limbs. A distinctive feature of mammalian musculature is the dome-shaped partition or **diaphragm,** which separates the coelom into an anterior **thoracic cavity** containing the heart and lungs, and a posterior **abdominal cavity** containing the ab-

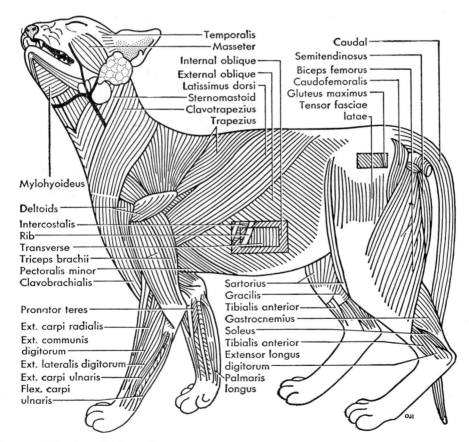

FIGURE 340. Superficial muscles of the domestic cat; some of the abdominal muscles are cut to show others that lie beneath.

dominal viscera. The cat has facial muscles which make possible a small degree of expression of emotional states. It is said, however, that man is the only animal that laughs.

See Chapter 31 for further information on the mammalian muscular system and its functions.

Digestive system

The **mouth cavity** (Fig. 341), on the anterior portion of the roof, bears a series of transverse ridges which help in holding the food. That part of the roof which has a bone foundation is known as the **hard palate.** Posterior to this is a fleshy flap, the **soft**

palate, which separates the mouth from the pharynx. At the sides of the posterior part of the soft palate are a pair of small reddish masses of lymphoid tissue called the **tonsils.** The **tongue** is attached to the floor of the mouth. It bears a number of **taste papillae** on the upper surface, which contain microscopic taste buds. The two orifices of the **auditory (Eustachian) tubes,** and the two openings of the **nasopalatine canals,** which connect the nasal and mouth cavities, are situated in the roof of the mouth behind and above the soft palate. There are 4 pairs of **salivary glands:** (1) the **parotids,** below the ears; (2) the **infraorbitals,** below the eyes; (3) the **submaxillaries,** behind the lower jaws; and (4) the **sublinguals,** next to

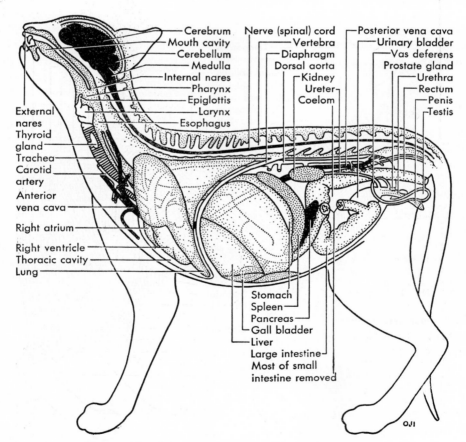

FIGURE 341. The internal structure of the domestic cat.

the submaxillaries. They pour watery and mucous secretions into the mouth cavity to moisten and lubricate the food.

The posterior continuation of the mouth cavity is called the **pharynx**. In the floor of the pharynx is the respiratory opening, the **glottis**, which is covered by a bilobed cartilaginous flap, the **epiglottis**, during the act of swallowing. The pharynx leads downward into the narrow, muscular **esophagus**. Following this is the **stomach**, behind the diaphragm; then comes the U-shaped **duodenum**, into which open the pancreatic duct from the **pancreas** and the bile duct from the **liver**.

The **small intestine**, which is several feet in length, leads into the **large intestine** (**colon**), which is continued as the **rectum**. At the junction of the small and large intestines, a short blind sac, the **cecum**, is given off. The cecum ends in a conelike sac, but there is no appendix as in man.

Circulatory system

The blood corpuscles of the cat are unlike those of the lower vertebrates, but characteristic of those in mammals; they are smaller and round,* instead of oval, biconcave, and without nuclei. The **heart** (Fig. 342) is completely 4-chambered, as in the pigeon, but the main blood vessel, the **aorta**, arising from the left ventricle, has only the left arch, whereas in birds the right arch persists. The right systemic arch of the cat is represented by the **innominate artery**, which is the common trunk of the right **carotid** and **subclavian arteries**. A **hepatic portal system** is present, but no renal portal system. The elongate **spleen**, a dark reddish organ, is on the left side behind the stomach.

The **lymphatic system** is important in the cat and other mammals. The fluid portion of the blood, because of the blood pressure, escapes through the walls of the capillaries,

---

* There is only one exception—in the camels they are oval in shape.

into the spaces among the tissues, and is collected into lymph vessels. These vessels pass through the **lymph glands** and finally empty into the large veins in the base of the neck. The lymphatics which collect nutriment from the intestine are called **lacteals**.

Respiratory system

The cat and all other mammals breathe air by means of **lungs** (Fig. 341). The glottis opens into the **larynx**, from which a tube called the **trachea** or windpipe arises. The trachea is held open by incomplete rings of cartilage; it divides into two **bronchi**, one bronchus going to each lung. These distribute air through smaller and smaller branches that end in microscopic air sacs (**alveoli**) of the lungs. The alveoli are surrounded by a capillary network of blood vessels in which the oxygen and carbon dioxide exchange of gases takes place. The larynx is supported by a number of cartilages and across its cavity extend two elastic cords called the **vocal cords**, with which the cat's squalls are produced. The lungs are conical in shape and lie freely in the thoracic cavity suspended by the bronchi.

Air is drawn into the lungs by the enlargement of the thoracic cavity. This is accomplished both by pulling the ribs forward and thus separating them, as in most reptiles, and by means of the diaphragm. The diaphragm is normally arched forward; when it contracts, it flattens, thus enlarging the thoracic cavity. The increased size of this cavity results in a slight negative pressure around the lungs; the lungs consequently expand and air rushes in (**inspiration**). Air is forced out of the lungs (**expiration**) by the elastic contraction of the lungs when the diaphragm and rib muscles relax.

Excretory system

The **urine** excreted by the two **kidneys** is carried by two slender tubes, the **ureters**, into a thin-walled muscular sac, the distensi-

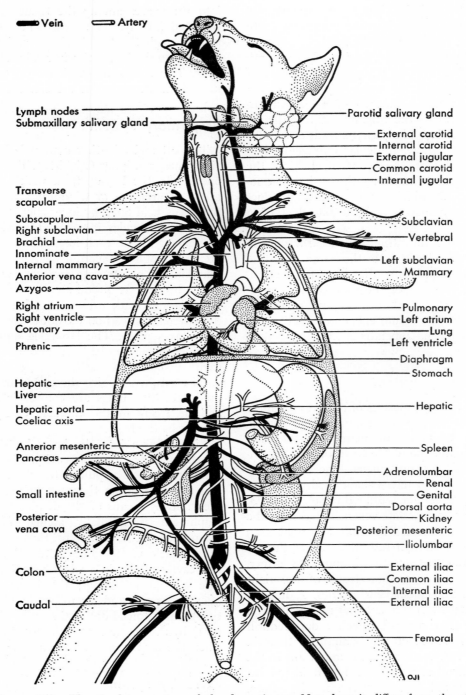

Vein   **Artery**

Lymph nodes
Submaxillary salivary gland

Transverse
scapular
Subscapular
Right subclavian
Brachial
Innominate
Internal mammary
Anterior vena cava
Azygos
Right atrium
Right ventricle
Coronary
Phrenic

Hepatic
Liver
Hepatic portal
Coeliac axis
Anterior mesenteric
Pancreas
Small intestine
Posterior
vena cava
Colon
Caudal

Parotid salivary gland
External carotid
Internal carotid
External jugular
Common carotid
Internal jugular
Subclavian
Vertebral
Left subclavian
Mammary
Pulmonary
Left atrium
Lung
Left ventricle
Diaphragm
Stomach
Hepatic
Spleen
Adrenolumbar
Renal
Genital
Dorsal aorta
Kidney
Posterior mesenteric
Iliolumbar
External iliac
Common iliac
Internal iliac
External iliac
Femoral

OJI

FIGURE 342. The circulatory system of the domestic cat. Note how it differs from the circulatory systems of vertebrates previously studied.

ble **bladder** (Fig. 343). At intervals the muscular walls of the bladder are voluntarily contracted, forcing the urine out through the **urethra**. In the male the urethra passes through the penis.

Nervous system

The cat possesses a brain, cranial nerves, spinal cord, spinal nerves, and an autonomic nervous system.

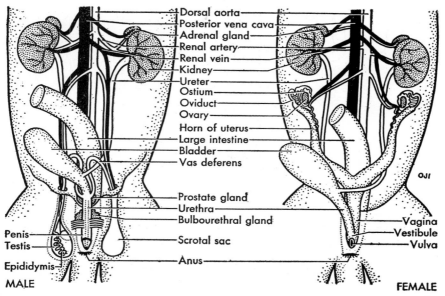

Dorsal aorta
Posterior vena cava
Adrenal gland
Renal artery
Renal vein
Kidney
Ureter
Ostium
Oviduct
Ovary
Horn of uterus
Large intestine
Bladder
Vas deferens

Prostate gland
Urethra
Bulbourethral gland

Penis
Testis
Scrotal sac
Epididymis
Anus
MALE

Vagina
Vestibule
Vulva
FEMALE

FIGURE 343. Urogenital organs of the domestic cat, in ventral view. This illustration shows that the urinary and reproductive organs of mammals are closely associated.

The **brain**, as in other mammals (Fig. 344), differs from that of the lower vertebrates in the large size of the **cerebral hemispheres** and **cerebellum**. The cerebral hemispheres are slightly marked by depressions or **sulci**, which divide the surface into lobes or **convolutions** not present in the pigeon. This increase in cerebral tissue is doubtless correlated with the greater intelligence of the cat. The **olfactory lobes** are very large and club-shaped. The **optic lobes** are each divided by a transverse furrow into two. The whole surface of the cerebellum is thrown into numerous folds. Its high degree of development is probably related to the excellent muscular coordination in the cat, which enables it to turn in the air and make a "four-point landing" when dropped.

There are 12 pairs of **cranial nerves** from the brain, and from the **nerve cord** a pair of spinal **nerves** emerges between successive vertebrae.

Sense organs

The organs of smell, taste, sight, and hearing in the cat are very similar to those of man in location and function (see Chap. 33). The eye of a cat has a pupil which varies in size and shape, depending on the amount of light striking the iris. The metallic luster which makes the eyes of cats "shine" at night is due to light-reflecting crystals in part of the eye. The large **outer ear** (Fig. 396) serves to collect sound waves; the **middle ear** transmits the vibrations of the **tympanic membrane** or **eardrum** by means of three **auditory bones** (malleus, incus, stapes), which extend across the tympanic cavity to the inner ear. This is un-

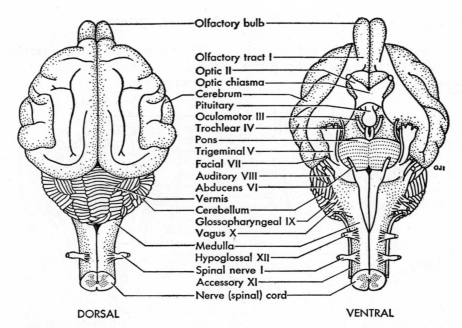

Olfactory bulb
Olfactory tract I
Optic II
Optic chiasma
Cerebrum
Pituitary
Oculomotor III
Trochlear IV
Pons
Trigeminal V
Facial VII
Auditory VIII
Abducens VI
Vermis
Cerebellum
Glossopharyngeal IX
Vagus X
Medulla
Hypoglossal XII
Spinal nerve I
Accessory XI
Nerve (spinal) cord

DORSAL   VENTRAL

FIGURE 344. The brain of a cat shows the complexity of the brain which characterizes mammals and is doubtless one of the reasons why they have become a dominant group.

like the ears of amphibians, reptiles, and birds, which have only one bone, the columella. The **cochlea** of the **inner ear is** spirally coiled and not simply curved as in the pigeon. The **nasal cavities** are large, indicating a highly developed sense of smell.

Endocrine glands

In the cat the ductless glands consist of the thyroid, parathyroids, pituitary, islets of Langerhans, adrenals, and gonads. Their functions, much like other mammals, are discussed in Chapter 33.

Reproductive system

The two **testes** of the male lie in oval pouches of skin called **scrotal sacs**, one on either side of the copulatory organ, the **penis** (Fig. 343). The **sperms** pass from each testis into minute convoluted tubes called the **epididymis**; they then enter the sperm duct, or **vas deferens**, which leads into the abdominal cavity and opens into the **urethra**. During **copulation** the sperms pass

into the urethra and are transferred to the female by the penis. At the base of the urethra is the **prostate gland;** and just posterior to the prostate is a pair of **bulbourethral (Cowper's) glands.** The secretions from these glands are added to the sperms, making the seminal mass more fluid and neutralizing the acidity resulting from the passage of urine through the urethra.

The two **ovaries** of the female are ovoid bodies exhibiting small, rounded projections on the surface; these are the outlines of the **Graafian follicles**, each of which contains an egg or **ovum**. Each ovary lies lateral to the **ostium**, which opens into a small **oviduct**. The latter is continued posteriorly as a thick-walled **uterus**. The two uteri unite medially to form the **body of the uterus** from which the **vagina** extends to the urogenital opening. On the ventral wall of the vestibule lies a small rodlike body, the **clitoris**, which corresponds to the penis of the male. The eggs are fertilized while in the oviduct and then pass to the uterus, where development takes place.

Development

The egg is fertilized and undergoes **segmentation** in the oviduct; it then passes into the uterus, where it receives nourishment and oxygen, and disposes of wastes by way of the mother's blood circulation through a structure called the **placenta**. This is formed from the fetal membranes and united with the mucous membrane of the uterine wall. The interval between fertilization and birth, known as the **period of gestation**, is 60 days.

STRUCTURES OF OTHER MAMMALS

Hair

The hairs which distinguish mammals from all other animals (Fig. 345), unlike feathers which are modifications of horny scales, are new structural elements of the skin. However, in function the hair and feathers are similar in that both are insulating devices. When hairs are shed, new hairs

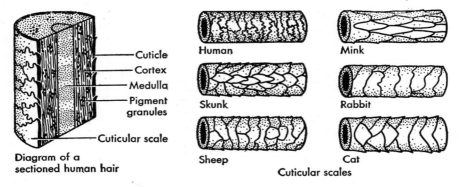

Cuticle
Cortex
Medulla
Pigment granules
Cuticular scale

Diagram of a sectioned human hair

Human
Mink
Skunk
Rabbit
Sheep
Cat
Cuticular scales

Figure 345. Structure of various mammalian hairs. The hair is a complex structure, covered with a sheath of scales, which superficially suggest shingles on a roof. The fact that many mammals can be identified from the external cuticular scales makes a knowledge of them useful in both crime detection and the fur industry.

usually arise to take their place. Secretions from the **sebaceous glands** keep the hairs glossy.

The two main types are (1) **guard hairs** which are long and strong, and (2) woolly hairs which are shorter and constitute the **underfur.** In some animals the woolly hairs have a rough surface, as in the sheep, which causes them to cohere and gives them their felting quality. Certain of the stronger hairs may be moved by muscle fibers. The muscles of the skin are responsible for the erection of spines or the bristling of the other hairs.

Scales

Scales are present on the bodies of a few mammals, notably on the pangolin (Fig.

354), and on the tails of certain rodents such as the beavers, rats, and mice.

Claws, nails, hoofs, etc.

These are all modifications of the horny covering on the dorsal surface of the distal ends of the digits (fingers and toes). The chief forms are shown in Fig. 346. When on the ground the foot rests partially or entirely upon the digital pads. Dermal papillae occur on the digital pads, often forming concentric ridges such as those that produce the fingerprints of man. The sole is softer than the nail plate.

Other epidermal horny thickenings are the **hornsheaths** of the ox and other ruminants, the **nasal horns** of the rhinoceros, and

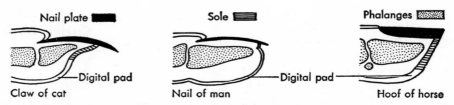

FIGURE 346. Diagrammatic longitudinal sections through the distal ends of the digits of mammals. Claws, nails, and hoofs are all modified scales. The hoof of the horse is a modified nail and essentially similar to a human fingernail. (Partly after Wiedersheim, after Gegenbaur and Boas.)

the "whalebone" (baleen) of certain whales. **Dermal plates** of bone form the exoskeleton of the armadillos (Fig. 354E).

Skin glands

Mammals possess a greater number of glands than reptiles or birds; these are for the most part sebaceous and sweat glands, or modifications of them (Fig. 211). The **sebaceous glands** usually open into the hair follicles and secrete a greasy substance which keeps the surface of the skin soft and the hair glossy. The sweat glands secrete a fluid composed chiefly of water, containing a small amount of solutes, mainly sodium chloride; this fluid evaporates, thereby cooling the skin and regulating the body temperature. In carnivores generally, sweat glands are much reduced in numbers; the panting of a dog utilizes evaporation on the tongue for the same purpose. The **lacrimal glands,** the secretions of which keep the eyeballs moist, the **scent glands** of many species, and the **mammary glands** are all modifications of skin glands.

Teeth of mammals

The teeth of mammals are of considerable value in classification and indicate also food habits. Whalebone whales, monotremes, and many edentates are without teeth in the adult stage; and in some forms, for example, the spiny anteater, they have never been found even in the embryo.

The embryologic development of mammalian teeth is like that of other vertebrates. The principal forms and the relations of their three constituents are shown in Fig. 347. The **enamel** (in black) is the outer hard substance; the **dentine** (stippled) constitutes the largest portion of the tooth; and the **cement** (dotted line) usually covers the part of the tooth embedded in the tissues of the jaw. The central **pulp cavity** of the tooth contains nerves, blood vessels, and connective tissue. A tooth has an open pulp cavity during growth, which in some cases continues throughout life.

The teeth of fishes, reptiles, and amphibians are, with some exceptions, similar, and the dentition of these animals is therefore said to be **homodont** (same). The dentition of mammals, on the other hand, is almost always **heterodont** (different); there being usually 4 kinds of teeth in each jaw: (1) the chisel-shaped cutting teeth or **incisors** (Fig. 347), (2) the conical tearing teeth or **canines,** (3) the anterior grinding teeth or **premolars,** and (4) the posterior grinding teeth or **molars.**

In most mammals the first set of teeth, known as the **milk (deciduous) dentition,** is pushed out by the permanent teeth which last throughout the life of the animal. The milk molars are followed by the premolars, but the permanent molars have no predecessors.

The relation of the form of the teeth to the food habits of the animal is quite obvious; for example, sharp conical teeth are adapted for capturing fish, large canine teeth are suitable for capturing and killing prey,

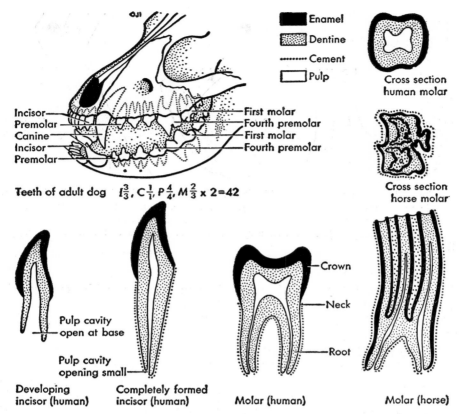

Enamel
Dentine
Cement
Pulp

Cross section
human molar

Incisor
Premolar
Canine
Incisor
Premolar

First molar
Fourth premolar
First molar
Fourth premolar

Teeth of adult dog $I\frac{3}{3}$, $C\frac{1}{1}$, $P\frac{4}{4}$, $M\frac{2}{3}$ x 2=42

Cross section
horse molar

Pulp cavity
open at base

Pulp cavity
opening small

Crown

Neck

Root

Developing
incisor (human)

Completely formed
incisor (human)

Molar (human)

Molar (horse)

FIGURE 347.   Mammalian teeth. *Above, left,* teeth of dog. The teeth of a mammal are of a definite number and are collectively referred to as the dentition. Their number is expressed as a dental formula that includes those of the upper and lower jaws of one side. The dental formula of the dog is given and multiplied by two to show the total number of teeth. *Upper and lower, right,* the structure of mammalian teeth shown diagrammatically in cross and longitudinal sections.

and large molars are useful for grinding food. Not only can the kind of life of extinct animals be determined from their teeth, but the type of contemporary plant life can be reconstructed, and some conclusions can be drawn regarding the no-longer-existing digestive organs of these animals.

Foot posture of mammals

The primitive type of foot posture is called **plantigrade**. The entire palm or sole rests on the ground, and neither the wrist nor the ankle is raised above the ground (Fig. 348). This type gave way to the **digiti-**grade posture, the animals walking upon their digits with the bones of the wrist and ankle, and the upper ends of the palms and soles raised above the ground. The third type of foot posture is the **unguligrade,** characteristic of hoofed animals. These ungulates walk on modified nails or hoofs, such as those of the horse.

Development of mammals

The eggs of most mammals develop within the body of the mother; the exceptions are the monotremes which lay eggs, thus showing their close relationship to rep-

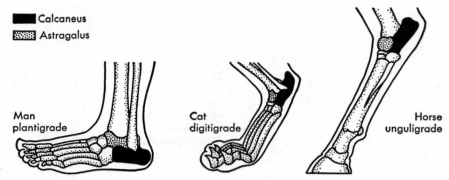

Calcaneus
Astragalus

Man
plantigrade

Cat
digitigrade

Horse
unguligrade

FIGURE 348. Feet of mammals (left hindfoot). Man, generalized, with 5 digits (toes); the entire sole rests on the ground (plantigrade). Cat, with 4 toes, heel raised; walks on digits (digitigrade). Horse, most specialized, with only 1 digit (third); walks on hoof which covers the end of his toe (unguligrade). Note that a sprinter runs on his toes to attain maximum speed on the track.

tiles. Their eggs are incubated by the female and are hatched in the same manner as those of reptiles and birds. The young of marsupials, such as the Virginia opossum (Fig. 351A), are born in a very immature condition. At birth an opossum immediately climbs by a hand-over-hand movement through its mother's hair until it reaches the pouch, where it remains attached to a nipple for about 40 days. In the nine-banded armadillo, a single egg gives rise to 4 young (Fig. 351B), a phenomenon known as **polyembryony**; this rarely occurs in man.

During their development the embryos of mammals, as well as those of birds and reptiles, produce two membranes: (1) the **amnion** and (2) the **allantois**. Because of the presence of these membranes, the mammals, birds, and reptiles are often grouped together as Amniota, while the amphibians, fishes, elasmobranchs, and cyclostomes, which do not possess these membranes, are designated as Anamniota.

The segmentation of mammals' eggs is complete (except in monotremes) and takes place either in the oviduct as in the rabbit, or in the uterus as in the sheep. Figure 349 presents photographs of stages in the segmentation of the rabbit's egg and development of the human embryo; and Fig. 350 illustrates the early development of the human embryo with embryonic membranes.

The placenta of some marsupials and all the Eutheria arises in the following manner: the young embryo becomes connected to the uterine wall by means of its outer epithelial layer, now known as the **trophoderm**. This later becomes coated wholly or in part on its inner side by somatic mesoderm and constitutes the membrane known as the serosa. Later on, the splanchnic mesoderm of the peripheral and distal part of the allantois becomes applied to the serosa, and the two structures constitute the embryonic membrane called the **chorion**. The chorion develops vascular villi which are lined with an epithelium only one cell in thickness. These thin-walled chorionic villi sink into pits eroded in the wall of the uterus. Blood from the maternal blood vessels oozes into these pits.

The connection of the chorion of the fetus with the uterine wall gives rise to the placenta, by means of which the nourishment and respiration of the fetus are provided for in the body of the mother. Although the blood of the fetus and that of the mother are not in direct communication, the membrane which separates them is so thin that substances such as gases, foodstuffs, and nitrogenous wastes pass through

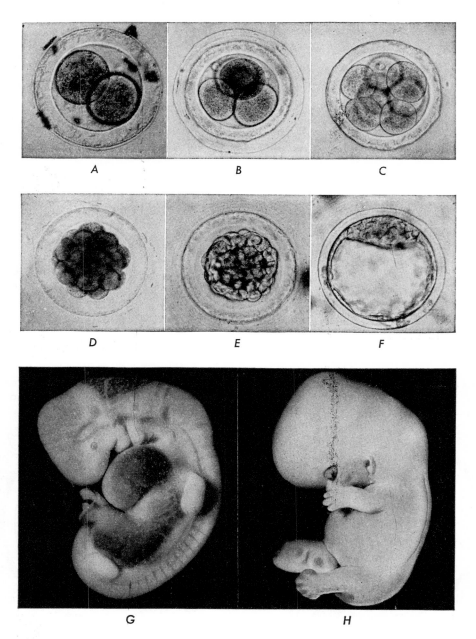

Figure 349. Photographs illustrating the development of the mammalian egg. A–F, stages in the development of the rabbit's egg. A, two-cell stage, 24 hours after fertilization; the surrounding membrane is the zona pellucida in which are embedded several sperms; the polar body lies near the upper end of the cleavage furrow. B, four-cell stage (29 hours). C, eight-cell stage (32 hours). D, morula stage (55 hours). E, trophoblast stage (71½ hours), showing the differentiation of cells into the outer trophoblast layer and the inner cell mass from which the embryo arises. F, blastocyst stage (90 hours), showing the segmentation cavity, trophoblast, embryonic disk (above), and zona pellucida with part of the albuminous coat around it. G–H, human embryos. G, one month old (6.7 mm.), showing arm and leg buds, growing at caudal end, umbilical cord, heart, branchial bars, olfactory pit, and eye. H, six weeks old (19 mm.), showing developing hands and feet, elbow and knee, nose, eye, and ear. The cranial vault appears too large for the body, due to the fact that it is a hollow vesicle. (Photos A–F by courtesy of P.W. Gregory; G–H by courtesy of Carnegie Institute of Washington, Department of Embryology.)

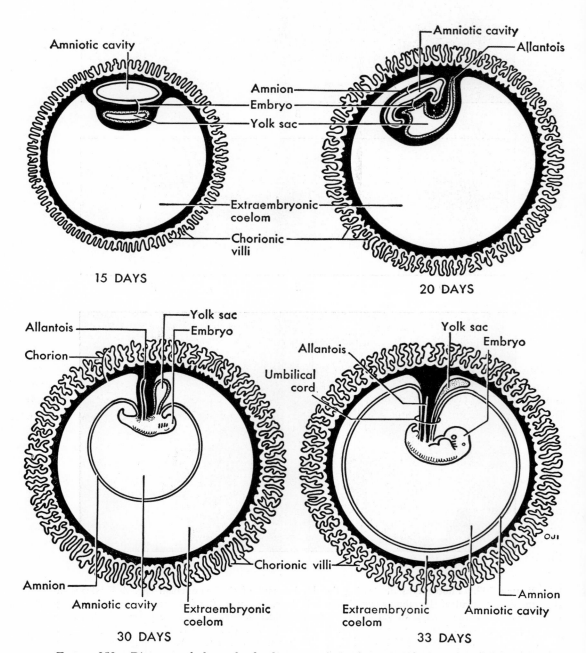

Figure 350. Diagrams of the early development of the human embryo surrounded by the protective embryonic membranes. Note the rootlike villi which grow into the wall of the uterus.

478

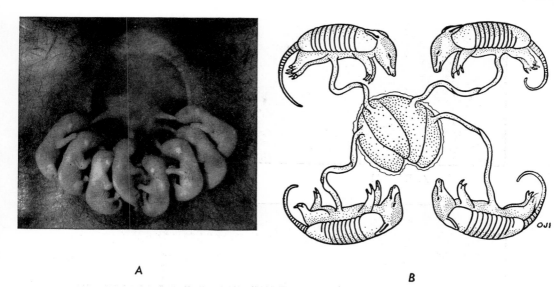

A   B

FIGURE 351. A, young American opossums attached to the mammary glands in the brood pouch of their mother. When born the young opossum is strikingly undeveloped and smaller than a honey bee. The opossum is considered the most primitive of America's mammals and is often referred to as a "living fossil." Except for its larger size, it is almost the same as its ancestor of millions of years ago. B, four fetal nine-banded armadillos that have developed from a single egg. (A copyright by General Biological Supply House, Inc., Chicago.)

it. The placenta presents great variations in the individual orders, in its special development and in the mode of its connection with the uterine walls.

Hibernation and migration

During the winter, mammals either remain active like the rabbit, or hibernate to tide them over the winter scarcity of food and cold rigorous weather. During hibernation the metabolism drops to a low level, the temperature of the body decreases, and the animal falls into a profound torpor. Respiration almost ceases, the heart beat is slowed, and no food is taken into the body; but the fat masses stored up in the autumn are consumed, and the animal awakens in the spring in an emaciated condition. Chipmunks and ground squirrels hibernate in underground nests, and some bats in caves or buildings.

Comparatively few mammals migrate. Among those that do are the fur seal, reindeer, bison, red bat, and some whales. The fur seals (Fig. 352F) that breed on the Pribilof Islands in Bering Sea spend the winter months making a circuit of about 6000 miles. The reindeer of Spitzbergen migrate regularly to the central portion of the island in summer and back to the seacoast in the autumn. Some bats and certain birds leave their northern summer habitats when food becomes scarce and migrate southward for the winter.

The lemmings of Scandinavia are celebrated for their curious mass movements. They multiply on high plateaus until the food supply is exhausted; then they swarm over the valleys in vast hordes, swimming lakes and streams, and turning aside for nothing, eating crops in their paths. Remnants of the lemming army finally reach the sea, plunge in, and perish. There are many theories to explain why the lemmings jump into the ocean and drown, but probably none is better than the one, that they attempt to swim the ocean as they have other bodies of water and fail in the too great undertaking.

A. Duckbill   B. Manatee

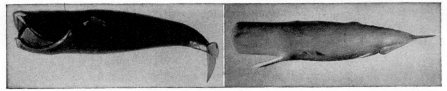

C. Whalebone Whale   D. Sperm Whale

E. Walrus   F. Fur Seal

FIGURE 352. Some interesting aquatic mammals. A, duck-billed platypus, *Ornithorhynchus anatinus*, 24 inches long, with thick fur and webbed feet. It possesses both reptilian and mammalian characteristics. B, manatee, *Trichechus*, 14 feet long. Note flipperlike forelimbs, absence of hindlimbs, and rounded tail with horizontal fin. C, whalebone whale, or right whale, *Eubalaena glacialis*, 50 to 60 feet long. Note fishlike form, finlike forelimbs, and horizontal bilobed tail. D, sperm whale or toothed whale, *Physeter catodon*, male 60 feet long. Note fishlike form, flipperlike forelimbs, absence of hindlimbs, and horizontal bilobed tail. E, walrus, *Odobenus rosmarus*, 10 feet long, 2000 to 3000 pounds. Note legs adapted for swimming, and long canine teeth (tusks). F, fur seal, *Callorhinus ursinus*, 6 feet long. Note streamlined body, webbed forefeet and hindfeet, and thick fur. (A courtesy of Pacific Discovery, photo by H.C. Reynolds; B courtesy of N.Y. Zoological Society; C, D, E, and F courtesy of American Museum of Natural History.)

OTHER MAMMALIA

Mammals differ widely from one another in their mode of life and in their adaptations to their environments. Space limitations allow us to describe only a few groups, but the references at the end of this chapter give a wealth of information on mammalian life. Note the many adaptations mentioned in your collateral readings.

Egg-laying mammals

These most primitive mammals are confined to the Australian region, that is Australia, Tasmania, and New Guinea. The young, before hatching, live on the yolk contained in the egg. After hatching, the young are for a time nourished by milk from the mother's mammary glands. The best-known species are the spiny anteater echidna (Fig. 353), and the duck-billed platypus (Fig. 352A). The platypus is a

FIGURE 353. Spiny anteater (*Echidna*). One of the egg-laying mammals. Like the duck-billed platypus, its egg shell is not limy, but leathery. The egg is incubated in a pouch where the newly hatched young are kept for a time. The echidna has numerous hard sharp quills and an underfur of coarse hair. It possesses amazing digging powers which enable it to disappear quickly. These animals are typical anteaters with a long and slender bony tongue, adapted to catching ants and other insects. Australia has a strange assortment of animal life, due largely to its geographic isolation. (Courtesy of Harold C. Reynolds.)

beaverlike animal; it is aquatic and constructs burrows. It feeds chiefly on freshwater invertebrates. The female, after laying her eggs, curls around them and remains inactive for about two weeks. At the end of this time, the young are hatched. The male has a claw on its heel which is connected with a poison gland.

Pouched mammals

Pouched mammals (marsupials) occur mainly in Australia and neighboring islands, but a few are natives of the Americas. The young are born in an embryonic condition, having no hair for protection, no eyes, and no ears, but having good olfactory organs and usually well-developed front feet. At first they live in a pouch on the abdomen, where they feed on milk by means of teats. The young of the **American opossum** (Figs. 337 and 351A) remain in the mother's external pouch until they complete their natal development. Many species of marsupials, such as kangaroos (Fig. 354) and **koalas** (Fig. 355) are distributed over the Australian region.

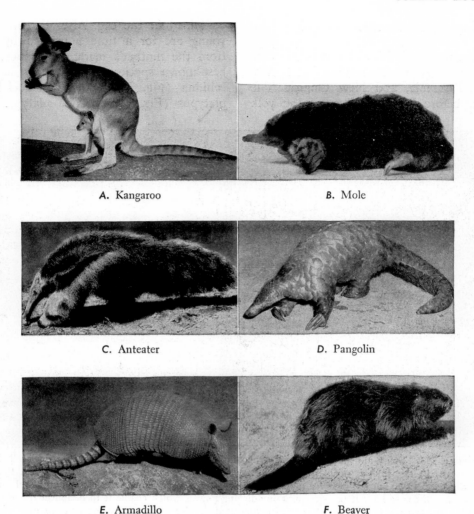

A. Kangaroo   B. Mole

C. Anteater   D. Pangolin

E. Armadillo   F. Beaver

FIGURE 354. Some mammals showing interesting adaptations. A, order Marsupialia, kangaroo, or more specifically a wallaroo, *Macropus robustus*, (4 feet long). Note young in pouch or marsupium, large hindlimbs, small forelimbs, and large tail. B, order Insectivora, mole, *Scalopus aquaticus* (6 inches long). Note forefeet adapted for digging, sensitive nose, and rudimentary eyes. C, order Edentata, giant anteater, *Myrmecophaga tridactyla* (7 feet long). Note long snout and sharp foreclaws for digging. D, order Pholidota, giant pangolin, *Manis gigantea* (3 to 5 feet long). Note large scales, long snout, and large claws for digging. E, order Edentata, nine-banded armadillo, *Dasypus novemcinctus* (12 to 15 pounds). Note bony shell, scanty hair, and long claws for digging. F, order Rodentia, beaver, *Castor canadensis* (3½ feet long). It has chisel-like teeth, webbed hindfeet, and a flat scaly tail. It builds its home in forest ponds, which it makes by building dams. (Courtesy of N.Y. Zoological Society.)

Insect-eating mammals

Insect-eating mammals are considered the most primitive of those that nourish their young before birth by means of a specialized placenta. They are entirely absent from the Australian region and from most of South America. They are nocturnal in habit and feed principally on insects which they seize with their projecting front teeth and cut into

FIGURE 355. Koala, Australian "teddy bear." Female first carries young in a pouch, then later on her back, as is shown in this photograph. Adults are about two feet long. They live in trees and feed on the leaves of the giant gum (eucalyptus) tree of this region. (Courtesy of Victorian Railways.)

pieces with the sharp-pointed cusps on their hind teeth. Most of them travel on the ground, but a number of them live in burrows, a few are aquatic, and some live in trees. **Moles** (Fig. 354B) and **shrews** are common species in this country. The shrews are of special interest for several reasons: they are the smallest mammals (some weigh less than a dime) and their metabolic rate is the highest of all animals in this group. The masked shrew is reported to breath 850 times per minute and has a pulse rate of about 800 beats. A poisonous substance in the saliva helps the shrew in the capture of mice and other prey.

The only true flying mammal

Bats possess forelimbs that are modified for flight. The forearm and fingers are elongated and connected with each other, with the hindfeet, and usually with the tail, by a thin leathery membrane. Because of their remarkable powers of locomotion, bats are very widely distributed, occurring on small islands devoid of other mammals. Most of the more than 600 species are small and chiefly nocturnal. During the day most of them seek darkened retreats such as caves, tree hollows, and houses, where they hang head downward, suspended by the claws of one or both legs. At night, bats fly about actively in search of insects. Some live on fruit, and a few suck the blood of other mammals. The **little brown bat,** which is abundant in eastern North America, appears to have a well-developed homing instinct. Experiments show that it tends to return to the same cave used as a daytime retreat.

The **true vampire bats** inhabit tropical America. They live on the blood of horses, cattle, and other warm-blooded animals, and sometimes they attack sleeping human beings. Their front teeth are very sharp, but the back teeth have practically disappeared. The skin of their victims is cut by the front teeth, and the oozing blood is lapped up. It has been proved that vampire bats in Mexico transmit paralytic rabies, a disease to which many animals, including man, are susceptible. Other diseases known or suspected to be vampire-bat-borne include yellow fever, scrub typhus, Chagas' disease, all affecting humans; and a tropical trypanosome disease of horses known as murrina.

The expression "blind as a bat" indicates a common misconception, for the bat does have eyes and appears able to see well. Nevertheless, a completely blinded bat can fly about in a room hung with crisscrossing silk threads without touching the threads. It guides itself by the echoes of supersonic sounds it makes which are thrown back from objects in its path. Thus it will be seen that long before man ever thought of radar, the bat employed this principle. It can catch its food in pitch darkness while dodging all sorts of objects.

A. Otter   B. Skunk

C.   Elephants   D.

E. Tapir   F. Pronghorn

FIGURE 356. Interesting mammals. A, order Carnivora, American otter, *Lutra canadensis*. Note broad webbed feet, and strong muscular tail. B, skunk, *Mephitis mephitis* (2 feet long). C, order Proboscidea, African elephant, *Loxodonta africana*. Note long prehensile trunk with tusks (incisor teeth), loose skin, large ears, and hollow back. D, Indian elephant, *Elephas maximus* (10 feet high at shoulder). Note smaller ears and arched back. The upper lip and nose of the elephant are drawn out into a trunk, a remarkable grasping organ. E, order Perissodactyla, tapir, *Tapirella bairdii* (3 feet high at shoulder). Note long, prehensile nose. F, order Artiodactyla, pronghorn antelope, *Antilocapra americana*. Note even number of toes, branched horns, and white rump patch. (Courtesy of N.Y. Zoological Society.)

484

FIGURE 357. Chipmunk (*Tamias*). A beautiful little rodent that lives in crevices in rocks, under logs, or in burrows in the ground. It becomes quite tame if fed and is a favorite of children and adults in some parks. (Courtesy of N.Y. Zoological Society.)

FIGURE 358. The chinchilla. These animals were introduced into the United States in 1923 by Chapman, who obtained 11 animals from Chile. Since then many chinchilla ranches have been established in the United States. Chinchilla fur has a downy softness, but it is not as serviceable as some other furs. (Courtesy of N.Y. Zoological Society.)

Toothless mammals

The toothless mammals either have no teeth or a few that are not well developed. They include sloths, anteaters, and armadillos. **Sloths** inhabit the tropical forests of Central and South America, live in the treetops, and hang to the underside of the branches by means of two or three long curved claws. The **great anteater** (Fig. 354C) has a long, narrow snout, long claws on the forefeet with which to tear open anthills, and a long, slender tongue serving to capture ants. **Armadillos** (Fig. 354E) possess armor of bony scutes; and when they are disturbed, some roll up into a ball for protection.

Gnawing mammals

Among the gnawing mammals are squirrels, beavers, rats, mice, pocket gophers, porcupines, chinchillas, and golden hamsters. Their front teeth are efficient chisels and grow constantly. The common **tree squirrels** are all excellent climbers. **Chipmunks** usually live on the ground among rocks. **Ground squirrels** are sometimes called "gophers" in northeastern states where true gophers do not occur. **Prairie dogs** of our western plains are burrowing rodents. **Woodchucks** or ground hogs also live in burrows. **Beavers** (Fig. 354F) are adapted for life in the water, possessing webbed hindfeet and a broad flat tail. Another adaptation is ear and nose valves, which close under water. The beaver can gnaw logs below the surface of water as well as above. The common **house mouse,** the **Norway rat,** and **black rat** have all been introduced into this country from the Old World. **Porcupines** (Fig. 337) possess spines, which normally lie back, but can be elevated by muscles in the skin. The **chinchillas** of South America are of medium size and noted for their very soft fur.

Omnivorous mammals

These are mammals which eat both plant and animal food; examples are common house rats, red fox, bears, raccoons, pigs, and man.

Carnivorous mammals

The flesh-eating mammals live in two types of habitats, terrestrial and aquatic. The teeth of carnivores (Fig. 347) are perhaps their most characteristic feature. The front teeth or incisors are small and of little use; the canines are very large and pointed, enabling the animal to capture, kill, and tear its prey; the premolars and the first molar in the lower jaw have sharp cutting edges; the other molars are usually broad crushing teeth; the fourth premolar of the upper jaw and the first molar of the lower jaw bite on one another like a pair of scissors and are called shearing teeth.

Wolves and **foxes** walk on their toes (digitigrade, Fig. 348). The red fox is the most common of all the foxes in America. The **arctic** or **blue fox** may become perfectly white in winter, enabling it to creep up on its prey unseen. Wolves may hunt in packs and must be controlled where they destroy great numbers of deer, calves, and sheep; they are shot and trapped whenever possible.

The cat family includes the **cat, puma** (also called mountain lion, cougar, or panther) (Fig. 366), **leopard, lion, tiger, lynx,** and **cheetah.**

Bears are all plantigrade (Fig. 348); they are large awkward-appearing animals with rudimentary tails.

The **mustelids** constitute a large family of small fur-bearing animals. About 50 species inhabit North America. The **otter** is adapted for swimming by webbed feet and a powerful tail. The **mink** is also fond of water. The **weasel** is one of the smallest of the mustelids and very bloodthirsty. The **skunk** (Fig. 356B) is notorious because of the powerful odor of a secretion which it can eject from a pair of scent glands which open into the anal canal.

The **aquatic carnivores** are greatly modified for life in the water. Both fore- and hindfeet are fully webbed and serve as swimming organs. The body has acquired a fishlike form suitable for progress through the water. They are chiefly marine, but a few inhabit fresh water or swim up rivers. The **fur seal** (Fig. 352F) breeds on the Pribilof Islands in Bering Sea, but at other times occurs along the coast of California. The **California sea lion** is often seen in captivity. Adult male walruses (Fig. 352E) may weigh over a ton; the canine teeth of the upper jaw are very long, and are used to dig up mollusks and crustaceans from the muddy bottoms and to climb up on the

blocks of ice in the Arctic seas where they live.

Whales

The whale is the largest living animal; it is adapted to life in the water. It possesses a very large head with elongated face and jaw bones; the forelimbs are modified as paddles (flippers), and there is no external trace of hindlimbs; the tail is flattened horizontally and forms two lobes, the "flukes"; the eyes are small; and there is no external ear. In the sperm whale the nostrils form a single opening; and the warm moist air which is forced from it condenses in the cold atmosphere, appearing like a spout of water. Only a few hairs are present about the mouth. Beneath the skin is a thick layer of fat or blubber, which takes the place of the insulating hair of most mammals. The teeth on the lower jaw of the sperm whales are numerous and conical in shape; in whalebone whales there are no teeth, but there are numerous parallel horny plates of whalebone on the sides of the upper jaw.

The **sperm whale** (Fig. 352D) reaches a length of 75 feet and is the largest toothed whale. Moby Dick was a sperm whale, and, according to the novel and the movie by that name, one of enormous size. In the large head is a cavity filled with as much as a ton of fine oil (sperm oil). Other species of toothed whales are the common **dolphin,** the **narwhal,** the **killer whale** (Fig. 337), and the common **porpoise.**

The **sulfur-bottom,** a whalebone whale, inhabits the Pacific from California to Central America. The **blue whale** (Fig. 359) is the longest of all whales and the largest animal in the history of the world. It reaches a length of 105 feet and a weight of about 125 tons. It summers near polar ice packs of both poles, but winters in temperate waters. Other species of whalebone whales are the **gray whale,** the **humpback whale,** and the common **rorqual.** Some whales may

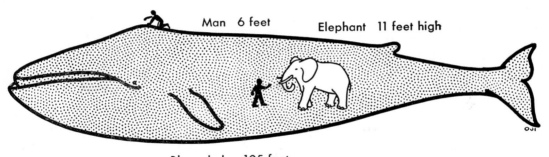

Man 6 feet   Elephant 11 feet high

Blue whale   105 feet

FIGURE 359.   Relative size of a blue whale, the largest living animal, and an African elephant.

disappear from the sea, unless protected by law, because modern ships go out to hunt these animals, equipped with airplanes, radar, whale guns, and other refined apparatus.

Sea cows

Sea cows differ considerably in structure from whales. Their bones are heavy, enabling them to remain on the bottom; the teeth are broad and crushing; the lips are large and movable and are used to seize seaweeds and other water plants upon which they feed; the forelimbs are flexible flippers; and the tail is rounded and not notched as in whales. The **Florida manatee** (Fig. 352B), is a genus of "sea cow." The sea cows and manatees probably account for some of the tales of the so-called mermaids.

Elephants

Elephants are the largest land animals, weighing as much as 14,640 pounds. The two species of living elephants are the **Asiatic elephant** (Fig. 356D), and the **African elephant** (Fig. 356C). Both species are covered by a thick loose skin with a thin coat of hair; they have long, muscular proboscises (trunks) with nasal openings at the tips; they are provided with tusks which are elongated incisors; they possess small eyes, small tails, and enormous ears, and are without canine teeth. The skull is massive,

due to thick bones containing air spaces; and the grinding teeth are very large and possess complicated ridges.

Hoofed mammals

Hoofed mammals are divided into those with an odd number of toes and those with an even number of toes. **Horses, tapirs,** and **rhinoceroses** have an **odd number** of **hoofed toes,** the axis of symmetry passing through the third digit. None is native to the United States, but many remains of extinct species have been found in this country. The **tapirs** occur in Central and South America, and in Sumatra, Java, and the Malay Peninsula. The American tapirs have long, prehensile noses (Fig. 356E).

The majority of the **big game animals** belong to the **even-toed hoofed mammals.** The axis of symmetry passes between digits 3 and 4. Here belong the **peccaries, pigs, hippopotami, camels, llamas, hollow-horned ruminants, pronghorn antelopes** (Fig. 356-F), **giraffes,** and **deer.** The term **ruminant** has been given to the animals belonging to the camel, deer, giraffe, pronghorn antelope, and ox families, since they ruminate or chew their cud. The food of these animals is swallowed without sufficient mastication; it is later regurgitated in small quantities and thoroughly chewed. A typical ruminant possesses a stomach consisting of 4 chambers (Fig. 360).

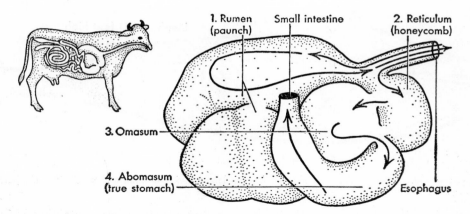

1. Rumen (paunch) Small intestine 2. Reticulum (honeycomb)

3. Omasum

4. Abomasum (true stomach)

Esophagus

FIGURE 360. A 4-compartment stomach of a ruminant animal (cow). The arrows show the course of roughage such as hay. Grains such as corn go directly to the reticulum. This type of stomach permits the animal to consume large amounts of grass; after which it seeks a place safe from its enemies, where it can rechew its food. (After *Anatomy of the Domestic Animals,* by Sisson and Grossman. Copyright 1938 by W.B. Saunders Company.)

Primates

Primates are of special interest because the order includes man. Primates inhabit chiefly the warm parts of the world. Most are arboreal in habit and are able to climb about among the trees because the great toe and thumb are opposable to the other digits, adapting the hands and feet for grasping. A few primates lead a solitary life, but most of them go about in troops. Fruits, seeds, insects, eggs, and birds are the principal articles of food. One young is usually produced at a birth; it is cared for with great solicitude. Eleven families of living Primates are recognized, and some interesting representatives of these are described here.

The **lemurs** are of small or moderate size and usually possess a long nonprehensile tail. They are mostly confined to Madagascar and neighboring islands. Their food is mostly plants and small animals.

The **aye-aye** is found in Madagascar; it is one of the most remarkable of the lemurs and is about the size of a cat. Its toes are long and end in pointed claws.

Tarsiers live in the Philippines and adjacent islands. They are about the size of

FIGURE 361. Rhesus monkey. (*Macaca mulatta,* formerly *M. rhesus.*) Its humanlike behavior always attracts a crowd at the "zoo." The rhesus (Rh) factor, which is found in about 86 per cent of the white population in the United States, was first found in this monkey. (Courtesy of N.Y. Zoological Society.)

rats and have large eyes and rounded pads at the ends of their toes.

The **marmosets** are little primates ranging from Central America to Brazil. They are about the size of small squirrels; the body is covered with soft fur. The great toe has a flat nail, but the other digits bear claws.

The **typical South American monkey** (Fig. 363A) is of small or medium size; the thumb, as well as the great toe, is opposable; all digits possess nails; the tail is usually long and prehensile, aiding in climbing; the space between the nostril openings is wide; there is no vermiform appendix. They are known as **night monkeys, titis, squirrel monkeys, sakis, howlers, capuchins,** and **woolly** and **spider monkeys.**

The **Old World monkeys** (Fig. 363B) usually possess long tails, which are never prehensile; their buttocks are provided with thick patches of callous skin on which they rest in a sitting posture; the nostrils are

Figure 362. Gibbon. It is the smallest of the apes and the only one that habitually walks erect like man. It is a tree dweller with very long arms, legs, hands, and feet; sometimes called the acrobat of mammals. (Courtesy of N.Y. Zoological Society.)

separated by a narrow space; and some have cheek pouches. Many species live in Asia and Africa, including the **baboons, macaques,** and **langurs.**

The **anthropoid apes** (Pongidae) are the primates most nearly related to man. Like man they have a vermiform appendix. The tail is absent; the forelimbs are longer than the legs; locomotion is often bipedal, and when the ape is walking, the feet tend to turn in; and the knuckles help preserve equilibrium. There are 4 genera in the family: (1) *Hylobates* or gibbons (Fig. 362), (2) *Simia* (formerly *Pongo*) or orang-utans, (3) *Gorilla* or gorillas (Fig. 363C), and (4) *Pan* or chimpanzees (Fig. 363D).

Gibbons (Fig. 362) are arboreal; they have slender bodies and limbs, are omnivorous, reach a height of not over three feet, and when walking, they are not assisted by the hands. There are more than a dozen species inhabiting southeastern Asia and the East Indies.

There is one or probably two species of **orang-utans** confined to Borneo and Sumatra. They live principally in the treetops, where they construct a sort of nest for themselves. Orang-utans are herbivorous. They are about 4½ feet in height; when walking, they use their knuckles as well as their feet. The brain of this species is more nearly like that of man than of any other animal.

The **gorilla,** *Gorilla gorilla* (Fig. 363C), inhabits the forests of western Africa. It is arboreal, feeds mainly on vegetation, has large canine teeth, reaches a height of 5½ feet and a weight of about 500 pounds, walks on the soles of its feet, aided by the backs of the hands, and is ferocious and untamable. The lowland gorilla is blackish-brown in color; the mountain gorilla (*Gorilla gorilla beringeri*) is black.

The **chimpanzee,** *Pan troglodytes* (Fig. 363D), also lives in West Africa. It resembles the gorilla, but has shorter arms and a smoother, rounder skull. In many respects the chimpanzee is more nearly like man than any other living mammal. It is easily tamed when young.

The family Hominidae contains the single living species *Homo sapiens* or **man.** Man differs from the other primates in the size of the brain, which is about twice as large

A. Spider Monkey

B. Barbary Ape

C. Gorilla

D. Chimpanzee

FIGURE 363. Primates. A, spider monkey, *Ateles ater*, a New World (South American) species. It has a prehensile tail which functions as a fifth appendage and a great toe and thumb opposable to other digits. B, barbary ape, *Macaca sylvana*, an Old World monkey. C, gorilla, *Gorilla gorilla*, (5½ feet long, weight 500 pounds). It is the largest and possibly the most intelligent of the great apes. D, chimpanzee, *Pan troglodytes*. It has large ears, long lips, and nails on fingers and toes. (Courtesy of N.Y. Zoological Society.)

as that of the highest ape, and in his erect bipedal locomotion. The hairy covering is not well developed, and the great toe is not opposable. The mental development of man has enabled him to accommodate himself to every climate and to dominate all other animals.

Domesticated mammals

The most common domesticated mammals are the dog, horse, ass, camel, cattle, sheep, llama, goat, pig, rabbit, and cat. Dogs have become changed under domestication, until there are now more than 200 breeds. The immediate ancestors of the horse are not known, but the more remote are well known (see Chap. 36). The ass is descended from the African wild ass, *Equus asinus*. The Arabian camel is thought to have originated from wild stock in Mongolia. The cattle of Europe and America were probably derived from the aurochs, *Bos primigenius*, of Europe.

Sheep have probably arisen from wild sheep of the genus *Ovis*. Goats have been domesticated since the earliest times, and their wild relatives are abundant in many parts of the world. Our domesticated pigs are descended from the wild boar, *Sus scrofa*, of Europe. The remote ancestor of the common house cat was probably the African wildcat *Felis libica*.

Fossil mammals

Many of the orders of mammals are known only from fossil forms. The earliest known remains are of small species. In Cretaceous times the evolution of the existing orders of placental mammals took place. The Cenozoic Era is called the "Age of Mammals," since this interval of about 60 million years between the Mesozoic Era and the present time witnessed the ascendency of mammals and the inauguration of their dominance over all other animals.

Among the fossil mammals found in North America are: (1) the archaic ungulate, *Uintatherium* (Fig. 364), which was almost as large as the largest existing elephants and possessed three pairs of conspicuous protuberances upon the dorsal surface of its head; (2) the enormous tortoise armadillo, *Glyptodon* (Fig. 364), which was almost 9 feet in length and was provided with an arched shell of immovable bony plates; and (3) the mastodon (Fig. 364) of Europe, Asia, and South Africa, as well as of North America, which resembled our modern elephants in size and shape, and of which more than 30 species have been distinguished.

COMPARATIVE LIFE SPAN OF ANIMALS *

How long does a certain mammal live is a frequent question and one about which too little is known. Under natural conditions animals rarely live their maximum potential age because of high death rates due to disease, predators, and other factors. The most reliable information about the life span of animals comes from zoological parks where accurate records are kept and animals live under conditions that permit them to reach more nearly their maximum age. For example, a mouse, which may live only a few months in the wilds, can survive years in captivity.

The following examples of extreme old age of animals, from insects to mammals, were chosen from reliable records of zoological parks and aquaria all over the world.

MAMMALS	YEARS
Elephant	69
Horse	50
Hippopotamus	49
Chimpanzee	40
Grizzly bear	32
Bison	30
Lion	30

* The comparative tables of the life span of animals is reproduced by permission from *Iowa Conservationist*, 16:133 (1957) and was prepared by D.H. Thompson and R. Mann.

Glyptodon, an armadillolike species

Mastodon

Uintatherium, a 7-foot tall species living in Wyoming during the Upper Eocene

FIGURE 364. Reconstructed fossil mammals that once lived in North America.

Tiger	25
Elk	22
Mountain lion	20
Beaver	19
Wolf	16
Squirrel	16
Chipmunk	12
Cottontail	10
House mouse	4

BIRDS	YEARS
Turkey buzzard	118
Swan	102
Parrot	80
Great horned owl	68
Eagle	55
English sparrow	23
Canary	22
Hummingbird	8

REPTILES	YEARS
Giant tortoise	152
Box turtle	123
Alligator	68
Snapping turtle	57
Cobra	28
Cottonmouth	21

AMPHIBIANS	YEARS
Giant salamander	55
Toad	36
Bullfrog	30
Mud puppy	23
Green frog	10
Newt	7

FISH	YEARS
Catfish	60
Eel	55
Carp	47
Mosquito fish	2

INSECTS	YEARS
Cicada	17
Ant (queen)	15

RELATIONS OF MAMMALIA TO MAN

The relations of mammals to man are so varied and complex that only a very general account can be given here. In the first place, domestic mammals are of almost inestimable value to man. They serve as beasts of burden; they are used as food; and their hides are used for clothing. Musk is obtained from the glands of certain mammals, ivory from the tusks of elephants and walruses, oil from the fat of whales; ambergris,

a product of the intestine that is used in the manufacture of perfumes, is also obtained from whales. The largest chunk of ambergris found was a 900-pound mass off the coast of New Zealand. It brought approximately $400,000 to the finder. Some of the more important game mammals of North America are the moose, wapiti, deer, bears, mountain lions, foxes, wildcats, squirrels, and rabbits. Some of these are exceedingly destructive; others, like the deer, are of considerable value as food. The various states protect many of the game animals during certain seasons of the year, and in some cases for a period of years, to prevent their extermination.

FIGURE 365. Grizzly bear. One of America's fiercest and most dangerous big game animals. (Courtesy of N.Y. Zoological Society.)

The majority of the species of fur-bearing animals of North America are carnivores. This group includes the otter, mink, weasel, marten, wolverine, and badger. Most of these animals are now scarce, and furriers are forced to use the skins of other species, such as the skunk, muskrat, raccoon, fox, lynx, black bear, and rabbit. Natural furs now compete with man-made acrylic fibers in coats designed to appear like mink and other furs. The annual production of raw furs in the United States reaches a value of many millions of dollars. The muskrat is the leading fur-producing animal in the United States, and it brings the greatest financial return of any single fur-bearing animal. In certain states where marshland is managed for the maximum production of muskrats, the profit per acre is as much as on surrounding farmland. Fox and mink farming has developed into a fairly large and profitable industry. Black and silver foxes are color phases, or inherited variations of the red fox. New color mutations of the red fox which are being ranch-bred include platinum, pearl, and white face. Some of the newer mutant furs have scarcity value and sell for high prices.

FIGURE 366. Mountain lion, *Felis concolor,* a large predatory mammal; it kills calves, deer, and other large animals. (Courtesy of N.Y. Zoological Society.)

Many, many mutations have occurred in the mink to produce new fur colors. Some of these are very beautiful and have a scarcity value.

The rat is the worst mammalian pest known to man. The damage it does throughout the world results in losses amounting to hundreds of millions of dollars annually. But these losses, great as they are, are of less importance than the fact that rats carry from house to house and from seaport to seaport the germs of the terrible bubonic plague or "black death."

Predatory mammals feed upon the flesh of other animals; if these animals preyed upon are beneficial to man, the predatory mammal may be considered injurious, but if the animals preyed upon are harmful to man, the predatory mammal is beneficial. The harmful predatory mammals include the

wolves and cougars, which subsist largely upon big game, sheep, cattle, and horses; and the house cat, which destroys millions of birds in this country annually. Other predatory mammals are occasionally harmful, but usually beneficial.

FIGURE 367. Ocelot, *Felis pardalis.* This beautifully colored cat is an inhabitant of Texas and tropical America. (Courtesy of N.Y. Zoological Society.)

There is great danger in introducing a new kind of mammal into this country. The brown rat reached this country about 1775 and is now one of the worst mammalian pests. Rabbits, which were introduced into Australia about 1788, soon became so numerous that legislative action was taken for their destruction. By the middle of the nineteenth century, rabbits were a menace to sheep raising. In 1907, a one-thousand-mile fence was built from north to south, all the way across the continent, to stop them from invading western Australia. The mongoose of India destroys rats, lizards, and snakes; it was introduced into Jamaica and other tropical islands, and at first proved very beneficial, but later it became a great pest, destroying poultry, birds, young domesticated animals, and even fruit. These disastrous results led Congress to prohibit importation of most birds and mammals, unless special permission is obtained from the government.

FIGURE 368. Timber wolf (*Canis*). A cousin to the dog, and of high intelligence. It is now becoming scarce in some places where it was once abundant. (Courtesy of N.Y. Zoological Society.)

A BRIEF CLASSIFICATION OF LIVING MAMMALIA

(For reference purposes only)

Class Mammalia. Mammals or "animals" are warm-blooded; possess hair at some stage of existence; and have mammary glands in the female, which secrete milk to nourish the young. Approximately 5000 species.

Subclass 1. Prototheria. Egg-laying mammals. They are confined to Australia, Tasmania, and New Guinea. The two oviducts open directly into a cloaca along with the intestine and urethra, as in birds and reptiles; in certain respects the skeleton agrees with that of the reptiles.

Order 1. Monotremata. Monotremes. Exs. *Ornithorhynchus anatinus*, duck-billed platypus (Fig. 352A); *Tachyglossus*, spiny anteater (Figs. 337 and 353).

Subclass 2. Theria. Mammals bearing the young alive.

Infraclass 1. Metatheria. The young are born in a very immature condition and are carried in a marsupium or pouch; usually no placenta.

Order 1. Marsupialia. Marsupials. They possess abdominal pouches or marsupia in which they carry their immature young. Exs. *Didelphis marsupialis*, American opossum; *Phascolarctus*, koala (Fig. 355).

Infraclass 2. Eutheria. Mammals with an efficient placenta attached to wall of uterus. The young are born in an advanced stage.

Order 1. Insectivora. Insectivores. Moles, shrews (Fig. 337) etc.

Order 2. Dermoptera. "Flying lemurs." Ex. *Galeopithecus volans*, flying lemurs (Fig. 337).

Order 3. Chiroptera. Bats (Fig. 337). Ex. *Myotis lucifugus*, little brown bat, flying mammals.

Order 4. Primates.* An arboreal offshoot of the primitive placental stock. Ex. Baboon (Fig. 337).

Suborder 1. Lemuroidea. Lemurs. Ex. *Lemur varius*.

Suborder 2. Tarsioidea. Tarsiers. Transitional between lemurs and monkeys. Ex. *Tarsius spectrum*.

Suborder 3. Anthropoidea. Monkeys, apes, and man. Ex. *Homo sapiens*. Mam-

---

* The position of the primates in the midst of the mammalian series instead of at the end, where they are sometimes placed, may seem strange to students, but man, the apes, and other mammals belonging to this group retain a larger number of primitive characters than do the orders that are placed below them in this classification. The primates excel principally in the development of the nervous system, but are comparatively primitive when the bones, muscles, teeth, and other organs are taken into account.

mary glands always in pectoral region.

Order 5. Carnivora. Carnivores. The flesh-eating mammals. Ex. *Mephitis mephitis*, skunk (Fig. 356B) and hyena (Fig. 337).

Order 6. Hyracoidea. Hyraxes of Africa and Asia Minor; rabbitlike habits, but actually ungulates. Ex. *Hydrax abyssinicus* (Fig. 337).

Order 7. Proboscidea. Elephants and fossil relatives, mammoths and mastodons. Ex. *Elephas maximus*, Indian elephant (Fig. 356).

Order 8. Sirenia. Sea cows. Ex. *Trichechus manatus*, manatee (Fig. 352B).

Order 9. Perissodactyla. Odd-toed hoofed mammals. Ex. *Tapirella bairdii*, Baird's tapir (Fig. 356E), and zebra (Fig. 337).

Order 10. Artiodactyla. Even-toed hoofed mammals. Ex. *Antilocapra americana*, pronghorn antelope (Fig. 356F), and hippopotamus (Fig. 337).

Order 11. Edentata. Sloths and armadillos. Ex. *Dasypus novemcinctus*, 9-banded armadillo (Fig. 337), southern Texas.

Order 12. Pholidota. Scaly anteaters. Ex. *Manis*, pangolin (Fig. 337), Africa and southeastern Asia.

Order 13. Tubulidentata. Aardvarks (Fig. 337). Ex. *Orycteropus*, an anteater, but not related to the previous order. These animals are confined to Africa.

Order 14. Cetacea. Whales, dolphins, and porpoises.

Suborder 1. Odontoceti. Toothed whales. Ex. *Physeter catodon*, sperm whale (Fig. 352D).

Suborder 2. Mysticeti. Whalebone whales. Ex. *Eubalaena glacialis*, right whale (Fig. 352C).

Order 15. Rodentia. Gnawing animals (except rabbit group). Ex. *Castor canadensis*, beaver (Fig. 354F).

Order 16. Lagomorpha. Hares, rabbits (Fig. 337) and pikas (conies). Ex. *Lepus californicus*, jack rabbit.

SELECTED COLLATERAL READINGS

Beddard, F.E. "Mammalia." *Cambridge Natural History*, Vol. 10. Macmillan, London, 1902.

Bourlière, F. *Mammals of the World; Their Life and Habits.* Knopf, New York, 1955.

Burt, W.H., and Grossenheider, R.P. *A Field Guide to the Mammals.* Houghton Mifflin, Boston, 1952.

Cahalane, V.H. *Mammals of North America.* Macmillan, New York, 1947.

Flower, W.H., and Lydekker, R. *An Introduction to the Study of Mammals Living and Extinct.* Black, London, 1891.

Hamilton, W.J., Jr. *American Mammals; Their Lives, Habits, and Economic Relations.* McGraw-Hill, New York, 1939.

Henderson, J., and Craig, E.L. *Economic Mammalogy.* Thomas, Springfield, Ill., 1932.

J. of Mammalogy. Quarterly journal published since 1919 by the American Society of Mammalogists.

Leach, W.J. *Functional Anatomy of the Mammal.* McGraw-Hill, New York, 1946.

Miller, G.S., and Kellogg, R. *List of North American Recent Mammals.* Bull. 205, U.S. National Museum, Washington, 1955.

Mochi U., and Carter, T.D. *Hoofed Mammals of the World.* Scribner's, New York, 1953.

Palmer, R.J. *The Mammal Guide.* Doubleday, New York, 1954.

Reighard, J., and Jennings, H.S. *Anatomy of the Cat.* Holt, New York, 1935.

Romer, A.S. *The Vertebrate Body*. Saunders, Philadelphia, 1949.

Seton, E.T. *Lives of Game Animals*, 4 vols. Doubleday, Doran, New York, 1925–1928.

Simpson, G.G. *The Principles of Classification and a Classification of Mammals*. American Museum of Natural History, New York, 1945.

Troughton, E. *Furred Animals of Australia*. Scribner's, New York, 1947.

Young, J.Z. *The Life of Mammals*. Oxford Univ. Press, New York, 1957.

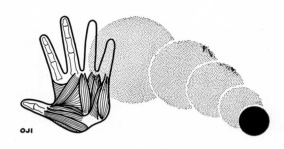

CHAPTER 31

Skeletal Systems
and Movement

THE advantages of having a skeleton were made evident by our study of the animals that do not have one. The jellyfish can float and swim in the sea, but on land it is helpless. All vertebrates, such as fishes, birds, and man, have skeletons. Imagine man without a skeleton—he could not build the sky-scrapers, the bridges, or the jets that enable him to fly faster than the birds—he would be a mass of tissue with little form and strength. The skeletal structures determine the form of an animal. They serve three purposes: (1) to provide a support or framework for the softer parts of the body, (2) to protect the soft parts, and (3) to supply a firm surface for muscle attachment.

Types of skeletal structure

In general we may recognize two types of skeletons: (1) **exoskeletons** that are built up on the outside of the body and to whose inner surface muscles are attached and (2) **endoskeletons** that are built up inside of the body, are surrounded by soft tissues, and have muscles attached to their outer surface. Besides these, there are many skeletal structures, especially among the lower invertebrates, that furnish support and protection but consist of more or less isolated parts that are not joined together into a unified whole.

Motion and locomotion do not depend much on the presence of skeletal structures in the lower invertebrates; but in the rest of the animal kingdom, movements of animals require either an exoskeleton or an endoskeleton for the attachment of muscles.

Protection and support

Protection and support are secured among the lower invertebrates in various ways. **Protozoa** may secrete a shell, such as that of *Arcella* (Fig. 17), or they may build up a shell of tiny grains of sand held together by a secretion, such as that of *Difflugia* (Fig. 17). The protection these shells provide en-

498

ables such organisms to survive under conditions that would destroy the naked types such as amoebas; but as far as one can observe these naked protozoans are just as widespread and abundant as those with shells. Many other protozoans secrete internal skeletons of calcium carbonate or silicon, which serve mainly to support the soft bodies. Calcium carbonate shells make up the globigerina ooze, and silicon shells make up the radiolarian ooze that covers so much of the sea bottom. The **coral polyp** secretes a supporting skeleton of calcium carbonate, into which it can contract and thereby secure protection. The spicules and spongin of sponges effectively prevent the collapsing of a body that would otherwise be nothing but a jellylike mass; in fact, massive sponges could never have evolved without the support of skeletal structures.

Exoskeletons

Exoskeletons are characteristic of the arthropods, but many lower invertebrates secrete a **cuticle** which similarly serves to protect the softer parts beneath. In many **Protozoa** the pellicle also aids in maintaining the shape of the body. The soft body of many colonial **coelenterates** such as *Obelia* is supported and protected by a chitinous tube called the perisarc. The exoskeleton of an **arthropod** consists of a substance called chitin. Chitin is secreted by the outer layer of the body wall and is made hard by nonchitinous substances such as calcium carbonate in the crayfish. What amounts to an exoskeleton is present in certain **vertebrates**, such as the bony carapace and plastron of the turtle covered by epidermal plates, the bony shell of the armadillo, the epidermal scales of the scaly anteater, the scales of fish and reptiles, the feathers of birds, and the hairs of mammals.

The chitinous exoskeleton of an arthropod, such as that of the crayfish and of the grasshopper, no doubt protects the animal from certain enemies, but many amphibians, reptiles, birds, and mammals feed on practically no other types of animals. Such a skeleton, however, serves for the attachment of muscles and makes locomotion possible. The arthropod skeleton covers the entire body, but it is very thin at certain points, thus enabling the animal to move parts of the body and the appendages.

Movements without a skeleton

Movement in the lower invertebrates is usually accomplished without the assistance of a skeleton. Thus amoebas use pseudopodia for this purpose; the flagellates, flagella; and the ciliates, cilia. Many **protozoans** possess **contractile** fibrils called myonemes, which are of particular value in contracting the body; the nature of the contraction is probably similar to that of true muscles. The larvae of sponges are flagellated and free-swimming, but the adults are attached and incapable of moving from place to place. Openings, however, such as the osculum and certain pores can be closed by muscle cells, the myocytes, which form a ring around them. The epitheliomuscular cells of the coelenterates are generally considered to be the most primitive type of muscle cells. Also we encounter in coelenterates, for the first time, what may be considered a muscular system. In sponges the myocytes are localized groups of cells; whereas in the coelenterates, cells in the epidermis contain longitudinal muscle fibers; and those in the gastrodermis contain circular muscle fibers. The longitudinal fibers bring about contraction of the entire body and the bending of the body and tentacles; the circular fibers by their contractions extend the body or tentacles and are responsible for the peristaltic waves that occur when food is swallowed.

Three sets of muscle fibers are present in **planarians** and many other flatworms: (1) an outer circular layer, (2) an internal longitudinal layer, and (3) dorsoventral fibers

(Fig. 70). These muscle fibers, like those in higher animals, are mesodermal in origin. The body wall of an annelid is very muscular, containing an outer circular layer and an inner longitudinal layer (Fig. 92). Special muscles are present for moving the setae, and in the polychaetes, for moving the parapodia as well. The setae are chitinous skeletal structures that aid in locomotion. Leeches and certain other parasitic types, such as trematodes, are provided with muscular sucking disks that are used for attachment and for purposes of locomotion.

In many **mollusks,** locomotion is due to the activity of muscles in the foot. In the bivalves the shell may be closed by transverse adductor muscles. The tube feet of **echinoderms** are highly specialized locomotor organs, which are extended by a fluid driven into them by the contraction of circular muscles in the walls of the ampullae, inside the shell, and contracted by longitudinal muscles in their own walls.

Movements with an exoskeleton

In **arthropods** with an exoskeleton, circular and longitudinal muscles such as occur in annelids are replaced by special muscles which extend from one segment of the body to another, or between the joints of the appendages, and are fastened to the inside of the shell. In the crayfish, sudden contractions of the powerful flexor abdominal muscles bend the abdomen forward and drive the body backward. Crayfishes are able to walk in any direction by means of muscles within the legs that act much like those in the legs of insects. In the **grasshopper** and in most other insects, wings as well as legs serve as locomotor organs. Wings may be raised by contraction of tergosternal muscles and lowered by contraction of dorsolongitudinal muscles, as shown in Fig. 135. The rate of wing beat may be as low as 9 strokes per second in butterflies and as high as 330 strokes per second in the house fly.

INTERNAL SKELETONS OF VERTEBRATES

Skeletons of aquatic vertebrates

The vertebrate skeleton gives support and protection to the body and furnishes a firm surface for muscle attachment. Aquatic vertebrates differ from terrestrial vertebrates in the character of both the axial and appendicular sections of the skeleton. Since they are held up by water, aquatic vertebrates neither need nor possess the sturdy type of skeleton required in land animals for holding the body above the ground. The appendages of fish are paired pectoral and pelvic fins, which contain weak skeletal structures (Fig. 254); they serve primarily for balancing and steering rather than for locomotion. Other types of vertebrates such as frogs, salamanders, turtles, alligators, penguins, herons, whales, and seals have skeletons variously adapted to an aquatic existence.

Human skeleton

In general the **skeleton of man** resembles that of the frog and has similar functions. Some of the principal bones are labeled in Fig. 369; the parts of the skull are shown in Fig. 370, and of a vertebra in Fig. 371. The **cranium** consists of 8 bones: **occipital, parietal** (2), **frontal, temporal** (2), **ethmoid,** and **sphenoid.** The 14 bones of the face are the **nasal** (2), **vomer, inferior nasal conchae** (inferior turbinate) (2), **lacrimal** (2), **zygomatic** (2), **palatine** (2), **maxilla** (2), and **mandible.** In each **ear** are 3 bones, the **malleus, incus,** and **stapes;** and in the **neck** a single **hyoid bone.** The **vertebral column** averages about 28 inches long; it consists of approximately 33 bones, but in adults 5 are fused to form the **sacrum,** and 4 to form the **coccyx.*** The sacrum and coc-

---

* The number of coccygeal bones varies from 3 to 5. They represent bony remnants of the tail of lower animals.

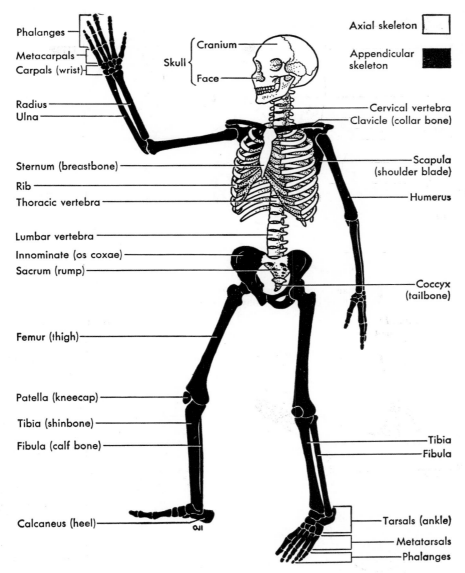

Axial skeleton

Appendicular skeleton

Phalanges
Metacarpals
Carpals (wrist)
Radius
Ulna
Sternum (breastbone)
Rib
Thoracic vertebra
Lumbar vertebra
Innominate (os coxae)
Sacrum (rump)
Femur (thigh)
Patella (kneecap)
Tibia (shinbone)
Fibula (calf bone)
Calcaneus (heel)

Skull { Cranium
Face

Cervical vertebra
Clavicle (collar bone)
Scapula (shoulder blade)
Humerus
Coccyx (tailbone)
Tibia
Fibula
Tarsals (ankle)
Metatarsals
Phalanges

FIGURE 369. The skeleton of man. The sex of an individual can be determined from the skeleton, also the approximate age of the person at death.

cyx in the female are less curved and pointed more backward than in the male. This is an adaptation for childbirth. The other vertebrae are the **cervical** (7) in the neck, the **thoracic** (12) in the thorax, and the **lumbar** (5) in the loins; these move freely on one another. The neural arch encloses the spinal cord.

In man the **thorax** is a bony cage consisting of the **sternum, costal cartilages,** and 12 pairs of **ribs.** The first 7 pairs of ribs are attached to the sternum by costal cartilages and are called **true ribs;** the next 3 pairs are attached to the costal cartilages of the ribs just above them and are known as **false ribs;** and the last 2 pairs are free in front and

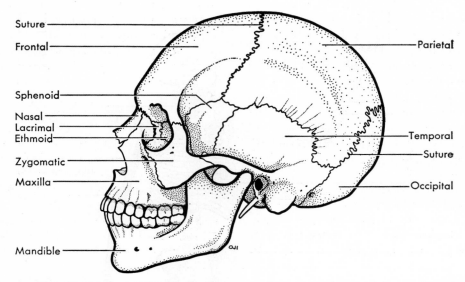

FIGURE 370. Skull of man. Note the distinct sutures between the bones of the cranium; these sutures close and are nearly or completely obliterated in old age.

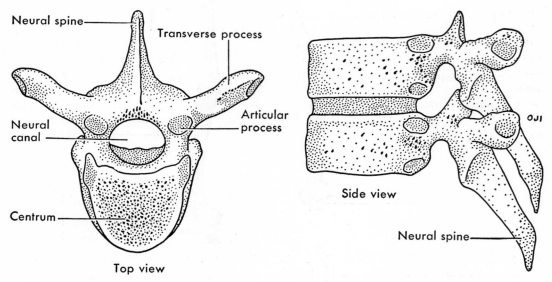

FIGURE 371. Vertebrae of man. Their structure makes possible a flexible vertebral column. Movements can be made forward, backward, and sidewise.

hence called **floating ribs.** Some individuals have an extra rib which is called a gorilla rib because it represents the normal condition in gorillas and chimpanzees.

The bones of the **appendicular skeleton** are those of the **shoulder (pectoral) girdle** (4), **pelvic girdle** (2), **upper limbs** (60), and **lower limbs** (60). The **shoulder girdle** consists of 2 **clavicles** and 2 **scapulae.** The bones in each arm are the **humerus, ulna, radius, carpals** (8), **metacarpals** (5), and **phalanges** (14).

Each side of the **pelvic girdle** is made up of 3 bones, the **ilium, ischium** and **pubis,** united into a single **innominate (os coxae) bone.** The bones in each leg are the **femur, patella, tibia, fibula, tarsals** (7), **metatarsals** (5), and **phalanges** (14). The total number of bones in the adult human skeleton is 206, consisting of the cranium (8), face (14), ears (6), neck (1), vertebrae (26), ribs (24), sternum (1), shoulder girdle (4), pelvic girdle (2), upper limbs (60), and lower limbs (60).

Primitive vertebrates tend to have a larger number of skull bones than the more recent forms. Some fishes have 180 skull bones; amphibians and reptiles, 50 to 95; and mammals, 35 or fewer, with man having only 29.

Protection and movement

The vertebrate skeleton provides **protection, support, surfaces for the attachment of muscles,** and **leverage for locomotion.** The cranium protects the brain; the vertebral column protects the spinal cord; the sternum and ribs protect the organs in the thorax; and sockets protect the eyes and ears. Bending movements of the body and of the neck are made possible by the movable parts of the vertebral column. Breathing movements involve enlargement of the thoracic cavity by contraction of the diaphragm and a number of other muscles of inspiration, which force the sternum and ribs upward and outward, and a subsequent decrease in the size of the thoracic cavity by the elastic recoil of the parts previously stretched. The bones of the skeleton serve for the attachment of muscles that move the limbs and other parts of the body such as the lips, nose, eyelids, etc. Many bone surfaces are large for the attachment of important muscles; in man are the hipbone (innominate Fig. 369) for the muscles that help maintain an upright position, and the shoulder blade (scapula) for the muscles that move the forelimbs; and in birds, the enormous sternum for the muscles of flight.

Joints

Locomotion in vertebrates require movable joints (Fig. 372). These are of several types: (1) **gliding joints,** such as those between the carpal bones, which allow only gliding movements; (2) **hinge joints,** such as the elbow, which permit motion in one plane only; (3) **pivotal joints** with a rotary movement in one direction, such as between

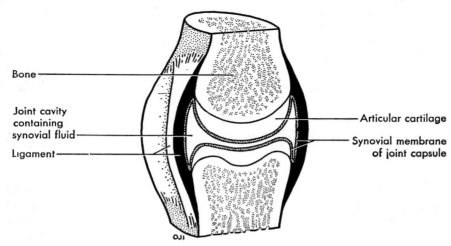

Bone

Joint cavity containing synovial fluid

Ligament

Articular cartilage

Synovial membrane of joint capsule

FIGURE 372. A diagram of a joint surface (longitudinal section) showing some of its characteristics. This is a freely movable joint.

the axis and atlas, which permits turning the head from side to side; and (4) **ball and socket joints** with a rounded head lying in a cuplike cavity, such as the shoulder and hip joints.

MUSCLES AND MOVEMENT

Movements in animals are effected principally as a result of the contractility of muscle fibers, but contractility is a general property of protoplasm and can be observed in the absence of muscle fibers, as in the flagella and cilia of protozoans. Certain protozoans also contain contractile fibrils, the myonemes, that resemble myofibrils in the muscle fiber of a vertebrate. As already noted, the epitheliomuscular cells of coelenterates are the simplest of all cells that are specialized for purposes of contraction.

Smooth muscle

Muscular tissue in higher animals is usually classified, according to its structure and localization, into three types (Fig. 373): (1) smooth, (2) skeletal,* and (3) cardiac. **Cardiac muscle** occurs only in the hearts of vertebrates. **Smooth muscle** is characteristic of invertebrates and of the visceral organs of vertebrates. It is composed of spindle-shaped cells, from 0.015 to 0.5 mm. long, and from 0.002 to 0.02 mm. in diameter, each with a single nucleus near the center. Smooth muscle cells may be either isolated or aggregated into small groups; or they may exist in parallel layers of considerable size. Smooth muscles contract more slowly than other types. Changes in the shape and size of the visceral organs are due to the contraction of smooth muscles, such as peristalsis in the intestine. Such muscles are present in

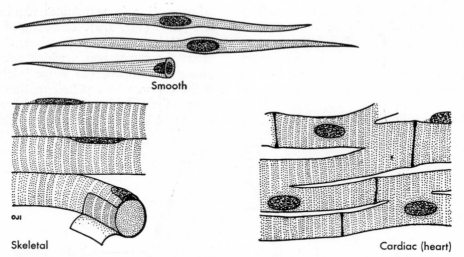

Smooth

Skeletal

Cardiac (heart)

FIGURE 373. Microscopic structure of the three types of muscle cells (fibers). Skeletal muscle is also called striated; but inasmuch as cardiac (heart) muscle is also striated, this terminology results in some confusion.

the walls of blood vessels and the bladder, around the openings of glands, in the skin where they may raise the hair, in the

* Skeletal muscle is also called striated, but inasmuch as cardiac muscle too is striated, the use of the term striated for skeletal muscle may result in some confusion.

trachea and bronchi, and in the reproductive ducts. Since they are not under voluntary control, they are called **involuntary muscles.** Smooth muscles, because they are the first kind to have developed in animals, are thought to be the most primitive.

Skeletal muscle

Skeletal muscle is what we know as **flesh.** It makes up about 40 per cent of the weight of a man. Most of it is located in the limbs, where it effects locomotion, and in the body wall; it is present also in the diaphragm, tongue, upper third of the esophagus, pharynx, larynx, and around the eyeballs. When viewed with a microscope, each myofibril in skeletal muscle appears to consist of alternate light and dark segments; these segments are arranged in a muscle so that all of the light ones lie side by side, and all of the dark ones also lie side by side, giving the whole muscle a striated appearance. The blood supply is rich and appears in amounts of from 1400 to 4000 capillaries per cubic millimeter, which, however, is much less than in heart muscle. Since these striated muscles are the type that are attached to the skeleton, they are called **skeletal muscles;** and since their movements are more or less under voluntary control, they are known as **voluntary muscles.**

The fibers of skeletal muscles are spindle-shaped and may be from one to 40 mm. long and from 0.01 to 0.15 mm. in diameter.

Each is a multinuclear cell, the nuclei usually lying just beneath the surface membrane. Myofibrils run lengthwise through the cell. The fibers are bound together into muscles by connective tissue, and the muscles thus formed are attached to bones by means of tough strands of connective tissue called tendons. The end of the muscle that is attached to the more stationary part of the skeleton is called the **origin,** and the other end, which is attached to the part moved when the muscle contracts, the **insertion.** Some of the skeletal muscles of man are shown in Figs. 374 and 375, and the origin, insertion, and function of a few of these are given in the accompanying table. Skeletal muscles contract more quickly than smooth muscles, and since each fiber may act separately, various gradations in the force of the contractions are possible. Muscles used in locomotion are usually present in pairs that are "antagonistic." For example, when the biceps contracts it bends the arm at the elbow; since muscles exert no force when they relax, an opposing muscle, the triceps, on the opposite side of the arm is required to extend the forearm again as shown in Fig. 232.

THE NAME, ORIGIN, INSERTION, AND FUNCTIONS OF SOME OF THE
SKELETAL MUSCLES OF MAN (*Illustrated in Fig. 374*)

NAME OF MUSCLE	ORIGIN	INSERTION	FUNCTION
Deltoid	Clavicle and scapula	Humerus	Abducts * the arm.
Biceps	Scapula	Radius	Flexes ** elbow and supinates † forearm and hand.
Triceps	Scapula and humerus	Ulna	Extends forearm.
Pectoralis major	Clavicle, sternum, etc.	Humerus	Adducts †† and draws arm across chest and rotates it inward.
Serratus anterior	Ribs and intercostals	Scapula	Carries scapula forward, assists trapezius and deltoid, etc.
Gluteus maximus	Ilium, sacrum, etc.	Femur	Extends, abducts, and rotates femur.
Tensor fascia lata	Ilium	Fascia lata	Abduction and rotation of thigh and tightening of fascia lata.
Sartorius	Ilium	Tibia	Flexes leg on thigh and thigh on pelvis.
Quadriceps femoris	Innominate (os coxae), femur, etc.	Tibia	Extends leg and flexes thigh.
Gracilis	Pubis	Tibia	Adducts thigh and flexes leg.
Gastrocnemius	Femur	Calcaneus	Flexes leg and extends foot.
Soleus	Fibia and tibia	Calcaneus	Extends foot.
Peroneus	Fibula	Metatarsals	Extends foot.

* Abduct means to draw away from (L. *ab,* from; *ducere,* draw).
** Flex means to bend (L. *flexus,* bent).
† Supinate means to bring the palm upward (L. *supinus,* bent back).
†† Adduct means to draw toward (L. *ad,* toward).

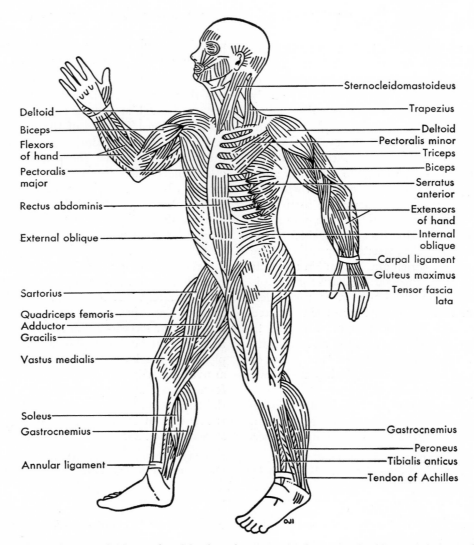

Deltoid
Biceps
Flexors of hand
Pectoralis major
Rectus abdominis
External oblique
Sartorius
Quadriceps femoris
Adductor
Gracilis
Vastus medialis
Soleus
Gastrocnemius
Annular ligament

Sternocleidomastoideus
Trapezius
Deltoid
Pectoralis minor
Triceps
Biceps
Serratus anterior
Extensors of hand
Internal oblique
Carpal ligament
Gluteus maximus
Tensor fascia lata
Gastrocnemius
Peroneus
Tibialis anticus
Tendon of Achilles

FIGURE 374. Superficial muscles. Muscles of man with the external oblique and pectoralis major removed from the left side to show others that lie beneath.

Cardiac heart muscle

The cardiac muscle in the vertebrate heart consists of cells that are less distinctly striated than those in skeletal muscle. These fibers are connected with one another so that they form a syncytium. Impulses pass quickly through the ventricles of the heart due to these connections, and the reaction is that of one large muscle cell. The automatic rhythmic contraction of the heart, day after day, as long as we live, is its most striking characteristic.

Muscles of the face

Some of the **muscles of the face,** of which there are about 30, and of the neck are shown in Fig. 375. The facial muscles make possible the expression of many emotional states. The primates have the greatest development of these muscles, but some animals such as the dog can express a limited degree of emotion, but in vertebrates below the mammals, the face is expressionless.

The **frontal** elevates the eyebrows and causes the transverse wrinkles of the forehead; the **orbicularis oculi** closes the eyelids; the **masseter** is a muscle of mastication

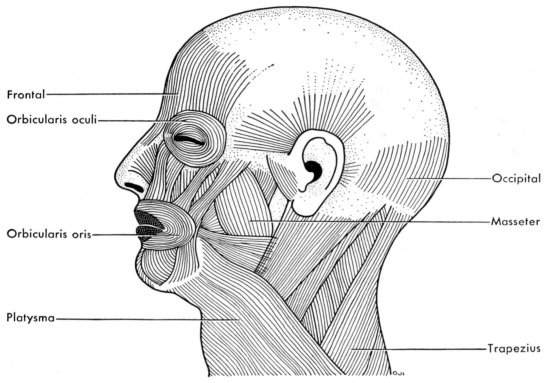

Frontal

Orbicularis oculi

Orbicularis oris

Platysma

Occipital

Masseter

Trapezius

FIGURE 375. Superficial muscles of the face and neck of man. The facial muscles are of special interest because they make possible the expression of emotions such as joy and anger. (After Gerrish.)

and raises the lower jaw, closing the mouth; the **orbicularis oris** closes the lips; and the **platysma** is a neck muscle that draws the lower jaw and the corners of the mouth downward.

Physiology of muscle contraction

The stimuli that bring about muscular contraction may be nervous, chemical, or physical. The reaction is a shortening and thickening of the muscle, but no alteration in volume. Chemical changes of a very complicated nature occur, but the exact nature

of these is not completely understood. However, it is known that when a muscle contracts, it functions as a machine which converts stored potential chemical energy to mechanical energy. The efficiency of the process of changing chemical energy into mechanical energy is only about 25 to 40 per cent. The greater part of the energy liberated is in the form of heat; everyone knows that exercising the muscles makes one warmer. About four-fifths of all the body heat is derived from this source.

It has been demonstrated that in the contraction of a muscle, oxygen is used, carbon dioxide is released, glycogen disappears, lactic acid is formed, and changes occur in certain organic phosphates which are present. There is much evidence that the energy used in the shortening of a muscle comes from the breakdown of adenosine triphosphate (ATP). It appears that all animal movements such as those of the arms, legs, wings, and fins are traceable to ATP. In the recovery process, glycogen is broken down into lactic acid; some of this acid is oxidized to carbon dioxide and water, and the remainder is reconverted to glycogen. There are other intermediate reactions involved.

A summary of some of the better-known chemical reactions in muscle contraction, in the sequence in which they occur, may be expressed thus:

1. Adenosine triphosphate (ATP) → adenosine diphosphate (ADP) + phosphate + energy for muscle contraction.
2. Glycogen → complex intermediate stages → lactic acid + energy for resynthesis of ATP.
3. About $\frac{1}{5}$ of the lactic acid + oxygen → carbon dioxide + water + energy, for resynthesis of the remaining $\frac{4}{5}$ of the lactic acid to glycogen.

Some of the reactions in the summary are reversible, and an unknown number of enzymes are involved in the chemical reactions.

Oxygen is not used in the actual shortening of a muscle; a muscle can contract for a time without oxygen, for it is required only in the chemical reactions associated with recovery. In **strenuous muscular exercise,** such as in a 100-yard dash, lactic acid accumulates because oxygen cannot be supplied as rapidly as it is used. This results in what is called an **oxygen debt,** which is repaid by rapid deep breathing for some time after the race.

True fatigue is caused, in part at least, by the effects of waste products (carbon dioxide, lactic acid, acid phosphate) which accumulate during exercise. The loss of nutritive substances may also be a factor in fatigue, but the accumulation of wastes is probably of major importance.

Rest is necessary after violent exercise to enable the blood to carry the metabolic waste substances to the excretory organs and nutritive materials to the muscles. Exercise stimulates circulation and brings about an increase in size, strength, and tone of the muscles.

SELECTED COLLATERAL READINGS

Goss, C.M. (ed.). *Gray's Anatomy,* Lea & Febiger, Philadelphia, 1954.

Gray, J. *How Animals Move.* Cambridge Univ. Press, London, 1953.

Heilbrunn, L.V. *An Outline of General Physiology.* Saunders, Philadelphia, 1952.

Stiles, Karl A. *Handbook of Histology.* McGraw-Hill, New York, 1956.

Toldt, Carl. *An Atlas of Human Anatomy.* Macmillan, New York, 1928.

OJI

CHAPTER 32

Metabolism and Transport in Animals

Our studies of the various types of animals have included the subject of nutrition and have prepared us for a general review of the nutritive processes "from amoeba to man." Here we propose to consider (1) what constitutes the food of different types of animals, and of animals in general, (2) how this food is captured and ingested, (3) how it is digested, (4) how it is transported about the body, (5) how it is absorbed, (6) how it is stored or built up into protoplasm, (7) how it is utilized to produce energy before or after being assimilated, and (8) how waste products are eliminated. The processes involved constitute nutrition. The term metabolism may also be applied to these processes, but it is here used in a restricted sense for the chemical reactions that take place within the cells.

Food

All substances taken into the body that are used to build up protoplasm and to produce energy are foods. The principal foods of animals are organic compounds (carbohydrates, fats, and proteins) built up by other organisms, water, inorganic salts, oxygen, and vitamins. Most animals cannot synthesize organic compounds from inorganic substances as plants do, but must feed on other living organisms, their remains, or their products. Only certain chlorophyl-bearing protozoans, such as the euglena, can manufacture their food out of inorganic substances; all other animals use plants, or other animals that feed on plants, for their nutritive material.

Photosynthesis

The manufacture of food by certain protozoans and by most plants from inorganic substances is known as photosynthesis (Fig. 376). Organisms that are able to carry on photosynthesis contain a green substance, chlorophyll, which is closely related chem-

509

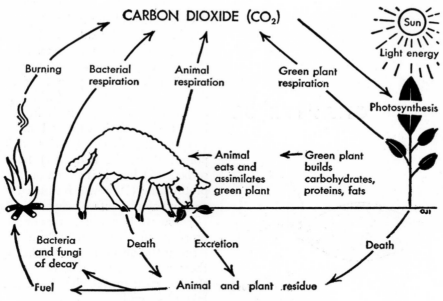

FIGURE 376. The carbon cycle in nature.

ically to the hemoglobin in our own blood, and which in the presence of sunlight brings about a combination of carbon dioxide and water to form a carbohydrate (glucose). It has been estimated that the amount of energy fixed annually in plants by photosynthesis is equivalent to that obtainable from 300 billion tons of coal. The carbon dioxide is obtained principally from the air, and water is absorbed from the soil by the roots of the plant. The chemical equation for this may be expressed as follows:

$$6H_2O + 6CO_2 + \text{Light energy} + \text{Chlorophyll} \rightarrow C_6H_{12}O_6 + 6O_2$$

$$\underset{\text{Water}}{6H_2O} + \underset{\substack{\text{Carbon}\\\text{dioxide}}}{6CO_2} + \text{Light energy} + \text{Chlorophyl} \rightarrow \underset{\substack{\text{Sugar}\\\text{(glucose)}}}{C_6H_{12}O_6} + \underset{\text{Oxygen}}{6O_2}$$

The sun furnishes the energy required for these chemical combinations. The oxygen that is freed escapes from the tissues of the plant by diffusion. In most plants the glucose is converted almost immediately into starch, the form in which food is usually stored in plants. Starch can be made synthetically in the laboratory from glucose.

The carbon in living animals is returned to the environment as a result of fermentation and respiration, and of decay when the animals die, as illustrated in Fig. 376. Dead animals are disintegrated by bacteria with the aid of enymes; carbohydrates become carbon dioxide and water, and proteins become carbon dioxide, water, and ammonia or free nitrogen.

Nitrogen-fixing bacteria

Plants are of value in another way: with the aid of certain bacteria, they recover nitrogen from the soil and restore it to organisms. Nitrogen-fixing bacteria live in the soil, or in root nodules, which they have stimulated certain leguminous plants, such as clover, and peas, to grow. The number of different kinds of bacteria known to be capable of nitrogen fixation has greatly increased in recent years. Also certain bluegreen algae living in the soil of rice fields in India are very active nitrogen fixers. With energy supplied by the glucose resulting from photosynthesis, the bacteria are able to combine atmospheric nitrogen (the air con-

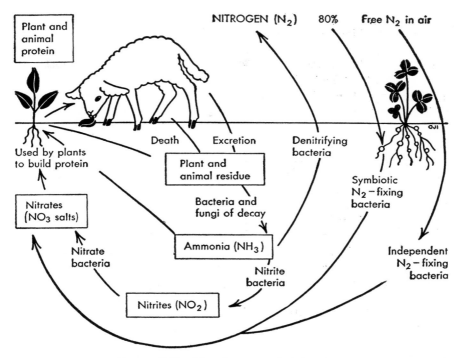

FIGURE 377. The nitrogen cycle in nature.

sists of 78 per cent free nitrogen) with atmospheric oxygen to form potassium nitrite (KNO_2) and sodium nitrite ($NaNO_2$). From these nitrates, minute plants (bacteria) are able to form other nitrogenous substances such as nitrate (NO_3) and ammonia (NH_3). By linking these with the carbohydrates formed by photosynthesis, amino acids are produced, which the plant then constructs into proteins. These plant proteins constitute one of the principal food elements of animals. The nitrogen cycle is illustrated in Fig. 377.

Energy

During photosynthesis, light energy from the sun is transformed into chemical energy. In all nutritive processes, energy transformations occur. Energy may be defined as "the capacity to do work." It may appear to us in the form of motion, heat, chemical changes, light, electric currents, etc. Two

types of energy are recognized: kinetic and potential. Kinetic energy is the energy of movement and potential energy that of position. For example, a brick that is held 6 feet above the ground possesses potential energy equal to the kinetic energy required to raise it to that height against the force of gravity. Dropping the brick brings about the transformation of this potential energy into the kinetic energy of motion, and into that of heat when the brick strikes the ground. Potential energy is stored in food. When one type of energy is transformed into another, according to the law of conservation of energy, the quantity of energy remains the same. "Conservation of energy" means that the total energy of the universe is constant, none being lost and none being gained; all changes are due to transformations.

Mechanical energy appears in the movements of animals and in the streaming of protoplasm; for example, cyclosis in the paramecium. The energy of heat is manifested by all animals, but it is particularly obvious in the "warm-blooded" birds and mammals. Chemical energy takes part in the building up and breaking down of proto-plasm within cells (metabolism). Light energy is exhibited by a few animals but in small quantities. For example, it takes 2000 fireflies flashing simultaneously to produce the illumination of a single candle. Electric energy in very small amounts is involved in all of the activities of living cells, but may become concentrated as in certain fish such as the torpedo ray or the electric eel.

During photosynthesis radiant energy is absorbed and transformed into the potential chemical energy of organic compounds. Al-though practically all our energy is obtained from these organic compounds, a very small amount appears to be received directly from the sun and is utilized in the manufacture of vitamin D in the skin from sterols; this is of importance from the standpoint of general health. Most of the radiant energy which we receive daily from the sun eventually be-comes transformed into heat which is quickly dissipated.

Types of nutrition

Animals and plants that carry on photo-synthesis are said to be **holophytic.** Most animals feed on solid material, and nutrition involving the ingestion of such matter is called **holozoic.** Many animals, especially parasites that live within the bodies of other animals, absorb organic substances in solu-tion through the surface of their body; this type of nutrition is termed **saprozoic.**

Classification of animals according to their diet

Three principal types of animals may be recognized, based on their diets: herbivor-ous, carnivorous, and omnivorous. **Herbi-vorous animals** feed on vegetation and are adapted for that purpose. For example, leaf-eating insects possess chewing mouth parts; seed-eating birds may have short, thick bills

for breaking hard seeds; rabbits and other rodents are provided with sharp incisor teeth suitable for gnawing; and ruminants such as cattle have enormous stomachs of several chambers for storage of vegetation.

Carnivorous animals live on animal food. One order of meat-eating mammals is named Carnivora, but many mammals be-longing to other orders also eat meat. Such mammals often have enlarged canine teeth for holding their prey. Many of the types we have studied are carnivorous: paramecia eat other protozoans, coral polyps ingest only animal food; spiders and leeches suck up animal juices; and lampreys, dogfishes, perches, frogs, and some turtles all live on animals.

Omnivorous animals feed on both animal and vegetable matter. Many protozoans eat both miscroscopic plants and animals, as do also fresh-water mussels; earthworms feed largely on decaying vegetation but also in-gest animal food; and the greatest of all omnivores is man himself.

Food capture

Most animals that are capable of locomo-tion move about "seeking whom they may devour"; but a few species are sedentary and must either wait for food to come to them, or they possess some method of bringing it into range. The oyster, for example, becomes attached to some solid object by the left valve of its shell when very young, and the organic particles that constitute its food are drawn into the shell in currents of water created by the beating of cilia on the oyster's body. Sponges obtain their food in a similar manner.

Among the protozoans, food may be cap-tured by means of pseudopodia, flagella, or cilia. Tentacles provided with nematocysts are characteristic of the coelenterates. Star-fishes include bivalve mollusks among their prey, and are able to open their shells by a long, steady pull with their tubefeet. Many spiders build webs for capturing insects. The frog accomplishes the same thing with its sticky tongue. Many fish depend on speed for overhauling their prey. Birds that feed on animals likewise rely on the speed of flight as well as on sharp claws and hooked beaks. Claws and teeth are familiar mammalian weapons of offense.

Food selection

The fact that we can classify animals according to their diet indicates that they select their food. As already noted, amoebas seem to prefer the small flagellate *Chilomonas*. Hydras feed largely on such small aquatic animals as water fleas, worms, and insect larvae. The mouth parts of insects are supplied with sense organs that probably aid them in distinguishing different kinds of food. Many plant-eating insects and their larvae feed on one kind of plant, or on a small group of plants, and will starve if these are not available. Vertebrates likewise are more or less strictly limited in the character of the food they eat. This has led to such common names as fish hawk for the osprey, carrion crow for the black vulture, duck hawk, herring gull, kingfisher, flycatcher, anteater, sea cow, and fruit bat.

The **character of the food** depends largely on the habitat of the animal, whether marine, fresh-water, or terrestrial; on its period of activity, whether diurnal or nocturnal; on the size of the eater; on its method and speed of locomotion; on the structure of its organs or organelles for capturing its prey; on the type of its mouth parts; and on the structure of the digestive system. Sense organs also play an important role in food selection. These factors are all important and account in general for the character of an animal's food; but we still do not know why in many cases one type of food is preferred to some other type that seems to us to be equally desirable.

Ingestion of food

In many animals, the structures used in obtaining food are also employed for purposes of ingestion. This is true of the pseudopodia of amoebas, the cilia of paramecia, the tentacles of hydras, the muscular pharynx of planarians, earthworms, and certain sucking insects, the cilia of clams, and the tongue of the frog. In other animals, special methods of ingestion are employed. In sponges, food particles drawn into the central cavity by means of flagella are engulfed by the collar cells. In hydras, the mouth and body wall force the food into the gastrovascular cavity, but small particles are ingested by the nutritive cells of the inner body wall. In the crayfish and in many insects, the food is held by certain of the mouth parts while it is crushed or bitten into small pieces by the mandibles or jaws. A starfish does not ingest the large bivalves it attacks, but everts its stomach, inserts it between the valves, and digests the soft parts of the prey outside its body. The lamprey attaches to fishes with its suckerlike mouth and horny teeth, and rasps away the flesh with its tongue, then feeds on blood. Most fish do not chew their food but hold it with their teeth and swallow it at once. Many other vertebrates, such as snakes and birds, swallow their food whole. Mammals, for the most part, chew their food before swallowing it; their teeth are modified for this purpose; for example, the grinding teeth of herbivorous types (cattle, horses, etc.), and the cutting teeth of carnivores (dogs, cats, etc.). The relation between the structure of the teeth and the character of the food in mammals is worth detailed study.

DIGESTION AND DIGESTIVE SYSTEMS

Digestion

The apparatus between the mouth and the anus is for getting food into the blood. The process of digestion is the breaking down of food material so that it is in a soluble form and can pass through membranes and protoplasm; that is, it can be absorbed. Certain foods such as water, oxygen, mineral salts, and glucose and other simple sugars, can be absorbed in the form in which they are ingested; but most of the food of animals consists of carbohydrates, fats, and proteins, which will not usually diffuse through membranes and protoplasm. The proteins must be broken down into amino acids, the fats into glycerol and fatty acids, and the carbohydrates into simple sugars. The products of digestion are used by the body to: (1) produce energy when they are oxidized, (2) be built up into protoplasm, (3) be stored for future needs, or (4) manufacture special substances, such as hormones.

In most animals, certain **mechanical processes** take part in digestion such as the chewing of food, the movement of food through the digestive canal, and the grinding or mixing activities within the digestive tract. **Chemical digestion** is a process of hydrolysis. During hydrolysis a complex compound combines chemically with water, and complex molecules are split into two or more simpler molecules. For example, common sugar (sucrose) when combined with water gives rise to the two simple sugars, glucose and fructose, as follows:

$$\underset{C_{12}H_{22}O_{11}}{\text{Sucrose}} + \underset{H_2O}{\text{Water}} \rightarrow \underset{C_6H_{12}O_6}{\text{Glucose}} + \underset{C_6H_{12}O_6}{\text{Fructose}}$$

The molecular formulas for glucose and fructose are the same, but the atoms of which they are composed are differently arranged; such substances are known as isomers. Hydrolysis is brought about by enzymes which are secreted by the protoplasm. Enzymes act only on the surface of food particles, so, obviously, the previous mechanical breakup of food into small pieces speeds up the digestive process. In higher animals, glands are specialized for secreting these enzymes.

Two types of digestion can be recognized in animals, **intracellular** and **extracellular**. In protozoans and sponges, food particles are digested inside food vacuoles within cells; and even in coelenterates such as the hydra, and in certain higher animals, some of the food is digested within cells. Hydras also digest food outside of cells in a gastrovascular cavity. Coelenterates and flatworms each possess a digestive cavity with only one opening, whereas almost every animal above them in the scale of life is provided with a digestive cavity which has two openings, a mouth and an anus.

Digestive systems

The digestive tracts of the earthworm, crayfish, grasshopper, mussel, and vertebrates are constructed on the same general plan. The bodies of these animals are essentially double tubes, as is clearly seen in the earthworm. The outer tube is the body wall, and the inner tube is made up of the digestive canal. Between the two tubes is a body cavity. All organs which make up the digestive canal, together with the other organs that aid in digestion, constitute the digestive system.

Many of the peculiarities in digestive systems are correlated with the character of the food and with the feeding habits of the animals. For example, we have noted the following: a **planarian** captures and ingests food with the aid of a muscular, protrusible pharynx; its digestive system includes three main trunks and many lateral branches which carry food to all parts of the body; a circulatory system for this purpose is absent. The **earthworm** possesses a muscular pharynx for drawing food into the digestive canal, a crop for storage purposes, a gizzard for grinding up the food, and an intestinal fold, the typhlosole, to increase the secreting and absorptive surface of the intestinal wall; **lampreys** have somewhat similar intestinal folds. The **crayfish** stomach is constricted into two parts; the anterior part grinds up the food and passes it through a strainer into the posterior chamber. In the **grasshopper**, food is stored in the crop and ground up in the gizzard; 6 double gastric

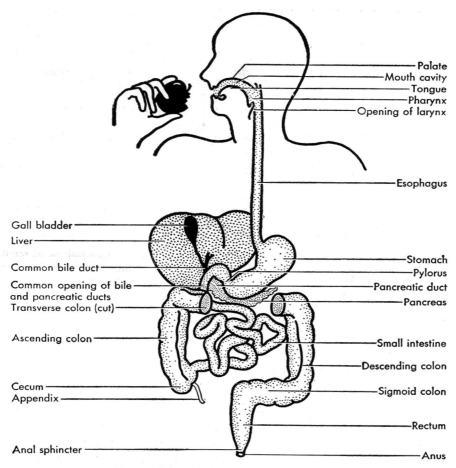

Palate
Mouth cavity
Tongue
Pharynx
Opening of larynx

Esophagus

Gall bladder
Liver
Common bile duct
Common opening of bile
and pancreatic ducts
Transverse colon (cut)

Ascending colon

Cecum
Appendix

Anal sphincter

Stomach
Pylorus
Pancreatic duct
Pancreas

Small intestine

Descending colon

Sigmoid colon

Rectum

Anus

FIGURE 378. The digestive system of man.

ceca pour secretions into the midgut. Part of the esophagus of the **spider** is dilated into a sucking "stomach"; 5 pairs of ceca open into the true stomach, and feces accumulate in a stercoral pocket near the anus. **Starfishes** specialize in pyloric ceca, a pair of which is located in each arm; two rectal ceca are also present.

In the **amphioxus**, pharyngeal grooves, bearing cilia and secreting mucus, aid in carrying particles of food into the intestine. A **frog** is characterized by a sticky protrusible tongue, small teeth for holding prey, an esophagus containing folds so that it can be distended to swallow large bodies, and a cloaca into which the excretory and re-

productive systems, as well as the digestive system, discharge their products. A cloaca is present in many other animals. The intestine of the **dogfish shark** is provided with a spiral valve which furnishes a large surface for absorption and prevents too rapid passage of food. **Snakes** possess peculiar jaws which can be opened so wide that prey 4 or 5 times the diameter of the body can be swallowed. The teeth of snakes are sharp and curved backward; they not only hold prey firmly but force it down the esophagus. Certain teeth in poisonous snakes are grooved or tubular for transfer of poison into a wound. Pigeons and many other **birds** have large crops; the stomach consists of two parts, the first being highly glandular and the second a grinding gizzard; two intestinal ceca are present. The teeth of the cat are highly specialized for seizing prey, and cutting flesh, and a short cecum (no appendix) opens into the intestine. **Plant-eating mammals** in general have large stomachs and large and long intestines, often with large ceca, for storing and digesting the enormous quantity of food necessary for their proper nourishment. The 4-chambered stomachs of ruminants are especially interesting. Flesh-eating mammals, on the other hand, are provided with smaller digestive organs, their food being more concentrated.

The digestive system and digestion in man

More is known about the digestion in man than about any other animal. All animals probably digest their food in a similar manner, that is, the process of digestion is, in general, the same throughout the animal kingdom from amoeba to man. The human digestive system resembles that of other vertebrates more closely than it does that of invertebrates; but even in such lowly animals as the earthworm, the organs that constitute the digestive system are given the same names as those in man, such as mouth, pharynx, esophagus, stomach, intestine, anus, and digestive glands. The parts of the digestive tract in man are as follows (Fig. 378):

1. Mouth cavity, containing (1) tongue, (2) openings of ducts of salivary glands, and (3) teeth.
2. Pharynx or throat cavity, shaped like an inverted cone.
3. Esophagus, a muscular tube about 9 inches long.
4. Stomach, a saclike dilatation of the digestive tube.
5. Small intestine, a muscular tube about 23 feet long, and from 1 to 1½ inches in diameter: duodenum, about 1 foot long; jejunum, about 8 feet long; ileum, about 14 feet long.
6. Large intestine, a muscular tube about 5 feet long and 2½ inches in diameter: cecum, a large pouch with vermiform (worm-shaped) appendix, about 3 inches long, at the end of it; colon, the main part of the large intestine; rectum, about 5 inches long; anal canal, about 1½ inches long.

The **mouth cavity** receives the food. Here it is chewed by the teeth, aided by the tongue which helps keep the food between the teeth. The **tongue** is also a special sense organ of taste and assists in swallowing the food. The **mucous membrane** lining the mouth contains minute oral glands which pour their secretion into the oral cavity. There it becomes mixed with the secretions from three pairs of **salivary glands** (Fig. 379) and is then known as saliva. Approximately 1000 ml. are produced per day. Secretion is an involuntary act stimulated by taste, sight, or smell of food. There are 32 permanent **teeth** as follows: incisors, 8;

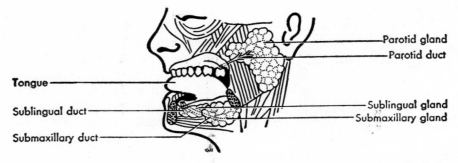

Tongue

Sublingual duct

Submaxillary duct

Parotid gland
Parotid duct

Sublingual gland
Submaxillary gland

FIGURE 379. Salivary glands and their ducts. (After Kimber, Gray, and Stackpole.)

canines (cuspids), 4; premolars (bicuspids), 8; and molars, 12. The first set of 20 teeth (incisors, 8; canines, 4; and molars, 8) are called milk or deciduous teeth because they fall out and are replaced during childhood. Each tooth may be divided into three parts: root, neck, and crown; and it consists of dentine, enamel which caps the crown, and cement which covers the root. The character of the teeth is closely correlated with the feeding habits of the respective animals.

The **pharynx** dilates to receive food and passes it on to the esophagus, where, as a result of peristaltic contractions, it is forced down through the **cardiac opening** of the stomach. The other opening of the stomach, that into the duodenum, is called the **pyloric opening**. Both openings may be closed by ringlike muscles or **sphincters**. Three types of **glands** occur in the stomach wall: (1) **cardiac glands**, which secrete mucin, a constituent of mucus; (2) **fundic glands**, which secrete hydrochloric acid and the enzyme **pepsin**, the latter being activated in the presence of the acid; and (3) **pyloric glands**, which secrete pepsin and mucin. The stomach retains the food until it becomes a semiliquid **chyme**, which is then passed on into the small intestine at frequent intervals. Certain cells in the mucous membrane of the stomach secrete a hormone called **gastrin**, which stimulates the secretion of **gastric juice**.

Digestion takes place principally in the small intestine. The chyme is here acted upon by **bile** from the liver and **pancreatic juice** from the pancreas; both usually enter the duodenum together through the same orifice. Simple tubular glands in the mucous membrane throughout the small intestine, and more complex duodenal glands in the submucous membrane of the duodenum secrete a digestive fluid named **intestinal juice**. Certain cells in the mucous membrane secrete the hormone **secretin** when an acid food mass from the stomach enters the intestine. Secretin is carried by the blood to the pancreas, which it stimulates to secrete

tory activity. **Peristaltic movements** and constricting movements carry the food along the small intestine, but circular folds tend to retard the movement, thus allowing more time for digestion and absorption. Minute fingerlike projections occur throughout the small intestine; these are called **villi** (Fig. 380). Digested food is absorbed into the blood and lymph vessels in these villi.

The **large intestine** consists of 4 parts: (1) cecum, with vermiform appendix, (2) colon, (3) rectum, and (4) anal canal. An **ileocecal valve** allows material to pass from the small intestine into the large, but not back again into the small intestine. A small pouch at the beginning of the large intestine is known as the **cecum**. Attached to the end of the cecum is a narrow tube about three inches long, the **vermiform appendix**; its principal importance appears to be the financial support of the surgeons who remove it. Material is carried through the colon by peristalsis. Digestion is continued here by digestive fluids that enter with the food from the small intestine, and absorption also takes place. Most of the water drunk with food and some that is secreted into the intestine in digestive juices is absorbed in the colon. Due to the absorption of water, the contents of the posterior end of the colon are in a semisolid condition. This fecal material consists largely of cellulose and other indigestible substances, bacteria, and excretions of the colon such as excess calcium and iron.

Besides the tongue, teeth, and salivary glands, the pancreas and liver are important glands of the digestive system. The **pancreas** secretes three types of enzymes: (1) **trypsin** * may convert proteins into amino acids, (2) pancreatic **amylase** (amylopsin) converts partly digested starches into sugar, and (3) **lipase** splits fat molecules into glycerol and fatty acids. The regulation

---

* Secreted in an inactive form, trypsinogen is changed to active trypsin by enterokinase, a coenzyme which is contained in the mucous membrane of the small intestine.

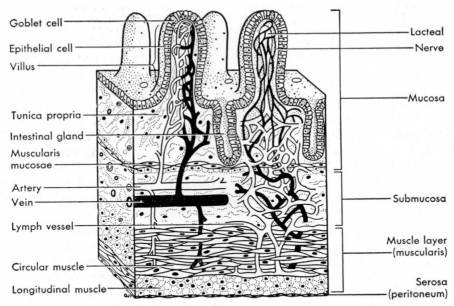

Goblet cell
Epithelial cell
Villus
Tunica propria
Intestinal gland
Muscularis mucosae
Artery
Vein
Lymph vessel
Circular muscle
Longitudinal muscle

Lacteal
Nerve
Mucosa
Submucosa
Muscle layer (muscularis)
Serosa (peritoneum)

FIGURE 380. Small intestine of man. Diagrammatic section showing villus at *left* with only blood vessels; that at *right* with only lacteal vessels and nerves; but all these structures occur in all villi.

of the concentration of each kind of amino acid in the blood is one of the most important functions of the liver. Other functions of the **liver** are the storage of glycogen, vitamins, iron, and copper; fat metabolism; production of heparin; protein detoxification; and secretion of bile, a liquid that may be stored in the gall bladder until needed. Bile contains bile salts that aid in the digestion of fat by bringing about physical division of fat droplets (globules) into smaller particles; this enables the lipase to act upon it more rapidly.

Chemical digestion

We have now reached the subject of what happens to different types of foods during the digestive processes.

Water

Most of our tissues contain from 75 to 90 per cent of water. It is the medium in which digestive changes occur, and in which dis-

solved food substances are absorbed, as well as the medium in which wastes are dissolved and removed by excretion. Water may be absorbed without change.

Mineral salts

Inorganic salts make up about one per cent by weight of the protoplasm and body fluids. Nevertheless, they are very important since they must be present in the proper concentration or our normal condition is greatly disturbed. For example, if the calcium content of the blood in mammals is greatly lowered, convulsions and death follow; and if calcium, sodium, and potassium are not present in the proper relative concentration, our hearts will not beat normally. The principal mineral salts contained in protoplasm are listed on page 16.

Calcium is a constituent of all protoplasm; 99 per cent of it is contained in the bones and teeth. Milk and leafy vegetables are the best sources of this mineral. Milk is also the best source of **phosphorus**, which is necessary for normal bone development. **Iron** occurs principally in the red corpuscles in the blood where it serves to carry oxygen; it enters our bodies especially by eating beef liver, egg yolk, whole grains, fruits, and green vegetables. **Iodine** is used by the thyroid gland in the production of the hormone **thyroxin,** which consists, in weight, of about 65 per cent of iodine; deficiency in the quantity of thyroxin may result in an enlargement of the thyroid gland to form a goiter. Iodine may be supplied by iodized salt, certain fish, lobsters, oysters, milk, leafy vegetables, and fruits from regions where the soil contains plenty of iodine. **Copper** is an essential element in nutrition although its role is not known; it occurs in liver, nuts, legumes, fruits, and leafy vegetables. Other salts in minute quantities are necessary for normal health. For example, a daily intake of 0.0003 gram of **manganese** is required.

Carbohydrates

The carbohydrates are the foods that provide energy most abundantly and economically. They contain carbon (C), hydrogen (H), and oxygen (O), the latter two being in the proportion of 2 atoms of hydrogen to 1 of oxygen as in water (H_2O). They occur as simple sugars, or as substances that can be converted into simple sugars by hydrolysis. Three kinds are recognized on the basis of the complexity of the molecule: (1) simple sugars (monosaccharides), (2) double sugars (disaccharides), and (3) complex carbohydrates (polysaccharides). A **simple sugar** contains 6 carbon atoms in its molecule and has the formula $C_6H_{12}O_6$. Simple sugars are soluble in water, can be absorbed in the intestine without further change, and consequently are not digested. **Glucose** is one which occurs in certain fruits, especially grapes, and in the blood; fructose (levulose) also is a simple sugar which occurs in fruits.

Double sugars (disaccharides) have the formula $C_{12}H_{22}O_{11}$ and are hydrolyzed during digestion into two simple sugars. One molecule of a disaccharide when combined with 1 molecule of water gives 2 monosaccharides as follows:

$$\text{Disaccharide} \quad \text{Water} \quad \text{Glucose} \quad \text{Fructose}$$
$$C_{12}H_{22}O_{11} + H_2O \rightarrow C_6H_{12}O_6 + C_6H_{12}O_6$$

Sucrose or cane sugar occurs in vegetables, fruits, and in many plant juices. **Lactose** or milk sugar occurs in the milk of all mammals. **Maltose** is a product of starch digestion and occurs in germinating cereals, malts, and malt products.

Polysaccharides when hydrolyzed break up into many simple sugars. Their molecular formula is written $(C_6H_{10}O_5)_n$, the n being a number supposed to range from 7 to 200 for different substances. For example, n for **starch** is large and for dextrin smaller, since each molecule of starch is hydrolyzed into several molecules of dextrin. **Dextrin** is then hydrolyzed into the disaccharide, maltose, and this into the monosaccharide, glucose. We obtain starch from grains, tubers, roots, etc. The solid matter of cereal grains consists of from 50 to 75 per cent starch, and of potatoes about 75 per cent starch. Another polysaccharide of which we ingest large quantities is **cellulose.** This is derived from the covering of starch grains and from plant cells; it resists digestion but by its bulk aids in peristalsis in the digestive tract. Glycogen is a polysaccharide which is stored in the liver and muscles. It is hydrolyzed to glucose in these organs, when needed by the body, and liberated into the blood. It is also hydrolyzed in the digestive tract when liver or muscle is eaten.

Hydrolysis by enzymes

Enzymes are complex substances produced by living cells. Their characteristics are as follows: (1) they are **catalysts,** that is, they bring about or hasten chemical changes in other substances without undergoing significant change in the process; (2) they are most effective in the body at body temperature; (3) each requires a definite type of medium—neutral, acid, or alkaline; (4) their action is specific, each acting on one type of food substance; (5) their action may be reversible, that is, they may aid in building up as well as breaking down substances. Enzymes are secreted into various parts of the digestive tract, bringing about hydrolysis (p. 514) of different substances in different organs as noted in the next paragraph.

Carbohydrate digestion

Two enzymes are present in saliva, ptyalin and maltase. **Ptyalin** (salivary amylase) hydrolyzes starch to dextrin and sugar (maltose). **Maltase** converts maltose to glucose. In the small intestine, the enzyme amylase from the pancreas hydrolyzes starch that was not acted upon in the mouth to maltose. Enzymes secreted by the small intestine continue the process: **maltase** hydrolyzes maltose to glucose; **invertase** (sucrase) acts upon sucrose and hydrolyzes it to glucose and fructose; and **lactase** hydrolyzes lactose to glucose and galactose. Glucose, fructose, and galactose are all simple sugars that can be absorbed into the blood.

Fats

Included among the fats are true fats or **lipids** and **compound fats** or **lipoids.** True fats are composed of carbon, hydrogen, and oxygen, as are carbohydrates, but less oxygen is present in proportion to the carbon and hydrogen; consequently this makes a more concentrated form of fuel. A molecule of fat can be split into two kinds of smaller molecules, one of glycerol (glycerin) and three of a fatty acid. For example, the fat known as stearin hydrolyzes as follows:

$$\text{Stearin} \qquad \text{Water} \quad \text{1 Glycerol}$$
$$C_3H_5O_3(C_{17}H_{35}CO)_3 + 3H_2O \rightarrow C_3H_5(OH)_3 +$$
$$\text{3 Stearic acid}$$
$$3HC_{18}H_{35}O_2$$

The best-known lipoid is **lecithin,** a substance that is abundant in the yolk of the hen's egg; it contains nitrogen and phosphorus in addition to carbon, hydrogen, and oxygen. Another type of lipoid is the sterols, which are solid waxy substances. The best-known sterol is cholesterol, which is excreted in bile and is widely distributed in the body. The fats we use are derived from plants and animals; some of the most common are fats ingested with meat, lard, butter, olive oil, cod-liver oil, etc.

Digestion of fat

No digestion of fat occurs in the mouth. In the stomach very little occurs, although a **gastric lipase** may begin the digestion of emulsified fats such as cream. Most fat is digested in the small intestine. An enzyme, **lipase,** from the pancreas splits the fats into glycerol and fatty acids that can be absorbed. **Bile** from the liver breaks up the fat droplets into small ones and thus hastens the action of the lipase.

Proteins

The proteins are always present in protoplasm and are, as the name means, of the first importance in the life of the cell. They are extremely complex; hundreds or thousands of atoms are required to form a single protein molecule. Proteins always contain nitrogen in addition to carbon, hydrogen, and oxygen, and are on this account often called **nitrogen compounds.** They sometimes contain sulphur, phosphorus, and iron also. A protein in our red blood corpuscles, hemoglobin, has been given the approximate formula $C_{3032}H_{4816}O_{872}N_{780}S_8Fe_4$. Protein molecules can be broken down into simpler molecules called amino acids; about 40 different kinds have been described as occurring in nature. Different combinations of these amino acids account for the differences between the proteins of different animals and of different tissues in the same animal. Our food contains proteins from animal sources such as meat, milk, fish, and albumin, and from plant sources such as glutenin from wheat, and legumin from peas, beans, peanuts, etc.

Digestion of protein

No protein digestion occurs in the mouth. In the stomach, the enzyme **pepsin** is effectively aided by hydrochloric acid to hydrolyze proteins into proteoses and peptones.

In the small intestine the enzyme **trypsin** from the pancreas may reduce proteins and partially digested proteins into amino acids. In the small intestine, **erepsin**, an enzyme, further acts on the split products of the gastric digestion of proteins to form amino acids. These amino acids are in a condition to be absorbed.

VITAMINS

Vitamins are organic food substances, present in very small amounts, and necessary for normal metabolism and growth. There is no generally accepted theory as to the way in which they influence nutrition. Some act as coenzymes, or influence enzyme systems within cells. Minute quantities are effective; for example, only 0.5 mg. of vitamin B_1 is required daily by a healthy adult; but the presence of vitamins is necessary in our food, or deficiency diseases develop. Plants and fish-liver oils furnish many vitamins, but some of them can now be manufactured in the laboratory. Rats, mice, and birds have been used a great deal for experimental work. The usual procedure is to feed an animal on a diet normal in every respect except for the absence of a particular vitamin, and to observe the results, which are usually similar to those that appear in man when he is deprived of the same vitamin.

Originally vitamins were designated by capital letters, but as their chemical structure became known, they have been given chemical names.

Vitamin A (Antixerophthalmic Vitamin $C_{20}H_{30}O$)

The precursor of this vitamin occurs in plants in the form of the pigment carotene, which in man is changed into vitamin A. Lack of this vitamin disturbs the secreting powers of mucous membranes; for example, the lacrimal glands do not keep the eye moist, which leads to a disease called **xerophthalmia**, "dry eye." The eyesight is impaired; resistance to certain infections decreases; and growth is retarded (Fig. 381). **Night blindness**, inability to see in the dark, has been known for centuries. This condition results from insufficient amounts of a photochemical substance in the eye known as **visual purple**, which is essential for good vision in dim light. In order to regenerate visual purple, vitamin A is required. Although few individuals show the more pronounced effects of vitamin A deficiency, such as xerophthalmia, nevertheless, a large number do suffer from some degree of night blindness. The chief sources of vitamin A are vegetables such as spinach, asparagus, carrots, sweet potatoes, butter, cream, eggs, liver, and fish-liver oils, especially halibut-liver oil.

Vitamin Thiamine (Antineuritic Vitamin, $B_1—C_{12}H_{17}N_4OSCI$)

Vitamin B_1 was the first member of the B complex to be differentiated. It prevents a disease known as beriberi, which is prevalent among Oriental people who live on a diet consisting largely of polished rice. Beriberi is characterized by loss of appetite and degenerative changes in the nervous system. Thiamine is abundant in brewer's yeast and whole cereals, that is, in cereals that have not been polished or milled so as to discard the vitamin, as is the case in polished rice and wheat from which white bread is made. It also occurs in peas, beans, nuts, and liver.

Vitamin Riboflavin (Vitamin G, $B_2—C_{17}H_{20}N_4O_6$)

Deficiency of riboflavin in the food results in soreness at the corner of the mouth

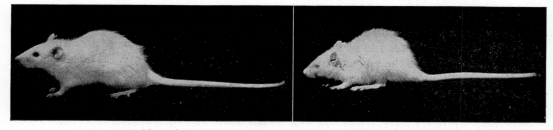

A. Normal   B. Deficient

Vitamin A

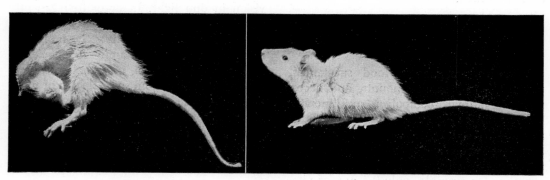

A. Deficient   B. After treatment

Vitamin B₁

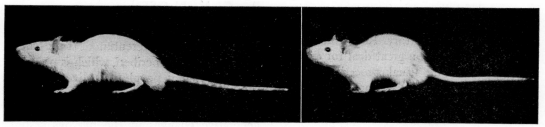

A. Normal   B. Deficient

Vitamin D

FIGURE 381. Effects of vitamin deficiency in rats. Vitamin A: two rats from same litter; A, weighed 123 grams, had bright eyes and sleek fur; B, had no vitamin A, weighed 56 grams, had infected eyes and rough fur. Vitamin B₁: A, rat 24 weeks old did not have enough vitamin B₁; B, same rat 24 hours after receiving food rich in vitamin B₁. Vitamin D: A, normal rat; B, rat that did not receive vitamin D, and hence is suffering from rickets. (Courtesy of U.S. Bureau of Human Nutrition and Home Economics.)

and inflammation of the cornea of the eye. This vitamin is contained in milk, green and leafy vegetables, egg white, liver, meat, and yeast.

Vitamin Niacin (Antipellagric Vitamin, P.P.—$C_6H_5NO_2$)

This constituent of the B complex protects against the disease known as pellagra, which is characterized by roughened skin on the hands, arms, feet, face, and neck, a sore mouth, pink tongue, diarrhea, and nervous disturbances. Its richest source is brewer's yeast, but it is also present in wheat germ, rice polishings, lean meat, milk, green vegetables, peas, and beans. Niacin is a constituent of certain coenzymes necessary for cellular functions.

Vitamin Pyridoxine (Vitamin B_6—$C_8H_{11}NO_3HCl$)

Although no deficiency disease for man has been identified, this vitamin has been shown essential for his health. It plays an important role in certain enzyme reactions in amino acid metabolism in the cell. It was first found to prevent dermatitis in rats. Yeast, whole cereal grains, milk, and liver are good food sources for B_6.

Pantothenic Acid ($C_9H_{17}NO_5$)

This vitamin is so widely distributed in foods eaten by man that apparently he gets enough; no deficiency disease is known in the human species. A deficiency, however, causes dermatitis in chicks; decreased adrenal cortex function in rats; and diarrhea and nerve degeneration in swine.

Pantothenic acid contributes to the formation of an important chemical compound known as coenzyme A. This coenzyme takes part in the metabolism of carbohydrates, lipids, and proteins. Yeast, cane molasses, meat, egg yolks, milk, and liver are some of the sources of this vitamin.

Vitamin Folic Acid (Vitamin M—$C_{19}H_{19}N_7O_6$)

Deficiency produces anemia and sprue in man. This vitamin is contained in green leaves, soy beans, yeast, and egg yolk.

Vitamin Biotin (Vitamin H—$C_{10}H_{16}N_2O_3S$)

This vitamin is necessary for the growth of birds, but in man it is not a dietary requirement for it is supplied by the intestinal bacteria. Deficiency symptoms are diarrhea, dermatitis, and nervous disorders. Sources for this vitamin are liver, kidney, and yeast.

Vitamin B_{12} (Cyanocobalamin—$C_{64}H_{92}N_{14}O_{13}PCo$)

Vitamin B_{12}, the antipernicious anemia vitamin that was first isolated from liver, is necessary for the formation of red corpuscles. A deficiency in man causes pernicious anemia. B_{12} is also essential for the growth of young animals. Sources of this vitamin are milk, liver, kidney, and lean meat.

Vitamin C (Ascorbic Acid—$C_6H_8O_6$)

The principal role of vitamin C is prevention of scurvy, a disease due to the breaking down of capillaries resulting in loosened teeth, bleeding gums, and fragile bones. The conquest of scurvy is one of the 10 greatest advances in medicine as listed in 1955 by Dr. L.H. Roddis. Ascorbic acid was isolated in pure form in 1932. It is present in citrus fruits, and tomatoes. Animals, except primates and guinea pigs, produce vitamin C.

Vitamin D (Antirachitic Vitamin—Calciferol—$C_{28}H_{44}O$)

Rickets is a disease involving softening of the bones, leading to deformities (Fig.

381), especially in young children. It is due to the absence in the food of sufficient amounts of certain organic compounds known as sterols. When a sterol obtained from yeast has been treated with ultraviolet radiation, it is known as calciferol and sold under the trade name of viosterol. A sterol occurs in the skin which is transformed into vitamin D when exposed to ultraviolet light. On this account sunlight is a preventive of rickets. Vitamin D also is present in fish-liver oils, eggs, enriched flour, and vitamin D milk. Too much vitamin D may result in harmful effects such as calcifications in the kidneys.

Vitamin E (Antisterility Vitamin —Tocopherol—$C_{29}H_{50}O_2$)

This vitamin is necessary for normal reproduction in some experimental animals such as rats, mice, and poultry. However, experiments have shown that goats, sheep, and rabbits have a normal reproductive capacity when on a diet deficient in vitamin E. These results should be a warning against the danger of making broad generalizations from experiments on one type of animal. This vitamin is so widely distributed in the foods used by man, such as green leaves and vegetable fats, that there appears to be no reason for concern about it. This vitamin is an antioxidant, which preserves easily oxidizable vitamins and fatty acids in foods, or in the body.

It has also been demonstrated that vitamin E deficiency may result in weakness and even degeneration of skeletal muscles. Muscles of animals deficient in this vitamin use oxygen at a much higher rate than normal.

Vitamin K (Antihemorrhagic Vitamin—$C_{31}H_{46}O_2$)

Deficiency of this vitamin is responsible for excessive bleeding due to delay in the clotting time of the blood. It is necessary for the formation of prothrombin, one of the substances essential for the clotting of blood. It appears that only under extraordinary circumstances does man suffer from a deficiency of this vitamin. Bile salts are necessary for absorption of vitamin K in the intestine. In cases of jaundice, due to the obstruction of a duct so that bile does not flow into the intestine, treatment with bile salts plus vitamin K is found to decrease the bleeding which usually occurs in this disease. It is also the custom to give this vitamin by injection or by mouth, accompanied by bile salts before operating on a patient with obstructive jaundice. Furthermore, treatment of a newborn baby with this vitamin prevents the tendency to bleed, which often exists. The chief sources of vitamin K are green leafy vegetables, and certain bacteria such as those of the intestinal flora.

Only some of the better-known vitamins and for the most part those that are of demonstrated importance in human nutrition are mentioned here. Investigations on vitamins are extremely numerous, and new discoveries are frequently announced.

ABSORPTION

Water, mineral salts, and digested food must be absorbed from the cavity of the digestive tract and pass into the circulating fluids, then be distributed to the tissues of the body before they can take part in cellular metabolism. Very little absorption takes place in the stomach, although alcohol is readily absorbed from it. Some water is absorbed by osmosis from the small intestine, but most of the water is absorbed in the large intestine. Inorganic salts diffuse through the intestinal wall, but some other cellular activity is also involved. The products of protein digestion (amino acids) are absorbed through the intestinal wall directly into the blood stream. However, glucose must first be changed at the cell surface into glucose phosphate; this is quickly absorbed by the cells lining the small intestine and glucose soon appears in the blood stream. Fatty acids form a complex with certain bile salts. This complex is soluble and passes by diffusion into epithelial cells. There it is converted into a lipid, and much of it passes into the lacteals in the intestinal villi, and is carried to the thoracic lymph duct which empties into a vein in the neck. Glycerol is absorbed by diffusion and enters the blood stream. Absorption of the fat-soluble vitamins A, D, and K develop in the presence of bile salts. Without bile, a deficiency of these vitamins may occur. The 5 million villi increase the internal surface of the small intestine enormously, thus rendering this part of the human digestive tract particularly favorable for absorption.

Diffusion and osmosis (Fig. 8) take part in absorption, but, as noted above, other cellular activities are involved. Small molecules such as those of amino acids pass through cell membranes by way of minute holes too small for large molecules, such as those of cane sugar and of proteins. This does not mean, however, that passage always occurs from the digestive cavity, where the concentration of digested substances is high, into the cells, where the concentration is lower. As a matter of fact, the absorptive cells seem to allow the passage of certain substances and reject the passage of others regardless of their concentration in the digestive cavity or within the cells. How this is brought about is still unexplained, but it must be regulated by cell activities which require expenditure of cellular energy; if cells are killed, substances should pass through their cell membranes according to the physicochemical laws of diffusion and osmosis, but actually they do not.

CIRCULATORY SYSTEMS AND INTERNAL TRANSPORTATION

Circulation in invertebrates

Having captured, ingested, digested, and absorbed food, the animal must now trans-port it to all parts of the body. In the **Protozoa**, this is accomplished by the streaming of the cytoplasm which carries the food vacuoles from one place to another. In the **sponges**, digested food is passed from cell to cell and carried from place to place by amoeboid wandering cells. In hydras and other **coelenterates**, food that is digested in the gastrovascular cavity comes in contact with the inner body wall throughout this cavity, is absorbed by certain gastrodermal cells, and part of it is passed on to other gastrodermal cells and to epidermal cells. A similar method of distribution occurs in the much-branched intestine of **flatworms**.

In the **earthworm**, we encounter a complicated system of tubes, the circulatory system, which carries digested food to all parts of the body. A similar system is present in most types of higher animals. In the **crustaceans** (crayfish), large body spaces (sinuses) are present in the midst of the tissues into which blood from the arteries accumulates and from which it passes into the heart after flowing through the gills. In the insects (grasshopper), the body cavity is a hemocoel filled with blood which bathes the tissues. In the **echinoderms** (starfish), the circulatory system is rather poorly developed; digested food passes into the coelom, where cilia keep the coelomic fluid in motion, thus distributing it.

Circulation in vertebrates

Blood and lymph

In the vertebrates the circulatory system (Fig. 386) consists of a heart, arteries, veins, and lymph vessels. **Human blood** is bright red in arteries and dark red in veins. It makes up about $\frac{1}{14}$ of the body weight. It consists in volume of about $\frac{1}{2}$ liquid plasma and $\frac{1}{2}$ formed elements (Fig. 382). The latter are (1) red corpuscles (erythrocytes), (2) blood platelets, and (3) white cells (leukocytes). The leukocytes are of 5 types: lymphocytes, monocytes, neutrophils, eosinophils, and basophils.

Human erythrocytes are anuclear circular disks, biconcave in profile. They measure approximately 0.0077 mm. in diameter. The framework of the erythrocyte is colorless and sufficiently elastic so that it can squeeze through openings smaller than its diameter. Erythrocytes contain **hemoglobin**, which consists of a protein (globin) and a nonpro-

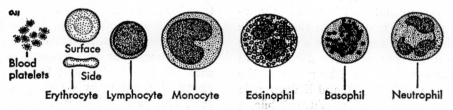

FIGURE 382. Human blood platelets and corpuscles.

tein pigment (hematin). Hemoglobin combines easily with oxygen to form **oxyhemoglobin** and gives up the oxygen in the tissues, becoming thereby **reduced hemoglobin**. The total surface area of the red blood corpuscles in a man is approximately ¾ acre.

If hemoglobin were merely dissolved in the blood fluid, as it is in invertebrates, the blood would be so thick that the heart would have to work much harder to pump it through the body.

Blood platelets are very minute disk-shaped bodies varying in number but averaging about 270,000 per cubic millimeter of blood. They release a substance that aids in the clotting of the blood. **Leukocytes** are capable of amoeboid movements; they wander about in the body and pass back and forth through capillary walls (Fig. 383). In man there are about 5 million erythrocytes and about 9000 white blood cells per cubic millimeter of blood.

The erythrocytes carry oxygen, which in combination with hemoglobin gives them their red color. The white blood cells devour foreign bodies in the blood such as bacteria and broken-down tissue and produce antibodies. The neutrophils are the first line of defense against invading organisms. In general, the chief functions of the blood are to carry oxygen from the lungs to the tissues, to carry waste products to the excretory organs, to carry food to the tissues, to trans-port hormones and other secretions, to help maintain a normal temperature, and to defend the body against infection.

Blood clotting

When a blood vessel is damaged so that blood escapes from it, the flow of blood is stopped by a clot which forms on the surface of the wound. This blood clot is composed of an interlacing network of fibers in which are enmeshed numerous red blood corpuscles. The chemical changes in the formation of the blood clot are complex and not very well understood. However, the fibers are not present in normal circulating blood; therefore it appears that the **fibrin** of which the fibers are composed is in a soluble form. The name **fibrinogen** has been given to this soluble form of fibrin. The substance that converts fibrinogen into the insoluble fibrin is **thrombin**. If thrombin were normally present in the blood, clotting would result, but instead it is in the inactive form of **prothrombin**. Prothrombin, in the presence of calcium and other plasma factors, is converted into thrombin. One of these factors, thrombokinase complex, is not normally present in the blood; therefore, before the chain of clotting reactions can take place, the thrombokinase complex must be formed from the plasma factors, platelets, and an extract from the injured tissue cells. Briefly summarized, the steps are as follows:

Thrombokinase + Prothrombin + Calcium = Thrombin
Thrombin + Fibrinogen = Fibrin
Fibrin + Erythrocytes = Clot

When the red blood corpuscles become trapped in the fibrin network, a clot is formed that prevents escape of blood from the wound. Another substance circulating in the blood, antithrombin, neutralizes the effect of any excess thrombin. In certain individuals, where one or more of these factors may be lacking, the blood clots so slowly that a minor wound results in severe bleeding. This condition, known as hemophilia, is hereditary.

Antibodies

Foreign substances, usually proteins of either plant or animal origin, when introduced into the blood of an animal, will cause the production of antagonistic substances collectively known as **antibodies.** The antibodies which the body produces when one is infected with a disease-causing organism such as bacteria are a part of the body's defense mechanism. They confer a degree of **immunity** to further infection to a given organism; this may be temporary or permanent. Man has taken advantage of this knowledge of immunity by injecting into the blood stream dead or attenuated organisms (vaccines) of the disease against which protection is sought, or in some cases a toxin may be injected. It is also possible to give an injection of an immune blood serum of a person who has had a disease such as measles and has built up immunity through the production of antibodies. If the serum injected is rich enough in the antibodies against measles, the disease is usually prevented or at least its severity is much lessened. The substance that is responsible for the development of a certain antibody is called an **antigen.** The antibodies are protein substances.

Human blood groups

In addition to antibodies produced as a result of contact with an antigen there are some **naturally occurring antibodies,** whose production is a normal event in certain individuals, and not the result of exposure to an antigen for which they are antagonistic. These were discovered when it was found in the transfusion of blood from one person (donor) to another (recipient) that the mixing of the bloods could be harmful instead of helpful. The harmful effects of some blood transfusions, it was discovered, were due to the clumping (**agglutination**) of the erythrocytes, which resulted from an antigen-antibody reaction. The first such unfavorable blood reactions investigated were due to what are now known as the A-B-O groups.

When blood from a donor belonging to the same blood group as the patient (recipient) is used, unfavorable reactions do not occur. Incompatibility of bloods results when the serum of one blood contains an antibody which reacts with the antigen in the erythrocytes of another to cause the clumping of the corpuscles. Landsteiner first found that there are two antigens designated **A** and **B** in the erythrocytes of man, and that the plasma may contain 2 kinds of antibodies called **a** and **b.** This makes possible 4 kinds of blood groups. The antibody **a** is antagonistic to antigen **A** erythrocytes, causing them to clump; likewise, antibody **b** causes clumping of blood corpuscles containing antigen **B.** Obviously antibody **a** must be absent from the blood of a person who has the **A** antigen; and by the same token, antibody **b** must be absent from the blood of an individual who possesses the **B** blood antigen. In other words, whatever antigen one has in his erythrocytes, the corresponding antibody is absent from his blood serum. The 4 A-B-O blood groups are designated **A, B, AB,** and **O,** where **O** indicates the absence of both antigens.

In transfusions, because the donor's blood is diluted in the recipient's blood stream, it is possible to ignore the effects of any antibodies in the donor's blood. The primary consideration is, what effect will the antibodies in the recipient's serum have on the antigens of the donor's red blood corpuscles? Thus it is possible, for example, to give a type **O** blood transfusion to a type **A** person, but the reverse, that is, giving type **A** to a type **O** person, would cause a severe reaction.

The relation of antigen, antibody, and blood group is summarized in the following table:

BLOOD GROUP	ANTIGEN IN ERYTHROCYTES	ANTIBODY IN BLOOD SERUM
A	A	b
B	B	a
AB	AB	None
O	None	a and b

Subgroups of the **A-B-O** blood groups have been discovered in recent years, some of which must be taken into consideration in making blood transfusions, thus complicating the work of the blood specialist.

The blood of individual anthropoid apes is assignable to one of the 4 human groups; for example, **A** and **O** have been found in chimpanzees. This is evidence of a close chemical relationship between the apes and man. Blood groups are also known in the rabbit, dog, and cattle, but none is identical with a human type.

Rh factor

The **Rh blood factor** is another important blood antigen found in man and monkeys. About 86 per cent of the white population of the United States have this antigen, hence are called Rh-positive; the remaining 14 per cent are without it and are therefore Rh-negative. Since the discovery of the Rh factor, it has been established that there are no less than six different antigens involved in the Rh system; of these, however, only the Rh antigen is usually of serious clinical significance.

There is no antibody that normally accompanies the Rh antigen as is true of the antigens of the **A-B-O** blood groups. However, the Rh antigen will cause formation of antibodies if the blood of an Rh-positive person is transfused into an Rh-negative person. If at some subsequent time another transfusion of Rh-positive blood is made to this Rh-negative person, then the Rh antigen reacts with the antibodies, causing a serious transfusion reaction, agglutination, which may result in death.

Another serious result of Rh incompatibility may be caused when an Rh-negative pregnant woman carries an Rh-positive child. Rh-positive erythrocytes may pass from the blood stream of the fetus into the mother's blood, where they stimulate production of antibodies (Fig. 420). These antibodies of the mother may diffuse into the blood stream of the fetus and cause destruction of fetal erythrocytes. This results in varying degrees of injury to the fetus, depending on the concentration (titer) of the antibodies present. The effects range all the way from a very mild anemia, scarcely detectable, to more severe anemic conditions, various structural abnormalities, abnormalities of the nervous system, sometimes causing mental deficiency, to miscarriage or stillbirth.

There are many other blood groups such as the P, M-N-S, Kell, Lewis, Lutheran, Kidd, and Duffy. This is a field in which there is much research activity, and new blood group antigens are frequently found. Since the presence of the antigens of one blood group system is independent of another, a person may have any one of many possible different blood groupings. Considering all of these blood group systems, the number of different blood type combinations possible is well up in the millions, which makes them useful in crime detection and in determining the parentage of a child.

Anthropologists have used the knowledge of blood groups in the study of the relationships of races. By a special technique it is possible to determine the blood groups of ancient bones and mummies.

The inheritance of some of the blood groups will be discussed in a later chapter on heredity.

Tissue fluid and lymph

Materials do not pass directly to the body cells from the capillaries or from the body cells to the capillaries, but they are dependent for this service on tissue fluid (Fig. 383), which bathes the cells, and by means of diffusion and osmosis brings about the exchange between blood and cells. Plasma filters out through the walls of the capillaries; it contains **leukocytes** but usually no erythrocytes. In the tissue spaces are minute tubes, the **lymphatics**; these are part of a

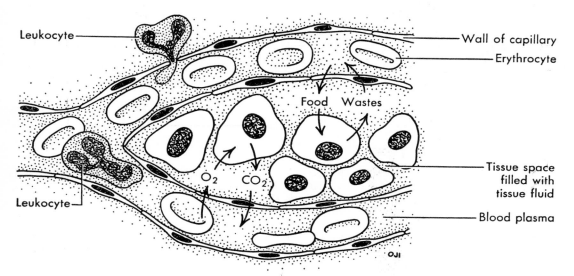

Leukocyte — Wall of capillary — Erythrocyte

Food Wastes

O_2 CO_2

Leukocyte — Tissue space filled with tissue fluid — Blood plasma

FIGURE 383. Drawing showing how tissue fluid serves as a medium of exchange between the blood vessels and body cells. Note diapedesis of a leukocyte through the wall of a capillary.

closed system of tubes (Fig. 386) which finally ends in two large tubes, the right lymphatic duct and the left thoracic duct; these return the **lymph,** which is tissue fluid that has entered the lymphatic vessels, to the blood by emptying it into veins in the neck region. The lymphatic vessels of the intestine are called lacteals (Fig. 380); these absorb fatty substances. Some tissue fluid is returned to the blood stream by reentering the capillaries.

Spleen

The spleen is a bean-shaped lymphatic organ lying immediately below the diaphragm on the left side. It is not essential to life; the body withstands its surgical removal successfully.

It serves as a reservoir for blood and can hold from $\frac{1}{5}$ to $\frac{1}{3}$ of all the blood in the body. By its contractions and expansions it can regulate the volume of circulating blood to changing needs. In the spleen, also, old red blood corpuscles are destroyed, and white blood cells (lymphocytes) and monocytes are produced.

Circulation in man and other mammals

The mammalian heart (Fig. 384) consists of 4 chambers, 2 thin-walled atria and 2 muscular ventricles. The pulmonary veins bring blood from the lungs to the left atrium; and other veins bring blood from the rest of the body to the right atrium. Blood from the atria flows into the ventricles beneath them, aided by the contraction of the atrial walls. When the ventricles are filled, they begin to contract, and the blood

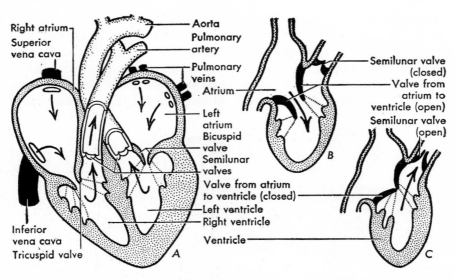

FIGURE 384. Diagram illustrating chambers of the heart and the action of the valves in man. A, internal structure of heart and direction of blood flow through it. B, blood is flowing from atrium to ventricle, and the semilunar valve is closed. C, the valve between the atrium and ventricle is closed, and blood is forced past the semilunar valve into the artery. Note that because of the upright position of the body of man, the anterior vena cava is called the superior vena cava, and the posterior vena cava is termed the inferior vena cava. (A after Walter and B after Peabody and Hunt.)

is forced from the right ventricle through the pulmonary artery into the lungs, and from the left ventricle through the aorta to the rest of the body. Valves prevent the blood from flowing back from the ventricles into the atria and from returning to the ventricles from the arteries (Fig. 384). The human heart contracts about 72 times per minute. What is responsible for the heart beat is not known; it appears to be due to factors within the heart itself and not to nervous control from outside, since some hearts continue to beat after they have been removed from the body.

Elastic tissue and muscle tissue are especially abundant in the walls of the arteries (Fig. 385); they regulate the flow of blood forward to the capillaries in the tissues. The pressure exerted by the blood against the walls of the arteries is known as the **blood pressure.** When an artery is cut, blood spurts from it, indicating that it is under pressure. Blood from a cut vein flows out continuously, indicating low pressure. Blood pressure depends on the force of the contracting ventricles of the heart, on the elasticity of the walls of the blood vessels, and on the resistance to the flow through the vessels. High blood pressure may be brought about by reduction in the elasticity of the small arteries, as in **arteriosclerosis.** If a finger is placed on the radial artery on the thumb side of the wrist, or on other arteries, a distention will be felt corresponding to the beat of the heart. This is due to the alternate dilatation and elastic recoil of the artery, due to the forcing of blood through it by the contractions of the heart, and constitutes the **pulse.** The character of the heart's action can be determined by feeling the pulse.

The **capillaries** (Fig. 383) are minute tubes with a thin wall, consisting of a single layer of cells which allow passage of material through them to and from the tissues. They form networks connecting the smallest

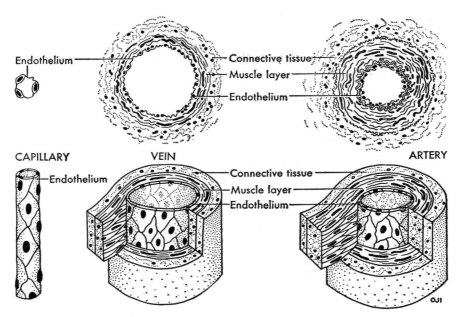

Endothelium — Connective tissue — Muscle layer — Endothelium —

CAPILLARY VEIN ARTERY

— Endothelium — Connective tissue — — Muscle layer — — Endothelium —

FIGURE 385. Structure of blood vessels. The muscle layer of an artery is thicker than the muscle layer of a vein of the same size; and a vein usually has a lumen of greater diameter than its corresponding artery.

arteries (**arterioles**) with the smallest veins (**venules**). It has been estimated that if all the capillaries in the human body were placed end to end, they would form a tube 62,000 miles long. Since each capillary is only about 1 mm. long, the total number is almost inconceivable. The wall surface of these capillaries is about 67,000 square feet or 1½ acres. Capillaries carry out the principal functions of the blood, such as taking in the secretions from the ductless glands, absorbing oxygen from and giving up carbon dioxide to the lungs, delivering waste products to the kidneys, absorbing food from the digestive system, and transporting food and oxygen to the tissues in exchange for cellular excretions.

The **rate of circulation** is so rapid as almost to defy our imagination. The entire blood supply passes from the heart, through the body, and back again to the heart in about 20 to 40 seconds. This means that the 5 quarts of blood in an average-sized man pass through his body from 3000 to 4000 times per day; this accounts for the rapid distribution of substances that gain entrance into the blood stream. The **velocity** of the blood flow differs in different arteries and veins, depending largely on the size of the vessel. In the large arteries, blood moves along rapidly; in the smaller arteries and capillaries, it moves more slowly. The rate of movement in the veins is less than in the arteries.

Distribution of digested food

Digested food that is absorbed by the cells of the intestinal walls, and which diffuses from them into the blood capillaries, is carried in the blood stream through the hepatic portal vein to the liver (Fig. 386). From the liver the blood passes into the hepatic vein and flows to the heart, which pumps it into the general circulation. Fats that enter the lymphatic vessels in the villi of the intestinal wall are carried by the lymph into the thoracic duct, which usually empties into the venous system in the region

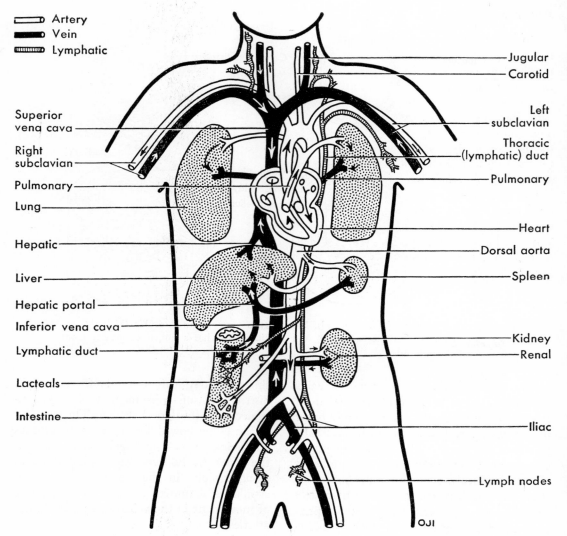

Figure 386. The larger blood and lymphatic vessels in man, together with some of the organs they serve. The lymph flows in only one general direction, toward the heart.

of the junction of the left subclavian and internal jugular veins. From here it is carried into the right atrium, then into the right ventricle, which forces it through the pulmonary arteries into the lungs. From the lungs it is returned by the pulmonary veins to the left atrium and then into the left ventricle, which forces it through the aorta to all parts of the body. From the capillaries, the digested food diffuses into the tissue fluid in the intercellular spaces, and from the tissue fluid into the cells where it is metabolized or stored.

Lymph nodes are located along the course of the lymph vessels. The node has a dual function: it produces lymphocytes, and is an organ in which lymph is filtered and purified as it flows through. Many kinds of cancers tend to spread by way of the lmphatic vessels.

Anemia

One of the commonest abnormalities of the blood is anemia. In this condition the number of red corpuscles may be reduced from the normal of about 5 million per cubic millimeter to 1 million or less. The erythrocytes may also be deficient in hemoglobin. The quantity of oxygen that can be carried to the tissues is correspondingly reduced. Of the several types of anemia, that known as **pernicious anemia** is of greatest interest. Before 1927 it was fatal in from 2 to 5 years after onset, but at that time, due to the investigations of Whipple on dogs, and Minot and Murphy on human beings, it was discovered that liver was an effective method of treatment. This is because there is an anti-anemic substance in the liver which stimulates the regeneration of red blood corpuscles.

Harvey and the circulation of the blood

No discussion of circulation would be complete without mention of the English physician William Harvey (Fig. 457). By means of experimental methods, he was able to demonstrate that the blood circulates through the body, being forced out of the heart and returning again to the heart (Fig. 387). This work threw an entirely new light on the subject of physiology in general, and had tremendous influence on the progress of this science.

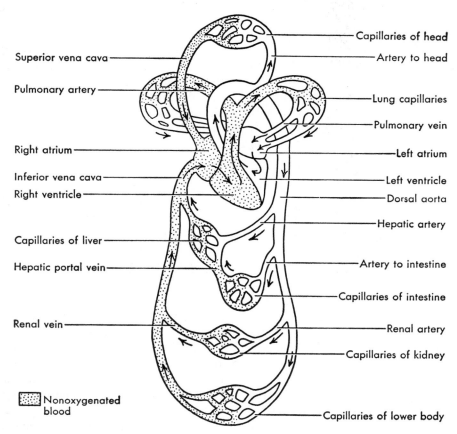

Capillaries of head
Artery to head
Superior vena cava
Pulmonary artery
Lung capillaries
Pulmonary vein
Right atrium
Left atrium
Inferior vena cava
Left ventricle
Right ventricle
Dorsal aorta
Hepatic artery
Capillaries of liver
Artery to intestine
Hepatic portal vein
Capillaries of intestine
Renal vein
Renal artery
Capillaries of kidney
Nonoxygenated blood
Capillaries of lower body

FIGURE 387. Diagram showing the general scheme of blood circulation in the human body.

RESPIRATORY SYSTEMS
AND RESPIRATION

Respiration is a process made necessary because uninterrupted liberation of energy is indispensable for the continued existence of the cells of the body. Usually animals obtain their energy from the burning of foods. Actual use of oxygen by the cells is called **internal** (**cellular** or **biologic**) **respiration,** as distinguished from **external respiration,** which involves the entrance of oxygen into the lungs and exit of carbon dioxide from them, and the transport of oxygen from the lungs to the cells and of carbon dioxide from the cells to the lungs. Internal respiration is the same for most cells, but external respiration differs among the various groups of animals.

Respiration in the **Protozoa** consists principally in the diffusion of oxygen, dissolved in water, through the surface protoplasm into the body, and of carbon dioxide through the surface protoplasm out of the body. The body surface is very permeable to oxygen and carbon dioxide; oxygen is in higher concentration in the water than in the protoplasm, and carbon dioxide is in higher concentration in the protoplasm than in the water, hence the diffusion of oxygen into the cell and of carbon dioxide out of the cell. In sponges, coelenterates, and many other **aquatic animals**, respiration occurs directly between the cells in the body wall and the water that bathes them.

Earthworms and other similar animals do not possess respiratory systems; they take in oxygen and give off carbon dioxide through the moist skin. Oxygen from the air diffuses into the cells in the skin and from these cells into the blood in the capillaries which lie in large numbers just beneath the surface layer of cells. The oxygen is transported by the blood to the various organs, and diffuses from the blood into intercellular spaces, and then into the cells. Carbon dioxide diffuses out of the cells into the blood, which carries it to the skin, where it diffuses from the blood into the cells of the skin, and out through the moist surface.

Insects and certain other types of arthropods possess respiratory systems consisting of networks of tubes, the **tracheae,** that carry air into and out of the body through a number of pairs of openings (spiracles) in the sides of the body segments. From the finest tracheae (tracheoles), gases diffuse into and out of the tissue cells. In these animals the circulatory system is of little importance for purposes of transporting gases.

In many aquatic animals with circulatory systems, respiration takes place with the aid of **gills.** For example, the crayfish possesses two rows of gills contained in branchial chambers, one row on each side of the thorax. Water flows into the posterior opening and out through the anterior opening of the branchial chamber; and oxygen diffuses from this water into and through the cells of the gill filaments, into the blood in the efferent gill channels. Carbon dioxide diffuses out of the blood in the afferent gill channels into the gill filaments and from there out of the body. Respiration is carried on in a similar fashion by fish. Certain so-called lungfishes take in oxygen and give off carbon dioxide by means of lungs as well as gills.

The **amphibians** such as the frog carry on respiration through the moist surface of the body, both while in the water and in the air, and also by means of **lungs.** Other groups of higher vertebrates respire with the aid of lungs. The lungs of the frog are simple, whereas those of the higher vertebrates are more complex. The essential feature of the lungs is the moist epithelial lining with oxygen-containing air in the cavities on one side, and blood in the capillaries on the other side. Oxygen from the lung cavities diffuses into the epithelial cells, and thence into the blood; and carbon dioxide diffuses from the blood into the cells, and thence into the lung cavities.

The lungs of **reptiles** are more complex than those of amphibians. Certain aquatic turtles possess cloacal sacs that act as auxiliary respiratory organs; these are comparable to the tracheal gills of dragonfly naiads, and the gill trees of sea cucumbers. In **birds,** the lungs are assisted by air sacs; and where the trachea divides into two bronchi, an enlargement known as a syrinx serves as a vocal organ.

Mammals are provided with respiratory systems similar to those of human beings. In man, air passes through the nose or mouth into the lungs by way of the larynx, trachea, bronchi, and bronchioles (Fig. 389). Air is warmed, moistened, and filtered in the nose. The **larynx** is a triangular organ; the Adam's apple, in man has 9 pieces of cartilage in its walls to prevent it from collapsing. The slitlike opening in the pharynx is the **glottis,** which is protected by a leaf-shaped lid, the **epiglottis.** Within the larynx are the **vocal cords.** Air forced out of the lungs may vibrate these cords, and the column of air above them gives rise to sounds. This may be compared to an organ pipe in which a reed and a column of air are set into vibration by a blast of air. Certain notes can be played on the organ which are remarkably similar to the human voice. The cavities of the pharynx, mouth, and nose act as resonators; the amplitude of the vibrations and the volume and force of the air current determine the loudness and intensity; and the length, tightness, and frequency of vibration of the cords determine the pitch of the voice. In women and children the vocal cords are usually short, and the voice is

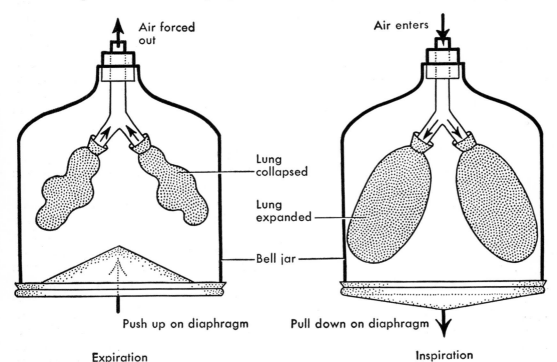

FIGURE 388. An apparatus to show the role of the diaphragm in breathing—rubber balloons in bell jars. The bottom of each jar is covered with a flexible rubber membrane. When the rubber membrane is pulled down, the space inside the jar is increased and pressure of air through the tube causes the balloons to expand. Similarly, when the diaphragm is lowered, the chest cavity becomes larger and air rushes into the lungs. In expiration, the diaphragm moves upward. An adult normally breathes on the average of about 16 times per minute.

high-pitched. In men the cords are usually longer, and the voice is lower. The **trachea** is a tube about 4½ inches long with **C-**shaped rings of cartilage in its walls; it branches into two **bronchi,** and these branch into many bronchial tubes or **bronchioles,** each of which terminates in an elongated saccule, the alveolar duct, which bears on its surface air sacs (alveoli). The number of alveoli in the human lungs has been estimated to be approximately 750 million. The area of surface exposed to the air within the lungs is over 800 square feet, or more than 50 times the skin surface of the body. The lungs (Fig. 389) are membranous sacs, each lying in a cavity lined with a serous membrane, the **pleura,** which lessens friction. When the pleura becomes inflamed, pleurisy results. The quantity of air that can be expelled from the lungs averages from 3500 to 4000 cc.

Breathing and the respiratory function of blood

Since no circulation of air occurs in the lungs, respiratory movements, which we know as breathing, are necessary. **Inspiration** is due to the enlargement of the lungs, following the enlargement of the chest cavity as a result of the contraction of the muscles of the diaphragm (Fig. 388), and other muscles of inspiration which cause the ribs to swing up and out. Air is drawn in through the trachea and bronchi. **Expiration** is produced by the contraction of the chest cavity due to the relaxation of the inspiratory muscles. The breathing movements are not controlled within the lungs but by a center in the medulla of the brain; if nerves to the lungs are cut, breathing ceases. The changes in the quantity of oxygen and carbon dioxide in the lungs during breathing are not great, as shown by the following figures:

	PER CENT
Inspired air:	Oxygen, 20.96
Expired air:	Oxygen, 16.02

4.94 loss

	PER CENT
Inspired air:	Carbon dioxide, 0.04
Expired air:	Carbon dioxide, 4.48

4.44 gain

Most of the oxygen that diffuses into the blood enters into a loose chemical combination with hemoglobin, producing thereby oxyhemoglobin, which gives the red color to arterial (oxygenated) blood. Oxyhemoglobin at the capillary level gives up its oxygen which diffuses into the cells, leaving the blood dark red or purplish in color (venous blood). The freed oxygen diffuses through the tissue fluid into the cells to take part in cellular or biologic respiration. The carbon dioxide resulting from metabolic processes within the cells diffuses into the blood, where it is less concentrated. Some of it combines with hemoglobin, and the remainder is transported in the blood stream to the lungs in the form of bicarbonates. In the lungs, carbon dioxide is freed from these bicarbonates and from the hemoglobin and diffuses through the cells into the air in the lung cavities. From the lung cavities, it enters the sea of air which surrounds man and in which he lives.

Some problems of space travel

A great sea of air engulfs the earth, and man lives at the bottom of it. Just as in the ocean, the pressure is greatest at the bottom. When he rises up in air to great heights, differences between pressures of high altitudes and those on the ground become evident. At sea level, the air man breathes has a pressure of 14.7 pounds per square inch. At high altitudes, the atmospheric pressure decreases, although the oxygen content varies little. At 18,000 feet the atmospheric pressure is only one-half that at sea level, and man must breathe air under pressure in order to obtain enough oxygen for the metabolic life processes. At altitudes greater than 18,000 feet, he suffers seriously from lack of oxygen unless special oxygen equipment is used. At about 43,000 feet, or 8 miles up, a man loses consciousness in 15 seconds and

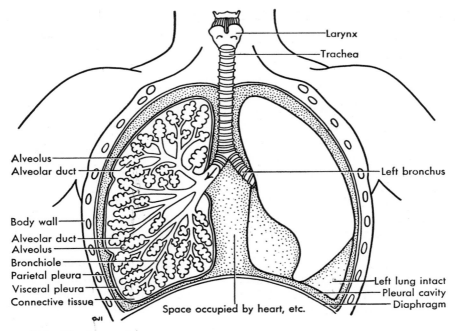

FIGURE 389. The lungs of man, each enclosed in a double-walled sac which is composed of visceral pleura and parietal pleura. The right lung is cut open to show the internal structure.

will die unless pure oxygen is supplied under pressure. The higher the altitude, the lower the temperature required to boil fluids. Hence, at approximately 63,000 feet, the pressure is so reduced that the body fluids, including the blood, literally boil.

It is obvious that the reduced atmospheric pressure of high altitudes requires a pressure cabin if one were to survive in space. Pilots flying jet planes above 48,000 feet must wear pressurized suits.

By taking advantage of what is known about aviation physiology, it has been possible for man to attain an altitude of about 24 miles above the earth. At such a height, one is so near the top of the ocean of atmosphere that less than 1 per cent is above him. Nevertheless, mice sent into outer space have returned alive in a pressurized rocket which reached a height of 36 miles. To conquer outer space, a thorough understanding of the physiology of respiration and circulatory functions is needed to provide the necessary safeguards.

When man moves into outer space, he enters a hostile environment, one for which he is not biologically adapted. Yet, there is serious interest in flight to the moon. At this writing men are being screened and tested in equipment that it is hoped will keep them alive in outer space.

EXCRETORY SYSTEMS AND DISPOSAL OF WASTES

Continuity of chemical reactions in cells depends on the removal of the waste products of their metabolic activity. The continual removal of metabolic wastes or excretions is necessary. A metabolic waste is known as an **excretion**; also the removal of metabolic wastes from the body is called excretion. Carbon dioxide is a waste product of metabolism, but it has already been dealt with in our discussion of respiration. As a result of metabolism, the cell needs to get rid of (1) certain soluble nitrogenous salts such as urea, (2) soluble inorganic salts such as sodium chloride, and (3) water, which is one of the chief products of oxidation. These substances usually escape from the cells by diffusion, are transported by the circulatory system, when this is present, and cast out of the body by means of an excretory system.

In fresh-water protozoans, most excretory substances diffuse directly into the surrounding medium; water, however, does not; it is eliminated by the contractile vacuoles. In the **lower invertebrates** such as sponges and coelenterates, excretory substances are eliminated by the cells in the body wall, with the aid of amoeboid wandering cells as transporting agents. Many of the flatworms are provided with a complex system of tubes, some of which end in peculiar cells with a bunch of cilia at the end, whose flickering movement has given them the name flame cells. The cilia create a current in the tubes, which carries the wastes out of the body through excretory pores. We encounter another type of excretory system in the earthworm, where coiled tubes termed nephridia extract waste products from the blood, and carry them, together with excretion-loaded coelomic fluid, out of the body through nephridiopores. The crayfish has one pair of excretory organs called green glands, which are probably homologous with the nephridia of earthworms. The organs of excretion in insects are long, slender Malpighian tubules that are coiled about in the body cavity and discharge excretory products into the anterior end of the hind-gut.

A large part of the water in vertebrates is excreted through the **lungs** by evaporation. **Sweat glands** also excrete water but are of little importance in the elimination of other excretory material. The sweat glands are very valuable, however, in the regulation of body temperature, since, by the evaporation of the water they excrete, heat is lost, which balances the heat constantly produced in the body. The **liver** excretes certain substances, such as the decomposition products of hemoglobin, which are carried in the bile into the duodenum and out of the body in the feces. The **feces** are not chiefly excre-

tory products of metabolism; most of their contents never have been a part of the protoplasm of the body.

The principal **excretory organs of vertebrates** are known as kidneys. The **kidneys** (Fig. 390) excrete urine, which is carried by two ureters to the bladder, and from the bladder to the outside of the body through the urethra. The kidneys of man are bean-shaped tubular glands, about 4½ inches long. The renal arteries, which come directly from the aorta, supply them with blood, and the renal veins carry the blood from the kidneys to the inferior venae cavae. In section, the following regions are revealed: an outer cortex, an inner striated medulla divided into about 8 to 18 cone-shaped pyramids, and the expanded end of the ureter known as the pelvis. Blood entering the kidney brings waste matter which is filtered from it, collected in renal tubules, and discharged into the ureter.

One kidney contains about a million renal corpuscles. The renal corpuscles and tubules are somewhat similar in structure and function to nephridia such as those of the earthworm. Each kidney begins in the cortex as a capsule surrounding a clump of capillaries, the glomerulus; this is where the blood plasma containing metabolic wastes filters into the tubules. The capsule opens into a convoluted tube that leads to the loop of Henle, where useful materials including some water are returned to the blood stream; this opens into a collecting tube which leads to the pelvis. From one to two quarts of urine are excreted per day by an average adult. Some of the constituents of normal urine are urea, creatinine, ammonia, hippuric acid, and purine bodies.

Abnormal kidney function is not to be taken lightly. Certain salts may form kidney stones in the pelvis of the kidney, and if they are too large to pass through the kidney ducts, they may cause great pain; sometimes requiring surgical removal. Some abnormal constituents which appear in the urine are albumen, acetone bodies, excess

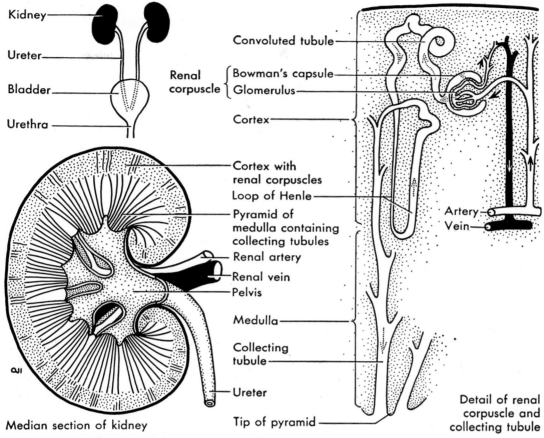

Kidney

Ureter

Bladder

Urethra

Renal corpuscle { Bowman's capsule / Glomerulus }

Convoluted tubule

Cortex

Cortex with renal corpuscles

Loop of Henle

Pyramid of medulla containing collecting tubules

Renal artery

Renal vein

Pelvis

Medulla

Collecting tubule

Ureter

Tip of pyramid

Artery

Vein

Median section of kidney

Detail of renal corpuscle and collecting tubule

FIGURE 390. Excretory system of man. *Upper left*, diagram of entire system. *Lower left*, kidney in median section. *Right*, relations of renal corpuscle tubules, and blood vessels. Solid arrows, path of blood; dotted arrows, path of excretion.

glucose, pus, and blood. A urine analysis is an index of bodily function and is of great assistance in medical diagnosis.

Although both kidneys are needed to eliminate the wastes of a pregnant woman, a kidney may be removed from certain individuals, with the remaining one ridding the body of metabolic wastes satisfactorily.

SECRETIONS

Secretions are substances that are manufactured by the protoplasm within certain cells and are used by the cells that synthesize them, or they are discharged from the cells and used elsewhere in the body. During secretion, oxygen is used up and carbon dioxide is produced, indicating that the process requires the energy liberated by oxidation. Secretory cells may discharge their products continuously or store them until the proper stimulus brings about their discharge at one time. Usually these specialized cells contain visible secretory granules. In some cases it is difficult to distinguish between secretions and excretions, but usually the former are of use to the body, and the latter are waste products that would bring about the death of the animal if they were not eliminated.

Protozoa all produce secretions, for example, the digestive enzymes that are poured into the food vacuoles, and the skeletons of the foraminiferans and radiolarians. In **Metazoa,** cells or organs are specialized for secretion of particular substances; such cells or organs are called glands. **Unicellular glands** occur abundantly in the lower invertebrates, such as those that secrete the spicules and spongin in sponges, and the hypnotoxin in the nematocysts of coelenterates. They also occur in higher animals,

including vertebrates, where they may be found in all mucous membranes. Most glands in higher animals, however, are **multicellular** and consist of epithelial tissue specialized for this purpose. Some of the types of glands are illustrated in Fig. 391.

Glands and their secretions may be separated into two types: (1) glands that secrete directly to the outside or into a cavity, or discharge their products through a duct, are **duct (exocrine) glands** and produce external secretions; and (2) glands that discharge

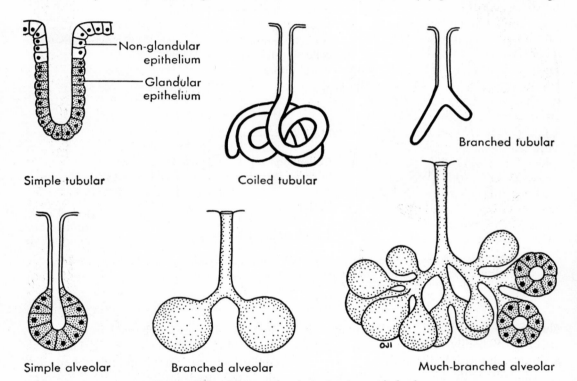

Non-glandular epithelium

Glandular epithelium

Simple tubular

Coiled tubular

Branched tubular

Simple alveolar

Branched alveolar

Much-branched alveolar

FIGURE 391.   Diagram showing some types of glands.

their products directly into the blood or lymph are **ductless or endocrine glands** and produce **internal secretions.** Glands of external secretion vary greatly in the character of their products. Some of the principal types are as follows.

1. Protective glands that secrete **mucus,** as in the skin of the earthworm and frog; **exoskeletons,** as the cuticle of the earth-

worm, crayfish, and grasshopper; and **shells,** such as those of mussels. Many types of glands secrete substances that protect the eggs of animals: the cocoon of the earthworm, the egg case of the cockroach, the shell of birds' eggs, and the substance that fastens the eggs of the crayfish to her swimmerets.

2. Skeletal glands that secrete the calcare-

ous and siliceous skeletons of protozoans, the spicules and spongin in sponges, the coral in coral polyps, and the calcareous plates in starfishes.

3. Digestive glands that secrete digestive juices; a list of those in man is presented on page 517.

4. Nutritive glands that secrete milk and other products that serve as food for the young, such as the mammary glands of mammals, and those lining the crop of the pigeon that secrete the cheesy substance called pigeon's milk.

5. Poison glands that secrete poisonous substances for purposes of defense or offense, such as those in the skin of frogs, toads, and salamanders, in the sting of the bee and the scorpion, and those located in the heads of the Gila monster and the rattlesnake.

6. Constructive glands that produce silk with which caterpillars build cocoons and spiders build webs, and wax with which bees construct honeycomb.

Many other examples of glands could be listed from those we have encountered during our studies of animals.

UTILIZATION OF FOOD IN THE BODY

Now that we have learned what food is, where it is obtained, how it is captured, how it is ingested, how it is digested, how the products of digestion are distributed throughout the body and absorbed, how oxygen is obtained during respiration, how secretions are formed for digestion and for other purposes, and how the wastes involved in these processes are eliminated, we are ready to consider the utilization of food in the body. What becomes of oxygen, water, mineral salts, vitamins, carbohydrates, fats, and proteins, and what are the requirements of animals with respect to these food substances?

Oxygen

Oxygen enters cells from the medium in which the cells live (water in many aquatic animals, and tissue fluid or blood in higher animals); it is used in building up proteins within the cell and in the production of energy by oxidation.

Water

Water makes up about 60 to 90 per cent, by weight, of protoplasm. It is ingested in greater amounts than all other substances combined, and it is also an important excretion. It is the vehicle of the principal foods and excretion products, for most of these are dissolved as they enter or leave the body. In fact, as clearer ideas of the physicochemical organization of protoplasm have developed, it has become evident that the organism itself is essentially an aqueous solution in which are spread out colloidal substances of great complexity. As a result of these conditions, there is hardly a physiologic process in which water is not of fundamental importance.

Mineral salts

Salts are essential constituents of cells and of the environment in which cells live. They take part in the building up of protoplasm and in the activities of various types of cells. For example, iron is a necessary constituent of hemoglobin, iodine of the hormone thyroxin of the thyroid gland, and calcium and phosphorus of the bones. In many cases only a minute quantity of a mineral is required, but without this health would be impaired or life impossible. For example, the necessary daily quantity of iron is only 0.006 gram and of iodine only 0.00001 gram, but calcium and phosphorus are required in great abundance.

Carbohydrates

Carbohydrates are furnished to the cells in the form of simple sugars. They may com-

bine with other compounds to form protoplasm, or they may be oxidized to furnish
energy for the cells; this oxidation occurs
at a relatively low temperature, due to the
activity of enzymes within the cells. Certain
amounts of glucose are converted in the
liver and muscles into glycogen, which is
often called animal starch. Stored glycogen
can be reconverted into glucose and utilized
when needed between meals.

Fats

Fats and fatlike bodies may be built up
into the protoplasm of cells; they are especially abundant in cell membranes and
are largely responsible for the semipermeabil-
ity of these membranes. They may be
stored in special fat cells that are scattered
throughout the body. When insufficient
food is taken into the body, these fat reservoirs are utilized for production of energy
and heat, a process that requires more time
than is the case with glycogen. An example
of a chemical equation involving oxidation
of a typical fat (tripalmitin) into carbon
dioxide and water with the liberation of
energy is as follows:

$$\text{Fat} \qquad \text{Oxygen} \quad \text{Carbon dioxide}$$
$$2C_{51}H_{98}O_6 \ + \ 145O_2 \ \rightarrow \ 102CO_2 \ +$$
$$\text{Water}$$
$$98H_2O \ + \ \text{Energy}$$

Proteins

The amino acids that result from digestion of proteins are much more important
than carbohydrates or fats in the synthesis of

protoplasm. Amino acids are the "building
blocks" of proteins. In order to grow, the
human body must have amino acids. It
needs them to build muscles, skin, hair, nails,
the various organs, etc. The growing cell is
provided with a mechanism which enables it
to put together the various amino acids in
the number and proportion required to
make a specific protein. Amino acids may
be oxidized in production of energy but this
is a minor function. Very little protein is
stored in the body; but when carbohydrates
and fats are used up, the proteins supply
energy, that is, the protoplasm itself is oxidized. The proteins in the animal body can
be built up from amino acids, but the body
can also convert them into simple sugars,
and simple sugars into fat.

SELECTED COLLATERAL READINGS

Baitsell, G.A. *Human Biology.* McGraw-Hill,
New York, 1950.
Carlson, A.J., and Johnson, V. *The Machinery
of the Body.* Univ. Chicago Press, Chicago,
1953.
Gaffon, H. (ed.). *Research in Photosynthesis.*
Interscience Publishers, New York, 1957.
Gerard, R.W. (ed.). *Food for Life.* Univ. of
Chicago Press, Chicago, 1952.
Kimber, D.C., Gray, C.E., Stackpole, C.E., and
Leavell, L.C. *Textbook of Anatomy and
Physiology.* Macmillan, New York, 1956.
Mitchell, P.H. *Textbook of General Physiol-
ogy.* McGraw-Hill, New York, 1956.
Scheer, B.T. *Comparative Physiology.* Wiley,
New York, 1948.

CHAPTER 33

Coordination

and

Behavior

The **behavior** and reproduction of an animal depend on the coordination of its organs. This coordination in the higher invertebrates and vertebrates is accomplished largely through the agency of a nervous system and sense organs, and by means of a number of chemical substances (hormones) secreted by the ductless (endocrine) glands. The relations of the nervous system and endocrine glands are complex and closely associated. Naturally, the higher an animal is in the scale of life, the more complex these agents of coordination become. We have studied the reactions of a number of different animals, and their various types of nervous systems, sense organs, hormones, and behavior; now we are ready to consider the subject as a whole.

Coordination in lower invertebrates

Irritability and **conductivity** were found to be fundamental characteristics of protoplasm. Amoebas and other **protozoans** that lack specialized organelles for reception of stimuli, nevertheless, respond to changes in the environment much as do higher animals that possess sense organs and nervous systems. However, some of the more complex ciliates are supplied with a system of fibrils (**neuromotor apparatus**), some of which are conductile, for example, coordination of ciliary action. Reactions to stimuli in **sponges** are hardly more advanced than in protozoans, unless the studies of deCeccatty prove to be correct. If the researches going on now in America confirm deCecatty's report of a primitive type of nervous system in sponges, then it will be recognized that true nerve cells first appear in sponges rather than in the hydra (coelenterate). However, if no nerve cells are present, then stimuli are transmitted very slowly from cell to cell. True nerve cells unquestionably appear in the hydra, where sensory cells (**receptors**)

543

serve for reception of stimuli and are in direct continuity with fibers from nerve cells (**conductors**) which send out processes to the contractile fibrils (**effectors**) in the epitheliomuscular cells. All together, these constitute a sort of nerve net or plexus. The coelenterates have a **receptor-effector** nervous mechanism.

Coordination in higher invertebrates

A definite nervous system is present in the **flatworms** and **round worms**. Flatworms have long nerve cords connected by transverse nerves, a concentration of nervous tissue (the brain) near the anterior end of the body, and sense organs such as "eyes." More complex are the nervous systems of the **earthworm, crayfish, grasshopper,** and **frog**; in them and in other lower animals, sense organs of many kinds are present. In all of these, as well as in man, the **mechanism of reaction** is the same: a stimulus is received by a sense organ, the impulse is conducted by the nervous system, and the response is carried out by muscles or glands, which are, therefore, effectors.

The chief advances shown by the annelid type of nervous system over that of the coelenterates involves the concentration of ganglion cells to develop a central nervous system, and the addition of association neurons within the central nervous system to mediate impulses between afferent and efferent neurons. These advances made possible the one-way conduction and reflex arcs, instead of the diffuse nerve pathways typical of the coelenterates.

Nervous coordination

Nervous coordination is brought about by the activities of **neurons** as shown in Fig. 236. The **reflex arc** as described in the earthworm (Fig. 95), is the functional unit of nervous action. With the help of **association neurons**, which are located within the central nervous system, more complex activities are performed. The same basic mechanisms of nervous coordination exist in vertebrates. Thus the differences, from earthworm to man, are due to an increased number and specialization of receptors, association neurons, and effectors. It is a **receptor-association neuron-effector** system.

Coordination by means of the **central nervous system** is largely responsible for behavior as far as voluntary muscles are concerned, but coordination of the activities of involuntary muscles and glands is also necessary. This is accomplished by the **autonomic nervous system.**

In some cases **hormones** take part in reflexes. For example, in a blind catfish, bright light stimulates photoreceptors of the skin which send nervous impulses to the pituitary gland; here a hormone (intermedin) is secreted which is carried by the circulatory system to chromatophores in the skin, causing them to enlarge and darken the skin color. This type of reflex is known as a **neurohumoral reflex.**

It is interesting to note that in some invertebrates as well as vertebrates the passage of a nerve impulse from one neuron to another, or to a motor end organ, appears to be due to the liberation of a chemical mediator.

Nervous systems and sense organs of vertebrates

The nervous system and sense organs of the frog and certain other vertebrates have been described.

Brains of vertebrates

The differences in the **brains of the various classes of vertebrates** are probably more striking than those exhibited by any of the other organs in the body, as the diagrams in Fig. 392 indicate. In the **cyclostomes** both the cerebral lobes and cerebellum are quite small. In the **fish** the optic lobes and medulla are especially large; the size of the cerebellum depends on the swimming ability of the species. In **amphibians** the olfactory lobes are large and elongated; the optic lobes are smaller; the cerebellum is a mere transverse band; and the medulla is produced by a broadening of the spinal cord. In **reptiles** the olfactory lobes are usually not well developed; the cerebral hemispheres are much larger and a little gray matter is present in the cortex; the optic lobes are quite small and the cerebellum is larger; and both

pineal and parietal bodies are present, the latter forming a median eye in *Sphenodon*. In **birds** the brain is short and broad; the olfactory lobes are very small; the cerebral hemispheres are large, but the gray matter is limited to the posterior region; the optic lobes are comparatively large and spread apart by the large cerebellum. In **mammals** the olfactory lobes are well developed; the cerebral hemispheres are very large, due to the growth of the gray matter in the cortex;

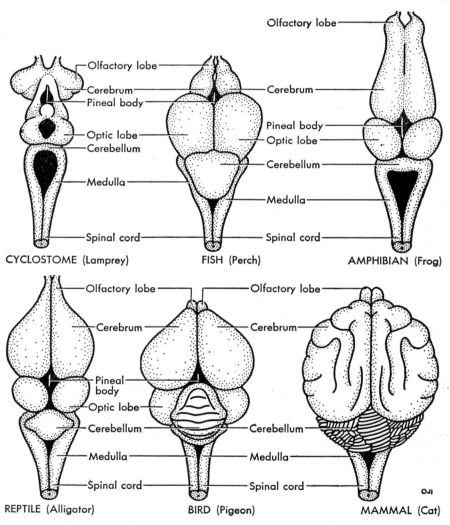

Figure 392. Diagrams showing the dorsal surface of the brain of 6 types of vertebrates and designed to illustrate differences in the degree of development of the different parts. Note especially the progressive increase in size of the cerebellum and cerebrum.

the 4 corpora quadrigemina derived from the optic lobes are covered by the cerebrum; the cerebellum is large and divided into 3 parts; the medulla is comparatively short. These differences in brains are correlated with the character of the activities of the different vertebrate types and with the degree of development of their senses.

Human brain

The **human brain** (Fig. 393) differs especially from that of all other animals in the relative **size of the cerebral hemispheres** and the **quantity of gray matter** they contain. The average weight of the human brain is about 1350 grams, whereas that of a gorilla, having approximately the same body weight, is only 430 grams, and that of a dog of equal weight only 135 grams. The **cerebrum**, which is the seat of intelligence and conscious sensations, of memory associations, and of the control of voluntary movements, comprises about 80 per cent of the total weight. The surface of the cerebrum is

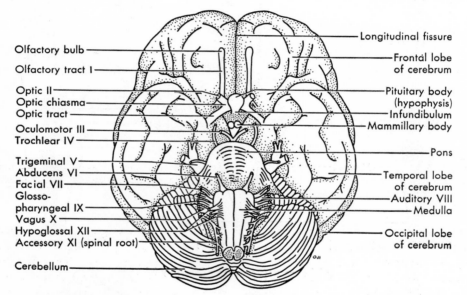

FIGURE 393. Brain of man, ventral surface. The numbers I to XII indicate the cranial nerves. (After Gerrish.)

thrown up into ridges or **convolutions**, which increase the area tremendously. The gray matter is correspondingly increased. This gray matter consists of the bodies of about 10 billion nerve cells.

Localization of function in the brain

The cerebrum, cerebellum, and medulla, each has its own particular functions. Impulses are conducted between the spinal cord and the brain through the **medulla.** In the medulla are groups of cells which influence the heart beat, blood pressure, and the rate and volume of respiration. Here also various reflex activities are controlled, including sneezing, coughing, vomiting, winking, and the movements and secretions of the digestive tract.

The **cerebellum** helps to maintain posture, equilibrium, and the tone of voluntary muscles; none of its activities comes into consciousness. If it is injured, normal voluntary movements are impossible; for example, the hand may have difficulty in grasping an object; there may be difficulty in walking due to inability to control the muscles of the legs, or difficulty in talking because of lack of coordination in the muscles moving the tongue and jaw.

The **cerebrum** governs all mental activities: it is the seat of consciousness, associative memory, reasoning, and intelligence; it originates voluntary acts and influences many reflex acts. Laughing, weeping, urinating, defecating, and many other acts are examples of the latter. The brain, with its various centers of activity, is to the nervous system what the wiring arrangements and switchboards are to the central office of a telephone system.

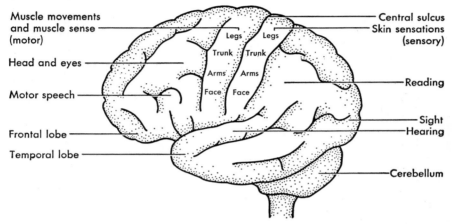

Figure 394. Diagram of the left side of the human brain to show the main lobes and the areas concerned with certain functions. The cerebrum, which reaches its greatest development in man, is by far the largest part of the brain.

The motor areas are located in front of the central sulcus, a groove, as indicated in Fig. 394, and the sensory areas are behind it. These sensory areas include those of sight (visual), hearing (auditory), and skin sensations. The regions surrounding these are association areas, which are concerned with the higher psychic activities.

Sense organs and sensations

The principal sense organs of the frog and other vertebrates are the **nose, eyes,** and **ears.** In some of the lower vertebrates, conspicuous **lateral line organs** tell of water movements and the pressure of current against the body (Fig. 253). **Sensory cells** of several types are also located in various parts of the body. Sensations result when receptors are stimulated, and impulses are transmitted to the brain by afferent nerves.

The "sensations" of lower animals must be interpreted on the basis of what we know regarding those of man. They may be grouped according to the types of receptors involved. Thus we may recognize **mechanoreceptors,** such as pressure on the skin; **chemoreceptors,** such as smell and taste; and **radioreceptors,** such as those for light, heat, and cold, which are excited by radiant energy, etc.

The **sense of touch** results from the stimulation of **tactile receptors** by contact with objects. In **man,** the papillae of the dermis, especially of the palmar surface of the hands and fingers, which contain tactile corpuscles, give the skin its sense of touch. The sense of **hunger** is due to receptors in the stomach wall that are stimulated by contractions of this organ when empty. The sensation of **appetite** may be due to similar receptors, but is probably aroused by the nerves of taste and smell. **Thirst** is a sensation result-

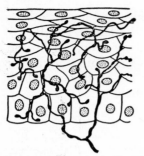

Free sensory nerve endings in
cornea of eye

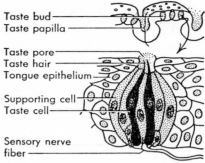

Taste bud
Taste papilla

Taste pore
Taste hair
Tongue epithelium

Supporting cell
Taste cell

Sensory nerve
fiber

Taste bud in longitudinal section showing
taste cells and afferent nerve fibers associated with them

Receptor of heavy pressure, Pacinian
corpuscle in mammary gland

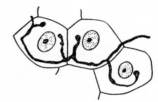

Motor nerve endings on gland cells of
pancreas

Figure 395. Receptors and effectors, the nerve endings of sensory and motor nerves. (After Kimber, Gray, and Stackpole.)

ing from stimulation of nerves in the pharynx or in other tissues affected by prolonged deprivation of water.

Proprioceptors are receptors that occur in connection with muscles, tendons, and joints; they are stimulated by the activities of these tissues and are responsible for the **coordination** necessary for proper posture and for the movements of the body. To the nerves in the skin of man are due the sensations of **pressure, heat, cold,** and **pain.** The skin surface is a mosaic of sensory spots; more than 2,000,000 are pain points, 500,000 are pressure points, 150,000 are cold points, and 16,000 are warm points.

The sensation of **taste** is due to the contact of substances in solution with taste buds, chemical receptors (**chemoreceptors**), that are distributed over the surfaces of the tongue, soft palate, fauces, tonsils, and pharynx. The 4 primary taste sensations are (1) **salty,** (2) **bitter,** (3) **acid,** and (4) **sweet.**

The sensation of **smell** results from the contact of minute particles dissolved in water with olfactory nerve endings (chemoreceptors) in the nose. The nose is a testing place of the chemical nature of the air taken into it. Man is a poor smeller compared with dogs and many other mammals.

The essential part of the **auditory apparatus** (Fig. 396) of land vertebrates is the **cochlea. In man and other mammals** there is an **external ear** or **pinna** which collects sound waves. In aquatic animals this is not necessary since water carries the sound waves to the tissues, which transmit them directly to the internal ear. The **middle ear** or **tympanic cavity** is separated from the external ear by the tympanic membrane (**eardrum**); the **Eustachian tube** leads from the middle ear to the pharynx. The **internal ear** includes an **osseous labyrinth** comprising the **saccule, utricle,** the three **semicircular canals,** and the **cochlea.** Within the osseous labyrinth is the **membranous** labyrinth filled with **endolymph.** The cochlea is a spiral canal of 2¾ turns. The **auditory nerve** is divided into two, one part becoming the cochlear nerve and the other the vestibular nerve. Air waves entering the external ear bring about vibrations of the eardrum which are communicated through the 3 bones, the **malleus** (hammer), **incus** (anvil), and **stapes** (stirrup), to the fluid in the internal ear; this stimulates the nerve

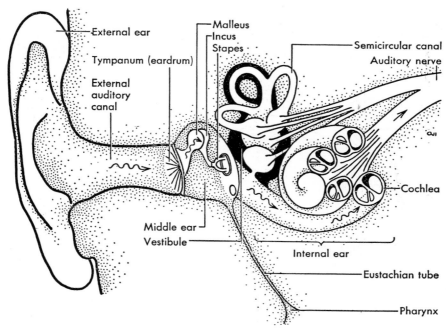

FIGURE 396. A dissection of the human ear to show the parts that have to do with receiving sound and the part which is concerned with balance.

endings in the **organ of Corti,** and impulses are transmitted by the auditory nerve to the center of hearing in the brain. The organ of Corti lies within the cochlea and contains 5 rows of sensory "hair cells" which are the sound receptors.

Equilibrium in man is a complex thing that depends on vision, proprioceptors, sensitiveness to pressure on the soles of the feet, and organs of equilibrium within the internal ear. The latter consist of two small sacs, the saccule and utricle, and semicircular canals. On the bottom of the saccule and the utricle there is a membrane of sensory hairs on which rest many tiny crystals of lime (**otoliths**). This balancing mechanism gives knowledge of linear accelerations, and tilt and pull of gravity, due to the inertia of the crystals which causes the sensory hairs to bend. The semicircular canals also contain "hair cells" like those of the saccule and utricle. These hair cells are sensitive to the movement of a fluid which fills the canals. Any acceleration or deceleration of head movement causes the fluid to flow in different directions in the canals, thus stimulating the hair cells to send impulses to the brain. The receptors in the canals are strongly affected by vertical movements like those of an elevator and by the rolling and pitching motions of ships and planes.

The **eyes** are the most complex of the sense organs of vertebrates. The principal elements of structure and the method of action may be pointed out by means of a diagram of the human eye (Fig. 397). The eye is nearly spherical. It consists of three concentric coats enclosing transparent substances, as follows.

1. The outer or **sclerotic coat** is the white of the eye. It is composed of connective tissue and serves as a protective covering. In front of the **lens**, the sclerotic coat forms a transparent area called the **cornea**.

2. The middle or **choroid coat** is beneath the sclerotic coat; it is supplied with blood vessels and contains a great deal of black pigment which prevents light from entering except through the cornea. The choroid coat is separated from the sclerotic coat and is perforated just in front of the lens; the opening is the **pupil**, and a part of the choroid surrounding the pupil is the **iris**.

3. The inner coat, the **retina**, is the most important since it is the light-sensitive layer. It is composed of two types of receptors,

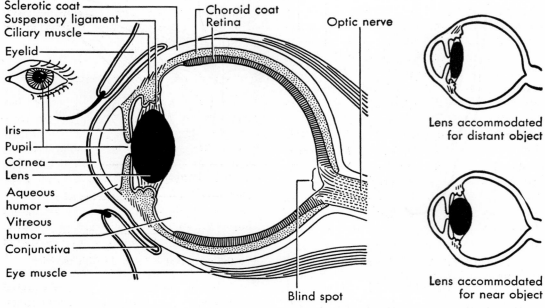

Sclerotic coat
Suspensory ligament
Ciliary muscle
Eyelid
Choroid coat
Retina
Optic nerve
Iris
Pupil
Cornea
Lens
Aqueous humor
Vitreous humor
Conjunctiva
Eye muscle
Blind spot
Lens accommodated for distant object
Lens accommodated for near object

FIGURE 397. *Left,* the general structure of the eye of man, showing the mechanism of sight. *Right,* changes in the shape of the lens to focus on distant and near objects.

rods (about 120 million in a human eye) and **cones** (about 7 million). The rods are concerned with colorless vision, while the cones are concerned primarily with color vision. The rods contain a pigment known as **visual purple (rhodopsin).** Light falling on the rods bleaches visual purple, which must be present for vision in dim light. Visual purple is related to carotene compounds, and vitamin A is thought to be a stage in its regeneration; vitamin A deficiency produces "night blindness." At the point where the optic nerve enters the retina, there are no rods or cones. This part of the retina is called the blind spot because it is not sensitive to light.

The lens is biconvex and transparent. It is attached to the choroid coat by a **suspensory ligament.** The space anterior to the lens is called the **anterior cavity,** this in turn is divided into **anterior** and **posterior chambers.** These two chambers are separated by the iris. The anterior cavity is filled with a fluid called **aqueous humor.** The **vitreous humor,** a jellylike substance, occupies the space between the lens and the back of the eyeball.

The eye is like a camera in certain respects. With the aid of the lens, an image of the objects in front of the cornea is formed on the sensitive retina as on photographic film. The eye is accommodated for recording images of near and far objects by changes in the convexity of the lens. These changes in the lens are caused by its own elasticity, and by the pull exerted upon it by the elastic choroid coat and the **ciliary muscles.** In viewing near objects, the ciliary muscle counteracts the pull of the choroid coat and allows the lens to assume a more convex shape, whereas distant objects are made distinct by the flattening of the lens.

The eye is moved by 6 muscles: 4 straight (**rectus**) and 2 **oblique.** Folds of skin, the **eyelids,** protect the eye in higher vertebrates. In the vertebrate there may be three eyelids: an upper and a lower lid which act vertically, and a lateral lid (nictitating membrane) which moves outward from the inner angle of the eye. In some reptiles the eyelids are transparent and fused over the eye. Terrestrial vertebrates have **lacrimal glands** in connection with the eye; the secretion from these keeps the surface of the eyeball moist and washes away foreign particles.

HORMONES; CHEMICAL COORDINATORS

We have seen how the nervous system coordinates the separate responses of an animal, as for example, coordination of muscles in writing, talking, and walking. These activities involve the working together of various sets of muscles, and the nervous system is very effective in quickly correlating and regulating these activities. In contrast, the **endocrine system** usually acts slowly over long periods of time in effecting coordination. The endocrine system is composed of specialized tissues, and, in some cases, glands, which produce chemical substances called **internal secretions** (**hormones**). Most multicellular glands in animals have ducts and are called **glands of**

external secretion (exocrine); an example is the liver which discharges its secretion through a duct into the intestine. The endocrine glands, however, are ductless, and hence are called glands of internal secretion because their hormones pass directly into the blood or other body fluids. A hormone is a chemical coordinator which has some regulatory effect upon cells that may be some distance from the origin of the hormone. A hormone may be either excitatory or inhibitory in its influence on the activities of various tissues and the behavior of an animal.

Hormones of invertebrates

Most of the research on hormones has been done on vertebrates. As a result, comparatively little is known about hormones in the different invertebrate phyla. There is good evidence of hormones in nematodes, annelids, arthropods, mollusks, and some other invertebrates. Hormones in certain of the arthropods are discussed in an earlier chapter. Destruction of certain gonadal tissue of some crabs often results in partial sex reversal, somewhat similar to that observed in chickens. In the bug *Rhodnius,* the hormone controlling molting is secreted by glands in the head. Molting and metamorphosis in certain arthropods are under the control of hormones.

Hormones of man

In striking contrast to the situation among invertebrates, in which little is known about endocrine function, a great many investigations have been conducted on many vertebrates. The methods used have been either to remove an endocrine gland or to study the effects of injected hormones. Additional information has been obtained from research on animals in which the endocrine glands were diseased. Some experiments have been performed on the effects of transplanting glands. Several of the hormones such as thyroxin have been synthesized by chemists. The hormones now sold are either synthesized or come from mammals. Insulin, which makes it possible for diabetics to live, is extracted from beef pancreas.

Because of the similarity of the action of hormones in most vertebrates, the following discussion will deal with the human endocrine system. The most important of the ductless glands in man are the thyroid, parathyroids, adrenals, pituitary, islets of Langerhans, and gonads (Fig. 398). Hormones are also produced by the membrane lining the intestines, and possibly the stomach. There is still no convincing evidence of endocrine function in the pineal and thymus glands.

Thyroid

The thyroid is a bilobed gland, which weighs about an ounce and lies in front of the trachea below the larynx; it influences the general rate of metabolism in the body. It secretes a hormone called thyroxin, which contains about 65 per cent iodine by weight. When too little thyroxin is secreted, the thyroid may become much enlarged to form a **goiter.** When the thyroid fails to function properly in early life, children may become dwarfed and mentally deficient, a condition known as **cretinism.** In goiter districts, supplemental iodine should be supplied, especially in the diet of pregnant women. This is frequently accomplished by the use of iodized salt. If the thyroid of an adult atrophies or is removed, **myxedema** occurs, which results in the subcutaneous tissues becoming infiltrated with mucoid substance, causing the face and hands to swell. Overactivity of the thyroid or **hyperthyroidism** is known as **exophthalmic goiter** or Grave's disease. Thyroxin has been chemically isolated and crystallized, and also synthesized.

Parathyroids

The parathyroids are 4 small glands on the posterior surface of the thyroid. They produce a secretion which contains a hormone that exercises a profound influence on the metabolism of calcium and phosphorus in the body. A deficiency of this hormone results in low blood calcium and violent twitching of the muscles, a condition known as tetany; an excess, as in parathyroid tumors, may cause excessive withdrawal of calcium from the bones.

Adrenals

The adrenals are 2 small glands perched like cocked hats on top of the kidneys. Each consists of 2 parts, the cortex and medulla. The **cortex** secretes about 30 known compounds. Chemically, these are steroids. One of the best known of these steroids is cortisone, which has proved beneficial in some types of arthritis. Removal of the adrenal cortex causes death.

Injury to the cortex of the adrenals results in Addison's disease, which is characterized by anemia, low blood pressure, intestinal disturbances, sometimes deep bronzing of the skin, and ending in death if not treated.

The **medulla** secretes the hormone **epinephrine (adrenalin).** It mimics the action of sympathin which is secreted by the tips of the nerves of the thoracolumbar division of the autonomic nervous system. It has been suggested that the secretion of adrenalin constitutes a reserve mechanism that comes into action at times of stress. Under emotional excitement, such as fear or anger, additional adrenalin is secreted, and the individual is prepared for "fight or flight" by acceleration of the heart, and blood vessel constriction, which raise the blood pressure; in addition, the blood sugar is elevated by conversion of liver glycogen. Adrenalin is widely used in treating asthma.

Pituitary or hypophysis

The pituitary gland (Fig. 398) is about the size of a pea, and is located at the base of the brain in a depression of the sphenoid

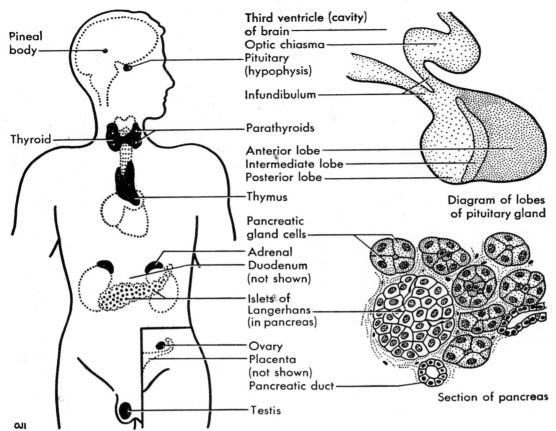

Pineal body

Thyroid

Third ventricle (cavity) of brain
Optic chiasma
Pituitary (hypophysis)

Infundibulum

Parathyroids

Anterior lobe
Intermediate lobe
Posterior lobe

Diagram of lobes of pituitary gland

Thymus

Pancreatic gland cells

Adrenal
Duodenum (not shown)

Islets of Langerhans (in pancreas)

Ovary
Placenta (not shown)
Pancreatic duct

Testis

Section of pancreas

FIGURE 398. *Left*, a diagram to show the approximate location of some of the endocrine glands in man. Although the pineal body and thymus are included, they are not known definitely to be organs of internal secretion. *Right*, section of a pituitary gland showing lobes and microscopic structure of the pancreas.

bone. It consists of an anterior lobe and a posterior lobe. The **posterior lobe** secretes two or more hormones, collectively called **pituitrin.** Injection of pituitrin into the circulatory system raises the blood pressure, decreases the amount of urine formed, and causes the contraction of smooth muscles, especially those of the uterus, and the contractile elements in the mammary glands which cause the "let down" of milk.

The **anterior lobe** secretes several hormones. These (1) control skeletal growth, (2) stimulate the growth of the gonads and maintain them in functional condition, (3) stimulate milk secretion, (4) stimulate the thyroid, and (5) stimulate the adrenal cortex. An excessive amount of secretion

of the growth hormone in the young stimulates development of the long bones resulting in **giantism;** when this occurs in adults, the bones, especially of the limbs and face, become thickened, resulting in **acromegaly.** The pituitary also secretes a hormone which increases the sugar content of the blood, thus having effects opposite to those of insulin.

The influence of the pituitary gland on other endocrine glands gives it the name of the "master gland."

Ovary

Several hormones are secreted by the ovary. **Estrogens** are formed in the Graafian

FIGURE 399. A photograph to show variation in growth. The pituitary giant is 20 years old and 81¾ inches in height. The pituitary dwarf is 26 years old and 52 inches in height. (From Smiley and Gould.)

follicles; they control the menstrual cycle, sexual behavior, and the development of the accessory genital organs and secondary sex characteristics. **Progesterone** is secreted by the **corpus luteum**; it regulates the menstrual cycle and plays a part in the development of the mammary glands and in preparing the female for pregnancy. **Relaxin**, another ovarian hormone, makes child birth easier by relaxing the ligaments of the pelvic girdle.

Testis

The interstitial cells of the testis secrete a hormone, **testosterone**, which influences

sexual behavior, and controls the development of the male accessory genital organs and the secondary sex characteristics.

Pancreas

The prancreas is a gland weighing two or three ounces, situated behind the stomach. The masses of cells in the pancreas, known as the **islets of Langerhans** (Fig. 398), produce an internal secretion containing the hormone **insulin.** This hormone is necessary for normal regulation of sugar metabolism; it aids utilization of the glucose in the blood; it accelerates synthesis of sugar to glycogen; and it retards production of sugar in the liver from fat and protein. If the pancreas does not secrete a sufficient amount of insulin, an excessive amount of sugar is present in the blood, a condition resulting in the disease known as **diabetes mellitus** (sugar diabetes).

Gastric mucosa

There is some evidence that the mucous membrane of the pyloric end of the stomach may produce a hormone called **gastrin**, which is carried by the blood to the gastric glands and stimulates the secretion of gastric juice.

Intestinal mucosa

Parts of the mucous membrane of the intestine produce a hormone called **secretin**, which was the first hormone discovered (1902). Secretin is carried by the blood to the pancreas, causing it to secrete pancreatic juice at once. Another action of secretion is to increase the flow of bile. A second intestinal hormone is **cholecystokinin**, which causes the gall bladder to empty.

Influence of hormones on one another

Finally, it is interesting to note that the hormones secreted by the different ductless glands may affect one another; for example, if the anterior lobe of the pituitary gland is removed, both the testes and ovaries regress and secrete little, if any, of their respective hormones. Furthermore, several of these hormones may have a similar function, or, on the other hand, they may be antagonistic. Only when all are behaving properly is an equilibrium established among the various physiologic processes in the body, so that we feel and react like normal human beings.

Other chemical coordinators

It has been pointed out that the amount of carbon dioxide in the blood controls the respiratory center in the brain and hence regulates the rate of breathing.

Both the force and the rate of the heart beat can be altered, depending on the requirements of the body. The rate of the heart beat can be greatly slowed by the presence of a chemical substance, **acetylcholine**, while the presence of an adrenalin-like substance, **sympathin**, will increase its rate and force. Such substances are called **neurohumors** (**neurohormones**) because they are liberated at nerve endings. Acetylcholine is given off by the **cranio-sacral** (**parasympathetic**) division of the autonomic system, and sympathin is liberated by the nerve endings of the **thoracolumbar** (**sympathetic**) division of the autonomic nervous system. There is an increasing amount of evidence indicating that the effects of the autonomic nervous system are not brought about directly by nerve impulses themselves, but by chemical substances which the impulses cause to be liberated from the nerve endings. These chemical substances from nerve endings, after performing their physiologic functions, are destroyed by enzymes.

Both electrical and chemical theories have been advanced in order to account for the transmission of impulses across the synapse between neurons. The evidence, as it now stands, is not sufficient to establish beyond reasonable doubt that transmission of impulses from one neuron to another is only by a neurohumor substance. The new knowledge of neurohumors, however, is making it necessary to discard many old concepts of the coordinating mechanism in animals.

ANIMAL BEHAVIOR

We have defined behavior as the reactions of the whole organism to its environment and have described the behavior of the amoeba, euglena, paramecium, hydra, earthworm, crayfish, and frog. The behavior of all these animals has much in common. In the first place, as already noted, one of the fundamental properties of protoplasm is its irritability or ability to respond to stimuli, that is, to react to changes in the environment.

Protozoans

The behavior of such simple animals as the **amoeba** is based on the inherent responsiveness of the protoplasm of a single cell. Such primitive behavior patterns would not make possible the active lives of more complex animals. Even among protozoans, as in the paramecium, organelles involving fibrillar conduction serve to coordinate the activities of different parts of the cell.

Extensive studies indicate that there is no evidence of the existence of differences of fundamental character between the behavior of protozoans and that of the lower metazoans. The study of behavior lends no support to the view that the life activities are of an essentially different nature in protozoans and metazoans. The behavior of protozoans appears to be no more and no less machinelike than that of the metazoans; similar principles govern both.

Sponges

Sponges are active when in the larval stage, swimming about by means of flagella;

but later they become attached to some solid object for life. Certain adult sponges are capable of slight contractions of the body and of feeble bending movements; but greater activity occurs within the body, due to contractile cells, which are arranged about the osculum and pores. Stimuli of various sorts applied directly to the contractile cells result in the opening and closing of the osculum, pores, and canals, and in changes in the flow of water. Transmission to other oscula does not occur. There appears to be present, however, a sluggish type of transmission through the protoplasm, such as seems to occur in certain protozoans. This is transmission, without highly differentiated nervous elements, such as are present in the usual nerve transmissions. Studies of the behavior of sponges indicate that no true neurons exist. Sponges, therefore, have cells that act as effectors but do not possess special receptors or adjustors.

Hydra

A distinct advance in behavior is evident in the **hydra,** where specialized nerve cells form a sort of network in the body wall, which enables the animal to perform complex coordinated movements of the entire body. Simple reflexes in hydras are those that involve movement of a part of the body that is stimulated, for example, bending a single tentacle. Reception of stimuli and transmission of nerve impulses by sensory cells, conduction, and discharge of impulses by neurons, with the resultant action of effectors such as contractile and secretory cells, all occur in the hydra.

Earthworm

In the **earthworm** we encounter a highly developed nervous system and definite sense organs. Most of the nerve cells are concentrated in the ganglia of the nerve cord. Here a sensory neuron may come in contact with several motor neurons by means of axon branches, and the motor neurons may come in contact with several sensory neurons by means of their dendrites. Such contacts are known as **synapses.** Besides this, **association neurons** are present in the central nerve cord, and nerve impulses may pass from one of these to another throughout the entire length of the cord. This association of neurons results in complex reflex arcs which are characteristic of all the higher animals. The cerebral ganglia at the anterior end of the earthworm are slightly larger than the ganglia elsewhere as a result of the concentration of sensory neurons in that region of the body. It is the anterior end which first encounters changes in the environment during locomotion.

The concentration of nerve cells in the head region, which is known as cephalization, continues as one proceeds up the animal series, culminating in the large brain of man.

Instinct

The reactions of the earthworm to various external stimuli are much more complex than those of the hydra. As in all animals, they are for the most part of benefit to the animal, and vary according to the physiologic state of the individual. Such reactions as withdrawal of a worm into its burrow, as a result of vibration or of sudden illumination at night, are due to compound reflexes and are commonly spoken of as **instincts** These instincts consist of a chain of coordinated reflexes of the organism. Instinctive acts are performed without any previous experience and are characteristic for each type of animal. For example, certain caterpillars spin cocoons, spiders spin webs, birds build nests, and honey bees construct honeycombs. In many cases such instinctive acts are carried out only once during the lifetime of the organism. This type of behavior is dependent on inherent reflex arcs, and instincts are often referred to as **inherited behavior;** each species of animal inheriting its own particular types of instincts. Where simple reflexes end and instincts begin, it is difficult to state.

Habit formation, learning, and intelligence

During the study of the behavior of lower animals, experiments have been devised, as in the crayfish, that seem to indicate the formation of habits. **Habit formation** among the vertebrates is quite common. It consists of the development of a particular type of behavior as a result of previous experience. Driving an automobile, tying a shoe lace, and winding a watch all become more or less automatic as the result of a constant repetition of reflexes. Habits are of great value since they enable us to perform acts without conscious effort.

Learning differs from habit formation since it involves replacement of the normal or usual stimulus by another as the result of repeated association. Such a reaction depends to a large extent on **conditioned reflexes**. A conditioned reflex may be illustrated by the famed physiologic studies on the dog. The salivary glands of a newborn dog are reflexly stimulated when it tastes food, and they respond by pouring saliva into the mouth. As the dog grows older, the sight of food calls forth the outpouring of saliva before the food has been tasted; thus the taste of the food is replaced by the sight of the food. The dog learns by experience that when he sees food, he will soon taste it; and nervous pathways are developed by the sight of food that bring about salivary stimulation. The investigator rang a bell each time food was presented and found that after a few repetitions the dogs secreted saliva when the bell was rung without the presence of food. Thus one conditioned reflex became the basis for another.

The ability of an animal to form conditioned reflexes determines largely its capacity to learn by experience. Retention of what has been learned by experience is called **memory**. The **intelligence** of an animal depends on its ability to profit by experience. Intelligent behavior is manifested to a high degree by man, to a lesser degree by other mammals and birds, and almost not at all by the rest of the animal kingdom. Next to man, anthropoid apes and then the monkeys exhibit the greatest development of intelligence.

SELECTED COLLATERAL READINGS

Best, C.H., and Taylor, N.B. *The Living Body, A Text in Human Physiology*. Holt, New York, 1952.

Gardner, Ernest. *Fundamentals of Neurology*. Saunders, Philadelphia, 1952.

Hoskins, R.G. *Endocrinology*. Norton, New York, 1950.

Parker, G.H. *Animal Colour Changes and Their Neurohumours*. Cambridge Univ. Press, London, 1948.

Scott, J.P. *Animal Behavior*. Univ. Chicago Press, Chicago, 1958.

Turner, C.D. *General Endocrinology*. Saunders, Philadelphia, 1948.

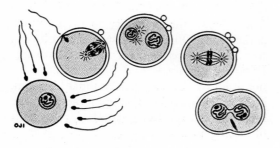

CHAPTER 34

Reproduction and
Development

Every species must reproduce itself or it will soon disappear from the earth. Reproduction is one of the fundamental properties of protoplasm and is exhibited by all animals, both one-celled and many-celled. The theory of spontaneous generation that once prevailed has given way to the concept that **all life arises from preexisting life.**

ASEXUAL REPRODUCTION

Binary fission in protozoans

The simplest type of reproduction occurs among one-celled animals and is known as **binary fission.** This is a type of asexual reproduction because it is reproduction without the intervention of sexual cells or gametes. In certain species such as the amoeba, fission is nothing more than cell division; but in the more complex protozoans it may involve working over the protoplasm of each daughter cell. For example, in the paramecium both anterior and posterior daughters must produce a new contractile vacuole, and a new cytopharynx must be developed. Binary fission may be transverse as in the paramecium, or longitudinal as in the euglena. Binary fission may also occur in cysts as in the euglena. **Multiple fission,** which occurs in many protozoans, especially among the sporozoans, is usually a succession of binary fissions within an envelope; but sometimes, as in the malaria organism (Fig. 33), the nucleus may divide a number of times, and then the entire cell segments into as many daughter cells as there are nuclei.

Fission in metazoans

Among many-celled animals, fission cannot be considered common. Planarians may divide transversely, each part then becoming organized into a normal animal. Any missing parts of a new individual are regenerated. Some annelids as well as certain anthozoans may also reproduce in this way.

Budding

Budding is also an asexual process. Several kinds of budding have been described in the animals we have studied. Often, as in the hydra, the bud grows out from the body, and when completely differentiated, frees itself from the parent; this is known as **external budding**. The bud does not always resemble the parent; for example, in the hydroid *Obelia*, buds from the asexual polyp give rise to sexual jellyfishes. In cases of polymorphism, as in the Portuguese man-o-war, several types of individuals may arise by budding from a single larva. A type of budding called **internal budding**, which results in the formation of gemmules, is a normal process in certain sponges and Bryozoa.

REGENERATION

Regeneration in invertebrates

When an animal, such as the paramecium, planarian, or an annelid, divides by fission, each daughter reorganizes itself into a normal complete animal. In nature, reorganization may also occur in animals that suffer injuries; parts may be lost, or the entire animal may be cut in two. The wounds of injured animals heal if they are not too severe, large parts may be replaced, or a part may reorganize itself into a complete normal animal. This ability we call regeneration.

Many interesting cases of regeneration have been cited. **Sponges** are especially remarkable, since an entire sponge may regenerate from a group of dissociated cells. Cuttings of sponges will grow and develop into complete sponges much as cuttings of plants do. The regenerative powers of the **hydra** have been known for at least 200 years. **Flatworms**, such as the planaria, have long furnished material for studies of regeneration. How frequently **earthworms** in nature lose parts of their bodies and regenerate them again is not known, but their powers to do so occur largely through the

activities of totipotent cells; these migrate to the region of injury and differentiate during regeneration. Legs, claws, eyes, antennae, of the **crayfish** may be replaced if lost. If the tentacle that bears the eye of a **snail** is removed, a new tentacle with eye may regenerate 20 times in succession in a single animal. Starfishes are famous for their ability to replace lost parts, and specimens with regenerated arms are common in nature. **Sea cucumbers** may lose a large part of their internal organs, but they are able to replace them in most cases.

Regeneration in vertebrates

Regeneration occurs in vertebrates as well as in invertebrates. It is especially noteworthy in **salamanders** where tails, limbs, and eyes appear to be replaced easily. In one experiment, the tail of a salamander was removed and a new one regenerated 8 times in succession. **Lizards** often escape enemies such as birds, which grasp them by the tail; the tail breaks off at a special breaking point; the lizard escapes, and a new tail (without bones) is regenerated. In man and many other vertebrates regeneration is more restricted. In many of the higher vertebrates, the regeneration process is responsible for the healing of external wounds, for the renewal of the epidermis and hair, and for the production of new red blood corpuscles.

It will be noted from this discussion that the more primitive animals in both the invertebrate and vertebrate series have the greatest ability to regenerate lost parts. Also, the power of regeneration is greater in young than in old ones.

Heteromorphosis

The part regenerated is not always the same as the part lost. This type of regeneration is known as heteromorphosis. For example, if an entire eye of a crustacean is cut away, it may be replaced by an antennalike structure.

Compensatory regulation

Somewhat resembling regeneration is the compensatory reaction of certain organs as a result of various types of bodily changes. If one kidney is removed, the other kidney increases its activity so as to function for both. If muscular exertion is increased, thus requiring a greater blood supply, the heart increases in size and power. If certain muscles are exercised, they increase in size.

Autotomy

Certain parts of the body may be subjected to injury more than others. When this is true, a definite breaking point may be present and the injured animal automatically severs the part at this point. This process is known as **autotomy**. Well-known examples of autotomy are furnished by the crayfish, which may break off injured legs at a point near the base (Fig. 119). Healing and regeneration appear to take place at this point more readily than elsewhere. The **starfish** casts off its injured arms near the base at the fourth or fifth ambulacral ossicle.

SEXUAL REPRODUCTION

Sexual reproduction is reproduction by means of gametes. There are two types of gametes that are visibly different and are referred to as eggs and sperms. These usually unite in sexual reproduction, but in some cases eggs may develop normally without union with a sperm, as in rotifers, or they may be induced to develop by artificial means, as in the case of sea urchin eggs when the chemical nature of the medium is changed.

Parthenogenesis

The development of an egg that has not united with a sperm is called parthenogenesis. In **rotifers**, the summer eggs develop normally without being fertilized. In **aphids**, stem mothers that are parthenogenetic and viviparous hatch from eggs that have lived through the winter. Their offspring are wingless parthenogenetic females. These give rise to wingless parthenogenetic females, but after a time winged females are produced which migrate to other plants. As fall approaches, males and oviparous females appear, mating occurs, and fertilized eggs are laid that remain dormant over winter and give rise to stem mothers in the spring.

Sperms are stored up in the seminal receptacle of the queen **honey bee**. She seems to be able to lay fertilized or unfertilized eggs, according to the size of the honeycomb cell in which the individual is to develop. Fertilized eggs develop into queens and workers, whereas the unfertilized eggs develop into drones. Many other cases of normal parthenogenesis among invertebrates could be cited.

Certain eggs that normally must be penetrated by a sperm before they will develop can be made to undergo development, at least for a short time, by means of various stimuli; this is known as **artificial parthenogenesis**. The eggs of many invertebrates have been stimulated to develop by changing the chemical constitution of the medium. Pricking, shaking, and raising the temperature may stimulate development. Frogs and rabbits are reported to have been reared from such eggs; they had a mother but no father.

Recently, parthenogenetic turkeys (Fig. 400) have become less rare as a result of U.S. Department of Agriculture studies of natural parthenogenesis in turkey eggs. The exact cause of the parthenogenetic development is not known. But Dr. M.W. Olsen, investigating this problem, thinks that the incidence of parthenogenesis has been increased by selection; he also suspects that a vaccination program in some way enters into the picture.

FIGURE 400. A turkey gobbler without a father. This photograph was taken when the bird was 32 weeks old and weighed about 15 pounds. (Photo courtesy of M.W. Olsen, U.S. Department of Agriculture, Beltsville, Md.)

Paedogenesis

The larvae of the gall fly (*Miastor*) produce eggs that undergo parthenogenetic development to produce other larvae. Such parthenogenesis among larvae is called **paedogenesis.**

Neoteny

The larvae of the tiger salamander under certain conditions will become sexually mature, mate, and produce fertile eggs; this phenomenon is known as **neoteny.**

Evolution of sex

In one order of flagellated protozoans, the Phytomonadina, which are considered by many to be plants, are a group of types which can be arranged in such a way as to illustrate different grades of organization from a loose association of cells to one approaching a metazoan, and also to illustrate the evolution of sex.

Spondylomorum

Spondylomorum (Fig. 401) is colonial in habit with 16 cells in each colony. These cells are practically independent; each reproduces by fission to form a colony like the parent colony. No gametes are known.

Chlamydomonas

Chlamydomonas (Fig. 401) is a unicellular type that reproduces asexually by simple cell division (fission) into 2, 4, or 8 daughter cells and also produces gametes of one size, which fuse together in pairs; the resulting zygotes undergo fission, resulting in a number of unicellular individuals. In this organism and similar forms, we apparently observe the origin of sex cells and of sex.

Pandorina

Pandorina (Fig. 401) is a colonial form of 4 to 32 cells embedded in a gelatinous matrix, each independent of the others. New colonies are asexually produced by division of each cell in the mother colony into a new daughter colony. In sexual reproduction, gametes of unequal size are formed; the female gamete is the larger. Male and female gametes fuse to form zygotes; and since sexual reproduction usually consists of the fusion of a larger female gamete with a smaller male gamete, the process in *Pandorina* seems to furnish an early stage in the evolution of sex.

Eudorina

Eudorina (Fig. 401) is a colonial type with 32 cells. Each cell may reproduce a colony asexually by fission. At times the cells of certain colonies become large; this

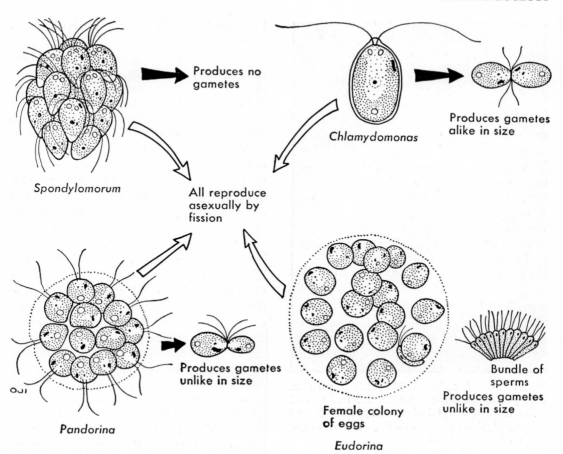

Spondylomorum — Produces no gametes

Chlamydomonas — Produces gametes alike in size

All reproduce asexually by fission

Pandorina — Produces gametes unlike in size

Eudorina — Female colony of eggs

Bundle of sperms — Produces gametes unlike in size

FIGURE 401. Evolution of sex in the flagellates.

is characteristic of female colonies. In male colonies, each cell divides to form 16 or 32 small cells (sperms). These fuse in pairs with the large cells (eggs) in the female colony to form zygotes. This species produces sharply distinguished male and female gametes.

Volvox globator

Volvox globator (Fig. 22, p. 48) represents the final stage in the series. The thousands (one species, 50,000) of asexual cells in a colony are united by protoplasmic strands; physiologic continuity is thus established between the cells, a condition not found in the colonies previously described.

If a single cell from the colony is cut out and isolated from its neighbors, it will round off like a tear-drop and swim about by means of its two flagella. In this state it resembles *Chlamydomonas*, but after a time the isolated cell dies. Most of the cells of the colony contain an eyespot, chloroplasts, contractile vacuoles, and two flagella; these are called "body" or somatic cells. The production of daughter colonies is accomplished by special reproductive cells which are set aside for this purpose.

The **asexual method** of reproduction is as follows: certain cells of the colony become larger than others and lose their flagella; they increase in size, and each divides by longitudinal division into a great number of cells. As the cells divide, they bulge inward to form a pocket, the new daughter colony, without fusing with a gamete.

The **sexual method** of reproduction may be observed in colonies which contain as many as 50 large nonflagellated cells. Some of these grow larger and may be recognized as female gametes (eggs); others produce by longitudinal division a flat plate containing many spindle-shaped male gametes (sperms). One sperm fuses with each egg. The zygote thus formed secretes a surrounding wall and remains in this condition for some time. Eventually the zygote breaks out of the wall and produces a new colony by multiple division. However, the zygotes are retained in the parent colony until the somatic cells of the latter die and disintegrate.

In *Volvox*, true somatic cells are encountered for the first time, that is, cells which are unable to reproduce the colony. In the other forms described, every cell has the capacity of reproducing the whole. *Volvox* also contains true germ cells, that is, cells that are set aside for purposes of reproduction. Furthermore, a clear case of **natural death** occurs in the somatic cells when they fall to the bottom of the pond and disintegrate. The situation in *Volvox* is similar to that in higher animals in which the body consists of many cells which may be separated into somatic cells and germ cells. The latter are either male or female. In most cases the fusion of a male cell with a female cell is necessary before a new organism can be reproduced. At any rate, some of these germ cells maintain the continuation of the species by producing new individuals, while the somatic cells perish when the organism dies.

Looking back over this series, it will be seen that there is a trend from a small simple aggregation of cells to a large and highly complex colony composed of cells that show considerable division of labor. Also, there is the origin and progressive development of sexual reproduction.

Germ plasm and somatoplasm

As already noted, when the germ cells become mature, they separate from the body, giving rise to a new generation, whereas the somatic cells die. This has given rise to the idea that the somatic cells constitute a sort of vehicle for the transportation of the germ cells. From this idea has developed the **theory of the continuity of germ plasm,** according to which the germ plasm is a self-perpetuating type of protoplasm, which gives rise to both the protoplasm of the gametes (**germ plasm**) and to the protoplasm of the somatic cells (**somatoplasm**) in each generation. The somatoplasm **dies** periodically, but the germ plasm is **potentially immortal.**

Metagenesis

Metagenesis is not common in the animal kingdom but occurs frequently in certain groups. **Metagenesis,** or alternation of an asexual generation with a sexual generation, is not uncommon among the coelenterates. For example, the asexual generation of the hydroid *Obelia* (Fig. 57) reproduces by budding; some of these buds are small jellyfish which produce either eggs or spermatozoa; the fertilized eggs develop into asexually reproducing hydroids. Gametes are produced by the jellyfish *Aurellia* (Fig. 60), and the fertilized eggs develop into a very small hydroid stage which produces jellyfishes by budding.

Oogenesis and spermatogenesis

The gametes that are set aside during embryonic development become either the female type, oogonia, or the male type, spermatogonia. In certain species, for example in *Miastor*, a definite number of germ cells is produced in one animal; in some other animals, the number appears to be indefinite. In *Volvox* (Fig. 22) and in sponges, the gametes are scattered, and no definite gonads are recognizable; but in the hydra (Fig. 50), the gonads consist of groups of interstitial cells which form conical (male) or ball-shaped (female) projections on the stalk. In the hydra, eggs and sperms need no ducts in order to escape from the body. Flatworms, earthworms, and other higher invertebrates and vertebrates possess gonads, in which the eggs and sperms develop, and ducts for carrying them to the outside. These essential reproductive organs are often very complicated; those of the various types may be found by looking in the index under the names of the different animals, or under the term "reproduction."

Reproductive ducts and glands

The reproductive ducts of the female are usually one or two **oviducts** that carry the eggs from the gonads (ovaries) directly to the outside, or to a cloaca, uterus, etc. The male ducts are usually one or two **vasa deferentia** which carry the sperms directly to the outside, or into an ejaculatory duct, etc. The male ducts are often enlarged near the posterior end into **seminal vesicles** (Fig. 224), where sperms are stored until needed; and **seminal receptacles** may be present in the female for a like purpose. In many animals, **glands** are associated with the gonads and their ducts, as for example, yolk glands in planarians (Fig. 68); cement glands in insects; oviduct glands that secrete the gelatinous coat of the frog's egg (Fig. 223); glands that secrete the albumin, shell membrane, and shell of the bird's egg; and the prostate and Cowper's glands that add their secretions to the spermatozoa in mammals.

Fertilization and egg laying

Both structures and activities are frequently combined in order to insure fertilization of the eggs of different animals.

In many **aquatic animals,** such as fish and frogs, the eggs are laid directly in the water, and sperms either come in contact with them by chance or are poured over them by the male, as in the frog. In other aquatic animals, for example the crayfish and in most **terrestrial animals,** the sperms are injected into the female by the male, where they unite with the eggs at once, or are stored until required. Animals that lay their eggs either before or after fertilization are **oviparous.** In certain types of animals the eggs are retained in the body until they hatch, as in certain sharks, fish, amphibians, lizards, and snakes; the term **ovoviviparous** is applied to this procedure. The fertilized egg in most mammals is nourished within the body by food from the blood of the mother that passes through a special embryonic organ called the placenta. Mammals of this type and other animals that give birth to young that develop from eggs within the body of the mother and are nourished from her blood stream are called **viviparous.**

EMBRYOLOGY
(DEVELOPMENT)

Descriptive embryology

Embryology is the subdivision of biology which deals with the fertilized egg and its development. Historically, embryologists were interested initially in describing the visible changes in the fertilized egg as it develops, and in comparing the developmental events observed in the egg of one species with those observed in the eggs of other species. The first visible event in development is the subdivision of the fertilized egg into a number of cells, the process of **cleavage** (Figs. 41, 56, 237, 258, 350, and 349). Sooner or later the individual cells (**blastomeres**) rearrange themselves individually around a cavity called the **blastocoel** (Figs. 41, 56, 237, and 349); this constitutes the **blastula** stage. Subsequently groups of blastomeres shift their positions in such a way that several distinct **germ layers** become recognizable (Fig. 402); these are named according to their positions relative to one another. The outermost layer of cells is then called the **ectoderm;** the innermost layer which forms the wall of the archenteron is called the **endoderm;** the middle layer located between ectoderm and endoderm is called the **mesoderm.** The stage of development during which formation of germ layers occurs is called the **gastrula.** The

mass movements of groups of cells during gastrulation are referred to as **morphogenetic movements,** since they constitute the initial step in transforming the simple blastula into the rough outlines of the future body; genesis of form is under way. Details of gastrulation differ considerably in eggs of different species, but the end result is essentially the same in all.

In most triploblastic animals, a cavity soon forms within the mesoderm, and con-

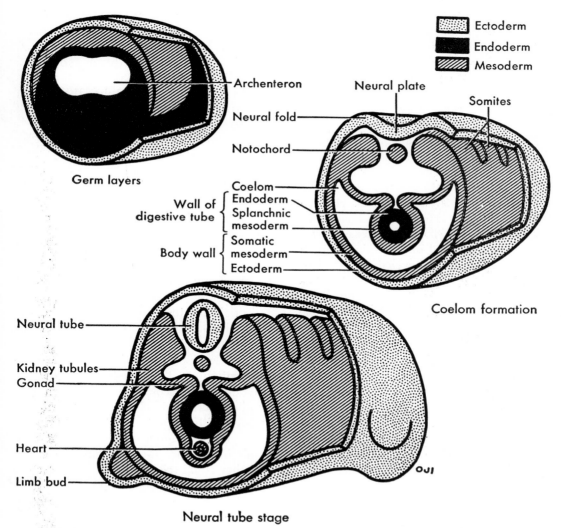

FIGURE 402. Stereograms of parts of early stages in the development of a chordate embryo; successively older stages are shown from germ layers to neural tube. Only the areas of mesoderm in which the kidney tubules and gonads will develop are labeled, and not the actual developing structures.

sequently is completely bounded by this germ layer; this cavity is the coelom (Fig. 402). The outer layer of mesoderm adjacent to the ectoderm is now called the **somatic mesoderm;** together with the ectoderm it forms the body wall. The inner layer of mesoderm adjacent to the endoderm is now called **splanchnic mesoderm;** together with the endoderm it forms the wall of the digestive tube. If the developing egg belongs to a chordate, coelom formation does not extend into the dorsal-most mesoderm. The mesoderm located in the dorsal midline forms a longitudinal supporting rod, the **notochord.** The mesoderm to each side of the latter becomes separated into a row of mesodermal blocks, the **somites.** The arrangement of these pairs of somites along the length of the embryo is the basis of metamerism in the chordate body.

A most interesting change then occurs in the ectoderm located directly above the notochord and somites (Fig. 402). It becomes thickened into a flat plate of cells, the **neural plate;** the edges of this plate are then elevated as **neural folds.** These folds continue to approach one another until they fuse in the middorsal line, forming a dorsal, hollow, **neural tube,** covered by ectoderm (Fig. 402). Once this developmental stage is reached (the **neurula**), subsequent developmental processes are relatively simple, although they result eventually in the formation of complex organs. The anterior end of the neural tube enlarges to become the **brain;** different antero-posterior levels of the brain enlarge to different degrees, thereby indicating the 5 major subdivisions of the adult brain. The lateral walls of the second such subdivision fold outwards (normal embryo, right side of Fig. 403), then fold back upon themselves (normal embryo, left side of Fig. 403), thereby forming the major part of the eye, the **optic cup.** The ectoderm overlying this optic cup thickens, then folds towards the optic cup (right side of Fig. 403), forms a vesicle, and finally separates from the ectoderm to become the **lens**

of the eye (left side of Fig. 403). At the anterior end of the brain a pair of infoldings of the ectoderm marks the beginnings of the **nostrils.** On each side of the hindbrain a similar infolding of the ectoderm forms an **auditory vesicle** which separates from the ectoderm; each of these vesicles later on transforms into the complex inner ear mechanism (membranous labyrinth). The posterior end of the neural tube remains less complex and becomes the **spinal cord.**

Similarly, the digestive tube becomes modified at different antero-posterior levels to form the posterior part of the mouth, pharynx, esophagus, stomach, and intestine. At certain levels of this digestive tube the walls fold outwards to form several derivatives of the digestive tube: the trachea and lungs, the common bile duct, liver, gall bladder, and pancreas.

At appropriate levels of the body, the lateral body wall thickens and protrudes outward to form the **limb buds** (Fig. 402), which develop later into the legs. Certain areas of the mesoderm form the **heart,** others the **kidney tubules,** and still others the **gonads** (Fig. 402).

Thus as development continues beyond the gastrula stage, different groups of cells, which originated by cleavage of the fertilized egg, and which accordingly contain parts of the original cytoplasm of the egg and the same chromosomes as the zygote, develop in different directions; we speak of this stage of development as the stage of **cellular differentiation.** The question then arises, why do cells become different from one another during development? Descriptive embryologists suspected that interaction between adjacent groups of cells might play a role in cellular differentiation. For example, they could see that the lens always developed from the ectoderm immediately adjacent to the optic cup. Perhaps the optic cup exerts some influence on the overlying ectoderm which causes it to differentiate into a lens. How could this suspicion (hypothesis) be tested?

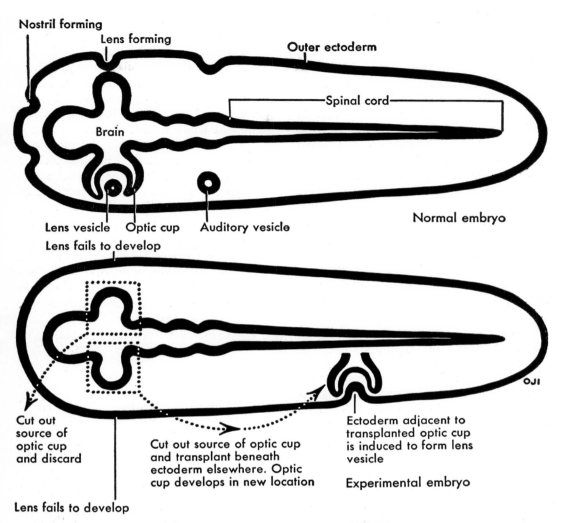

Nostril forming

Lens forming

Outer ectoderm

Spinal cord

Brain

Lens vesicle   Optic cup   Auditory vesicle

Normal embryo

Lens fails to develop

Cut out
source of
optic cup
and discard

Cut out source of optic cup
and transplant beneath
ectoderm elsewhere. Optic
cup develops in new location

Ectoderm adjacent to
transplanted optic cup
is induced to form lens
vesicle

Experimental embryo

Lens fails to develop

FIGURE 403. Experimental embryonic induction of the lens in an embryo. Diagrams are schematic dorsal views of normal and experimental chordate embryos.

Experimental embryology

Embryonic induction

It was possible to design instruments so delicate that operations could be performed on young embryos to dissect out and discard that part of the brain wall which would later form the optic cup (experimental embryo, Fig. 403, right side). Such an operation constitutes an **embryonic extirpation.** Would the ectoderm in that region form a lens in the absence of the optic cup? It did

not do so. But was this sufficient proof that the development of the lens depended on the passage of some influence from the optic cup to the lens-forming ectoderm? Perhaps the lens-forming ectoderm was merely damaged during removal of the source of the optic cup. To rule out this possibility another type of experiment was indicated. Suppose the source of the optic cup was removed from its normal position and was placed beneath the ectoderm elsewhere in the body of a young embryo (experimental embryo, Fig. 403, left side). Such an operation is called **embryonic transplantation.** Would the optic cup continue to develop in its new location? If so, would it stimulate the overlying ectoderm to form a lens? The answer to both questions is yes. Thus it is clearly evident that the optic cup does indeed exert some influence on the overlying ectoderm which causes the latter to differentiate into a lens. The process of stimulation is called **embryonic induction.** This approach to the study of development which revealed the role of embryonic induction in the process of cellular differentiation of a lens is called **experimental embryology.** By systematic investigation of all other regions of the developing embryo where similar causal relations between adjacent groups of cells were suspected, experimental embryologists have demonstrated convincingly that interaction between adjacent groups of cells does play an exceedingly important role in embryonic differentiation in many species.

Having demonstrated the existence of embryonic inductions, the next step was to study the mechanisms of induction. Does the optic cup produce a specific chemical substance which diffuses to the nearby lens-forming ectoderm and stimulates the latter to differentiate into a lens? Or does the optic cup stimulate the adjacent ectoderm physically in some way? Similarly, experimental embryologists ask questions concerning changes in the reacting cells during and following embryonic induction. Increasingly, today's approach to development is to identify and study the chemical and physical bases of embryonic differentiation.

Organizer theory

It has been found that the very first appearance of a definite head-tail axis, and of a nervous system, in the early embryo, is due to interactions between mesoderm cells and the overlying ectoderm. This was first shown by Spemann, who was awarded the Nobel prize for a scientific achievement of tremendous importance. Spemann demon-strated this by transplanting the dorsal lip of the blastopore (the opening into the archenteron) of one salamander gastrula to a site in another gastrula where a nervous system would not normally form. It was found that the transplanted dorsal mesoderm (chordamesoderm) **induced** the ectoderm with which it was in contact to become a neural tube. The transplanted mesoderm, itself, **self-differentiated** into notochord, somites, and other structures, so that a small embryo was formed from the combination of **host** and **donor** tissues. No other region of the early gastrula was found to have this inductive ability, so the chordamesoderm of the salamander gastrula has been called the **organizer.** Much important work still needs to be done in this fascinating field of **experimental embryology.**

METAMORPHOSIS

Metamorphosis occurs commonly during the development of invertebrates and occasionally in vertebrates. By metamorphosis is meant a sudden, marked change in the course of development. Such changes occur even among the protozoans, where, for example, the ciliated embryos of Suctoria, after swimming around for a while, settle down, become attached, and transform into tentacle-bearing adults. Similarly, the free-swimming, flagellated embryos of **sponges** metamorphose into permanently attached animals with an osculum at the outer end and spicules in the body wall (Fig. 49). No free-swimming larva appears in the life cycle of the hydra, but in many other **coelenterates,** such as *Obelia* (Fig. 57) and *Aurellia* (Fig. 60), a ciliated planula becomes attached and metamorphoses into a hydroid. Many marine **annelids** and **mollusks** pass through a trochophore stage from which the adult develops. In many species of **starfishes,** the egg develops into a larva called a bipinnaria (Fig. 429), which is bilaterally symmetrical; the free-swimming bipinnaria settles to the bottom and changes into a minute, radially symmetrical starfish.

Metamorphosis in insects

Perhaps the most striking of all types of metamorphosis occurs among the insects (Figs. 140 and 141). In this class the character of the metamorphosis, whether complete or incomplete, is an important means of classification. No metamorphosis takes place in certain orders; in other orders, the larvae or nymphs are recognizably similar to the adults and are active throughout their immature life; but in most of the insects, metamorphosis is complete, and the caterpillars, grubs, maggots, etc., become quiescent pupae. Within the pupa, many of the larval tissues break down into a liquid form, which is utilized by groups of larval cells called imaginal disks, to build up both internal and external organs of the adult. The adult eventually emerges from the pupal covering.

Metamorphosis in chordates

Several very conspicuous cases of metamorphosis among the chordates are worth mentioning besides those already studied. Among the **tunicates** (Fig. 206), the tadpolelike larva with its notochord, neural tube, digestive tract, heart, pharynx, and gill slits, becomes attached and undergoes **retrogressive metamorphosis**, during which most of the larval organs are lost or become degenerate. Larval **lampreys** were given the genus name *Ammocoetes* before their relation to the adult lamprey was known. They resemble the amphioxus (Fig. 201) very closely in structure, and seem to represent a sort of intermediate stage between primitive chordates and primitive vertebrates. After about 8 years of free life, the ammocoete larva acquires the structure and habits of the adult lamprey. Metamorphosis from an aquatic larva with gills to an air-breathing terrestrial or semiterrestrial condition is ex-

hibited by the frog (Fig. 238) and many other amphibians.

PARENTAL CARE

While parental care of eggs and young is widespread in the animal kingdom, in some instances, it may be lacking entirely. Certain aquatic forms such as starfishes and sea urchins shed their eggs and sperms into the water and allow currents to bring them together. Under these conditions, enormously large numbers of gametes must be produced to insure a sufficient number of fertilized eggs to prevent the race from dying out. Other aquatic species lay their eggs after fertilization where conditions are favorable for their development; for example, the eggs of fish and frogs are laid in the water and those of certain turtles in the warm sand. The newly hatched young must shift for themselves, since their parents pay no attention to them.

Care of eggs

Protection and food are provided by the parents of certain animals, who then seem to consider their duty done, and they give their offspring no further consideration. Egg cases are common protective devices, such as the cocoons of the earthworm (Fig. 97), cockroach, and other insects. The solitary wasps have become famous, since they not only hide their eggs in a burrow or in a protective nest, but they deposit near them a supply of partially paralyzed insect larvae for the young to feed upon when they hatch.

Eggs may be cared for by parents in various ways. The crayfish attaches them to her swimmerets (headpiece, p. 197); the water flea *Cyclops* carries them about with her in two egg sacs; certain spiders carry them in a silk cocoon, and the fresh-water clams may hold their eggs and young in their gills throughout the winter (Fig. 177). The Surinam toad carries eggs in epidermal pouches on her back until they hatch, and the male obstetrical toad transports strings of eggs, wound about his hindlegs, and deposits the newly hatched young in water. The male sea horse is provided with a brood pouch in which the eggs are well protected. Most birds build nests, some of which are hardly more than a few blades of grass, whereas others are really amazing works of art (Fig. 319). The eggs laid in these nests are kept warm or incubated by the female, male, or by both, until they hatch. Several species, for example the cowbird, lay their eggs in other birds' nests, thus forcing the foster parents to incubate them and care for the young.

Care of young

Most of the invertebrates and cold-blooded vertebrates do not care for their young, but a few of them do. Young cray-fish remain with the mother for about one month. Worker honey bees attend the larval bees with great care; they provide those who are to develop into workers with royal jelly for two days, then a mixture of pollen and honey for 5 to 6 days. Those who are to become queens are fed only royal jelly, a nutritious albuminous material. This latter is a secretion of the pharyngeal glands of young worker bees. The male fresh-water dogfish builds and guards the nest and the young until they are about 4 inches long. The male stickleback also builds a nest and guards the eggs and young.

Birds

Birds and mammals are particularly solic-itous of their young, although this varies greatly in different species. Birds that are able to run about soon after they hatch are precocial; they neither need nor receive as much care as those that hatch in a very immature condition (altricial birds). Al-tricial birds must be fed in the nest for a long time. The whip-poor-will and killdeer are examples of precocial birds, and the prairie horned lark and chimney swift, of altricial birds (Fig. 320).

Mammals

All mammals care for their young, pro-viding them with protection and nourish-ment (milk) until they can take care of themselves. The egg-laying duckbill of Aus-tralia (Fig. 352A) holds her young to her abdomen with her tail, where they lick or suck from her hair, milk that is secreted by her mammary glands. Opossums, kangaroos, and other marsupials (Fig. 351) bring forth young in a very immature condition and protect and nourish them in a brood pouch on the abdomen. Young opossums are only about $\frac{1}{2}$ inch long when born; they crawl into their mother's pouch, where they feed on milk until they are able to creep out upon her back, scurrying in again in case of danger. Among the higher mammals, the young may become independent soon after birth, as in guinea pigs, or they may be born blind and helpless, like mice and kittens. The degree of parental care, in general, in-creases as one proceeds up the vertebrate scale to the more complex forms; and the number of offspring produced annually de-creases. The period of helplessness is of great importance to the young, since they are taught at that time much that the race has learned through the ages.

SELECTED COLLATERAL READINGS

Arey, L.B. *Developmental Anatomy*. Saunders, Philadelphia, 1954.

Barth, L.G. *Embryology*. Dreyden Press, New York, 1953.

Huettner, A.F. *Fundamentals of Comparative Embryology of the Vertebrates*. Macmillan, New York, 1949.

Patten, B.M. *Foundations of Embryology*. Mc-Graw-Hill, New York, 1958.

Romer, A.S. *The Vertebrate Body*. Saunders, Philadelphia, 1953.

Shumway, W., and Adamstone, F.B. *Introduction to Vertebrate Embryology*. Wiley, New York, 1954.

Spemann, H. *Embryonic Development and Induction*. Yale Univ. Press, New Haven, 1938.

Waddington, C.H. *Principles of Embryology*. Macmillan, New York, 1956.

Willier, B.H., Weiss, P.A., and Hamburger, Victor (eds.). *Analysis of Development*. Saunders, Philadelphia, 1955.

Witschi, E. *Development of Vertebrates*. Saunders, Philadelphia, 1956.

CHAPTER 35

OJI

Heredity

SELECTION has long been used in producing superior animals, such as the beautiful and sensitive race horse, the luxuriously furred blue-ribbon cat at the pet shows, and the pointer with its keen sense of smell. But what is more recent and more important, the knowledge of heredity has been used to produce the prize-winning steer at the fair to be sold for its steaks and roasts, and the golden-eared hybrid corn.

The knowledge of heredity has made great socio-economic contributions to human welfare; it has been estimated that the use of hybrid corn in this country represents an economic advantage of about a billion dollars a year. Applications of the principles of genetics produce superior domestic animals and farm crops. Also, research in human genetics is increasing our understanding of the relation of heredity to abnormalities and diseases, both physical and mental. Modern genetics is also giving insights into the biological basis of human nature.

HEREDITY

A knowledge of the reproduction and development of animals provides a good foundation for the discussion of heredity. In a legal sense we may inherit lands, buildings, and various articles; but we are not concerned here with this type of heredity; we are concerned with biological inheritance. We inherit from our parents the potentialities for various traits (characteristics) that can be observed, and the determiners of many other characteristics that we never exhibit. As a rule, when we discuss heredity, we do not refer to those traits that are common to all members of a group or species, but to variations in body and mental traits that may be possessed by both parents and offspring. Thus we are not ordinarily concerned with the fact that both father and son, each, have two eyes, but we are concerned about the color and other characteristics of their eyes. This is because the eye color of the son may not be the same as that of the father. From time immemorial, humans have taken note of the resemblance of children to their parents and tried to determine whether a child had its father's nose or its mother's, and the same for other features. The characteristics of the son may be like those of neither the father nor the mother, and thus we may discover that heredity involves differences as well as likenesses between parents and offspring.

The study of heredity deals with the origin of similarities and the differences between parent and offspring. It is concerned with the nature of these similarities and differences, their sources, and how they develop. Briefly stated, **heredity** is a study of the transmission, from generation to generation, of developmental potentialities (genes) and how they come to expression.

Genes

The gene is the chemical unit of heredity, which is transmitted in the chromosome, and which by interaction with the internal and external environment may control the development of a trait. Although the exact physical nature of the gene is not known, there is some evidence for regarding it as a complex chemical substance; the essential genic material is desoxyribonucleic acid (abbreviated DNA). Investigations on the nature of genes are difficult because they cannot be isolated for study or seen with a microscope. One of the most important properties of a gene is its ability to reproduce itself, for each gene must be duplicated in each cell division. The way in which a gene duplicates itself is unknown, but it probably depends on enzyme activities.

The fertilized egg in the case of man and of other higher animals and the unfertilized egg in parthenogenetic species contain the sum total of the genes that largely constitute the heredity of the individual. We have already discussed in Chapters 8 and 34, the origin of the egg and sperms, fertilization,

chromosome behavior, and embryonic development. The study of genetics requires further study of these phenomena, since the distribution of the genes which are responsible for the heredity of any individual is accomplished during the processes that occur before and at the time of fertilization. Of particular interest are the chromosomes and their behavior, since the genes are contained in the chromosomes. We shall therefore begin our discussion of genetics with a description of what at present biologists believe to be the structure of the chromosomes.

Chromosome structure

The **chromosomes** are deeply staining structures found in the nuclei of cells. Their morphology and behavior are described in the accounts of mitosis in Chapter 2, the origin of eggs and sperms on page 80, and illustrated in Fig. 404. Figure 10 illustrates the structure of a chromosome in different phases of mitosis.

Chromosomal constitution of somatic cells

During the life of the individual, from the fertilized egg (zygote) to the period of sexual reproduction, every cell in the body contains the same number of chromosomes, a number which is usually constant for and characteristic of the species. In sexually reproducing organisms, since the chromosomes of the zygote result from a union of sperm and egg, the zygote chromosomes consist of a paternal and a maternal set. The chromosomes composing the paternal set generally differ from each other in length, shape, and in the genes they contain. Similarly, the maternal set is composed of different chromosomes. However, for each chromosome of the paternal set, there is a chromosome in the maternal set which is similar to it in form and genic content. Chromosomes which show such close resemblance to each other are spoken of as being **homologous.** The zygote and its cellular descendants all contain the number of homologous pairs of chromosomes characteristic of the species.

The formation of eggs and sperms

Obviously, if the sperm and egg which combine to form the zygote contained the same number of chromosomes as somatic (body) cells, the number of chromosomes present in a species would double every generation. However, during the formation of eggs and sperms, an orderly process known as **maturation (meiosis)** prevents this doubling from occurring. The most important single effect of maturation (Fig. 404), is a reduction of the number of chromosomes in eggs and sperms to one-half the number contained in somatic cells. Though the details of this reduction are variable in different species and somewhat complicated in all species, the process can be described simply as a single duplication of each chromosome, followed by two nuclear divisions.

The two divisions in maturation are spoken of as the **reductional** and **equational divisions** for reasons which will become clear in what follows. Early in the first or reductional division, each chromosome duplicates itself to form two chromatids (Fig. 10), which do not separate until later in maturation.

A second important process, **synapsis,** also occurs in the primary oocyte or spermatocyte. Synapsis describes the process whereby the two members of a homologous pair of chromosomes come to lie very close to each other. Because a synapsed pair of chromosomes is composed of four elements, the two chromatids of each duplicated chromosome, the whole structure is called a **tetrad** (Fig. 404). In synapsis, the chromosomes may lie so close together that under the microscope the tetrad may appear as a single dense unit. During synapsis, exchanges may occur between the chromatids of the

two homologous chromosomes, a phenomenon called crossing over, to be discussed in a later section. While the chromosome pairs are still in synapsis, they migrate to the equatorial plate of the first division spindle. When they arrive, they become oriented in such a way that one member of each pair is directed toward one pole of the spindle, the other member toward the opposite pole. The first division is then completed by the separation of the homologous members of each pair (separating black from white, in the diagram Fig. 404). This is a **reduction division.** Note that the chromosomes in each of the secondary oocytes and spermatocytes are not an assortment of any combination of chromosomes, but a very orderly group consisting of one chromosome from each pair of homologous chromosomes contained in the parental cell (primary spermatocyte or oocyte). In other words, while a somatic cell contains two chromosomes of each kind (similar in length, form, and genic content) to be found in a species, a secondary oocyte or spermatocyte will contain only one of each kind. For example, human somatic cells contain 46 chromosomes (23 pairs) whereas a human secondary oocyte contains 23 (one from each pair).

The second division, the **equational division,** may follow closely on the first. The essential feature of the second division is extremely simple. You will recall that following duplication, each of the chromosomes of the first division was made up of two sister chromatids. In the second division, every chromosome becomes oriented on the two spindles. The sister chromatids then separate from each other (black from black and white from white in Fig. 404). The separated chromatids are known as chromosomes.

Following maturation, the **immature egg** or sperm (spermatid) matures to become a **mature** sperm or egg, but there is no further chromosomal change. When a mature egg is fertilized by a sperm, the zygote resulting will again contain two chromosomes of each kind, as did the primary oocyte and spermatocyte from which the gamete (egg or sperm) arose. Further, with future mitotic divisions, all of the resulting somatic cells will contain the **diploid** (double) number of chromosomes. Only when maturation recurs will you find the **haploid** (single) number present in cells. Though chromosome pairs are present in somatic cells, they do not usually synapse in somatic cells.

Returning to the first maturation division, it should be remembered that the two members of a pair of homologous chromosomes in the primary spermatocyte or oocyte came originally from two sources, one from the father and one from the mother of the organism undergoing maturation. When the chromosomes orient on the first maturation division spindle, the paternal chromosome of a particular pair may go to the same pole as the paternal one from another pair, or it may go to the opposite pole. Each pair then is oriented independently of every other pair, and hence any combination of maternal and paternal chromosomes is possible in an egg or sperm, a fact which permits a wide variety of recombinations of genes, and hence traits, to occur. On the average, half of the chromosomes of an egg or sperm will be of paternal and half of maternal origin, but one can predict that on rare occasions, a sperm or egg may contain by chance exclusively maternal or paternal chromosomes. This independent behavior of chromosome pairs in maturation is the physical basis for the **independent assortment of genes**, Mendel's Second Law.

Distribution of genes during fertilization and maturation

Since the homologous chromosomes consist of genes that affect the same traits, Fig. 405 may be used to understand the distribution of genes during fertilization and maturation. Instead of writing the complete descriptive name of each trait, the geneticist assigns symbols to represent the character. For example (*a*) may be used to designate a gene for albinism and (*A*) a gene for pigment. Here, beginning at the left, the sperm containing genes represented by (*A*) and (*B*) fertilizes the egg containing genes (*a*) and (*b*) to form a zygote (*AaBb*); next shown, without including the steps that lead up to it, is reduction division in an individual with the genotype (*AaBb*). The possible arrangements of the chromosomes on the spindle at the reduction division is a matter of chance. Those shown not only can occur but do so with equal frequency. It depends on how the chromosomes are arranged in the equatorial plane at reduction division as to what combination of chromosomes and genes will result in the gametes. With 2 pairs of chromosomes, as used in this illustration, there are 4 different possible combinations of chromosomes to form 4 different kinds of gametes as indicated: (*AB*), (*ab*), (*aB*), and (*Ab*).

Alleles

Two genes at the same position (locus) in the homologous chromosomes, but producing somewhat different effects on the individual are called **alleles**. For example, the gene responsible for red-green color blindness is an allele of the alternative normal gene. An individual is **homozygous** for a trait when both the genes at corresponding loci in homologous chromosomes are identical. An individual is **heterozygous** for a trait if the two genes at any one locus in homologous chromosomes are different for a given trait. An organism may be homozygous for some pairs of genes and heterozygous for other pairs.

Dominants and recessives

In a heterozygote the genes are of two types, dominants and recessives. A gene is said to be dominant when the trait it represents appears in the heterozygote; its allele

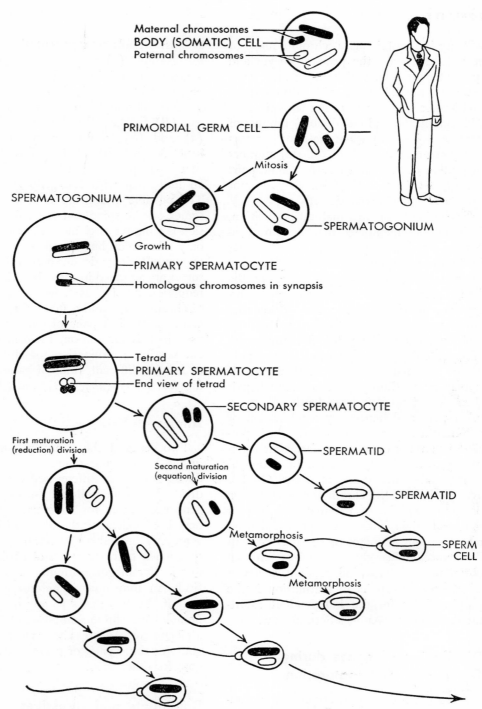

Maternal chromosomes
BODY (SOMATIC) CELL
Paternal chromosomes

PRIMORDIAL GERM CELL

Mitosis

SPERMATOGONIUM

SPERMATOGONIUM

Growth

PRIMARY SPERMATOCYTE
Homologous chromosomes in synapsis

Tetrad
PRIMARY SPERMATOCYTE
End view of tetrad

SECONDARY SPERMATOCYTE

First maturation
(reduction) division

Second maturation
(equation) division

SPERMATID

SPERMATID

Metamorphosis

SPERM
CELL

Metamorphosis

FIGURE 404. The chromosome cycle in man. Diagrams illustrating the distribution of chromosomes during spermatogenesis, oogenesis, fertilization, and early embryonic development. The primordial germ cells are represented as containing 4 chromosomes of two different lengths; one of each length having been derived from the mother (maternal) and the other from the father (paternal). All chromosomes in the zygote received from the sperm are thereafter paternal, and those received from the mature egg are thereafter maternal, regardless of what they

576

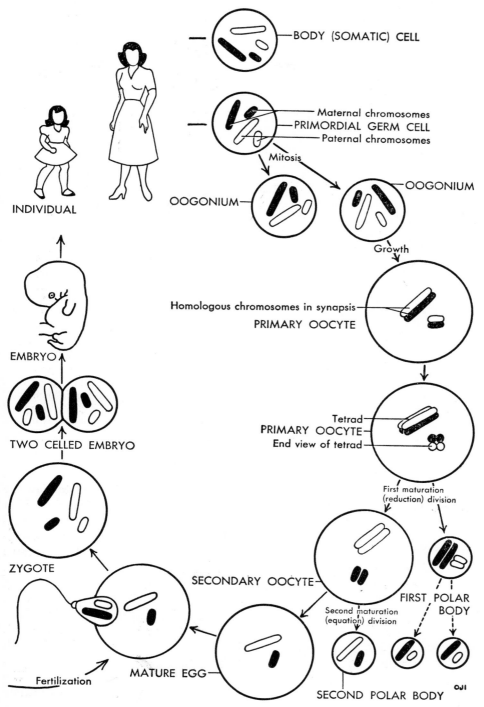

BODY (SOMATIC) CELL

Maternal chromosomes
PRIMORDIAL GERM CELL
Paternal chromosomes

Mitosis

OOGONIUM

OOGONIUM

INDIVIDUAL

Growth

Homologous chromosomes in synapsis
PRIMARY OOCYTE

EMBRYO

TWO CELLED EMBRYO

Tetrad
PRIMARY OOCYTE
End view of tetrad

First maturation
(reduction) division

ZYGOTE

SECONDARY OOCYTE

FIRST POLAR
BODY

Second maturation
(equation) division

MATURE EGG

Fertilization

SECOND POLAR BODY

were in the mature gametes. In the interest of simplicity, the 23 pairs of chromosomes in man are represented here by only two pairs; however, the principle of maturation is exactly the same for two pairs of chromosomes as for 100 pairs. These diagrams illustrate well the continuity of chromosomes.

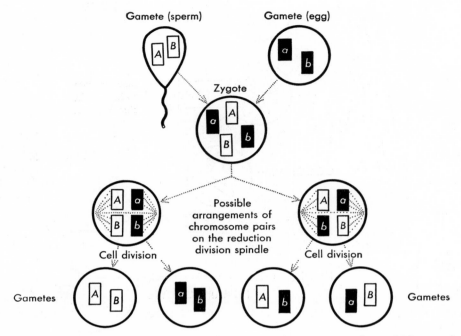

FIGURE 405. Diagram to show the union of gametes to form a zygote, from which an animal is eventually developed; when this individual forms gametes with 2 pairs of chromosomes, there are 4 possible combinations of the chromosomes to form 4 different kinds of gametes as follows: (AB), (ab), (Ab), and (aB). Details of the maturation process as shown in Fig. 404 are omitted to save space. It is a genetic custom to represent dominant genes in chromosomes with capital letters and recessive genes with small letters.

in such a case is said to be recessive. For example, in the fruit fly *Drosophila*, the gene for red eyes is dominant and that for white eyes recessive; in man, it appears that freckles are dominant and the absence of freckles is recessive; and in cattle, hornlessness is dominant, and horns recessive. Similarly among plants, Mendel found tallness in peas dominant, and shortness recessive (Fig. 408). The result of dominance and recessiveness in allelic genes is that heterozygous individuals do not exhibit all that they inherit from their parents, since some of the genes are recessive.

When we say that we inherit certain traits, we mean that heredity potentialities (the genes) are the things that are really inherited, and never the developed trait. We do not inherit our father's nose, but we may inherit from our father a gene for a nose that looks like his.

Genotype and phenotype

The term **genotype** is used to describe the sum total of the genes inherited from both parents; these include both the dominant genes, whose corresponding traits appear in the individual, and the recessive genes that may have no detectable effect. The term **phenotype** is used to describe the individual as shown by his expressed traits. (Frequently phenotype is incorrectly defined as the appearance of the individual; this definition is limited to physical traits such as hair color, but does not include physiologic traits such as the blood groups.) The following examples will serve to illustrate what actually happens.

Homozygotes

When a homozygous individual with black curly hair mates with a homozygous

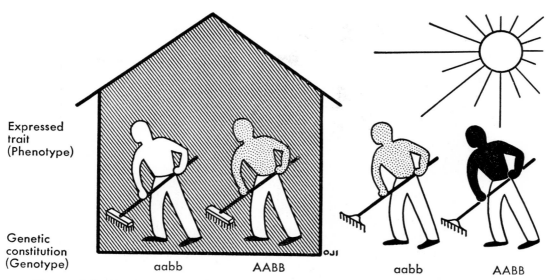

Expressed trait (Phenotype)

Genetic constitution (Genotype)

aabb   AABB   aabb   AABB

Figure 406. Sketch showing the difference between phenotype and genotype. The potential difference in skin pigmentation of a white person and a Negro is controlled by genes (genotype), but the actual color of the skin (phenotype) will depend greatly on the extent of the individual's exposure to sunlight.

individual with black curly hair, the offspring will all have black curly hair. Similar results are obtained with respect to any trait when the parents are homozygous, since the genes that control the development of the trait are all of one type. Since some organisms are known to have thousands of different kinds of genes, any cross between individuals may serve as a test of the inheritance of any or of all the traits in which the two individuals differ. The investigator may concentrate his attention on as many, or as few traits, as he wishes. Usually the smaller the number of traits studied simultaneously, the easier it makes the interpretations. No more than two pairs of traits will be used in this book. We will start with the simplest possible situation in which the inheritance of one pair of alleles is studied.

Monohybrids

A monohybrid is the result of a cross between parents differing in respect to a single gene. One of Mendel's (Fig. 463) experiments with peas will serve to illustrate this

situation. He crossed tall pea plants with short pea plants. Figure 408 presents a diagram of the results. Here each parent contains two genes for height; one parent has the dominant genes (SS) for tallness; the other, recessive genes (ss) for shortness. The offspring in the first filial (L. *filia*, daughter; *filius*, son) generation (F_1) are all alike, each receiving a dominant gene (S) from the tall parent, and a recessive gene (s) from the short parent. These offspring are all tall since the gene for tallness (S) is dominant; but they carry within them the recessive gene (s) for shortness.

During maturation, as indicated in Fig. 404, 2 types of male gametes and 2 types of female gametes are produced by the members of the F_1 generation; one half of each are provided with a gene for shortness (s) and the other half with the gene for tallness (S). Fertilization brings about the results shown, that is, 25 per cent of the zygotes will receive 2 genes for tallness (SS); 25 per cent will receive 2 genes for shortness (ss), and 50 per cent will receive 1 gene for tallness and 1 for shortness (Ss). The F_2 generation will consist of 75 per

FIGURE 407. Garden of the Augustinian monastery at Brno, Czechoslovakia, measuring only 20 feet by 120 feet, in which Mendel experimented with the garden pea. After 8 years of study, he stated his conclusions in what are now known as Mendel's laws. This photograph was made by Professor Hugo Iltis many years ago when the garden was essentially the same as it was at the time of Mendel's investigations. (Courtesy of Mendel Museum, Fredericksburg, Va.)

cent tall plants, [33⅓ per cent homozygous (SS) and 66⅔ per cent heterozygous (Ss)], and 25 per cent homozygous short plants (ss). Therefore, 2 phenotypes appear, tall and short, but 3 genotypes are present (SS, Ss, and ss). When a monohybrid cross is made, as described above, 1 phenotype appears in the F_1 generation and all the organisms are like the dominant plant. There is also but a single genotype (Ss). In the F_2 generation, however, there are 2 phenotypes, 75 per cent of the offspring (SS and Ss) on the average being tall, and 25 per cent (ss) short; but there are 3 genotypes, 25 per cent with 2 genes for tallness (SS), 50 per cent with 1 gene for tallness and 1 for shortness (Ss), and 25 per cent with 2 genes for shortness (ss). Mendel actually obtained in the F_2 generation, 787 dominant tall plants and 277 recessive short plants.

The headpiece at the beginning of this chapter shows that when black cocker spaniels, both of which are heterozygous for black and brown coat color, are mated, a ratio of 3 black to 1 brown is obtained. Thus it appears that black is dominant to brown in these dogs.

Dihybrids or the inheritance of two independent genes

A dihybrid organism is the result of a cross between parents differing in 2 genes (Fig. 409). For example, round shape of peas is dominant over wrinkled shape, and yellow color is dominant over green. If homozygous yellow-round peas are crossed with green-wrinkled peas, the F_1 generation of pea plants will bear only yellow-round peas. If the F_1's are crossed, the traits appear to be inherited independently. During the reduction division, 4 types of female and 4 types of male gametes will be produced. How these will recombine when fertilization

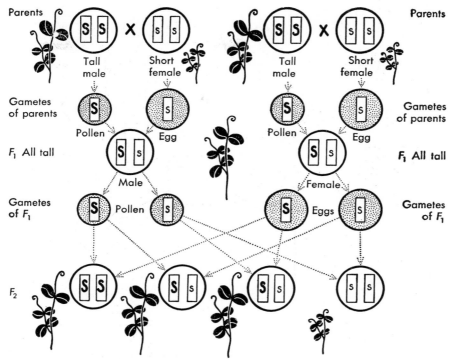

Parents

Tall male × Short female

Gametes of parents

Pollen Egg

F₁ All tall

Male

Gametes of F₁

Pollen

F₂

Parents

Tall male × Short female

Gametes of parents

Pollen Egg

F₁ All tall

Female

Eggs

Gametes of F₁

1 Homozygous tall: 2 Heterozygous tall: 1 Homozygous short
3 Tall plants: 1 Short plant

FIGURE 408. Inheritance in height in a cross between a tall and a short variety of the edible garden pea. Tall stem is dominant to short stem. S represents the gene for tallness; s represents the gene for shortness.

takes place is shown by use of a checkerboard (Fig. 409), which is a common method used by geneticists in illustrating the combinations of genes during hybridization. As shown in Fig. 409, the F_2 will consist of 9 genetically different combinations, and their phenotypes will be as follows: 9 yellow-round; 3 yellow-wrinkled; 3 green-round; and 1 green-wrinkled.

Mendel's laws

These are simple illustrations of what are commonly called Mendel's laws. **Mendel's First Law** is the **law of segregation** (separation); it states that there is a separation of the members of a pair of genes during maturation so that each gamete of an

individual contains one gene from each pair. Thus when two such gametes unite at fertilization, we shall have two genes for each trait brought back together in the individual. This is true because of reduction division. **Mendel's Second Law** is the **law of independent assortment**; it states that the distribution of each pair of genes to the gamete is entirely independent of the distribution of any other pair. This second law holds only if the pairs of genes are on separate (nonhomologous) chromosomes. As indicated in a later section on linkage, this condition is not always met. According to Mendel's laws, genes in the gametes behave in heredity as units and are distributed among the offspring according to mathematical rules. Thus with monohybrid par-

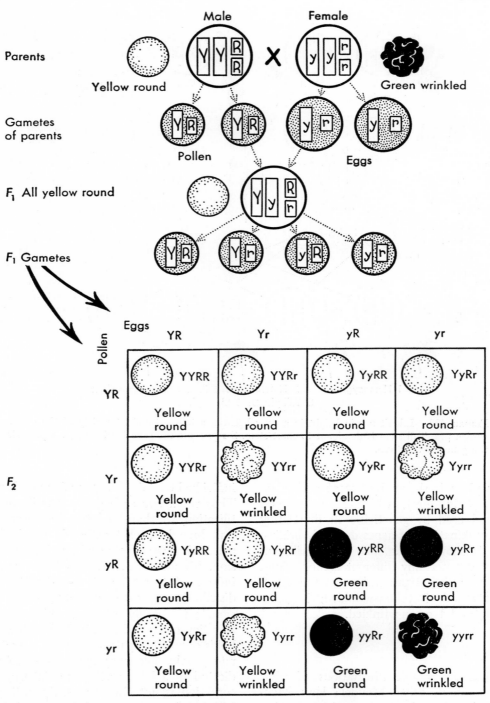

FIGURE 409. The inheritance of two independent traits is shown in a cross between yellow-round garden peas and green-wrinkled peas. Yellow and round are dominant genes in this case; the recessive genes are green and wrinkled.

ents, the Mendelian ratio in the F_2 generation is 3:1 (3 tall plants to 1 short plant, Fig. 408; in a dihybrid the ratio is 9 : 3 : 3 : 1 (Fig. 409); and in a trihybrid the ratio is 27 : 9 : 9 : 9 : 3 : 3 : 3 : 1. Where 4 different pairs of genes are concerned, there are 81 possible genotypes and 16 phenotypes; 5 different pairs of genes give 243 possible genotypes and 31 phenotypes. In man the somatic number of chromosomes is 46 * (Fig. 410), and the reduced number of chromosomes in the mature germ cells is 23. If these chromosomes are all different and each

is the bearer of genes, as we have every reason to suppose is true, the number of possible genotypes and phenotypes in human offspring is very large indeed.

Inheritance of sex

Thus far we have considered the 2 members of each pair of homologous chromosomes to be exactly alike; but in the males of most species of animals studied, including man, the members of one pair are dissimilar (Figs 410 and 411). One known as the **Y**

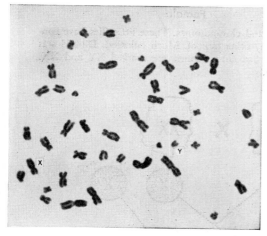

FIGURE 410. Chromosomes of man. This photograph shows the chromosomes of a normal male with one X, a smaller Y chromosome, and 44 autosomes. This is a metaphase stage when each chromosome is split into two chromatids. The illustration demonstrates clearly that the typical human chromosome number is 46. (Courtesy of Doctors Tjio and Puck, Dept. of Biophysics, Univ. of Colorado Medical Center.)

chromosome is often smaller than its mate, which is known as the **X chromosome**; in some species the Y chromosome is absent. These X and Y chromosomes are called **sex chromosomes**, in contrast to all the other chromosomes, which are termed **autosomes**. The X chromosome of the male resembles the chromosomes of a homologous pair possessed by the female. Thus the female has one pair of X chromosomes; and the male has one X chromosome, which may

---

* The chromosome number in man is still controversial, but 46 is probably correct. Several investigations with new and improved technics strongly favor the conclusion that there are 46 chromosomes. Kodani reports that all individuals possess 46 chromosomes, but some individuals have either 47 or 48. The explanation for the 47 or 48 chromosome count is the presence, either singly or in duplicate, of a supernumerary chromosome.

or may not have a Y chromosome as a mate. Experiments have shown that the X chromosome bears genes influential in determining sex. Figure 412 indicates how sex determination may depend on the distribution of these X chromosomes.

In Fig. 412, the primordial germ cells of man are shown with one X chromosome and one Y chromosome; and the primordial germ cells of a woman are shown with 2 X chromosomes. During maturation two types of sperms are produced, one with an X chromosome and the other with a Y chromosome, but only one type of egg with an X chromosome. Sex is determined at the time of fertilization, since the egg that is fertilized by the sperm with a Y chromosome becomes a zygote with only one X chromosome and develops into a male, whereas the

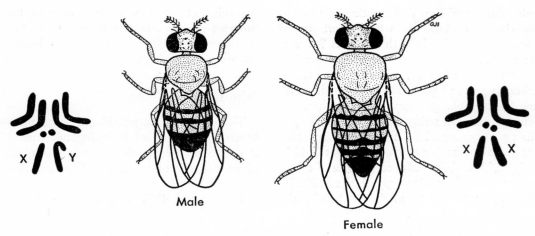

Male

Female

FIGURE 411. Fruit flies, *Drosophila melanogaster*, and chromosomes. These little flies have contributed more to our knowledge of genetics than any other animal. Much enlarged. Diploid sets of chromosomes (number found in somatic cells). Sex chromosomes are marked XY and XX. This is known as the XY type of sex determination.

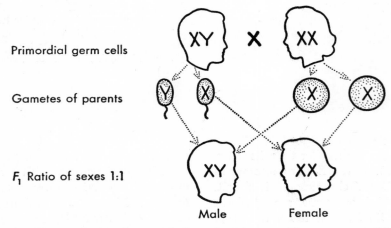

Primordial germ cells

Gametes of parents

F_1 Ratio of sexes 1:1

Male   **Female**

FIGURE 412. Diagram to show how sex is determined in man. The autosomes, which are the same in both sexes, have been omitted for purposes of simplification. Although a 1:1 ratio of sexes is expected, actually more males than females are born; the reason for this is still obscure. The mechanism that explains sex in man is not universal as to details, yet the fundamentals appear to be the same in organisms in which the sexes are separate.

egg that is fertilized by the sperm with an X chromosome becomes a zygote with two X chromosomes and develops into a female.

Research on sex determination in the fruit fly (Fig. 411) gives evidence that sex genes are located in the X chromosomes and also in the autosomes, and that in its final analysis sex determination is a matter of genic balance. It appears that the presence of two X chromosomes turns the balance in the direction of the female sex, and the presence of only one X chromosome results in the development of the male sex.

Sex-linked inheritance

The X chromosome, in addition to bearing genes influencing sex, also carries genes for many other traits. For example, in cases of color blindness in which the affected person cannot distinguish red from green, a color-blind father mated to a normal mother, as shown in Fig. 413, has no color-blind children, since the XY zygotes develop into normal males possessing one normal X chromosome and one Y chromosome which carries no gene for color blindness. Similarly

in this case, the X zygotes develop into normal females since only one X chromosome bears the gene for color blindness, which is recessive to the normal condition. In an F_2 generation, however, half of the grandsons and half of the granddaughters are free from this defect; and the other half of the granddaughters carry the gene for color blindness as a recessive, whereas the

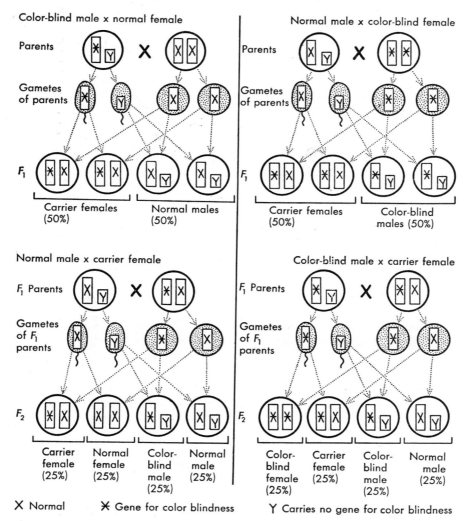

FIGURE 413. Inheritance of red-green color blindness in man. Diagram showing the 4 possible combinations of color blindness, excluding homozygous crosses, and the ways in which the defect is inherited from these combinations. The female, designated as a carrier, is one heterozygous for the gene for color blindness, but is normal in color vision. Marriages of brothers and sisters in the human species are so very rare that usually no F_2 is shown in texts; however, it is designated here to illustrate what commonly occurs in other species.

other half of the males are color-blind, having the gene in the X chromosome and no normal gene in the Y chromosome.

When a normal father is mated to a color-blind mother, all sons, but none of the daughters, are color-blind; and half of the grandsons and half of the granddaughters are likewise affected. Traits such as color blindness are said to be sex-linked, since their genes are borne by the X chromosome that also bears the genes influencing sex. Hemophilia (bleeder's disease) is another well-known sex-linked trait. There are many sex-linked traits; for example, the genes for over 30 sex-linked traits are known for man, and about 150 sex-linked genes have been found in the X chromosome of the fruit fly.

Linkage

It has been found by breeding experiments that the genes borne by the ordinary chromosomes or **autosomes** are also linked together in heredity, as one would expect, since at the reduction division, during maturation, entire chromosomes are separated. The number of linkage groups in an organism has always been found to be equal to the reduced number of chromosomes. Thus in the fruit fly, 4 groups of linked traits have been discovered, the genes for which have been located in the 4 chromosomes. Special technics have been developed in recent years for study of autosomal linkage in man. As a result, two well-established cases of autosomal linkage are known.

Crossing over

The clue to the localization of genes in the chromosome was furnished by the phenomenon known as crossing over. Certain crosses between fruit flies did not give the expected Mendelian ratios. The explanation suggested was that during the union of the chromosomes (synapsis), at the time of the reduction division and the subsequent separation of homologous chromosomes, an exchange of parts occurred between these homologous chromosomes. In other words, parts of a chromosome crossed over from one chromosome to its mate (homologue). A diagram of how this might occur is presented in Fig. 414.

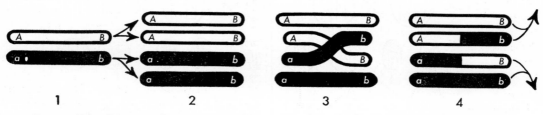

FIGURE 414. Diagram of crossing over during maturation (meiosis) with exchange of genes between homologous chromosomes. A, a; and B, b represent allelic pairs of genes in homologous chromosomes, which pair in synapsis: (1) pair of homologous chromosomes; (2) each chromosome becomes duplicated to form four chromatids (a tetrad); (3) crossing over takes place when one chromatid of each chromosome breaks and becomes reattached to the chromatid of the opposite (homologous) chromosome; (4) in the anaphase as shown by the arrows, the two groups of chromosomes go to opposite ends of the cell.

Location of genes

During the process of crossing over, those genes that are closest together in the chromosome would tend to remain together when the homologous chromosomes exchange parts. With this assumption as a basis, and with the results of thousands of breeding experiments as material to work with, the locations of hundreds of genes have been determined in the chromosomes of the fruit fly (*Drosophila*).

Multigenic traits

Up to this point we have assumed that there is one gene in the gamete for each trait exhibited by the adult, and this was for many years supposed to be the case. But now we know that many traits are determined by more than one gene. Several genes may work together in the development of a trait. When two or more genes are necessary for the development of a trait, it may be called a **multigenic (polygenic) trait**. A **modifying gene** is one which modifies in some way a trait determined by another gene. For instance, in man the gene for brown eyes is dominant to blue eyes; therefore, the difference between brown eyes and nonbrown in a given family probably depends on a single gene difference. But differences in amounts, kinds, and arrangement of pigment account for green, hazel, and brown eyes, which in turn appear to depend on other independent genes.

Lack of dominance

In all of Mendel's pea experiments, dominance was essentially complete so that there was no appreciable difference between the heterozygous and the homozygous individuals in the expression of a dominant trait. For example, (Ss) tall peas could not be easily distinguished from (SS) tall peas. However, there are many instances of **lack of dominance**, that is, the heterozygote is quite different from both the homozygous dominant and the homozygous recessive individuals.

One of the best illustrations of lack of dominance is provided by the blue Andalusian fowl. The "blue" appearance is due to very fine alternating white and black stripes. This type of fowl (F_1 in Fig. 415) is a hybrid (heterozygote) between black and white-splashed homozygous parents. When blue Andalusians (F_1) are interbred, the offspring (F_2) are 1 white-splashed, 2 blue Andalusians, and 1 black. The number

of visible types (phenotypes) here obtained is 3 instead of 2, which would have been true with complete dominance. Poultry breeders long tried by inbreeding to obtain pure blue Andalusian fowls, that is, fowls when bred together would produce only blue offspring. This is obviously impossible in the light of modern genetic information. The expression **incomplete dominance** or **partial dominance** is also used to describe cases of distinguishable heterozygotes, especially where the hybrids tend to resemble one parent much more than the other.

Examples of lack of dominance in man

In man it is probably rather common for heterozygotes to differ from both homozygotes. The form of the hair, with reference to curly and straight, as found in Caucasian people of European descent, illustrates a trait showing lack of dominance. The result of a mating involving curly and straight hair is offspring which have wavy hair, that is, hair intermediate in form between the homozygous parents. Certain of the blood groups are known to be inherited this way; and some diseases are known to have this mode of inheritance. Skin color in Negrowhite crosses, which involve at least two pairs of genes (Fig. 406), is another case in which dominance is lacking. The F_1's of a homozygous black and a homozygous white cross are all mulattoes of an intermediate color. The color of the skin of the offspring of mulattoes depends on the number of genes for black pigmentation distributed to each child, and may range from the extremes of white to black, although most of the progeny will show intermediate shades of color.

Penetrance

Penetrance refers to the regularity with which a gene produces a detectable effect. If every individual possessing a dominant gene develops the trait, the gene is said to have 100 per cent penetrance or **complete**

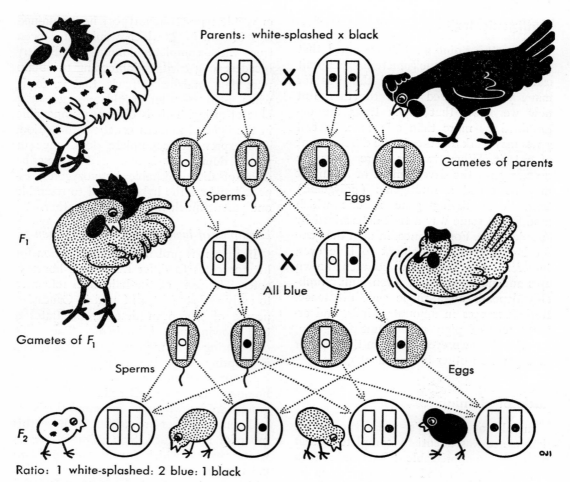

Parents: white-splashed x black

Gametes of parents

F_1

Sperms

Eggs

All blue

Gametes of F_1

Sperms

Eggs

F_2

Ratio: 1 white-splashed: 2 blue: 1 black

FIGURE 415. Lack of dominance. Cross between a white splashed fowl and a black Andalusian fowl. The hybrid (heterozygote) is called a blue Andalusian.

penetrance. If, however, a dominant gene does not cause the development of the trait in every case, the gene is said to have **reduced penetrance.** In other words, a dominant gene may possess a somewhat limited power to "penetrate" the developmental mechanism and cause a given phenotype. In all of Mendel's experiments with monohybrids, 100 per cent penetrance was present, hence the 3:1 ratio; but this ratio is not realized if the penetrance is reduced. Reduced penetrance of a dominant gene is sometimes called **irregular dominance.** The gene sometimes comes to expression in the heterozygous condition, and sometimes it does not. The causes of reduced penetrance are not very well understood, but modifying genes or external environmental factors, or both, are known to be responsible in some cases.

Some striking effects of environment on the penetrance of genes are produced by differences in temperature. On Siamese cats the dark pigment is produced only in the cooler parts of the body. The color of Himalayan rabbits corresponds to that of Siamese cats; the fur is white except on the feet, nose, and tail, where it is black. Ex-

FIGURE 416. Siamese cats. Pigment develops on the extremities as a result of temperatures lower than the rest of the body. (Photo by Chandoha, courtesy of Puss'n Boots Cat Food.)

perimentation has shown that whether the gene responsible for the development of the black extremities comes to expression depends on the temperature in which the fur develops.

Reduced penetrance is very common in man. Dominance with reduced penetrance has been found in human pedigrees of short metacarpals (brachymetapody) (Fig. 417), webbed toes (zygodactyly), hay fever, and many others.

The discussion of penetrance thus far has been limited to the dominant gene, but a recessive gene which does not always produce a detectable effect in the homozygous condition is also said to show reduced penetrance.

Expressivity of the gene

Expressivity refers to the variations in the way in which a particular gene expresses itself. Some genes have rather constant ex-

pressivity, regularly producing a definite degree of the trait; this is true of the genes for the A-B-O blood groups. On the other hand, many genes produce varying degrees of a trait in different individuals. For example, the gene for hay fever may cause only a little sneezing in one person and severe symptoms in another. The causes of variable expressivity of the gene are probably the same as those for varying degrees of penetrance.

Multiple alleles

Genes are probably composed of complex protein substances. The opportunities for change in such complex structures are greater than in simple ones. A single gene need consist of only one molecule of a protein to possess the capacity to change in several ways.

We have, up to now, considered conditions for which there are only two genes. Since all individuals have two genes at each

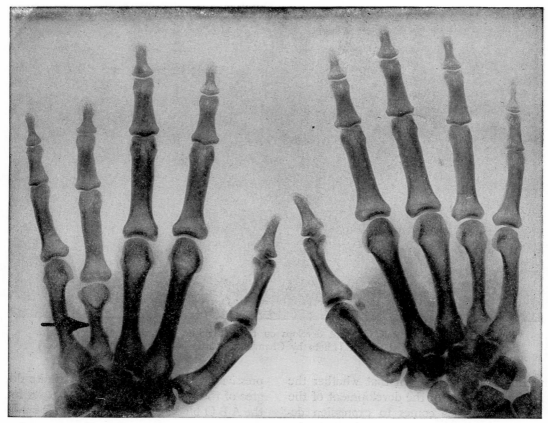

FIGURE 417. Short metacarpal (fourth of left hand) is due to a dominant gene which shows reduced penetrance. Some individuals in the heterozygous condition do not show the trait. Arrow points to short metacarpal. (From Karl A. Stiles, "The Inheritance of Brachymetapody." *J. of Hered.*, **30**:87–91, 1939.)

locus (one in each of the homologous chromosomes), one may have two of the same kind, or one of each of the two different kinds. Should one or both of these genes undergo a mutation (change) there will be 3 or more different kinds of genes for this particular locus on homologous chromosomes. Such genes are called **multiple alleles.** Any one of the genes is allelic to any other gene at that locus.

One of the best-known groups of multiple alleles concerns eye color in the fruit fly. The wild type is red, but the gene for this color has mutated to white (Fig. 440), buff, cherry, and at least 10 others. A fly must have any two of these genes—two genes for

red, or one for red and one for white, and so on.

A-B-O blood groups *

In man, the inheritance of A-B-O blood groups (p. 527) is determined by three such allelic genes. One of these genes causes the development of the A antigen, one the development of the B antigen, and the third results in the absence of both antigens. Since each individual must have two genes at this locus, one can readily ascertain that there are 6 different genotypes possible. Designat-

* The discussion of subgroups is beyond the scope of this book.

ing the three allelic genes by the letters representing the antigens they produce as A, B, and o (for none); **group A** will have the genotype AA or Ao; **group B**, BB or Bo; **group AB**, AB; and **group O** will be oo.

Gene A and gene B are not dominant to each other, but both are dominant to gene o. A gamete, whether sperm or egg, must carry a single gene as A, B, or o, and a zygote can have only 2 of these genes in duplicate or in a combination of any 2. The following table (Fig. 418) shows the relation of the possible genotypes to the blood groups. The superscripts usually used to show a multiple alleles series have been omitted to simplify the symbols.

GENOTYPE	BLOOD GROUP
AA Ao	A
BB Bo	B
AB	AB
oo	O

FIGURE 418. Table showing the inheritance of the A-B-O blood groups.

Rh factor

Although the inheritance of the **A-B-O blood groups** is relatively simple, the situation regarding the **Rh groups** is more complex. Their inheritance may be explained in two ways. One school of thought holds that 3 closely linked pairs of genes are involved, while the other explanation is based on an allelic series of at least 8 (probably more) genes. Since this discussion is not concerned with all the antigens of the Rh system, but only with the one most commonly involved in clinical problems, it is quite proper to think of the system in terms of two genes. The gene R causes the development of the Rh antigen, while its allele, r, does not. Thus persons of genotype RR or Rr will have the antigen and will therefore be Rh-positive, while those of genotype rr will not have it, and are classified as Rh-negative. In terms of dominance, one can think of R as being dominant to r. However, if one thinks of these genes simply as producing or not producing the Rh antigen, there is no need to be concerned with dominance.

In matings between Rh-positive and Rh-negative individuals, two patterns have been observed among the offspring. If the Rh-positive parent is homozygous (RR), then all the children will be Rh-positive, even though they are heterozygous as shown in Fig. 419. If, however, the Rh-positive parent is heterozygous (Rr), then one-half of the offspring are expected to be Rh-positive

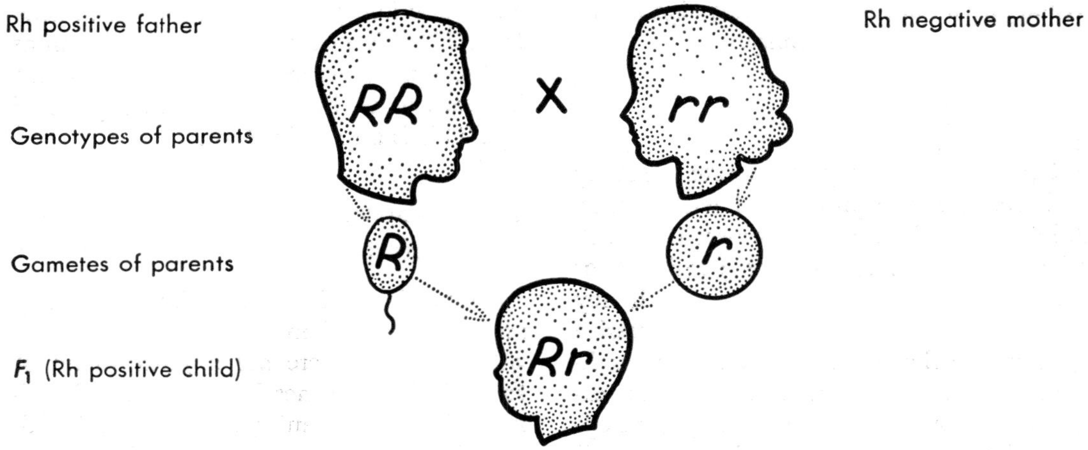

Rh positive father   Rh negative mother

Genotypes of parents

Gametes of parents

F_1 (Rh positive child)

FIGURE 419. Diagram showing one way in which Rh incompatibility may be inherited. The gene for the Rh-positive blood type is dominant to the gene for the Rh-negative blood type.

(*Rr*) and the other half Rh-negative (*rr*). This is because the chances are equal that either the *R* or *r* gene from the Rh-positive (*Rr*) parent will combine with the *r* gene of the Rh-negative (*rr*) parent.

In an earlier discussion (p. 528), the causes of Rh incompatibility were discussed.

The first and the second child born of parents with Rh incompatible blood groups usually escape harm, but by the time the third child is conceived there may be sufficient antibodies in the mother's blood to produce serious effects. The mechanism for Rh incompatibility is illustrated in Fig. 420.

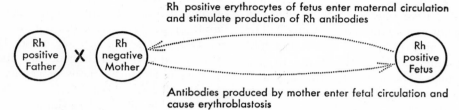

Rh positive erythrocytes of fetus enter maternal circulation and stimulate production of Rh antibodies

Antibodies produced by mother enter fetal circulation and cause erythroblastosis

FIGURE 420.   Diagram of the Rh mechanism in pregnancy. This illustration shows what may take place in pregnancy when an Rh-positive man is mated with an Rh-negative woman. The Rh-positive erythrocytes of the fetus cause the production of Rh-antibodies in the mother. The Rh-antibodies from the mother pass through the placenta and cause destruction of the red blood corpuscles in the fetus.

It should be remembered that if the mother has had a blood transfusion of Rh-positive blood this would serve as a stimulus for the formation of anti-Rh antibodies. In such a case, even the first child might suffer the effects of Rh incompatibility. Finally, for reasons as yet unexplained, the transfer of antibodies and red blood corpuscles across the placenta occurs only in a small percentage of cases. Thus in only one mating out of 28 between Rh-positive males and Rh-negative females is there any sign of the effects of Rh incompatibility.

Lethal genes

One factor that may complicate the study of heredity is the presence of lethal genes. A lethal gene is one which causes the death of an organism. It may be dominant or recessive and may affect the organism in any state of development. A lethal recessive gene is one that in the homozygous condition kills the organism. If this gene is sex-linked, all males will die in early developmental stages, and the offspring will be all

females, since the male receives only one X chromosome. Those females also will die that possess two X chromosomes containing homologous lethal genes. If a dominant lethal gene is located in the autosomes, only the one gene must be present in both males and females to bring about their death. Lethal gene traits have been demonstrated for many animals, including cattle, horses, sheep, swine, poultry, cats, dogs, guinea pigs, mice, rats, rabbits, and man. Infantile amaurotic idiocy is a late-acting lethal gene trait. There is a degeneration of the neurons of the central nervous system which results in death when the child is 2 to 3 years of age. This is a recessive trait.

Genes concerned with defects

Of particular interest to human society are the genes of man that are concerned with defects. There are a great many of these, including genes for hemophilia, blindness, deafness, insanity, and feeble-mindedness. These genes are segregated in maturation and distributed to offspring, just as are normal genes. The sex-linked recessive gene for one type of **hemophilia** is located in the X chromosome; males containing such a chromosome and females with two X chromosomes bearing this gene are hemophilic. Females with only one gene for hemophilia do not exhibit this condition. If a recessive gene for a defect is borne by an autosome, two allelic genes must be present in both males or females before the defect appears. Usually it is impossible to determine when an individual has only one recessive gene for a defect; hence it is often impossible to weed out defectives other than those that have two defective recessive genes, that is, those who actually exhibit the defects as a trait.

What is the effect of inbreeding?

Harmful genes are, for the most part, recessive. This fact has an important bearing on the results of inbreeding, that is, mating of closely related individuals. It is obvious that there may be various degrees of inbreeding, depending on the closeness of the relationship, varying from self-fertilization, through brother-sister matings, to the mating of distant cousins. It is the popular belief that the children of parents, closely related, for example, brother-sister marriages, are likely to be defective. Hence human laws nearly everywhere forbid brother-sister marriages and even first cousin marriages. Experiments with many plants and animals prove that in most instances, inbreeding weakens the race and outbreeding strengthens it. These results in man, in other animals, and in plants, are due to the fact that inbreeding tends to increase rapidly the homozygosity of a population, that is, progeny in whom pairs of allelic recessive genes are present. These individuals, since defects are usually recessive, will exhibit more defects. If, however, inbreeding is carried on so as to preserve advantageous traits, stocks may be secured that are much superior to the original and will remain so.

Thus we see that inbreeding in itself does not create weaknesses, but it does increase the opportunity for harmful recessive genes to come to expression.

Outbreeding tends to produce heterozygous dominants in which the defective genes will have normal dominant alleles and the defects will not appear. Hybrid corn is one of the many examples of the benefits of outbreeding to agriculture.

Origin of hereditary differences—mutations

The character of the genetic constitution of an animal depends not only on the distribution of genes during maturation and fertilization, but also on changes that may take place in the nature of the genes themselves. If these changes are heritable, they are known as mutations. A mutation may be defined as a sudden change in a gene resulting in a new hereditary trait (Fig. 439). Formerly, it was supposed that mutations were sudden, conspicuous, heritable modifications; but at present the heritability of the change and not its extent is considered important. It is apparent that mutations occur in the germ cell before the traits affected are exhibited by the adult organism; and that recessive mutations, which are the more frequent, will become visible only when the individual is homozygous for the mutant gene. Although we know that mutations occur in the germ cell, we do not know how those that occur spontaneously in nature originate. The great majority of mutations are undesirable; therefore, their production in man should, insofar as possible, be avoided.

Origin of artificially produced mutations

It has been proved that radiation can produce mutations in the germ plasm. When developing organisms are subjected to radiation, some of the genes in certain individuals become changed; these modified genes are inherited like normal genes and give rise to changes in the traits of the individual bearing them. Such gene mutations, as a result of radiation, have been described in both plants and animals. Besides single gene mutations, there are those which involve chromosome changes. An example is deletion, where a piece of a chromosome is lost. Ultraviolet light has produced both gene and chromosome mutations. Some other agents inducing mutations are: cosmic rays, high temperature, formaldehyde, mustard gas, and hydrogen peroxide. Of special importance is the fact that certain cancer-inducing chemicals also produce mutations.

Radiation genetics

Radiation genetics is the study of the effects of radiation on heredity.

Radiation

Of greatest present interest is the fact that radiation is known to increase mutations. Doubtless mutations have been produced among the Japanese by the effect of the atomic bombing in Japan in World War II. Muller has said, "I do not think that geneticists would question that recessive mutations so produced will go down for hundreds of generations." Geneticists seem agreed that an increase of mutation rates in human populations will add to the store of human misery. This is why there is world-wide concern about the genetic effect of any kind of increased radiation.

Fallout

A nuclear explosion emits great amounts of radiation, and even "small" explosions send appreciable amounts of material into the upper atmosphere. Here the prevailing winds cause the radioactive particles to move eastward and around the world in four to seven weeks.

Fallout affects human beings either directly through increasing external penetrating radiations, or indirectly by contaminating the food they eat or the air they breathe. Fallout is widely distributed over the whole globe, and everyone encounters some of its radioactive particles. However, the Atomic Energy Commission recently estimated the external dose from fallout to date to be from 0.001 to 0.005 roentgens per year. The latter figure is only a 5 per cent increase over the natural radiations we already receive. Moreover, it has been estimated that we receive about as much radiation from medical and dental X-rays as we do from natural sources. Hence any body (somatic) or genetic damage produced by fallout must be only a small fraction of that which is already being produced by natural and artificial radiations. Whether one considers a small increase in human suffering and death negligible depends on whether one is considering the question from the individual's or the population's point of view. Considering present radiation levels from both points of view, geneticists have reached the consensus of opinion that we must limit, as much as possible, exposures to fallout and other radiation sources under human control.

How do genes act?

An increasing number of investigations are concerned with the role of the gene in controlling development and the role of the gene in the synthesis of new substances. One organism much used in gene-action investigations is a bread mold, *Neurospora*, which has been found convenient for both genetic and biochemical studies. As found in nature, this bread mold is capable of synthesizing all its cell constituents from water, sugar, inorganic nitrogen, certain inorganic salts, and the vitamin known as biotin. By exposing the mold to X-rays, it has been possible to obtain mutant types which are unable to carry on the normal chemical activities of the wild strain. Investigators hypothesized that if the successive steps, chemical reactions, in these syntheses were controlled by a series of genes, and if one or more mutations were induced in the genes of this organism, that the requirements for its growth would change. Wild type *Neurospora* was irradiated in the hope of inducing mutations. Mutations were produced and mutant forms were found that require the addition of a particular vitamin, amino acid, purine, or pyrimidine, to the ordinary food before growth can occur, showing that the mutants have lost the ability to synthesize one of these substances. Loss of this capacity to synthesize vital substances would be lethal in nature. In every case, the loss of synthetic power has been found to be inherited.

Closer study of the mutants has shown that one gene is frequently responsible for one reaction in the synthesis of a given product. Thus one gene may control one of the chemical processes involved in the synthesis of niacin, another gene one of the processes in the synthesis of thiamine, and so on. One of the interesting results of these mold investigations is that the metabolic processes so far discovered are closely similar to, if not identical with, those of animals. This indicates that the findings made with this organism will probably be applicable to living things in general.

In some cases it seems that the relationship between genes and chemical reactions is more complex than in the examples given above, but there is no doubt that the kinds of chemical reactions which occur in a cell are controlled by the genes in its nucleus. The way in which genes exert this control is by controlling the production of the enzymes which catalyze the chemical reactions in question. Thus, for example, there is a mutant in *Neurospora* which fails to produce the enzyme tryptophane synthetase, and which is, therefore, incapable of synthesizing the amino acid tryptophane.

Several effects from one gene

Most genes, if not all, probably produce their effects by controlling one or another chemical reaction in the developing organism. Even if a gene controls just a single chemical reaction, the product of that reaction could be utilized in several different subsequent reactions. The amino acid tryptophane, for example, would be incorporated into many different proteins. Thus a single gene can have multiple effects even if it controls but a single chemical reaction.

An example is the gene-producing vestigial wing in *Drosophila* (Fig. 440). This gene not only reduces wing size, but also changes the positions of some of the body bristles, slows the growth rate, and shortens the length of life. Another example is a form of hereditary feeble-mindedness in man, which is always accompanied by the excretion in the urine of phenylpyruvic acid, a substance that a normal person oxidizes completely in his body. In fact, most genes seem to have multiple effects on the embryonic development of organisms.

Selection

Of interest, especially to agriculture, is the light that the study of genetics throws on the subject of selection. Man has for many centuries attempted to improve the traits of domesticated animals and plants by selecting for breeding purposes superior individuals. This has been effective to a certain extent, since, by this method, the progeny received the genes for the desired traits. However, the progeny also received the genes for traits (recessives) that did not appear in the parents. Also many of the traits selected were due to environmental influences and were not inherited. It seems evident that selection is effective only when heritable traits are involved and that more rapid progress is possible if the genotypic constitution of the parents is known.

Are diseases inherited?

Many geneticists have attempted to determine the relative roles of heredity and environment in relation to disease. On the basis of cause, diseases are of two kinds: (1) those that are primarily the result of hereditary abnormal structure and function of the organism and (2) those caused by parasites. To the first group belongs phenylketonuria, a metabolic defect which results in feeble-mindedness; to the second group belong the infectious diseases such as tuberculosis. Infectious diseases may be avoided if proper hygienic measures are adopted. An infectious disease is not hereditary in the sense that noninfectious diseases are. Actually, what may be inherited is a tendency or susceptibility to infectious disease. In other words, people differ in their inherent resistance to certain infections. Numerous experiments with experimental animals have shown conclusively that resistance and susceptibility to infectious diseases are hereditary. The mode of inheritance of some hereditary diseases is given in the list of human traits, Fig. 421.

Twins

Twins occur more frequently than most people realize; about once in every 85 human births, two are born at the same time. Twins are of peculiar genetic interest. There are two types, fraternal twins and identical twins (Fig. 422). **Fraternal twins** develop from two separate zygotes, and have, therefore, different genetic constitutions; they differ both genotypically and phenotypically, as do other progeny of the same parents. **Identical twins**, on the other hand, arise from a single fertilized egg, which splits into two at some time during embryonic development. Identical twins have the same genotypic constitution, since they arise from one egg. They are always of the same sex, and their characteristics, both physically and mentally, are remarkably similar. Any differ-

TRAIT	DOMI-NANT	RECES-SIVE	SEVERAL GENES
Structural			
Brown eyes	●		
Blue or gray eyes		●	
Premature grayness of hair	●		
Skin color			●
Albinism		●	
Split hand "lobster claw"	●		
Extra teeth	●		
Physiologic			
A-B-O blood groups			● M-A
Ability to taste P. T. C. (phenyl thiocarbamide)	●		
Psychologic			
Feeble-mindedness (certain types)		●	●
Huntington's chorea	● R-P		
Diseases *			
Red-green color-blindness		● S-L	
Near-sightedness (myopia)	●	●	
Absence of iris (anirida)	●		
Bleeding (hemophilia)		● S-L	
Cancer of eye (retinoblastoma)	● R-P		

FIGURE 421. Table of some human traits and their usual mode of inheritance. Key to the symbols: ● = inheritance of trait; R-P = reduced penetrance; S-L = sex-linked; M-A = several alternative genes; if more than one mode of inheritance is given for a trait, it means that in some families it is inherited in one way and in others in another.

* This is an artificial classification, because these diseases actually fall into structural or physiologic categories.

FIGURE 422. A pair of strikingly similar identical twins. Identical twins are usually very much alike in physical, mental, and personality traits. (Courtesy of The Toni Company.)

ences between them are due to environmental influences.

In twins, if the embryo division is not complete the result may be **conjoined twins**; these are popularly known as Siamese twins because the most widely publicized pair came from Siam (Fig. 423).

Quadruplets and quintuplets may include fraternals and identicals. At this date, the famed Dionne quintuplets of Canada, and the Diligentes "quints," born in Argentina, are the only groups of 5 which are known to have survived infancy. The Dionne girls were identical quintuplets.

False ideas about heredity

Telegony

This is the idea that one mating leaves an impression on the mother which affects later births. The belief is widespread, but, obviously, this is impossible, since the sperm that effects the union with the egg is the only one that contributes to the offspring and all others of that mating die. Thus there is no way in which they can have an influence in subsequent fertilizations.

Maternal impressions

This is another erroneous idea that modification in the development of the fetus results from experiences that occur to the mother during pregnancy. For example, a prospective mother sees the hand of a small child crushed accidentally, and so her baby is born with a deformed hand. Underlying this false notion is also the belief that the mother contributes to the heredity of her child throughout pregnancy. However, it is true that the health and nutrition of the mother may influence the development of the embryo, but this is a matter of physiology, which is quite another thing.

Prepotency

So-called prepotency refers to the supposed power of one parent to transmit its

FIGURE 423. Chang and Eng, the most famous pair of Siamese (conjoined) twins. The photograph clearly shows the band of flesh connecting them, which is evidence that conjoined twins are due to an incomplete separation of the embryo. They are always of the same sex. Chang and Eng were both married and said to have had 22 children. (Photo courtesy of F.H. Meserve.)

characteristics to its offspring to the exclusion of those of the other parent. Males are supposed to be particularly prepotent, but this is no doubt due to the fact that animal breeders pay more attention to males than to females for breeding purposes.

Inheritance of so-called acquired traits (characters)

Some of the traits selected by animal and plant breeders arise during the life of the individual as the result of environmental influences. Whether or not these acquired traits are inherited is a problem that has interested biologists for many years. None of the experiments designed to test the inheritance of acquired traits has given positive results, although there are a few cases that may be in doubt. It may safely be said that as yet there is no good evidence for the inheritance of acquired traits. This does not mean that the environment has no influence; on the contrary, development of the traits of an individual depends on both genetic and environmental components (Fig. 424).

Eugenics and euthenics

Eugenics is the science concerned with the application of the principles of genetics to the improvement of the human species. There is every reason to believe that the principles of heredity are as applicable to man as to other organisms, but the practical difficulties of actually applying these principles, at least to the conservation of the human species, are very great.

The study of human genetics is difficult for several reasons: (1) the impracticability of experimental breeding, (2) the small number of offspring in a family, and (3) the relatively slow breeding of man. Despite all these handicaps, significant achievements are being made in this field as is evident from the fact that in the last 15 years, centers for counseling on heredity have been established as a practical way of giving information to people with genetic problems.

Physicians are realizing more and more that human genetics has an important bearing on clinical problems, and relatively rapid progress is being made in the accumulation of information, which, when applied, proves helpful in the prevention and diagnosis of disease. The application of genetics to medical problems is a new science called **medical genetics;** it is making contributions to eugenics, for its practical application here seems more advanced than in some related fields.

Efforts are now being made to collect data which can be used in determining which human traits are hereditary, how these are inherited, and to what degree. Such information may aid in the solution of some of the socio-economic problems with which society is confronted.

Certain studies show that people with

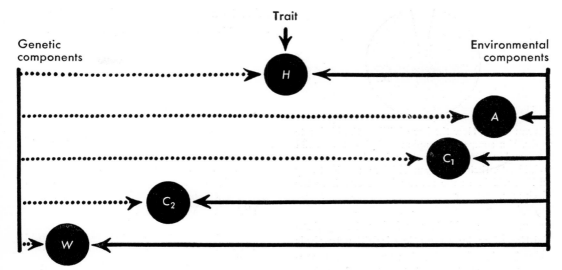

Trait

Genetic
components

Environmental
components

H

A

C₁

C₂

W

FIGURE 424. Diagram to show the relative influences (components) of heredity and environment in the development of traits. The black symbol lettered "H" illustrates a hypothetical trait, having about equal genetic and environmental components. The other symbols represent different traits (phenotypes); the length of the solid and dotted lines shows the relative importance of the genetic and environmental components. No trait could occur at either extreme since all traits possessed by an organism are influenced by both genetic and environmental factors. In many cases, one cannot measure the effects of one or the other, but in this diagram traits have been selected where the relative influences of environment and heredity are known. "A" symbolizes the phenotype albinism (absence of pigment), a trait which develops because of the presence of an allelic pair of recessive genes. Here the environment provides only the minimal essentials. "C₁" represents a cancer of the eye, retinoblastoma, a trait which is largely influenced by a single dominant gene. The environment, however, must play a part in its development. "C₂" symbolizes another malignancy, breast cancer, a trait for which there is statistical evidence of genetic factors, but there are also several important environmental factors known to be operating in the development of this trait. "W" represents the trait "writing," a behavior characteristic for which most of mankind possesses the necessary physical equipment. However, such a behavioral trait also requires training, an environmental component lacking in many cultures. An additional aspect of heredo-environmental interactions, not illustrated by the diagram, is the fact that the same phenotype may result from both a "weaker" and a "stronger" genetic component if the "weaker" is augmented by a "stronger" environmental component; in other words, the same genetic component may result in different phenotypes if different environments are provided. The best evidence for this may be found in the differences observed in "identical" twins in different environments.

hereditary feeble-mindedness have a much higher birth rate than normal people. Figure 425 shows how such an unfortunate differential birth rate works. It has been estimated that there are about three million feeble-minded persons in the United States. There have been many inaccurate statements about how little feeble-mindedness would be reduced in a generation if all feeble-minded persons of a previous generation had not reproduced. Most of the incorrect figures given have assumed that the feeble-minded marry at random as fruit flies mate in a bottle. It has been proved that this is a false assumption and that the feeble-minded tend to marry feeble-minded. It is impossible to determine exactly how much reduction in the feeble-minded would be effected in a generation if they did not procreate, but something would be accomplished.

Eugenics favors measures that may assist

FIGURE 425. How the law of differential birth rate works. If a competent couple multiplies at a 3-child rate, and a hereditary feeble-minded couple at a 9-child rate, their great grandchildren, provided they all live, will be as the above white sector is to the black area.

persons to avoid transmitting the potentialities of serious genetic disability to their offspring insofar as such measures are consistent with their own interests and welfare. However, much of the hope for man's improvement does not lie in genetic improvement, but in cultural, social, and scientific advance.

Therefore, the best chances of immediate progress are to be secured by **euthenics,** the science of improving man by providing the best possible environment. Euthenics, while not improving the genetic quality of the race, is a program of great value for human betterment. An organism develops from a fertilized egg in which the genetic potentialities of the individual are predetermined by the genes, but what the fertilized egg develops into is determined by the interaction of two powerful forces, the genes and the environment (Fig. 424). This makes obvious the importance of a favorable environment so as to give opportunity for the best possible expression of the genetic constitution.

What the environment may do for us is illustrated by the condition known as cretinism. The cretin is a feeble-minded dwarf who possesses a defective thyroid gland, which is unable to secrete sufficient hormones for the proper development of the body. If thyroid secretion is artificially sup-

plied to a young cretin, his condition may be improved or completely alleviated.

SELECTED COLLATERAL READINGS

Altenburg, Edgar. *Genetics.* Holt, New York, 1957.

Braun, W. *Bacterial Genetics.* Saunders, Philadelphia, 1953.

Colin, E.C. *Elements of Genetics.* McGraw-Hill, New York, 1956.

Crow, James F. *Effects of Radiation and Fallout.* Public Affairs Pamphlet No. 256, Public Affairs Committee, New York, 1957.

Dunn, L.C. *Genetics in the 20th Century.* Macmillan, New York, 1951.

Gates, R.R. *Human Genetics,* Vols. I and II. Macmillan, New York, 1946.

Lush, Jay L. *Animal Breeding Plans.* Iowa State College Press, Ames, Iowa, 1945.

Osborn, Frederick. *Preface to Eugenics.* Harper, New York, 1951.

Penrose, L.S. *The Biology of Mental Defect.* Grune and Stratton, New York, 1949.

Reed, S.C. *Counseling in Medical Genetics.* Saunders, Philadelphia, 1955.

Scheinfeld, A. *The New You and Heredity.* Lippincott, Philadelphia, 1950.

Schubert, J., and Lapp, R.E. *Radiation: What Is It and How It Affects You.* Viking, New York, 1957.

Sinnott, E.W., Dunn, L.C., and Dobzhansky, T. *Principles of Genetics.* McGraw-Hill, New York, 1958.

Snyder, L.H., and David, P.R. *The Principles of Heredity.* Heath, Boston, 1957.

Srb, A.M., and Owen, R.D. *General Genetics.* Freeman, San Francisco, 1952.

Stern, Curt. *Principles of Human Genetics.* Freeman, San Francisco, 1949.

Swanson, C.P. *Cytology and Cytogenetics.* Prentice-Hall, Englewood Cliffs, N.J., 1957.

Waddington, C.H. *The Strategy of the Genes.* Macmillan, New York, 1958.

Wagner, R.P., and Mitchell, H.K. *Genetics and Metabolism.* Wiley, New York, 1955.

CHAPTER 36

OJI

The Origin and History of Animal Life

Throughout our studies of animals, we have considered primarily the species that live on the earth at the present time; now we shall discuss questions such as: what is the origin of animal life on the earth, and what is the history of animal life from the earliest known fossils to the present time? This involves:

1. A review of the hypotheses to account for the origin of life.
2. A study of the relationships of different phyla to one another, and the relationships of groups within phyla.
3. An attempt to determine what types of variation occur within a species, and how these variations originate.
4. A study of the effects of natural selection in relation to these variations, and of the adaptations that result from the struggle for existence.
5. An examination of the various types of evidence indicating that organic evolution, the development of animal life to its present-day forms, has occurred.
6. A discussion of the principal theories that have been proposed to account for organic evolution.
7. A brief account of the development of man.

ORIGIN OF LIFE

Spontaneous generation

Previous to the end of the seventeenth century, the theory of **spontaneous generation** of animals was accepted by both scientists and philosophers. According to this idea, many species of animals were supposed to arise spontaneously from nonliving matter. For example, insects were believed to originate from dew, frogs and toads from the muddy bottoms of ponds under the influence of the sun, butterflies from cheese, and fly maggots from flesh. Even today, many uneducated people believe that mosquitoes are generated by stagnant water and that horse hairs, when placed in water, change into living "snakes." The classical experiment of the Italian Redi in 1680 exploded this theory in regard to the larger types of animals. Redi placed meat in widemouthed flasks; some flasks were left open, some were covered with gauze, and others with paper. The meat decayed in all vessels. Flies entered the open vessels and laid eggs which hatched into maggots. No larvae developed in the meat of the other vessels; but on the cloth of those covered with gauze, flies laid eggs which developed into maggots. Thus it was concluded from this experiment that the maggots arose from the eggs of flies and not from decaying meat (Fig. 426).

When microscopes were developed so

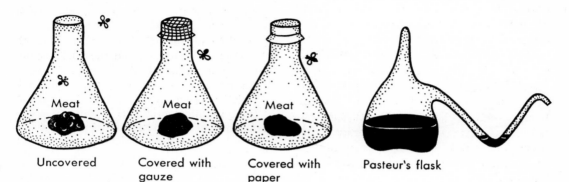

FIGURE 426. Spontaneous generation. Diagrams illustrating methods of disproving this theory. *Left*, the 3 flasks illustrate Redi's method of experimenting with blow flies. *Right*, Pasteur's flask as used in his experiments. This peculiar glass flask was completely closed except for an opening in the long glass tube on the right side. The flask was half filled with water, containing large numbers of microscopic organisms. By boiling at intermittent intervals, all the living organisms were killed, and the entire contents of the flask made sterile. At the same time, escaping steam condensed, and water filled the lowest part of the bent tube, so that a complete barrier was formed there. The water in the bent tube captured all organisms so that air from the outside which finally reached the sterile mixture at the bottom of the flask was sterile. The result was that within the flask proper no life developed, whereas in the water barrier in the bent tube a host of minute organisms developed.

that very minute organisms such as protozoans and bacteria were made visible, the advocates of spontaneous generation claimed that these tiny creatures arose from nonliving matter. Pasteur (1864) finally disproved their contention by protecting sterile hay infusions from the microorganisms in the air (Fig. 426); such infusions became populated if exposed to the air, but remained sterile if the air was heated or all particles were removed from the air before it reached the infusion.

Biogenesis

The theory of spontaneous generation, **abiogenesis,** thus gave way to that of **bio-**

genesis, which maintains that all life arises from preexisting life. If living animals do not arise from nonliving matter, it is natural to inquire how the world became populated with them, since both geologists and astronomers tell us that at one time, long ago, life could not have existed on the earth. The doctrine of **special creation,** that is, that each species of animal was specially created, is sufficiently refuted to the satisfaction of most biologists by the facts of organic evolution. Life must, therefore, have originated on the earth from nonliving matter, or it must have been brought to the earth from some other part of our universe. The latter idea, known as the **cosmozoic theory,** is so improbable as to be hardly worthy of consideration; even if it were true, it does not explain the origin of life, but only how life reached the earth.

Physicochemical theory

A number of theories have been proposed to account for the origin of life on the earth, during the period when the earth was cooling down from its original incandescent condition. The dominant theory now is that when environmental conditions became suitable for life, certain molecules became organized into the first living system. Even now, life might conceivably arise from nonliving matter if the various elements contained in protoplasm were to unite in the proper quantities, in the proper relations to one another, and under favorable conditions; but actually we have no real evidence of this.

However, this concept of the origin of life is made more plausible by recent research on viruses. These are the smallest living things, actually submicroscopic, and much smaller than the smallest bacteria (Fig. 427). Viruses have the characteristics of living organisms for they are able to grow, multiply, and even undergo mutations. Some animal diseases such as poliomyelitis (infantile paralysis) are caused by viruses. An interesting fact is that several viruses have been crystallized like inorganic substances. Of special interest is the fact that the tobacco mosaic virus has been separated into two nonliving substances, a protein and nucleic acid; when reunited, the combined substances had the characteristics of the living virus and caused infection in tobacco plants. However, such viruses do not appear to be the ultimate transitional form between living and nonliving matter, since, as they are known today, they can reproduce only in living cells.

Nevertheless, many think that the first primordial living particle was some kind of a simple viruslike particle. Of course, viruslike matter, to constitute the bridge between living and nonliving things, must have been

able to multiply in an inorganic environment, or in an environment of relatively simple organic compounds.

Where did the drama of the origin of life begin? Because the remains of the earliest forms of animal life are found in rocks which formed in oceans, and since the body fluids of all animals contain certain salts found in sea water, it seems logical to infer that life began in the sea.

We can only speculate on when life originated. There is fossil evidence of life 500 million years ago, and since many groups were well differentiated at that time it is possible that life existed a billion years ago.

Our final conclusion must be that we now are not sure how, where, or when life began.

INTERRELATIONS OF THE PHYLA OF ANIMALS

Invertebrates

This is a subject about which there has been much controversy. All zoologists seem to agree that the phylum Protozoa belongs at the foot of the "family tree" (Fig. 430); and although the amoeba is the type usually studied first, the flagellates seem to have given rise to the other three classes of protozoans. The sponges probably evolved from flagellated colonial protozoans of the *Proterospongia* type (Fig. 428), but they are believed to be an offshoot from the family tree and not in the main line of evolution.

Among the important difficulties encountered in attempting to determine relationships between phyla are the modifications that have taken place in both adult and larval stages. The result is that what may appear to be an ancestral condition may be nothing more than an adaptation to environment. On this account we can only speculate instead of arriving at definite conclusions. At any rate, the lower metazoans possess a **planula stage** in their life cycle,

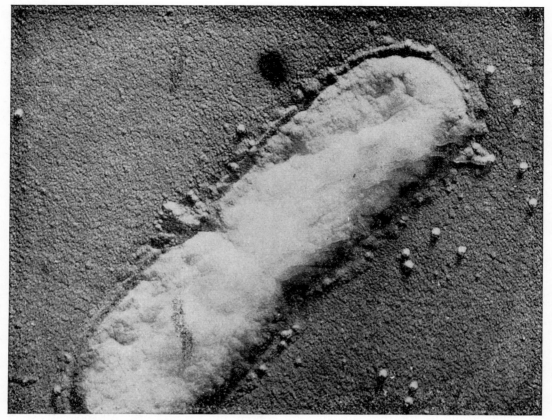

FIGURE 427. Electron micrograph of virus particles, which are the small spherical bodies scattered around the large oblong bacterial cell. The viruses are the smallest and simplest of living things. They appear to be on the borderline between living and nonliving states. Electron micrograph magnification 48,000 times. (Courtesy of A.P. Juenker, Michigan Department of Health.)

which appears to be an ancestral form that gave rise to coelenterates, and, as a side branch, to ctenophores. From planulae also evolved primitive bilateral animals with anteroposterior and dorsoventral axes—ancestral flatworms. From such an ancestral type, the flatworms may have arisen. Certain other phyla of invertebrates seem to be closely related through a common type of larval stage, the **trochophore**; these are the annelids, arthropods, and mollusks. Adult echinoderms are radially symmetrical, but their larvae are bilateral; and the phylum apparently also arose from a bilateral type of ancestor (Fig. 194).

Relations between vertebrates and invertebrates

Many eminent zoologists have attempted to trace the ancestry of the vertebrates to some invertebrate form. These investigations have resulted in a number of theories, but it is impossible in this place to give an account of each. That their differences are considerable may be inferred from the fact that arguments have been advanced in favor of annelids, arachnids, and echinoderms as invertebrate ancestors of the vertebrates.

The origin of vertebrates from an echinoderm-chordate line seems to have so many

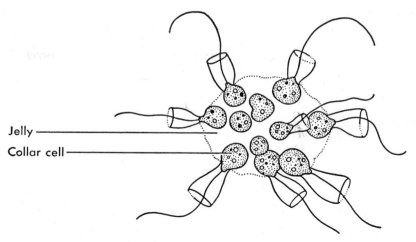

Jelly

Collar cell

FIGURE 428. *Proterospongia haeckeli,* a colonial flagellate that resembles what may have been a link between the protozoans and sponges.

points in its favor that this theory will be sketched briefly in the following paragraphs as an illustration of the method used in tracing vertebrate descent.

We have seen that there are a number of subphyla in the phylum Chordata that contain animals of a lower grade than the vertebrates. These are: (1) the subphylum Hemichordata (Fig. 203) which includes a few wormlike species; (2) the Urochordata (Fig. 205), which contains a number of saclike animals that exhibit chordate characteristic chiefly in the immature stages; and (3) the Cephalochordata, which has but a single genus—*Branchiostoma* (amphioxus) (Fig. 201).

The amphioxus appears to have much in common with the ancestor of the vertebrates. The essential structural characteristics which are possessed in common by the amphioxus and the vertebrates are the presence of (1) a notochord, (2) a dorsal nervous system, (3) a pharynx perforated by gill slits, and (4) a midventral endostyle.

If we accept the amphioxus as the invertebrate most closely related to the vertebrates, we may then seek for an ancestor of this form. Such an ancestor is supplied by the tunicates. The adult tunicates (Fig. 205) have retained very few of their primitive

characteristics, but the larva possesses a typical notochord, a neural tube, a series of gill slits, and an endostyle, which are similar in position and development to these structures in the amphioxus; and it seems probable that the adult tunicate once existed as an animal like the larval tunicate of today and that this remote ancestor was not only the progenitor of the modern tunicates, but was also the direct ancestor of the group to which the amphioxus belongs.

The search for a vertebrate ancestor more remote than the tunicates leads to a consideration of the marine wormlike animals of the subphylum Hemichordata. These species, as previously shown (Fig. 203) are provided with clearly defined gill slits, a structure which may be homologous to the notochord of the vertebrates, and 4 longitudinal nerve cords of which the dorsal is slightly more pronounced than the ventral and lateral ones. It appears, therefore, that a hemichordatelike animal may possibly have been a vertebrate ancestor of an earlier stage than the tunicates.

We must look to the larvae of the hemichordates for the link which may connect these lowest of the chordates with the other invertebrates, and thus complete our hypothetical line of vertebrate descent. The egg of the acorn worm (hemichordate) develops into a small larva called a tornaria (Fig. 429), which floats in the sea, is transparent, has a bilateral symmetry, and is provided with bands of cilia for locomotion. In habitat and structure, this larva corresponds almost exactly to a larval stage of the starfish and other echinoderms. This similarity leads to the possibility that a form resembling these larvae was the very remote an-

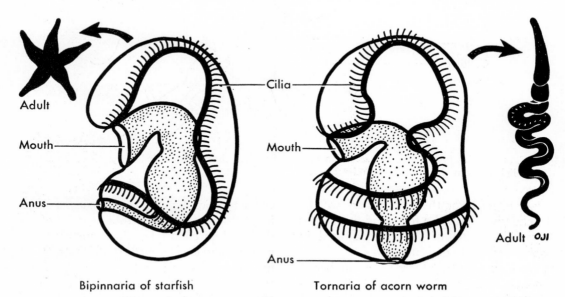

Bipinnaria of starfish   Tornaria of acorn worm

FIGURE 429.   Comparison of the starfish (echinoderm) and acorn worm (hemichordate) larvae. Note the striking structural similarities of the two.

cestor of both the echinoderms and the chordates, and that the lineal descendants of this hypothetical ancestor chose two paths, one of which, according to Wilder, leads to the echinoderms and the other to the acorn worms, tunicates, amphioxus, and eventually the vertebrates.

The question of the ancestry of the chordates is not solved by accepting their relationship to the hemichordates, since this latter group holds an uncommonly isolated position; in fact, as previously mentioned, some zoologists prefer these in an independent invertebrate phylum. Only from the structure of the acorn worm larva can there be concluded a distant connection with the echinoderms. We must resign ourselves to the thought that at the present time we are not in a position to assert from what ancestral form the chordates, and with them the hemichordates, were derived. The origin of the vertebrates is lost in the obscurity of forms unknown to us.

RELATIONS BETWEEN CLASSES OF VERTEBRATES

Anatomic and paleontologic investigations are continually changing our ideas regarding the interrelations of the vertebrates, and we can indicate only provisionally the possible line of descent of the vertebrates and the relations of one group to another.

FIGURE 430.   *Facing page*, a simplified family tree of the principal animal phyla. The lines indicate possible relationships. Evidence suggests an ancestral two-layered type as the basic stock above the protozoan stock. Relationships among other invertebrates are uncertain. There are no satisfactory clues as to the actual relationship between invertebrate and vertebrate animals. Like all such diagrams, this one reads from the bottom upwards.

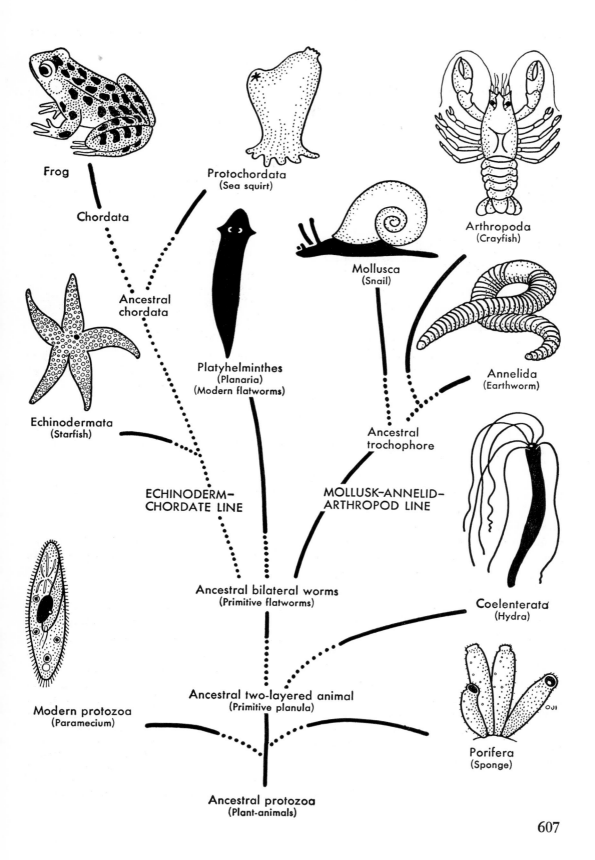

Frog

Chordata

Protochordata
(Sea squirt)

Ancestral
chordata

Echinodermata
(Starfish)

Platyhelminthes
(Planaria)
(Modern flatworms)

Mollusca
(Snail)

Arthropoda
(Crayfish)

Annelida
(Earthworm)

Ancestral
trochophore

ECHINODERM–
CHORDATE LINE

MOLLUSK–ANNELID–
ARTHROPOD LINE

Ancestral bilateral worms
(Primitive flatworms)

Coelenterata
(Hydra)

Modern protozoa
(Paramecium)

Ancestral two-layered animal
(Primitive planula)

Porifera
(Sponge)

Ancestral protozoa
(Plant-animals)

Cyclostomes and fishes

The lowest vertebrates, that is, the forms most nearly related to the primitive chordates such as the amphioxus are the cyclostomes. These (Fig. 240) are eel-like vertebrates without jaws and with cartilaginous skeletons. Although the cyclostomes represent a primitive level of vertebrate development, they are not themselves ancestral vertebrates.

The fossil record shows that the oldest and most primitive of fossil vertebrates were small, fishlike, jawless creatures called ostracoderms (Agnatha).

Next above the ostracoderms come the placoderms, which are extinct fishlike animals provided with jaws. The placoderms appear to have given rise to the bony fishes (Osteichthyes) and, as a side branch, to the elasmobranchs.

Amphibia

The lungfishes resemble the amphibians in so many developmental and structural features that they were once thought to be the actual amphibian ancestors. But it is known that these features were also present in their near relatives, the crossopterygians (bony fishes), from which it now seems probable that the amphibians are actually derived. The lungfishes now are regarded as a side branch from the same ancestral stock as that from which the crossopterygians originated.

Reptilia

The reptiles are descendants of ancient amphibians. Because of their method of reproduction, they became the first completely land vertebrates. The reptilian egg can be laid on land, thus making water existence unnecessary. The most primitive living reptiles are the Rhynchocephalia; these are represented by the single living species *Sphenodon punctatus* (Fig. 283) of New Zealand.

Aves

Birds sprang from reptilian ancestors; in fact, they have appropriately been called "glorified reptiles." This correctly implies that the birds are closely related to the reptiles, and one of the earliest known forms (*Archaeornis*, Fig. 331) might actually be called a flying reptile. The toothed birds are considered the forerunners of the modern toothless birds.

Mammalia

Mammals are of special interest since this class of vertebrates includes man. The earliest living mammals, the monotremes (egg layers) are descended from reptilian ancestors. Because of their reptilian characters, they are considered veritable "missing links." Although the monotremes are the most primitive of the mammals, they are so specialized in many ways that they cannot themselves be regarded as ancestral types. Above the monotremes are placed the marsupials (pouched mammals), and finally the Eutheria (placentals), which are the highest of all animals. The primates, the group that includes man, are discussed in a later section.

VARIATIONS WITHIN A SPECIES

An attempt was made earlier in this text to define a species. There it was noted that the individuals of a species may differ markedly among themselves. Such differences are known as variations. Careful studies of variations have revealed that they are of two principal types: (1) genetic or inherited variations and (2) environmental or noninherited modifications. This distinction is of the greatest importance, since only inherited variations can be passed on to offspring and can have any influence in changing the genetic constitution of the species. Zoologists have convincing evidence for the belief that such changes are necessary for the origin of new species, and in the course of time, of new genera, families, orders, classes, and phyla. It is therefore essential to determine the origin of inherited variations and the effects of the environment upon them. As already noted, the union of a sperm and an egg results in various combinations of genes, due to the method of distribution of the chromosomes during oogenesis and spermatogenesis, to crossing over, and to the chance association of ova and spermatozoa at the time of fertilization. Inherited variations are due not alone to chance combinations of genes, but also to actual changes in the genes, that is, to **mutations.** We know very little about the origin of gene mutations, but environmental factors such as radiation appear to be effective in bringing them about.

NATURAL SELECTION AND ADAPTATION

Natural selection

The activities of wild animals are directed mainly toward maintenance of the individual, which is really a struggle for existence. Ecologic studies are largely concerned with the methods employed by different types of animals in their struggles to adapt themselves to the physical and biological factors in their environment. Those that can withstand the conditions in their environment live, and the rest die. Darwin's theory of **natural selection** to account for the **origin of species** was based on this situation. He pointed out that there are almost always more individuals produced by members of a species than the environment can support. Thus any variations that better fit an individual for the struggle of existence will lead to its survival; this concept has been called the **survival of the fittest.** Thus nature selected those individuals that were best

adapted to their environment. These reproduced themselves, and their offspring presumably inherited the favorable variations responsible for their survival. Darwin knew that some variations were inherited and others not, but at that time the mechanism of heredity was not known. We now distinguish more clearly between heritable and nonheritable variations, and between large mutations and smaller mutations. Perhaps the most important point to be kept in mind is the fact that new species evolve slowly, and that natural selection has had hundreds of millions of years in which to operate, as the table on page 616 indicates.

Darwin's theory has withstood almost a century of criticism, and natural selection is still recognized as the guiding factor in the origin of species. Variations **do** occur; a struggle for existence **does** take place; and animals with certain types of variations **survive.** However, we cannot emphasize too strongly the fact that the heritable variations on which natural selection acts are not the direct result of environmental action, but are due to gene mutations and chromosomal recombinations of the individuals whose ancestors were subjected to the forces of natural selection.

Adaptations

That animals are adapted to the environment in which they live is obvious to anyone who has taken the trouble to consider their structure, physiology, and habits. In general, every living thing reacts adaptively to the external stimuli in the environment in which the species evolved. An adaptation may be structural, physiologic, or involve inherent patterns of behavior. We have noted, for example, how in insects the wings are adapted for flight, the legs for running, swimming, or other purposes, the mouth parts for biting or sucking, and the digestive tract for digesting solid or liquid food; and how in birds the wings and tail are adapted for flight, the feet for perching, wading, or swimming, and the bills for capturing insects, crushing seeds, or tearing flesh (Fig. 316). Such external adaptations are abundantly exhibited by all animals. They must fit a species for life in its environment, or that species cannot survive in the **struggle for existence** that is continually taking place. They involve all those activities necessary for the individual to maintain itself and to reproduce others of its kind.

Internal adaptations are concerned with the relations of the organs of the body to one another and with their physiologic activities. If these organs do not cooperate successfully in the manifold processes involved in locomotion, digestion, circulation, respiration, etc., the animal dies. How often individuals are rendered unfit by their internal adaptations is indicated by the large number of deaths that occur among people of the white race when exposed to tropical diseases, such as malaria and yellow fever. The principle of organic evolution and the evidence in favor of that principle depend on the assumption that the degree of adaptability to the environment determines whether an animal shall live or die in the struggle for existence.

Adaptive radiation and adaptive convergence

The methods of locomotion in mammals may be used to illustrate divergent adaptations in relation to various types of environment. Because of the competition for living space and food, there is a tendency for each group of organisms to spread out and utilize as many different habitats as possible. This evolution, from a single ancestral species to a variety of forms which occupy different habitats is called **adaptive radiation** or **divergent evolution**. Figure 431 illustrates that from a primative mammal, different forms have evolved that are adapted to various habitats. The specializations or adaptations indicated are for running, digging, swimming, hanging, flying,

and jumping. The great range of adaptability of the mammals has made it possible for members of this class to compete successfully with other types of animals on the surface of the earth, under the ground, in trees, and in the water, and to become the dominant animals in the long course of evolution.

Adaptive convergence or **convergent evolution,** which is the converse of adaptive radiation, may be illustrated (Fig. 432) by the streamlined body of a fish (shark), an extinct reptile (ichthyosaur), and a mammal (porpoise). Why should reptiles and mammals that live in water superficially resemble a fish in form? Natural selection has favored in aquatic animals, whether they be fish or mammals, those characteristics which fit them for life in water. As far as body form is concerned, the ancestors of a fish and a porpoise were probably much less similar than these animals are today. Note that the convergence has affected only some traits which are of special importance in adapting the mammal to life in water. Many body structures, such as the lungs, have not converged.

EVIDENCE IN FAVOR OF ORGANIC EVOLUTION

Practically all biologists believe in the evolution of plant and animal life, that is, in the principle that species of plants and animals now living have evolved from other species. The evidence for organic evolution is compelling. It is a well-established fact that all protoplasm is irritable; therefore, it should no longer be regarded as only a theory. One can hardly argue about the existence of established facts, one can only be ignorant of them. However, there are differences of opinion among biologists as to how evolution has taken place and as to its causes. The principle of evolution is based on a number of different types of evidence, some of which are presented briefly in the following paragraphs.

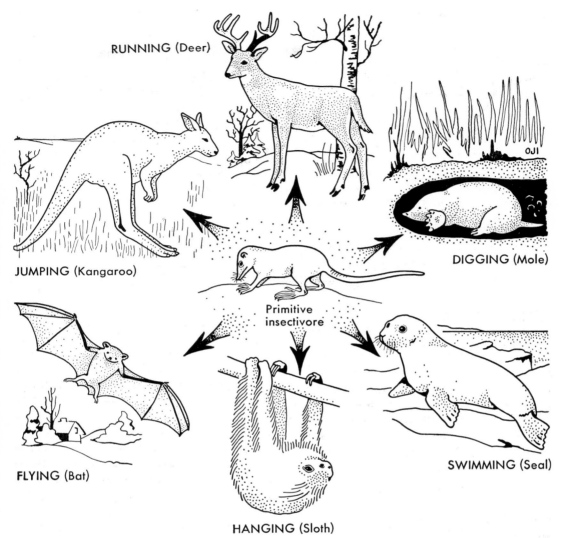

RUNNING (Deer)

JUMPING (Kangaroo)

DIGGING (Mole)

Primitive insectivore

FLYING (Bat)

HANGING (Sloth)

SWIMMING (Seal)

FIGURE 431. Adaptive radiation or divergent evolution. The various mammals have evolved from a common ancestor, the five-toed land mammal shown at the *center* of the diagram. Note how the structure of the limbs has been modified (specialized) to adapt them to a wide variety of environments.

Classification

One hundred years before organic evolution was generally recognized, biologists had classified animals according to their degrees of similarity into phyla, classes, orders, etc. Linnaeus (1707–1778), who introduced our present system of classification, was a firm believer in **special creation**. For the most part, the groups into which Linnaeus and others divided the animal kingdom contain animals that are actually closely related genetically. Also, the order adopted, beginning with the protozoans and proceeding to the more and more complex groups, is what one would expect if species arose from pre-existing species. The careful taxonomic studies of recent years, furthermore, have

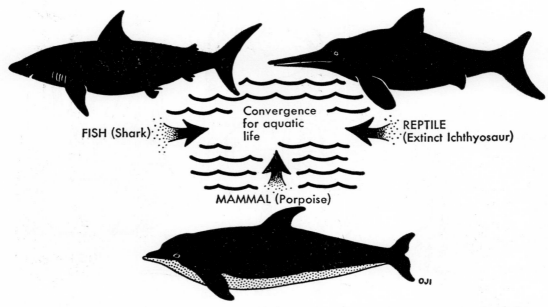

FIGURE 432. Adaptive convergence or convergent evolution. Although the fish, reptile, and mammal shown are not closely related, they have a marked superficial similarity because they are all adapted to living in the same environment.

revealed an abundance of intergrades for which the terms suborder, subfamily, sub-genus, subspecies, etc., have been coined. Classification, therefore, expresses the degree of kinship that exists among animals as required by the theory of organic evolution.

Domesticated animals and plants

Many plants and animals have been maintained under domestication for centuries by man. During this time various breeds have developed. In certain cases, we know that these breeds have all arisen from a single wild species; in other cases, they may have evolved under domestication from several wild species. That changes have taken place is undeniable. For example, the fantail, pouter, tumbler, and other types of pigeons may all have evolved from the blue rock pigeon. Horses, cattle, sheep, dogs, and fowls appear to have undergone similar changes. If these various breeds had been found in nature, no one would hesitate to consider them distinct species; yet we know that they have evolved from one or several wild species. Darwin wrote two large volumes on this subject, entitled *The Variation of Animals and Plants under Domestication* (1868), which make the idea of fixity of species seem very improbable indeed.

Comparative anatomy

The study of comparative anatomy brings out similarities and dissimilarities in structure (Fig. 433) and offers much evidence in favor of organic evolution. For example, the flipper of the seal, the wing of the bird, the wing of the bat, the leg of the horse, and the arm of man have evidently all evolved from the same type of ancestral appendage.

Vestigial organs, which are especially evident among vertebrates, furnish striking evidence of changes from ancestral condi-

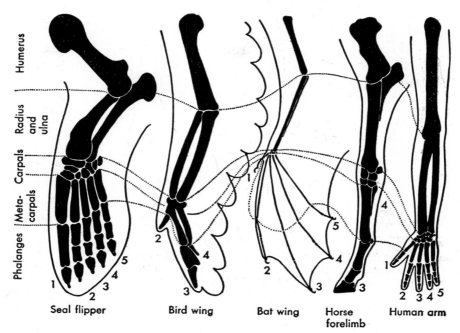

FIGURE 433. Homology and adaptation in bones of the forelimbs of vertebrates. The limbs are homologous in being of the same fundamental structure, based on common descent, but in each kind of animal they are adapted for special functions by modifications of an ancestral appendage.

tions. The eye of man, for example, has a vestigial nictitating membrane (Fig. 434), and the modern horse possesses splints in place of what were in its ancestors functional metacarpals and metatarsals (Fig. 437). Many organs during the course of evolution have changed in function; for example, the salivary glands in certain snakes have become modified into poison glands (Fig. 288).

Embryology

The **biogenetic law** was formulated many years ago by a German biologist (Haeckel) who observed that the early stages of vertebrate embryos were remarkably similar (Fig. 435). He thought that animals recapitulate in their developmental stages the phylogenetic history of the race. This conclusion was euphoniously stated as **ontogeny repeats phylogeny.** However, this broad generaliza-

tion was not entirely justified. A more accurate statement of this law is that an animal may repeat in its embryonic development some of the corresponding stages of its ancestors. This modification of the original statement of the biogenetic law is necessary because it is evident that structural changes have taken place in the embryonic and larval stages. For example, certain stages may be omitted; others may be added, the latter of course, have no ancestral significance. Despite such criticism of the biogenetic law, there can be no doubt that a study of the developmental stages of an animal give important clues regarding its ancestry.

Comparative biochemistry

Within recent years the discovery has been made that the biochemical characters of animals furnish convincing evidence in

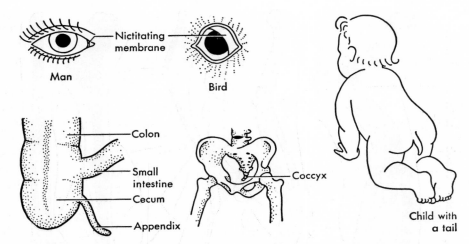

Figure 434. Vestigial organs are apparently useless remains of organs found in some animals, which are represented by useful structures in others. Eyes of man and bird, showing functional nictitating membrane (third eyelid) in the bird, and nonfunctional vestigial nictitating membrane in man. Vermiform appendix of man, a useless structure with a bad reputation, is not now regarded as a vestigial organ by some; the corresponding organ in herbivorous mammals apparently functions in digestion. Coccyx of man represents the bony remnants of the tail of lower animals, but an occasional child is born with a fleshy tail several inches long.

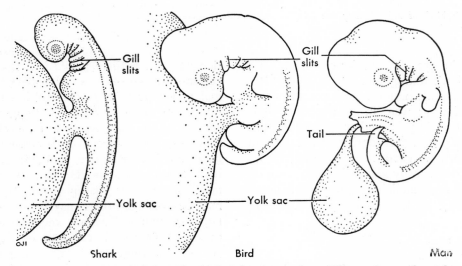

Figure 435. Gill slits in embryos of animals belonging to three different classes of vertebrates. We find gill slits in adult fish, but they are present only in embryonic birds and mammals.

favor of the principle of organic evolution. For example, studies have been made of the crystals formed by the hemoglobin of the blood, and comparisons show that the crystals of closely related species are more nearly alike in form than those of distantly related species. Thus the crystals in the blood of species belonging to one genus resemble each other more closely that they do those of species belonging to other genera. The relations of families, orders, etc., can also be determined in this way; for example, seals and bears are more closely related to each other than they are to dogs.

Additional evidence of animal relationships is provided by the degree of similarity between the blood protein of various animals. Thousands of tests by the antigen-antibody technique such as is used for blood grouping have shown a fundamental likeness between the blood proteins of all mammals. These blood tests have shown that man is closest genetically to the great ape; next closest, in order, are the Old World monkeys, the New World monkeys, and the tarsioids. Blood protein tests given to other animals give proof that dogs, cats, and bears are closely related, while sheep, goats, cows, antelopes, and deer form another closely related group. Sea lions and seals are more closely related to the carnivores than to the other mammals, as anatomic facts also indicate.

Hormones show similar reactions in different animals. If beef or sheep thyroid is fed to frog tadpoles, from which the thyroid gland has been removed, they metamorphose into normal frogs. The hormones used in treating endocrine deficiencies in man are obtained from other vertebrates.

Another point of similarity in most animals is the presence of enzymes essentially alike in their physiologic action. For example, trypsin, which acts upon proteins, occurs in many animals from protozoans to man; and amylase, which acts on starches, is present from sponges to man. It seems reasonable to suppose that similarity of biochemistry exists in such widely different animals because they have developed from a common ancestor. If each animal were a separate and special creation, then it is difficult to understand why such similarities in chemistry should run through living things.

Geographic distribution

According to students of geographic distribution, each species arose in a definite area, which is known as its center of origin;

from this area it tended to disperse, as already described. Many facts of present-day distribution can only be explained on the assumption that organic evolution has taken place. For example, continental islands possess faunas most closely related to those of the continents near which they are located, whereas the faunas of oceanic islands appear to have arisen by chance introduction of species from various regions. **Isolation** evidently plays an important role in evolution. Thus many animals on continental islands have evidently changed sufficiently, since these islands were cut off from the mainland, to be recognized as distinct species.

Fossil animals: historic record of evolution

From Darwin's time to the present, the remains of ancient animal life (fossils) have been regarded as strong evidence of evolution.

Fossil remains of animals are usually petrifactions, that is, parts that have been replaced by mineral matter, but the hard parts of the animals, such as bones, shells, and teeth, may be preserved intact, and parts of or entire animals may be preserved in ice (frozen mammoths in Siberia), amber (insects), asphalt (saber-tooth cats), and oil-bearing soil (mammoths). Casts of animals resulting from the dissolution of the hard parts and the filling up of the space with mineral matter, also give some idea of external features. Which animals become fossilized and which of these are discovered are more or less matters of chance. Furthermore, fossils are usually broken by the forces of nature and are therefore fragmentary when they are obtained. Nevertheless, from the evidence obtained from these fossils, paleontologists have constructed the accompanying table showing the geologic periods, arranged in the order of their succession, and the approximate time of origin of the different groups of animals (p. 617).

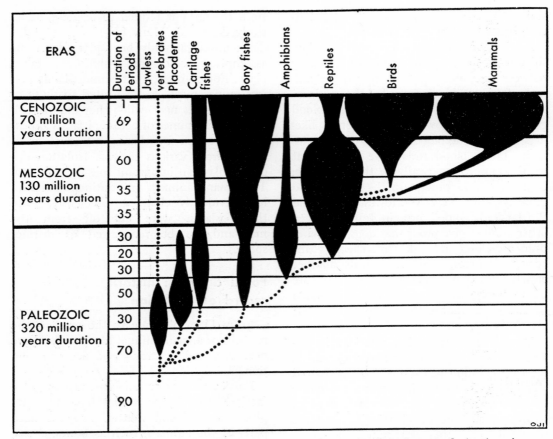

FIGURE 436. The distribution of the major vertebrate groups throughout geologic time is shown here in graphic form. Changes in width of the black areas indicates the relative abundance of each group through time; broken lines suggest possible sources and time of origin for certain groups. Like all geologic tables, this one reads from the bottom upwards. (After Colbert. *Evolution of the Vertebrates.* Copyright 1955 by John Wiley & Sons.)

Such a table shows that the invertebrates appeared first, since their remains occur in the oldest layers of rock, unaccompanied by remains of vertebrates; that the invertebrates became more complex in the succeeding periods; that the fishlike ostracoderms (low in the scale of vertebrate life) were the first fossil vertebrates to appear; and that these were followed by the fishes, amphibians, reptiles, birds, and mammals in the order that would be expected from a study of the structure of these vertebrates. This succession of the groups of vertebrates is even more dramatically shown in the accompanying diagram (Fig. 436). The most

convincing evidence derived from paleontology results from investigation of the lines of descent of single groups, such as the horses, camels, and elephants.

Evolution of the horse

One the best arguments in favor of the principle of organic evolution is furnished by our knowledge of the evolution of the horse. The horses now living in America are descendants of domesticated animals, which were brought to this country by the early settlers from Europe; but, in prehistoric times, the ancestors of our modern horse

THE DISTRIBUTION OF THE FOSSIL REMAINS OF ANIMALS IN THE LAYERS OF THE EARTH'S CRUST

ERAS AND ESTIMATED DURATION OF ERA IN YEARS	PERIODS AND EPOCHS	ANIMALS CHARACTERISTIC OF THE PERIODS
CENOZOIC (Age of Mammals) 70,000,000	Quaternary Recent Pleistocene	Man; mammals, mostly of species still living.
	Tertiary Pliocene Miocene Oligocene Eocene Paleocene	Mammals abundant; belonging to numerous extinct families and orders.
MESOZOIC (Age of Reptiles) 130,000,000	Cretaceous	Birdlike reptiles; flying reptiles; toothed birds; first snakes; bony fishes abound; sharks again numerous.
	Jurassic	First mammals; birds; giant reptiles; clams and snails abundant.
	Triassic	Sharks reduced to few forms; bony fishes appear.
PALEOZOIC (Age of Invertebrates) 320,000,000	Permian	Life transitional between Paleozoic and Mesozoic eras.
	Carboniferous (Age of Amphibians)	Earliest true reptiles. Amphibians; lungfishes; first crayfishes; insects abundant; spiders; fresh-water mussels; first land shells (snails).
	Devonian (Age of Fishes)	First amphibians; placoderms; sharks; mollusks abundant; first crabs; bony fishes appear.
	Silurian (Age of Invertebrates)	First truly terrestrial or air-breathing animals; corals abundant; ostracoderms, placoderms; brachiopods; trilobites; mollusks.
	Ordovician	Ostracoderms, trilobites, cephalopods, brachiopods, and bryozoans.
	Cambrian	Invertebrates only.
PROTEROZOIC		Simple marine invertebrates.
ARCHEOZOIC		Presumptive origin of life.

were native here, and some of the finest fossil remains of these ancestors have been found in America.

The evolution of the horse has been traced back through many distinct stages, extending through the **age of mammals** and the age of man. A brief description of 5 of these stages, together with Fig. 437, will serve to illustrate the principal changes that took place during this evolution. The structural features that became modified during this period were such as to adapt the horse to life on the open plains, where its food consisted of dry grasses.

The feet of the horse gradually lost the side toes; and only the middle toe and rudiments (splints) of the second and fourth digits * remain in our modern horses. The limbs became longer, enabling the animal to move about more rapidly; this change

* The digits are numbered 1 to 5, beginning on the thumb side.

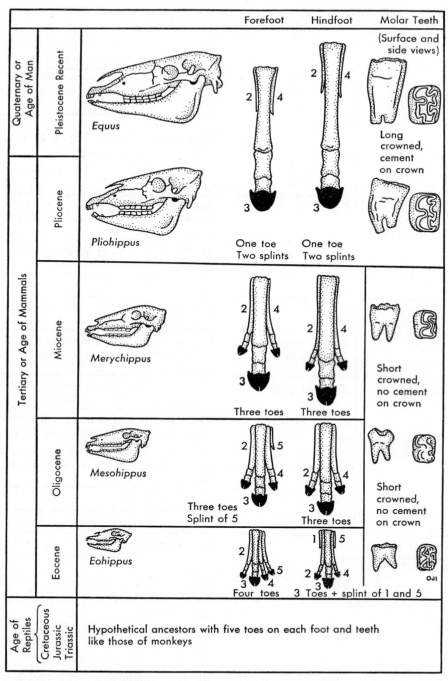

FIGURE 437. Diagrams illustrating the evolution of the horse. Digits or rudiments of digits (splints) are designated by numbers 1 to 5. (Modified from Matthew and Chubb.)

was correlated with an elongation of the head and neck, which was necessary in order to reach the ground. The front teeth were modified as chisel-like cropping structures; and the back teeth evolved from simple molars into wonderfully effective grinding organs with tortuous ridges of enamel and with supporting and protecting layers of dentine and cement. During the later periods, the molars elongated, and thus became adapted for grinding the dry grasses which caused them to wear down more rapidly than did the softer vegetation. During this evolution, the body gradually increased in size from that of the earliest known form, which was about as large as a domestic cat, to that of the horse of today.

Eohippus (dawn horse)

This tiny "dawn horse," also called *Hyracotherium* (Fig. 437), was only 11 inches high at the shoulder and about the size of a fox terrier. It lived during the Lower Eocene. *Eohippus* lived in North America and Europe and was a browsing forest dweller. Its forefeet have 4 complete toes each, but no trace of the first * (thumb); and the hindfeet have three complete toes each and the rudiments (splints) of the first and the "little finger" (fifth) which are shown in Fig. 437.

Mesohippus (intermediate horse)

This horse belongs to the Oligocene and reached the size of a sheep. Its forefeet possess three complete toes each, and the fifth digit is represented by a splint; the hindfeet also possess three complete toes each, but no splint. All three toes touched the ground, but the middle toe is larger and bore most of the weight of the body.

Merychippus (ruminating horse)

This horse lived in the Miocene, but became extinct in the Pliocene. It marks the transition from the primitive horse to the

---

* It was formerly claimed that the first toe was represented by a splint, but such a claim is not supported by any known specimen.

---

modern horse. The milk teeth are short-crowned and uncemented, like those of the primitive horse, but the permanent teeth are long-crowned and fully cemented grinders, suited to the harsh vegetation of the plains. Both its forefeet and its hindfeet possess 3 toes each.

Pliohippus (Pliocene horse)

This horse from the Upper Miocene and Pliocene is the first one-toed horse. Both fore- and hindfeet are one-toed, and the second and fourth toes are represented by splints. The crowns of the upper molars are similar to those of the modern horse, but they do not possess as complex a pattern of ridges on the surface. Pliohippus had a shoulder height of some 40 inches, about the size of a modern pony.

Equus (horse)

The modern horses of the Pleistocene and Recent epochs have lost the first and fifth digits entirely, and the second and fourth digits are represented by splints. The third toe alone sustains the weight of the body. The crowns of the molar teeth are much elongated with complex enameled ridges well adapted for grinding dry harsh vegetation. The lengthened skull is accompanied by a larger and more complex brain. This horse is about 60 inches tall, being considerably larger than any of its ancestors. The evolution of the horse has resulted in the development of an intelligent, long-legged, swift-running animal that is suited to live and feed on the open grasslands.

At the present time, true wild representatives of the genus *Equus* occur only in Asia (the Asiatic wild ass, *Equus hemionus*, and Przewalsky's horse, *E. przewalskii*) and in Africa (the African wild ass, *E. asinus*, and the zebras, *E. zebra*, and *E. burchelli*). The mustangs and broncos of our western plains and South America are not true wild horses, but are descendants of domesticated horses brought over from Europe.

The evolution of the elephant (see headpiece, p. 601), camel, dog, and many other

FIGURE 438. Evolution of the horse. Principal features of change in the horses through time are: (1) increased size; (2) increased length and mobility of the neck; (3) greater head size; (4) elongation of limbs; (5) reduction of toes; and (6) changes in teeth.

animals has been carefully worked out by paleontologists, but none quite so much in detail as that of the horse. Nevertheless, they show how much can be learned of the ancestors of vertebrates from a study of fossil forms.

THEORIES TO ACCOUNT FOR ORGANIC EVOLUTION

Early belief in organic evolution

The idea of organic evolution did not originate with Charles Darwin, as many people seem to believe, but from the time of the Greek philosopher Aristotle (384–322 B.C.), it has had a steady growth. Darwin, however, brought together an enormous mass of evidence in its favor and proposed a very plausible theory (natural selection) to account for it. He was so widely criticized by those who did not accept the theory, and so strongly defended by those who did, that the whole civilized world became conscious of the struggle and, for the most part, gave Darwin credit for the idea.

The immediate predecessors of Charles Darwin were Buffon, Erasmus Darwin, and Lamarck, and many others followed, especially Mendel and de Vries. Buffon (1707–1788) was a French writer on natural history who published evidence, such as we use today, to prove that species evolve from other species; he apparently believed that this was the result of environmental modifications that were inherited. He was followed by Erasmus Darwin (1731–1802), an uncle of Charles Darwin, who, in both poetry and prose, expressed a belief in organic evolution and in the hypothesis that changes take place as the result of the inheritance of environmental modifications.

Inheritance of acquired characters

Lamarck (1744–1829) was principally responsible for the belief, which prevailed during much of the nineteenth century, in the inheritance of acquired characters. According to the Lamarckian hypothesis of organic evolution, modifications due to use and disuse, or to direct action of environmental factors, are transmitted to the offspring; that is, traits acquired during an animal's lifetime are inherited by that animal's offspring. Such inherited modifications would account for the ability of antelope to escape their enemies by running rapidly, since the speed acquired by one generation would be passed on to the next, and so ad infinitum. Similarly, the giraffe would have acquired its long neck as a result of its habit of browsing, generation after generation, on the leaves of trees. These are examples of the supposed effects of use. If organs were not used, they were supposed to degenerate, as for example, the eyes of animals that live in caves.

Many investigators have attempted to obtain experimental evidence of inheritance of acquired traits, which must be proved before the Lamarckian hypothesis can be accepted. No evidence has yet been presented that is acceptable to most zoologists. Offspring do not appear to inherit modifications unless they are due to changes in the genes. The speed of the antelope, the long neck of the giraffe, and the degenerate eyes

of cave animals are correlated with the different environments in which these types of animals live and are best explained as the results of genetic change. Thus, the environment **indirectly** affects the genetic makeup of a species by operation of natural selection, which retains those genetic combinations best suited to prevailing conditions and discards those which are not fitted to them. The conclusion is that Lamarck's hypothesis is not valid.

Mutations in relation to evolution

De Vries (1848–1935) was a Dutch botanist whose principal studies were carried on with evening primroses. He observed sudden large changes in his primroses that were inherited and which he considered to be **mutations.** After 20 years of study, the same length of time devoted to the study of natural selection by Darwin, he published a book on mutations. His studies focused the attention of biologists on mutations, which have subsequently found to be of general occurrence.

Mutations were known to earlier breeders. Among these may be mentioned the short-legged sheep which appeared in a flock in Massachusetts in 1791 and from which was developed the Ancon breed of sheep. This mutation was of value to the farmer because these sheep could not jump over the low stone fences of New England. This breed became extinct about 90 years ago, but some 50 years later, a short-legged lamb appeared in the flock of a Norwegian farmer. From this, a new strain of Ancon sheep has been bred (Fig. 439).

Mutations have appeared frequently in animals bred for purposes of study, the most famous being those of the fruit fly, *Drosophila melanogaster* (Fig. 440). Investigators have examined millions and millions of flies belonging to this species and have described many different mutations in them.

As already noted, some mutations are due to changes in the genes which are respon-

FIGURE 439. The Ancon (short-legged) mutation in sheep (ewe in *center*, ram at *right*) compared with a normal ewe at *left*. This is the earliest recorded mutant among domestic animals. (Courtesy of *Life* magazine.)

sible for changes in the structure, physiology, or behavior of the organism. Such changes are now known to be numerous but small, and not rare or always conspicuous as was formerly supposed. How they arise is not known. They are inherited, however, and may be preserved or eliminated by natural selection. Thus, gene mutations are one source of the variability among animals which make possible the appearance of better-adapted individuals, and hence the evolution of the group.

Isolation as an evolutionary factor

Isolation of a group of animals from others of their kind seems to favor the progress of evolution in a species. This idea first originated as a result of the study of the faunas of oceanic islands. Such islands are usually inhabited by species that differ from those on the nearest mainland. Birds, bats, and insects are common inhabitants, no doubt, because wings give them the necessary powers of locomotion to reach islands, but amphibians and mammals, other than bats, are generally absent. Often the species of birds and insects on islands have become wingless.

Another example of isolation that has been carefully studied is that of snails living in the valleys along the sides of the mountains on Oahu in the Hawaiian Islands. They live in trees and ordinarily do not cross over the ridges from one valley to another. Practically every valley is inhabited by its own particular species or subspecies of snails, which differ in size, shape, or color of shell, but which are closely related. Chance colo-

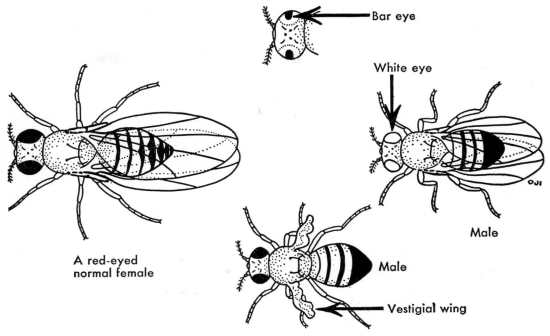

FIGURE 440. Mutations in the fruit fly, *Drosophila*, referred to by someone as "God's gift to geneticists." These are only a few of the thousands of mutations that are known to have occurred in this little fly.

nization with subsequent isolation appears to account for this situation. The original snail or snails in each valley possessed a set of genes that differed from those of snails in other valleys, since the genetic constitution of no two individuals (except identical twins) is alike. This fact, plus the probable mutations that took place and were perpetuated, would account for the diversity noted.

The types of isolation cited may be called **geographic isolation.** Other types of isolation also occur; for example, **seasonal isolation** exists when the breeding season of two groups of animals occurs at different seasons of the year; **sexual isolation** occurs when copulation is prevented for physiologic or psychologic reasons, when copulation is impossible on account of the morphology of the reproductive organs, when the spermatozoa are unable to reach or unite with the eggs, when the young hybrids that may develop from the fertilized eggs fail to reach

sexual maturity, or when sexually mature hybrids are unable to reproduce. Examples of all types of isolation mentioned might be cited and are more numerous than one would suppose.

THE BACKGROUND OF MAN

Zoologists do not maintain that human beings have descended from monkeys, as many people believe; but from a study of living primates and of their fossil remains, they are of the opinion that man and monkey both had common ancestors that lived many thousands of years ago. One authority's idea of primate descent is that the common monkeys of the present day separated from the ancestral stock at a very early period. The ancestral anthropoids gave rise to the anthropoid apes that are living today, such as the chimpanzee and gorilla as well as to the ancestors of man.

The early **human stage** is represented by two famous and closely related types: *Pithecanthropus* of Java, and *Sinanthropus* of China. The last stage is *Homo sapiens*. The line that has culminated in man of the present time is known from fossil remains, and new finds are being reported almost every year. The two physical factors that have been of prime importance in determining the evolutionary development of man from an apelike primate are: (1) the growth and high development of the brain and (2) the perfection of the erect posture.

African ape man
(Australopithecus africanus)

This first African ape man (Fig. 441) was discovered in the early 1920's by Dart; since then the rate of discovery has been very high. These fossils have been described under several generic names in Africa; and the remains may be parts of over 100 individuals.

Most authorities believe the Africa ape man fossils are the remains of a primate showing both the characteristics of the human family and the ape family. They are blended to such an extent that it is diffi-

Africa ape man
(Australopithecus)

Java ape man

Neanderthal man

Cro-Magnon man

FIGURE 441.   The African ape man and early men of Europe and Asia. These concepts of the appearance of prehistoric man come from fossil remains and are called restorations. (Africa ape man after E.H. Colbert and others after restorations by J.H. McGregor.)

cult to say whether they are ape or manlike.

The skull of *Australopithecus* resembled an ape; the volume of its brain is estimated at approximately 600 ml., which is only about half as large as modern man. The forehead, however, was more humanlike than that of living apes. The fossils give good evidence that the Africa ape man had a standing body posture approaching that of man rather than that of the ape. He also appears to have been an animal-hunting, flesh-eating, shell-cracking primate. No living ape lives on such a diet. It is believed by some authorities that these animals with both human and ape characteristics are ancesors of man, and our interest in them lies in the fact that they may be the beginning of the human line. However, for the time being, this is only a possibility.

Java ape man
(Pithecanthropus erectus)

The word *Pithecanthropus* means ape man and was applied to the remains of a creature that lived about 500,000 years ago because it possessed characteristics both human and apelike. The skull cap, femur, and two molar teeth were discovered in central Java in 1891, associated with the remains of certain extinct animals, which helped determine the geologic position (Upper Plio-

cene) of the ape man. These bones are sufficient for an anthropologist to reconstruct the animal to which they belonged. The cranial capacity of *Pithecanthropus* was about two-thirds that of modern man. The teeth are larger than human teeth. The femur resembles that of modern man, and its shape proves that *Pithecanthropus* stood erect.

Peking man
(Sinanthropus pekinensis)

The Peking man lived in a cave near Peking, China, where the teeth and parts of jaws and skulls of more than 35 individuals have been discovered. The teeth are human, but primitive; the skulls resemble that of *Pithecanthropus*, and the jaws exhibit apelike characteristics.

Heidelberg man
(Homo heidelbergensis)

The Heidelberg man is known from a lower jaw found near Heidelberg, Germany, in 1907. This jaw is heavy and much like that of a gorillalike anthropoid, but the teeth are small and of the human type. The conclusion of some anthropologists is that the jaw belonged to a man who had not evolved very far from the point of separation

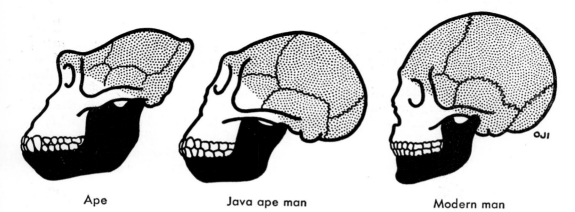

Ape   Java ape man   Modern man

Figure 442. Comparison of brain cases and faces of an ape, fossil man, and modern man. Note lack of chin in both ape and Java ape man; and as the brain increased in size, there was less jaw and face.

between man and the anthropoid apes, and who lived during the second interglacial period. Geologists tell us that during 4 different periods, great ice sheets from the arctic regions spread southward over Europe, replacing a semitropical climate with a frigid climate. Later, changes in temperature drove the ice northward and brought back the faunas and floras of warmer climates; these were the interglacial periods.

Piltdown man
(Ecanthropus dawsoni)

Fragments of a supposed fossil man were discovered in Piltdown, Sussex, England, in 1908 to 1915, by a lawyer named Dawson.

In 1953 some Oxford professors proved that the Piltdown man was not primitive, but the fragments were a mixture of ape and modern man—assembled by a prankster. Piltdown man was changed into the Piltdown hoax.

Neanderthal man
(Homo neanderthalensis)

A number of skeletons of Neanderthal man (Fig. 443) have been found in Europe. The Neanderthals lived in caves, made and used flints, understood the use of fire, and maintained definite burial customs. They ranged in height from about 5 to 5½ feet, but the thighbones were curved in such a

FIGURE 443. Neanderthal cave man, LeMoustier Cavern, Dordogne, France. He had a large brain, stocky body, slouching posture, and walked with a shuffling gait. From a painting by C.R. Knight. (Courtesy of American Museum of Natural History.)

way as to indicate that they did not walk erect as does modern man. The skull contained large orbits, and the brow ridges were prominent. The lower jaw was heavy and lacked a chin. The shoulders and arms were strong and the hands powerful. The Neanderthals flourished from 30,000 to 100,000 years ago.

Cro-Magnon man

The Cro-Magnons are extinct representatives of the living races of man (*Homo sapiens*). They (Fig. 441) were a mighty

race when they reigned in central France during the ice age. Their skeletal remains prove that they were tall and possessed large cranial capacity. Not only did they leave remains of their culture in the form of flint instruments and carved ivory in the caves in which they lived, but they also left evidence of artistic ability of a high order in the shape of drawings and paintings of animals now extinct on the walls of their caves.

Modern man (Homo sapiens)

The changes that have taken place during the development of modern man, *Homo sapiens,* have been chiefly mental rather than physical. Natural selection has brought about an evolutionary trend toward increasing brain power rather than body power. Intelligence has great adaptive value. Man's intelligence has enabled him to adapt himself to and control his environment. This has made him the dominant animal on the earth today, a position he will probably maintain for a long time to come.

Where did modern man first arise? We have no satisfactory answer to this question. Some students of this complex problem think Asia, but others equally competent consider Africa to have been the original home of man. Nor is it scientific to be dogmatic about man's pedigree. The general outlines of the evolution of man are fairly well defined, but many of the details are obscure or unknown.

SELECTED COLLATERAL READINGS

Barnet, S.A. (ed.). *Century of Darwin.* Harvard Univ. Press, Cambridge, 1958.

Colbert, E.H. *Evolution of the Vertebrates.* Wiley, New York, 1955.

Darwin, Charles. *On the Origin of Species by Means of Natural Selection, Or the Preservation of Favored Races in the Struggle for Life.* Appleton-Century, New York, 1875.

Dobzhansky, T. *Evolution, Genetics, and Man.* Wiley, New York, 1955.

Dodson, E.O. *A Textbook of Evolution.* Saunders, Philadelphia, 1952.

Dunbar, C.O. *Historical Geology.* Wiley, New York, 1949.

Hooton, E.A. *Up from the Ape.* Macmillan, New York, 1946.

LeGros Clark, W.E. *The Fossil Evidence for Human Evolution.* Univ. of Chicago Press, Chicago, 1955.

Moore, R. *Man, Time, and Fossils.* Knopf, New York, 1953.

Oparin, A.I. *The Origin of Life on the Earth.* Academic Press, New York, 1957.

Romer, A.S. *Man and the Vertebrates.* Univ. Chicago Press, Chicago, 1941.

Simpson, G.G. *Horses.* Oxford Univ. Press, New York, 1951.

————. *The Major Features of Evolution.* Columbia Univ. Press, New York, 1953.

Weiner, J.S. *The Piltdown Forgery.* Oxford Univ. Press, New York, 1955.

CHAPTER 37

Ecology and Zoogeography

No organism, plant or animal, ever exists in a vacuum. Every living thing is continually influenced by, and continually influences its surroundings. The inherited characteristics which enable a plant or animal to exist in terms of its surroundings constitute its heredity. The surroundings, with which it must conform, are its environment. **Ecology** is the science of the interrelationships of organisms in and to their environment.

One way of understanding the science of ecology is to start studying the nature of environments and to discover the demands they make upon organisms that inhabit them. We may begin by dividing environmental factors into those that are primarily physical—for example, light, temperature, chemicals, water, and substratum—and those that are primarily biological—for example, the presence of plants and animals.

A second approach is to study the organisms. The ecologist usually starts with a particular plant or animal population, or species, and his efforts are directed toward the discovery of the types of environmental conditions that can be tolerated by this particular group. He also concerns himself with conditions that actively or passively promote the welfare of the group in terms of survival and increase in numbers, as well as those that mitigate against its success.

It is significant that modern ecology is much less concerned with organisms as individuals than as groups. Ecologists have come to realize that it is the interaction of consistent environmental constants, changes, and cycles with relatively stable groups of organisms that is of importance to the orderly progress of evolution and survival. The experiences of any one individual are so variable and may be so atypical of those of the group to which it belongs that it obscures our understanding of the real problems presented by its environment. Any integrated group of organisms of one or of several species that occupies a consistent environment may be called a **population,** and it is populations, and not a particular individual, with which modern ecology is chiefly concerned.

The modern ecologist is also well aware of the importance of studying the physical-chemical environment and population, in terms of each other, at all times. This approach takes account of the constant interaction between the two and is called the ecosystem approach. Odum defines an **ecosystem** as "any entity or natural unit that includes living and non-living parts interacting to produce a stable system in which the exchange of materials between the living and non-living parts follows circular paths."

THE ENVIRONMENTAL OR HABITAT APPROACH

Before one can understand the interactions between environments and populations one must first learn of what an environment consists. The separate characteristics are called factors and may be classified as **physical, chemical,** and **biotic.** If the presence or absence of such a factor in a certain minimal quantity is necessary for the success of a population, it is called a **limiting factor. Physical factors** in the environment that are often of great importance as limiting factors are light, temperature, wind, water currents, fire, soil texture, pH (hydrogen ion concentration—acidity or alkalinity) of water and soil, presence or absence of certain inorganic salts, and the concentration of oxygen, carbon dioxide, and other gases. **Biotic factors** may exist in relation to the food supply, predation, or parasitism. A few of the more important environmental factors will be considered.

Physical factors

Light

Light is an important physical factor. We have seen what an influence light has on various types of animals such as the amoeba,

euglena, paramecium, hydra, earthworm, crayfish, insect, and frog. Without light, life on earth would be impossible. Only in the presence of light does photosynthesis take place for the manufacture of food for all organisms. By means of light, animals are able to move about freely and to carry on the necessary activities of life. Sense organelles, which detect light, are present in the protozoans, such as the euglena, and in most of the higher invertebrates and vertebrates. Thus we have encountered lensless eyes in planarians, eyes with lens and cornea in the sandworms, compound eyes in crayfishes and insects, eyes similar to those of vertebrates in the squid, and various types of vertebrate eyes in fish, frogs, turtles, birds, cats, and man.

The character of the lighting of an area has a profound effect upon the animals that live there. Everyone knows that certain plants will thrive in the shade, whereas others will not. This is likewise true of animals, not only of individuals, but also of aggregations. For example, the length of the period of daylight appears to be one of the factors that stimulate the migration of birds. In oceans and lakes many of the plankton organisms, that come to the surface at night, migrate downward by day. Many animals are nocturnal; some possess very large eyes with pupils that will admit a great number of rays in dim light. Certain fish that live in the ocean at depths where the light rays are few also have large eyes; many deep-sea fish manufacture their own light by means of luminescent organs. Among terrestrial animals that are nocturnal and possess large eyes are the tarsiers, night monkeys, and owls. Nocturnal animals, sometimes without large eyes, are provided with sensitive bristles on the face as in the shrews, or with some other means of finding their way around. Among the well-known animals that manufacture their own light by means of luminescent organs are the protozoan *Noctiluca*, ctenophores, certain marine worms, fireflies, glowworms, and certain deep-sea fish.

Temperature

We are well aware of our own sensitivity to temperature and what is true of man is equally true of many other animals.

Variations in temperature are generally less local than variations in light, and larger areas are therefore affected. The world may be divided into **zones** largely on the basis of differences in temperature, namely, **arctic**, **temperate**, and **tropical**. Most animals, even the amoeba and paramecium, react to differences in temperature, and each species has an optimum, which in the paramecium is between 24° C. and 28° C. Temperatures in sunlight and in shade differ and influence animals in their selection of a habitat. Even more notable differences occur in bodies of water between surface layers and deeper strata; animals react to these differences in temperature until they encounter their optimum which is the one at which they function best physiologically. An increase in temperature up to a certain point speeds up metabolism within the cells of the body and affects the activities of many animals. However, activity usually ceases before 45° C. is reached. House flies, for example, begin to move at about 6° C., carry on normal activity at about 17° C., increase their activity up to about 28° C., cease their activity at about 45° C., and die at about 46.5° C.

The effects of temperature on the presence or absence of animals in different habitats are varied. Certain species will not lay eggs until a favorable temperature is reached. Eggs develop more slowly at a low temperature and will not develop at all if the temperature is too low or too high. In some species, the adults die as winter approaches, but the race is maintained by means of "winter" eggs that can withstand the cold weather; other animals escape the cold by hibernation or migration. Some survive at high temperatures by estivation; certain animals live normally in hot springs at a temperature that would soon kill others accustomed to habitats of lower temperatures.

However, all living things are adapted to a comparatively limited temperature range; each animal has a different range in which life is possible as well as an optimum at which it lives best.

Chemical factors

The chemical nature of the medium is another important physical factor that influences the presence or absence of an animal in a particular habitat. As we have seen, protozoans, crayfishes, and many other animals react to chemical changes; these changes are often more conspicuous in an aquatic medium. For the most part, marine animals cannot live in fresh water, nor fresh-water animals in salt water. The presence or absence of certain chemicals may determine whether an animal can live in a habitat or not. For example, carbonate of lime (calcium carbonate) is necessary for building the shells of certain snails which cannot live where there is not a sufficient quantity of this chemical.

Water

Animals consist largely of water, and all require water. Since water is very irregularly distributed on the earth's surface, it has an important bearing on the character of the animals that live in various types of habitat. Plants are classified ecologically according to their water requirements. As just noted, the chemical content of the water determines to a considerable extent its availability as a habitat. The amounts of certain gases are also factors, for example, in deep water less oxygen and more carbon dioxide are usually present than in surface water. Organic compounds in water may serve as food for certain animals but prove fatal to others. Animals that live in dry regions usually possess some method of preventing evaporation of water; the horned lizard ("toad"), by means of a thick covering, can live for about 4 months in a desiccator; and the camel, by storing water in the reticulum of its stomach, can live for a week on dry food only, or for a month or more on green food. Certain species, such as the prong-horned antelopes, jack rabbits, and certain ground squirrels, can obtain all the water they require from green food.

Complete drying kills most animals, but members of some species can withstand considerable desiccation (drying). This is particularly true of small organisms such as the protozoans, rotifers, and minute crustaceans, which escape death by encysting or by laying eggs with heavy shells that resist evaporation. The water bears (Tardigrada) are famous for their ability to withstand desiccation for several years. Some animals, such as the lungfish, estivate during dry hot weather; while the earthworm and certain other burrowing animals make their way deeper into the soil where more moisture is present. Too much moisture is also a frequent hazard; animals such as the earthworm are flooded out of their habitats; they have been "rained up" out of their burrows and not "rained down" as some people suppose.

Substratum

Land. The substratum is another important ecological factor. On **land**, the character of the soil is an important factor in determining the nature of the vegetation and the types of animals that can maintain themselves upon it. Animals find different kinds of soil available for their homes and a place in which to escape from enemies, high temperatures, and desiccation. Countless animals live in the soil, notably protozoans, nematodes, worms, insects, burrowing amphibians, reptiles, and mammals. The type of soil, whether it be sand, loam, or clay, has a great influence on the ability of an animal to live in it.

Animals are adapted in various ways for life on or in the soil. The limbs of land vertebrates are under the body instead of on the sides, as are the fins on animals from which they evolved; this is necessary in order to sustain the weight of the body in a

medium (air) with a lower specific gravity than water. The legs of insects are derived from biramous swimming appendages, such as those of crustaceans. Sturdy bodies and enormously developed digging appendages with shovel-like claws have been developed by moles, mole crickets, and the nymphs of cicadas. Burrows must be reinforced to prevent cave-ins; the earthworm cements the wall with slime, the tiger beetle with saliva, and the trap-door spiders line their burrows with silk.

Water. Many aquatic animals inhabit the region on or beneath the bottom of water. *Neanthes,* the sandworm, burrows in the sand or mud of the seashore at tide level; the long-neck clam lives in the same type of habitat with its long neck reaching through the sand to the surface of the bottom. Corals and acorn barnacles live on various solid objects such as wood, shells, and corals, since they cannot attach themselves to mud or sand. The edible mussel *Mytilis edulis* attaches itself to rocks by means of a stringy secretion called a byssus. Oysters are not carried away by currents because they are attached to the substratum by one valve.

Types of environment

For purposes of convenience, environments may be classified as **fresh-water, marine, terrestrial,** and **symbiotic.** Each of these in turn may be broken down further into subdivisions such as lakes and streams as types of fresh-water environments. Furthermore, each environmental type has its own limiting factors.

Fresh-water environment

Fresh-water environments may first be subdivided into standing-water and running-water habitats. Examples of the former are lakes, ponds, and bogs, and of the latter, springs, streams, and rivers. It should be emphasized that there are no sharp boundaries among types, and that each may be in the process of becoming another, as when sedimentation gradually turns a lake into a bog.

Limiting factors of importance in fresh-water environments are temperature, transparency of the water, extent of water currents, and concentrations of oxygen and certain inorganic salts. All of these are subject to rapid change as when the evaporation of the water in a small pond increases the salt content of the water. Seasonal changes are also crucial in many cases.

Marine environment

Like the fresh waters, the seas are also aquatic environments. They differ from the former, however, in many aspects of ecologic interest. Because of their size, depth, and continuity, the ocean environments are more stable than those of the fresh waters.

The marine environments may also be broken down into smaller subdivisions. The relatively shallow waters of the continental shelves are called the **neritic zone,** and this may be further divided into zones related to tidal activity. The deep waters beyond the continental shelves constitute the **oceanic region.** Its subdivisions are vertical rather than horizontal. The **euphotic zone** is the upper portion of the oceanic region in which effective photosynthesis takes place. Because of this the euphotic zone is often called the "producing" region. The regions of the oceans, beyond the depth where light can penetrate, are called the **bathyal zones** when they occur on continental slopes, and they are called **abyssal zones** elsewhere. It should be noted that the fresh-water environments can also be subdivided in this manner, but such subdivisions are far less stable. Thus, one of the principal differences in approach between fresh-water and marine ecology is that geographic divisions have more weight in the former, while zonation is more important in the latter.

The limiting factors in the marine environments are generally the same as those of the fresh water, but their relative importance often differs. This is especially true of light, for there are few bodies of fresh water in which some light cannot penetrate to the bottom. Thus light is less of a limiting factor for the fresh-water environments. Salt concentration at a given place varies less in marine environments and has less significance as a limiting factor.

Terrestrial environment

The environments of the land are the most variable. They can be contrasted with the aquatic environments on the basis of a number of problems they offer to plant and animal populations.

On the land, moisture is always a limiting factor. Air, as contrasted with water, permits rapid temperature variation, but offers little variation in oxygen and carbon dioxide content. Also, air lacks the supporting ability of water and thus imposes a necessity for strong skeletal structure and special means of locomotion upon land animals. Land areas are not continuous, and this presents geographic barriers not generally present in aquatic, especially marine, environments. Finally, the nature of the substrate (soil) is of greater importance in land environments. To summarize: **climate** and **substrate** are the two groups of physical factors most important to land ecology.

In subdividing terrestrial environments, the most useful concept is that of the **biome,** the largest conveniently recognized community unit. A biome is a unit resulting from the interaction of a regional climate, regional biota (animal and plant life), and substrate. Examples are grasslands, tundras, coniferous forests, deciduous forests, and deserts.

Symbiotic environment

There are many examples in nature of two species habitually living in a more or less close relationship with one another, other than that of predation. All of these may be called **symbiosis,** and each species forms a more or less important part of the environment of the other. Since the environmental variation is almost endless in such cases, and since the limiting factors are often extremely subtle, a special section of this chapter is devoted to such relationships.

POPULATIONS AND COMMUNITIES APPROACH

Ecology can be subdivided in another manner with regard to the ways in which it is approached. If one studies the interrelationships of a single individual or species with its environment, he is concerned with **autecology**. If, on the other hand, whole populations are studied as units, the approach is called **synecology**. Today, the synecologic approach has largely replaced its autecologic predecessor, and, since this method deals with various levels of population organization, these should be well understood.

A group of individuals composed of members of a single species or several closely associated species, and occupying a definite environmental area, is called a **population**. All of the populations occupying a given geographic area constitute a **biotic community**. A biotic community together with its nonliving environment forms an **ecosystem**. It is on the level of the ecosystem that the principles of ecology can best be understood.

Biological principles with application to ecosystems

The part of the earth in which life exists is called the **biosphere**. Compared with the earth as a whole, this is a shallow surface region. It includes both the oceans and the atmosphere. The biosphere itself can be considered an ecosystem, consisting of smaller ecosystems, which in turn are made up of still smaller ones. In practice, ecologists study ecosystems of various sizes, depending upon the problems of interest at the time.

Also, the larger ecosystems provide examples of the broader ecologic principles while the smaller ones exhibit more clearly the specific and limited relationships.

Some of the biological principles which are a part of the ecosystems and which are also important are **habitat and niche, chemical cycles, biological interrelationships, limiting factors,** and **energy transfer** in ecologic systems. They will be discussed in this order.

Habitat and niche

Two of the most important concepts of ecology are those of habitat and niche. A **habitat** is the particular environment in which a population lives. Thus the catfish lives in slow-moving streams and lakes; these are said to be its habitats. A **niche** is the role of a population within its community and ecosystem. It includes such factors as what it eats, what its predators are, and how it changes the physical environment.

Chemical (inorganic-organic) cycles

The chemical elements of which all organisms are composed come from the environment, and eventually return to the environment after the organism dies. There are continual cycles of the chemical elements. Three examples will suffice to illustrate this principle.

Carbon cycle. Both plants and animals respire and give off carbon dioxide gas. This gas is of vital importance in the web of life. The carbon cycle is illustrated and discussed on page 510.

Nitrogen cycle. The proteins constitute one of the most important of the animal foods. All proteins contain the essential element nitrogen. The nitrogen cycle is illustrated and described on pages 510 and 511.

Mineral cycle. The importance of mineral salts to animals is discussed on page 518. Minerals dissolved in river or soil water form the basic supply for continental plants and animals. Upon their death (Fig. 444), the mineral components are again received by soil or water.

Biological (biotic) interrelationships

The web of life. Although we speak of solitary, gregarious, and social animals, no animal lives by itself alone; it must live in the same environment with others of its kind and with other species, where it is obligated to compete for space, food, mates, and protection from enemies.

Plants are also important factors in the biological environment, as are various factors of the physical environment. The com-

plexity of the "web of life" is shown in Fig. 444, which illustrates a typical **food chain** in a fresh-water lake. Dissolved mineral nutrients leached from the surrounding earth, coupled with nutrients derived from the decomposition of organic matter, provide food for the growth of the microscopic plant and animal life, such as plankton (Fig. 452). Use is made of this fact by the fishery biologist who attempts to increase fish production in a pond by use of commercial fertilizers.

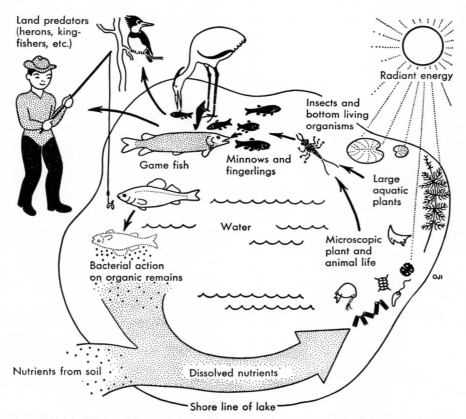

FIGURE 444. Food chain in a fresh-water lake. Arrows point from the organism eaten to those doing the eating. A food chain starts with the plant where photosynthesis produces the first food; the plants are eaten by herbivores, which are in turn eaten by a series of carnivores; each animal of the series is usually larger than the one preceding it (see headpiece page 628).

The plant plankton such as certain algae, together with the higher green plants, provide the chemical energy in such a lake community by their photosynthetic activity. The insects and bottom organisms feeding

upon the plants and smaller animals are, in turn, fed upon by the fishes which are the primary source of animal food for many animals such as herons, kingfishers, and even man. Under normal conditions, the food chain becomes completed when the fish and other organisms die and are destroyed by bacteria, thus making the materials again available to the plants. If a molecule of an element like phosphorus were made radioactive, the path of this tagged element would clearly demonstrate the chainlike nature of the feeding relationships of organisms living in this lake community. The relationship of food chains and the life cycles of parasites would also be demonstrated. Probably no living thing exists which does not serve as a link in some food chain.

Limiting factors

The presence and success of an organism or group of organisms depend upon a complex of conditions. Any condition, which is less than or exceeds the limits of tolerance, is said to be a limiting factor. By considering all possible limiting factors at once, instead of focusing upon each one separately, we are able to study their interactions. Thus an animal might be able to tolerate more heat in the presence of water than in its absence.

Energy transfer

In any ecosystem energy is continually being transferred from the physical environment to living organisms and from one group of living organisms to another (Fig. 445). This is the very basis of life. The account of the **web of life** illustrates some of the principles involved. It will be recalled that the web of life actually consists of a number of interlinked food chains. There are three types: the **predator chain** which starts with plants and proceeds from small to larger animals, the **parasite chain** which goes from large to smaller organisms, and the **saprophytic chain** which proceeds from dead material to microorganisms.

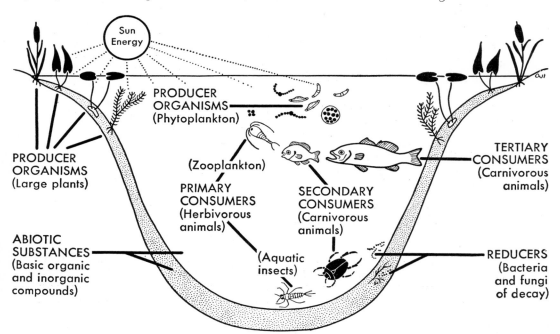

FIGURE 445. A fresh-water pond ecosystem. An ecosystem is a natural unit that includes living and nonliving parts, interacting to produce a stable system in which the exchange of materials between the living and nonliving follows a circular path. The ecosystem is the largest functional unit in ecology because it includes both the living and nonliving environment. (After *Fundamentals of Ecology* by E.P. Odum. Copyright 1953 by W.B. Saunders Company.)

Ecologic pyramid

The food chains in the web of life contribute to biological pyramids which may not be evident to the casual observer, but which exist throughout nature. We will consider here only the pyramid of biomass, which gives a picture of the food chain relations. To simplify this pyramid, we will consider only alfalfa, calves, and a boy. This also shows the important relationship between plants and animals.

Since all energy comes from sunlight, only the green plants can convert this energy into a form that can be utilized by animals. Studies have shown that it takes 20 million alfalfa plants to produce 17,850 pounds of alfalfa, to produce 4½ yearlings, weighing 2250 pounds. These 4½ yearlings are required to feed one boy to the age of 12, weighing 105 pounds (Fig. 446). This pyramid of biomass shows graphically that the actual protoplasmic mass, as well as numbers, becomes less toward the peak. Thus, to produce a given amount of human protoplasm, a great deal more calf protoplasm is required; and to produce a unit of calf protoplasm, a much greater weight of alfalfa is required.

Much is being written today about the "population problem." Will human populations exceed their food supply? It is easy to see that if the amount of biomass in the system, represented by the ecologic pyramid, is changed at any level, all the other levels would have to adjust to the changed conditions. How large a population the world can support depends on how much we can increase the food supply for man. It can readily be seen that the ecologic pyramid has socio-economic implications for human society.

Productivity

The productivity of an ecosystem is the amount of available food material of all types that it produces over a given period of time. **Primary productivity** refers to the food produced by **producer organisms** which are chiefly green plants. **Secondary productivity** is the amount produced by **consumer organisms,** principally animals. Animals are not merely consumers in relation to productivity; even if they are not consumed in turn by larger animals they return a certain amount of available energy to the ecosystem in the form of feces and their own dead bodies.

Interactions between species

Species may be treated as populations and, as such, are subdivisions of ecosystems. Two species can interact in various ways. If two or more species contend in rivalry for the same niche, it is called **competition;** only one species occurs in an ecologic niche in a habitat. If a larger species regularly consumes the smaller ones as food, the phenomenon is called **predation.** This involves the maintenance of a balance in the numbers of both species; the disappearance of the prey would result in the same fate for the predator. A similar balance exists between **parasite** and **host** species. Competition, predation, and parasitism are often called **negative interactions** between species. Examples of **positive interactions** are found in **commensalism** and **mutualism** which are considered under the general heading of **symbiosis.**

SYMBIOSIS

When two different species of organisms live together, the relationship is called symbiosis. Mutualism is sometimes erroneously called "symbiosis." Symbiosis is best used as a collective term to include mutualism, commensalism, and parasitism. The three terms —mutualism, commensalism, and parasitism —are usually employed for the main types of associations that exist between organisms of different species. However, there is no very sharp line of demarcation between them.

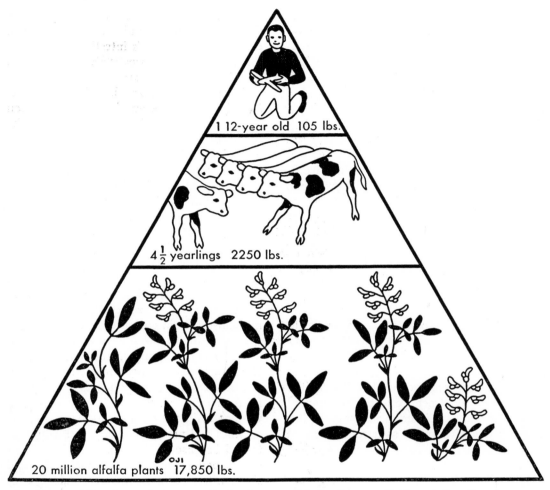

FIGURE 446. An ecologic pyramid, to show graphically the quantitative relationships in a simplified alfalfa-calf-boy food chain. An enormous mass of plant material is necessary to produce a relatively small amount of beef, and a large quantity of beef is required to grow a 12-year-old boy. Data from Odum.

Commensalism

Commensalism is a term that indicates an association in which one partner is benefited and the other is neither injured nor benefited; the one benefited is called a commensal. The term really means eating at the same table. This type of association probably occurs in all large groups of animals, sometimes between species belonging to the same phylum, class, or order, and sometimes between those of different phyla. For example, peculiar tropical fish called remoras are modified for life as commensals. The first dorsal fin forms a sucker by means of which the fish attaches itself to sharks, turtles, whales, other large aquatic animals, and floating objects such as boats. They are able to swim, but are more often carried about by other animals. Their food consists of other fish and probably scraps left from the meal of the shark or other animal to which the individual is attached. Many animals find the bodies of sponges excellent places in which to retreat for protection. The number and variety of these is indicated by the results of an examination of 12 living bath sponges reported by Pearse from the Dry Tortugas Islands near Florida. These 12 sponges, which ranged from 2 to 8 inches in diameter, contained 683 other animals belonging to 15 or more species, including annelids, brittle stars, crustaceans, and bivalves. A somewhat similar association is that of various types of animals that live in the nests of social insects. For example, termite nests are often inhabited by other species of insects; these are called termitophiles. Over 100 species of termitophiles have been recorded, including beetles, aphids, ants, millipedes, and isopod crustaceans. Ants and bees likewise serve as hosts for many other species of animals. Certain sessile animals attach themselves to free-swimming species; for example, barnacles to whales and protozoans to tadpoles, planarians, and snails.

Commensals may be internal as well as external. Most protozoans that live in the human digestive tract are of the commensal type. They do us neither harm nor good, but use our digestive tracts as a residence and may feed on waste fecal material as some of the amoebas do.

Mutualism

Mutualism is an association in which both species derive benefit; in other words, the relationship is mutually helpful, hence the descriptive term "mutualism." One of the best examples is that of termites and their intestinal flagellates (Fig. 447). The termites eat wood but cannot digest cellulose; but the flagellates in the termite intestine can, so food is available to both.

Without the flagellates the termites would starve to death in the midst of plenty, as has been proved by depriving termites of their flagellates. The flagellates receive the following benefits from this mutualistic relationship: (1) a constant food supply, (2) protection from enemies, and (3) a stable

environment. It has been demonstrated that these flagellates are unable to exist anywhere except in the termite's intestine.

A number of protozoans and coelenterates live in mutualistic symbiosis with algae, which are known as **zoochlorellae.** *Paramecium bursaria,* for example, is colored green by algae that live in its endoplasm. The zoochlorellae use the waste products of metabolism, including carbon dioxide, nitrogenous and phosphorous substances, and supply the paramecia with food and oxygen. Both the paramecia and algae can live alone, but they are mutually beneficial while living together. Protozoa may also contain brown or yellow unicellular organisms called **zooxanthellae** with which they are mutualistic. The green hydra owes its color to zoochlorellae that live in the endoderm. Brown and yellow zooxanthellae also live mutualistically in coelenterates.

Less intimate cases of mutualism occur between crabs, sponges, and coelenterates. Crabs may place sponges on their shells with the result that the sponge is transported from place to place, which may be of advantage to it; the crab is concealed from its enemies and prey, and if detected, is not attacked because of the disagreeable qualities of the sponge. Hermit crabs that live in snail shells often place hydroid coelenterates or sea anemones on top of the shell; the nematocysts of the coelenterates drive away enemies, and the coelenterates are carried about and probably obtain some of the food captured by the crab. The shore crab of the Indian Ocean is said to carry a sea anemone in each pincer, which it thrusts into the face of an approaching enemy and drives it away with the nematocysts.

Other interesting examples of mutualism occur among insects and vertebrates. For example, ants protect aphids, and in return "milk" honeydew from them, which they use as food. A fish lives among the tentacles of a jellyfish (Fig. 59) which give protection by their stinging cells. On the other hand the jellyfish benefits, for the small fish acts as a lure, attracting larger fish within the

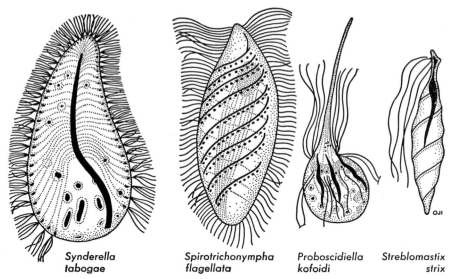

Synderella
tabogae

Spirotrichonympha
flagellata

Proboscidiella
kofoidi

Streblomastix
strix

FIGURE 447. Intestinal flagellates of termites. *Synderella* from *Cryptotermes longicollis*. *Spiro-trichonympha* from *Reticulitermes lucifugus*. *Proboscidiella* from *Cryptotermes dudleyi*. *Streblomastix* from *Termopsis laticeps*.

shooting distance of the tentacles loaded with poisonous stinging darts. Birds remove insects from the backs of buffaloes and rhinoceroses, and warn their hosts of approaching danger.

Some of the examples of plant-animal mutualism come from cross-pollination of certain plants by insects. Many orchids and other flowers with deep corollas (the second whorl of parts in a flower) are pollinated by moths with long tongues; pendulous flowers are pollinated principally by bees. The colors and odors of flowers are supposed to have evolved to attract pollinizing insects. Wasps, flies, butterflies, moths, ants, beetles, bees, and thrips are the most important pollinators. Most of these insects accomplish cross-pollination by pollen of flowers becoming attached to the hairs on their bodies and being brushed off on others; thus it is transferred from one flower to another. How important cross-pollination by insects may be is indicated by the fact that the Smyrna fig could not be grown in California until the tiny fig insect *Blastophaga psenes* (Fig. 448) was introduced in that state.

In certain cases, pollination results from a complicated series of instinctive acts as in the yucca moth *Tegeticula alba* (Fig. 449). Flowers of the genus *Yucca* depend entirely on this species. The moth visits the flowers in the evening, scrapes some pollen from a stamen, holds it underneath its head, and carries it to another flower. It clings to the pistil of this flower, and, thrusting its ovipositor through the wall of the ovary, lays an egg. It then mounts the pistil and forces the pollen it has brought down into the stigmatic tube. Another egg is laid in another part of the ovary, and more pollen is inserted into the stigmatic tube. These processes may be repeated half a dozen times in a single flower. This is a mutually beneficial relationship in that the yucca is cross-fertilized, and the moth larva is provided protection and food.

Parasitism

A parasite is an organism that lives its whole life, or a part of it, upon or within another organism (different species) from which it obtains its food. The host which harbors the adult stage of the parasite is

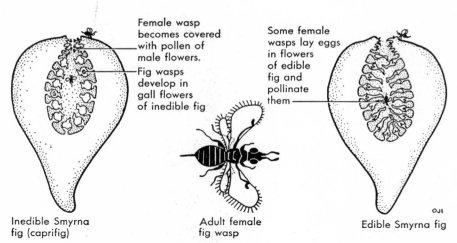

Female wasp becomes covered with pollen of male flowers.

Fig wasps develop in gall flowers of inedible fig

Some female wasps lay eggs in flowers of edible fig and pollinate them

Inedible Smyrna fig (caprifig)

Adult female fig wasp

Edible Smyrna fig

FIGURE 448. The female fig insect shown is necessary to the production of the edible Smyrna fig. Fig wasps do not develop in the edible fig even though eggs are laid in it. Both plant and insect benefit from the relationship.

the **definitive host.** The host which harbors the larval stages of the parasite is the **intermediate host.** A parasite that lives within the body is an **endoparasite,** and a parasite

FIGURE 449. Yucca moth female does not feed on yucca plant, but lays eggs in ovary and deposits pollen on the stigma. (Photo by Cornelia Clarke.)

that lives on the outside of the body is an **ectoparasite.**

Ectoparasites attack many aquatic animals. A small copepod crustacean, the fish louse (*Argulus versicolor*), is an ectoparasite

especially on pike and pickerel. It is brilliantly colored with red, green, and orange, and attaches itself to the host by the second maxillae which are modified into sucking disks. **Leeches** attack both aquatic and terrestrial animals.

The ectoparasites of terrestrial animals are principally arthropods. Human beings are attacked by lice, ticks, and many others. Probably most species of nonhuman terrestrial animals are inhabited by their own peculiar species of ectoparasites, such as the biting and sucking lice that infest poultry, and the ticks that feed on cattle and on many other animals.

Endoparasites occur in both aquatic and terrestrial animals and have been found in every species that has been properly examined. Certain protozoans live as endoparasites inside the bodies of other protozoans; others occur in species belonging to every group in the animal kingdom. Trematodes, tapeworms, and roundworms are common endoparasites. Arthropods may also live within animals; for example, the larvae of the bot fly live as endoparasites in the stomach of the horse. The larvae of mussels are parasitic in the skin or gills of the fish. Such endoparasites are all invertebrates.

Parasitism in the animal kingdom

Almost every large group in the animal kingdom contains parasitic species. There are very few of these, however, in certain phyla and large numbers in other phyla. A survey of the animal kingdom shows clearly that the parasites of principal importance are included in the phylum Protozoa, in several phyla of **worms,** and in the phylum Arthropoda. Among the Sarcodina are both free-living and parasitic species, including the amoebas of man and other animals. The flagellates also contain free-living and parasitic representatives, such as the intestinal and blood-inhabiting parasites of man and other animals. The sporozoans are all parasitic; among them are the coccidia and malarial parasites of man, and the parasites of the intestine, blood, and tissues of other animals. The ciliates are free-living or parasitic; *Balantidium coli* is the only species that is parasitic in man; various species inhabit other animals.

Very few parasites occur among the sponges and coelenterates. The flatworms include many free-living and parasitic species. The Turbellaria are mostly free-living, but the Trematoda and Cestoda are all parasitic. The roundworms likewise include free-living species and parasitic species that live in man and other animals; e.g., hookworms, ascarids, and others.

The Acanthocephala (spine-headed) worms are mostly parasitic in lower animals, and the Nematomorpha (hairworms) are parasitic in insects. Echinoderms are almost entirely free-living; annelids may be either free-living, such as the earthworm, or parasitic as the leeches. The mollusks are mostly free-living.

The arthropods are free-living or parasitic; many species act as intermediate hosts of parasitic protozoans and worms. Many crustaceans are parasites of fish; many insects are parasitic or serve as intermediate hosts; and a large number of arachnids are parasitic. The vertebrates are mostly free-living, but there are species that may be classed as parasites.

Origin and evolution of parasitism

We really know nothing definite about the origin and evolution of parasitism, since no one has ever observed a free-living species become parasitic, but many known facts are of value in any attempt to work out lines of descent. In the first place, the parasitic habit must have been more recently evolved than the free-living habit, since free-living forms must have existed before the parasites could obtain hosts on which to live. Ectoparasites probably evolved before endoparasites, because the change from a free-living existence to that of ectoparasitism does not appear to be so difficult as to that of endoparasitism. Inasmuch as there are free-living as well as parasitic species in many large groups of animals (e.g., the Sarcodina, Mastigophora, and Ciliata among the Protozoa), it is evident that the parasitic habit has arisen independently in each of these groups, and this type of evolution may therefore be considered of rather common occurrence.

PRINCIPLES ASSOCIATED WITH BIOTIC COMMUNITIES

It has been stated that a biotic community is essentially the group of populations in an ecosystem. They may be named after some conspicuous feature such as the most conspicuous or numerous animal or plant species (beech-maple) or after some physical feature (tropical rain forest). There is no set rule for the naming of communities. A **biotic community** (Fig. 450) is a more or less complex group of plants and animals that occupies a particular area and influences the life of each member. In this area, the environmental factors are such that certain types of plants and animals are able to live there. Other areas, where a similar environ-

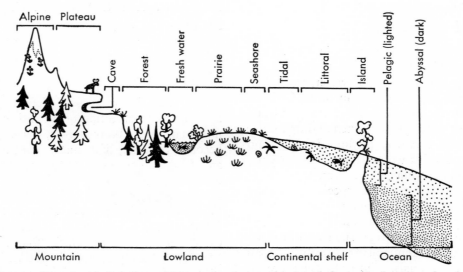

FIGURE 450. An ideal section at the margin of a continent to indicate the location of various types of ecologic environments available to animals. The different ecologic areas shown make possible different biotic communities.

ment exists, are likely to contain similar types of plants and animals. For example, fresh-water ponds are never exactly alike, but the environment in them is similar, and we look for the same kinds of plants and animals in them. Pond animals may be permanent or temporary residents, or merely visitors. Among the permanent residents are protozoans, some crustaceans, a variety of snails, and other small animals. Frogs, toads, and some salamanders are temporary residents; and water birds such as ducks and herons visit the pond to feed on the animals in it. Hundreds of different types of communities have been described and classified by ecologists.

There are a number of ecologic principles that are best understood in terms of communities; among these are **succession**, **dominance**, **stratification**, and **periodicity**.

Ecologic succession

When a community has reached the comparative stability of dynamic equilibrium, it is called a **climax community**. But every climax community has had a history of changes; such changes constitute **ecologic**

succession. A new habitat, as, for example, a pond resulting from the overflow of a river, may contain certain types of fish, including black bass and sunfish. Later the sides of the pond become overgrown with vegetation and the clean bottom becomes covered with deposits; the black bass and sunfish disappear because such an environment is not suited to them, but catfish may persist. Still later, just before the pond becomes a swamp, the mud minnow may replace the catfish. Finally, conditions become such that no fish are able to live in the habitat. Here are several stages, each differing in the type of fishes and other animals present. The final stage (Fig. 451) in the

FIGURE 451. *Facing page,* ecologic succession, simplified. Pond succession, from the practically bare bottom (pioneer) stage, which is gradually replaced by sequential stages, each more mature than the preceding one, until a climax is reached where the community becomes relatively stable. The stages shown here are based on studies in the Middle West. The succession in ponds with a different climate will not be the same in detail; and the climax will be different. Several intermediate stages are omitted. (Redrawn with modifications from *Basic Ecology* by R. and M. Buchsbaum, Boxwood Press, Pittsburgh.)

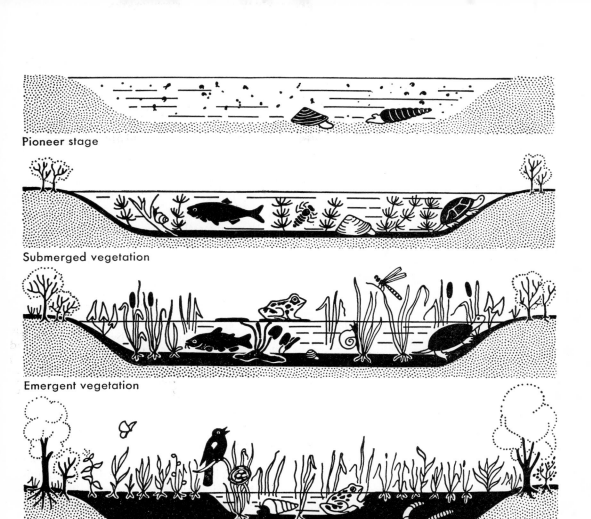

Pioneer stage

Submerged vegetation

Emergent vegetation

Temporary pond

Beech and maple forest climax

643

series of succession is a climax community. Ponds at the same stage in their development tend to contain the same kinds of animals; lakes of the same size and depth have similar faunas; and so on for each type of community.

Ecologic succession can also be observed in a jar of water containing a source of organic material and bacteria. For example, if a few pieces of hay are placed in a beaker of water, countless bacteria will appear in the water in a day or two. Soon minute flagellated protozoans make their appearance, feeding on the bacteria and on the products of bacterial decomposition. Next, ciliated protozoans (often *Colpoda*) become numerous; these eat bacteria but are themselves eaten by larger ciliates which soon become dominant. After all the smaller organisms are eaten, the large ciliates die unless green plants are established in the community. If this is done the plants and animals become adjusted to one another and a comparatively stable condition is established which we call a balanced aquarium (microcosm); this is essentially a climax community. In this community we find a few representatives of each preceding stage, but the greater numbers of green algae, rotifers, and crustaceans represent more recent stages.

Ecologic dominance

In many communities certain organisms will be more important than others because of their size and numbers, and these will have much to do with the determination of its character; they can be said to control or rule the community. Such organisms are called **dominants**. In land communities these are usually plants. For example, in a beech-maple community, these tall trees cast shade that limits the shorter plants to certain types, and these, in turn, limit the types of animal species that can live there.

Stratification

Stratification is the tendency for a community to arrange itself in vertical layers. In aquatic communities this is usually due to a stratification of physical factors such as light, temperature, or oxygen content of the water. Thus, the organisms that live on the bottom of a deep lake will not be the same as those near the surface. Similar divisions into layers occur in animal communities, but it is usually based upon the varying heights of vegetation such as grass, shrubs, and trees. Stratification often exhibits seasonal and daily changes. In a forest, certain animal species that are associated with the tree tops at night may live underground during the day. In fresh-water lakes there is often a seasonal reversal in temperature layers of the water and certain animal species will move with the shifting strata of temperature.

Periodicity

Periodicity is the tendency for communities to exhibit rhythms or cycles. These involve recurring changes in the activities or movements of organisms. Thus certain species may be active only during the day while others are active only at night.

In aquatic communities the zooplankton organisms generally move toward the surface at night and return to deeper waters during the day. These are called **daily rhythms**. There are also **seasonal rhythms**.

Types of communities

Fresh-water communities

As noted earlier, the major habitats are fresh-water, salt-water, and terrestrial. As an example of the subdivision of a major habitat into communities we may select fresh water. This type of habitat is less extensive than any of the others, but it is probably better known to most of us. First we divide the fresh-water habitat into communities of (1) flowing water and (2) standing water. Then we divide the flowing water into (1) rapidly flowing streams and (2) slowly flowing streams, and the standing water into (1) lakes, (2) ponds, and (3) swamps. Each of these may be further divided, for example, the ponds into (1) those with bare bottoms and (2) those whose bottoms contain vegetation. Each of these types of ponds contains a number of communities, such as those occupying (1) the beach above the water, (2) the shore-line, (3) the shore water, (4) open water (plankton and nekton), and (5) the bottom. All other habitats may similarly be subdivided.

Many of the animals we have studied live in fresh-water communities; these include protozoans, rotifers, hydras, planarians, crayfishes, helminthes, annelids, mollusks, and fishes. In **flowing streams** we find fish, flatworms, crayfishes, caddisfly larvae, and snails; these are adapted to withstand a current by swimming, by clinging to plants and rocks with claws, suckers, etc., and by seeking shelter in crevices or under stones. **Standing water** contains especially plank-

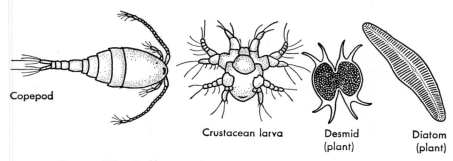

FIGURE 452. Some types of animals and plants found in plankton.

ton, organisms (Fig. 452) that float or swim feebly and are carried about by wave action and currents; they are mostly small and even microscopic, but some may be of considerable size. Larger swimming animals, the nekton, are also present. Animals that live on the bottom constitute the **benthos**. In **swamps** and **bogs** the quantity of oxygen is often reduced, which limits the variety of animals that obtain oxygen from the water; consequently most swamp animals are air breathers. The African lungfish is a notable example of an animal that may carry on respiration by means of either gills or lungs and is therefore able to live in water too foul for fish having only gills. The animals that live in **pools** are of particular interest because they must resist desiccation when the pool dries up or perish.

Marine (salt-water) communities

Animals that live in salt water have a great deal of space to occupy, since 72 per cent of the earth's surface is covered by the sea. Furthermore, animals live at all depths, and 84 per cent of the ocean is deeper than 1000 fathoms (6000 feet), and 7 per cent is deeper than 3000 fathoms (18,000 feet). The salinity of the ocean averages about 3.5 per cent, whereas that of fresh water is usually less than one per cent. The number of animals is greatest near the surface, where the light penetrates; here they are subject to tides and currents. Along the shores live large numbers of barnacles, sea anemones, and limpets, which attach themselves to rocks; clams, snails, starfishes, and sea urchins, which cling to rocks or hide in crevices; and many species of worms and clams which burrow into the sand or mud.

The animals of the **open sea** are called **pelagic.** As in lakes, they may be divided into plankton that float or swim feebly, and nekton that swim about freely. Among the **plankton** (Fig. 452) are Protozoa, especially the foraminiferans, radiolarians, and dinoflagellates; the medusas; the Portuguese man-of-war; ctenophores; small crustaceans; and pteropod mollusks. The **nekton** include fish, dolphins, birds, whales, etc.

Deep-sea animals are particularly interesting since they must be able to withstand unusual environmental conditions. The pressure is increased to several hundred atmospheres, and when a fish is drawn to the surface, the change in external pressure results in swelling of the body, bulging of the eyes, and protrusion of the stomach from the mouth. This is not true of all species because some have special adaptations that make toleration of considerable pressure change possible. Light penetrates to a depth of about 500 fathoms (3000 feet) in clear water; hence animals living below that depth must move about in total darkness or furnish their own luminescence. Many have no eyes. Below a depth of 600 feet only slight variations in temperature occur, the mean being about 2.5° C. Deep-sea animals may feed on each other, but they depend for their primary source of food on plants and animals that die and sink down from above, that is, they are principally scavengers. Most of the deep-sea bottom is covered with globigerina and radiolarian ooze. **Abyssal animals** that live below 2000 fathoms (12,000 feet) include fish, protozoans, worms, mollusks, sea cucumbers, and starfishes. The color of these abyssal animals is monotonous, usually dark brown or red.

Terrestrial communities

Terrestrial animals may live on the surface of the ground, under the surface, or largely in the air. Most terrestrial animals, such as Protozoa, insects and their larvae, nematodes, and moles live within 5 or 6 inches of the surface. Others such as rodents (gophers and prairie dogs), earthworms, and ants may burrow much deeper. Adaptations for a burrowing type of life have already been mentioned. The character of the soil and the amount of water it contains largely determine the types of animals that live in subterranean communities; for example, the earthworms need moisture. The principal kinds of soil are clay, and sand. Comparatively few species of animals live in pure clay soils; they include insect larvae, isopods, and prairie dogs. Clay soil rich in humus is usually well populated since it contains an abundance of food and is easily penetrated by burrowing. Earthworms actually eat their way through humus. Burrows in sandy soil cave in unless the walls are treated; hence fewer species live in this type of soil. Soils that are too rocky are unfit for burrowing, but many animals find the crevices between them a satisfactory hiding place.

Surface communities

Surface communities also depend largely on the character of the underlying soil, but even more so on the type of vegetation present. Thus ecologists recognize animal communities in coniferous forests and deciduous forests (Fig. 453), among shrubs and low plants, and on deserts. Many surface animals such as salamanders and slugs require moisture and hence are to be found only on wet soil or under logs and stones. Animals that move about quickly, like ground beetles, ants, rabbits, deer, and wolves, possess legs fitted for running or jumping. Representatives of some species that live in **trees** are adapted for boring, climbing, or clinging; these include boring beetles, climbing monkeys, squirrels, and clinging tree frogs with sucking disks on their toes.

Shrubs are inhabited by insects such as walkingsticks, beetles, and plant lice; by spiders, snails, and by representatives of many species of birds, including catbirds, brown thrashers, and field sparrows. Areas that are covered with **low plants,** such as

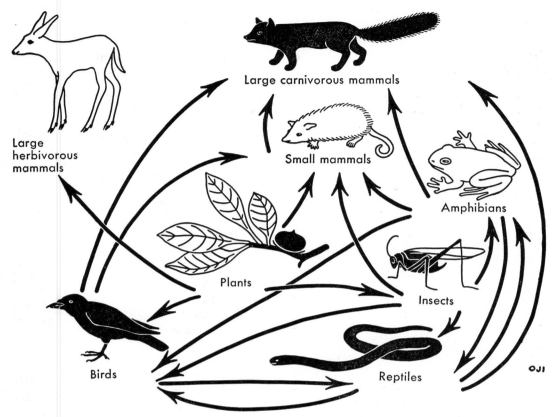

Figure 453. Food web in a forest community. Some of the possible food relationships have been omitted to simplify. The arrows point from animal or plant eaten to the animal that eats it. (Based on a diagram by James C. Braddock, Zoology Department, Michigan State University, and prepared expressly for this book.)

grasslands, are inhabited by insects, spiders, snakes, lizards, ground-nesting birds (prairie horned larks, vesper sparrows, etc.), mice, rats, antelope, bison, and many others. **Deserts** present very severe conditions, especially dryness (less than 10 inches of rainfall), high temperatures during the day and low at night, and a dearth of food plants. Ants, beetles, lizards, mice, rats, ostriches, and camels are characteristic desert inhabitants.

Aerial animals

Aerial animals may spend a large part of their time in the air, but they depend on the surface for rest and breeding purposes. The principal types of aerial inhabitants are insects, birds, and bats. Flying fish and flying reptiles, except the extinct Pterosauria, are not really aerial animals. The adaptations of flying animals are such as to provide a light rigid body, effective wings, acute vision, and in some the ability to capture food while on the wing. Thus in birds the bones are light; those of the forelimbs are modified into wings; the vertebrae of the trunk and the bones of the pelvic girdle are fused together to give rigidity; the sternum bears a large keel for attachment of the breast muscles; and the eyes are well developed and possess remarkable powers of accommodation. Birds that feed while in the air, such as chimney swifts and night hawks, have large mouths with bristles at each end that aid in capturing flying insects. Bats catch insects by means of their sharp teeth.

ZOOGEOGRAPHY

Presence and absence of species

Zoogeography is that branch of zoology which deals with the geographic distribution of animals. The available living space on the earth can be divided into 4 major habitats, namely, marine, fresh-water, terrestrial, and symbiotic, and these can be subdivided into minor habitats. But the species of animals are not exactly the same in environments of the same type in different localities; many bodies of fresh water capable of supporting certain species are free from them; each large land area usually supports a fauna that is distinct from that of every other large area; and certain species of parasites occur in human beings in one part of the world and not in others. That species are absent from a locality which is well fitted for them to live in is proved by the success of certain introduced species in this country, such as the English sparrow, starling, and gypsy moth. The principal problem involved is why a species does not occur wherever conditions are suitable.

The range

The areas occupied by different species may be small or large. Certain birds and bats, because of their remarkable powers of locomotion, are able to inhabit almost every large land area. Other species of animals may be very much restricted. Islands are especially noteworthy because of the species that occur there and nowhere else. Darwin's descriptions of the animals he found on the Galapagos Islands read like fairy tales. In many cases, the ranges of different species overlap, as shown in Fig. 454, but the range of each species, or genus, is rather definite. The size of the range is generally greater for a family than for a genus, and greater for a genus than for a species; but great differences exist in the size of the range of nearly related species. For example, the genus *Camponotus* (the carpenter ants) is found everywhere in North America (also on other continents) from the tops of the highest mountains to the lowest desert basins, from the Atlantic to the Pacific, and from the tundras of the north polar region to the tropical region along the Gulf; while another genus of ants, *SymphEidole*, has

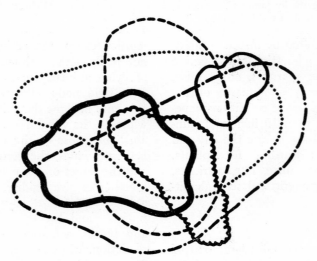

FIGURE 454. Geographic distribution of 6 different species of animals whose ranges are assumed to overlap, as indicated by the different types of lines. (After Walter.)

been found only in the Garden of the Gods in Colorado.

Continuous and discontinuous distribution

Certain species or genera are distributed continuously over an area, and this appears to be the general rule; but others are discontinuous. For example, two species of alligators are known; one lives in the southeastern United States and the other in China. Tapirs occur in tropical America and in Malaya on the other side of the world. Various physical and biological factors have been suggested to account for their present discontinuous distribution.

Changes in range

The extinction of a species in areas between present habitats seems probable, since in a number of cases fossil remains have been discovered in such areas. The study of fossil animals has shown how greatly the ranges of various groups have changed in the course of time. Dinosaurs, for example, once roamed over North America, but have disappeared not only from this continent but from the world of living creatures. The horse tribe was once native to North America, but no horses existed here when Columbus arrived. Modern horses were reintroduced by the Spaniards. Many species, such as the great auk and passenger pigeon, have become extinct within recent years, and the distributions of other species are known to have changed within historic times, or are changing now.

METHODS OF DISTRIBUTION

Dispersion

Every kind of animal produces a greater number of offspring than can be supported in its particular habitat. This **law of over-** **production** was particularly emphasized by Malthus (1766–1834) in his *Essay on Population* and led both Darwin and Wallace to formulate their **theory of natural selection** to account for organic evolution. Since parents and all their offspring cannot occupy the same area, there ensues a **struggle for existence**, as a result of which some individuals must migrate or perish. Animals tend to migrate from the region of their birth, and this normal migration accounts in a large part for the distribution of many species on the earth today. Even attached aquatic animals migrate; the larvae of sponges and the planulae of coelentrates swim about; and young clams may be carried by fish for long distances.

The range is usually enlarged by the animal invading new territory around the edges, but it is, of course, limited by its required environment; for example, a tree frog is not fitted for life on a grassy plain, and its range must end where the trees give way to grass. Certain types of migration are periodic and appear to have little influence on the breeding range; for example, the migration of birds, bison, and salmon. Sporadic migrations, such as those of the lemming and Rocky Mountain locust, usually come to naught, but they might be responsible for discontinuous distribution if the migrating hordes should encounter a new area with a satisfactory environment. The forced transportation of animals by the wind or by currents of water plays a minor role in distribution. Man has introduced many species, either purposely or accidentally, into new regions, but this has had relatively little effect on geographic distribution as a whole.

Barriers and highways

Animals are more or less confined to certain habitats by barriers; they are prevented from entering new regions by mountains or lakes, by lack of suitable food, by interfer-

ence from other animals, or by their own
physiologic makeup. Common barriers are
mountains, bodies of fresh or salt water,
open country for forest animals, and forests
for prairie-inhabiting species. The reverse of
a barrier is a highway. Apparently there are
routes of migration which are especially
favored.

LIFE REALMS

Life realms are natural regions of the
earth, distinguished by certain characteristics such as temperature, and often have no
relation to political boundaries. Wallace's
classification of the earth into 6 large regions
and each of these into 4 subregions (life

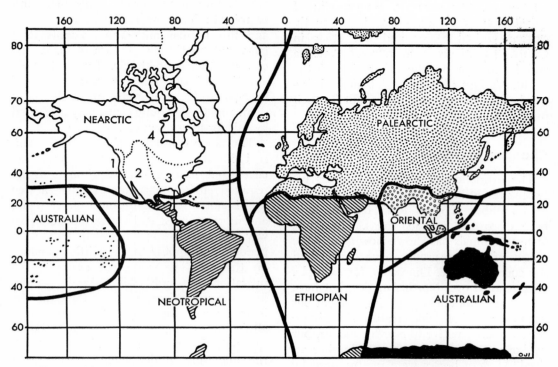

FIGURE 455. Zoogeographical regions of the world. Life realms are divided into zoological
regions and subregions. The subregions are designated by numbers for the Nearctic Realm only.

zones), as shown in Fig. 455, is the best
known. It is based on the distribution of
mammals. For example, most of North
America lies within the Nearctic Realm.
This realm is divided into 4 subregions: (1)
Californian, (2) Rocky Mountain, (3) Al-
leghenian, and (4) Canadian. The Nearctic
Realm is characterized by the presence of
certain groups of mammals and each subre-
gion by distinctive species or genera belonging to these groups. The members of each
large group of animals such as mammals,

birds, and mollusks are adapted to their own
peculiar conditions, hence life realms and
life zones must be determined for each
group, and the precise delimitation of regions for several groups together is practically impossible.

SELECTED COLLATERAL READINGS

Allee, W.C., *Cooperation Among Animals.*
Henry Schuman, New York, 1951.

————, Emerson, A.E., Park, T., Park, O., and Schmidt, K.P. *Animal Ecology*. Saunders, Philadelphia, 1949.

Buchsbaum, R. and Buchsbaum, Mildred. *Basic Ecology*. Boxwood Press, Pittsburgh, 1957.

Cott, H.B. *Adaptive Coloration in Animals*. Sidgwick and Jackson, London, 1941.

Darlington, P.J., Jr. *Zoogeography: the Geographical Distribution of Animals*. Wiley, New York, 1957.

Hesse, R., Allee, W.C., and Schmidt, K.P. *Ecological Animal Geography*. Wiley, New York, 1937.

McAtee, W.L. "Effectiveness in Nature of the So-called Protective Adaptations." *Smithsonian Misc. Collections*, Vol. 85, 1932.

Odum, E.P. *Fundamentals of Ecology*. Saunders, Philadelphia, 1953.

Sears, Paul B. *The Ecology of Man*. Science Service, Washington, 1957.

Tinbergen, N. *Social Behavior in Animals*. Methuen, London, 1953.

————. "Defense by Color." Scientific American, 197:49–54, 1957.

Weaver, J.E., and Clements, F.E. *Plant Ecology*. McGraw-Hill, New York, 1938.

CHAPTER 38

History of Zoology

THE unicorn, which decorates the heading of this chapter, is a mythical animal which illustrated early books and was used in designs for vases, tapestries, and many other articles. It is an example of the many misconceptions which man once had about animal life. Our knowledge of living things is still very limited, and this textbook attempts to give only a few of the fundamental facts and principles. Yet these facts and principles are based on the work of thousands of investigators, accumulated over a period of 2000 years or more. Of particular interest is the international character of the contributions to zoology. Beginning with the Greek scientist Aristotle, we can trace the growth of our subject through Rome, into northern Europe, and to the New World. No one nation has had a monopoly on science, and it would be difficult to select the one that has had the most influence on zoological knowledge. As a rule, certain outstanding scientists can be selected from each country to illustrate the milestones in zoological progress.

Aristotle (384–322 B.C.), a Greek scientist, was the father of natural history. He was preceded by many natural philosophers but rose above them largely because of his own personal observations and his use of the **scientific method.** Earlier philosophers tended to reach conclusions and then decided what the facts must be to agree with the adopted principle. Aristotle was a critical compiler and had a remarkable knowledge of comparative anatomy, physiology, and embryology.

Claudius Galen (about 130–200?) was one of the most famous of the Roman scientists; he was a physician who studied anatomy by means of dissection and carried out experiments on living animals. Galen's books were used in schools of medicine for many centuries, at a time when very little opportunity was afforded students for original observation.

The Middle Ages of over 1000 years following Galen's time were Dark Ages in zoological progress. People were content to rely on the work of Aristotle and other ancient philosophers which was often distorted beyond recognition. The struggle out of this distressing situation was difficult and did not succeed until the sixteenth century.

Andreas Vesalius (1514–1564) and William Harvey (1578–1657) were leaders in the revival of zoological investigation. Vesalius (Fig. 456) was a Belgian anatomist who in 1543 published a large treatise, *On the Structure of the Human Body*. This work is of particular importance since data contained in it were obtained by direct observation. To Vesalius, zoology owes the overthrow of reliance on authority.

FIGURE 456. Andreas Vesalius (1514–1564), the Belgian anatomist, who placed human anatomy on a firm basis of exact observation.

William Harvey (Fig. 457) was an English physician who published in 1628 an epoch-making monograph, *On the Motion of the Heart and Blood in Animals*. This book was a pioneering expression of the scientific method. Harvey was able to dem-

onstrate that the blood circulates through the body, being forced out of the heart and returning again to the heart. This work threw an entirely new light on the subject of physiology in general and had tremendous influence on the progress of zoology, since it transformed it into an experimental science.

FIGURE 457. William Harvey (1578–1657), the English physician, who, in 1628, was the first to demonstrate by experiment the circulation of the blood.

The discovery of the compound microscope early in the seventeenth century opened a new field for investigation and led to the remarkable work of **Robert Hooke** (1635–1703), an English scientist, to whom we owe the word cell; and to that of van Leeuwenhoek (1632–1723), a Dutch microscopist, who discovered bacteria and protozoans. Although spermatozoa were first observed by **Hamm**, another Dutchman, Leeuwenhoek studied the sperms of many animals. The microscope also enabled **Malpighi** (1628–1694), an Italian histologist, to place the subject on a firm basis. Hooke's *Micrographia* was published in 1665.

Antonj van Leeuwenhoek (Fig. 458) is known as the father of protozoology. He was born in Delft and at the age of 22 started in business as a draper. He became interested in microscopes and ground his own lenses. With his lenses he examined practically everything he could think of and made many interesting discoveries. In 1674, at the age of 42, he discovered free-living protozoans in a fresh-water pond, including what must have been *Euglena* and several species of ciliates. The same year he described parasitic protozoans, for the first time, in material obtained from the gall bladder of a rabbit. In 1681 he discovered human protozoan parasites in his own feces

and described what one can recognize as the intestinal flagellate *Giardia*. These and many other discoveries were recorded, mostly in the form of letters, to the Royal Society of London.

Leeuwenhoek's success was due to his lively curiosity, keen powers of observation, and his masterly skill in grinding lenses. He left behind him 247 complete miscroscopes and 172 mounted lenses. The best of these magnified 270 to 300 diameters. Besides free-living and parasitic protozoans, Leeuwenhoek discovered bacteria, rotifers, the cross-striations of muscle fibers, the viviparity of plant lice; and he described many other animals and plants and their structures and activities.

Marcello Malpighi (1628–1694) was the father of microscopic anatomy. Among the specimens he examined were the embryos of chicks, in which he recognized the beginnings of organs. This led him to the idea that the adult is preformed in the egg. Embryologists later discovered that the chick really develops gradually.

The **electron microscope** is one of the newer magnifying instruments. It makes magnifications up to 100,000 times possible. In this microscope, a beam of electrons is utilized, and the image may be recorded on photographic film.

Another development in microscopy is the **phase contrast microscope.** In living cells, some structures do not absorb visible light; hence they are not visible under the ordinary microscope. The phase microscope increases the contrast of these structures by optical means so that they may be observed. Therefore, phase microscopy is invaluable for the study of living cells.

Carolus Linnaeus (1707–1778), a Swedish scientist (Fig. 459), was the first great taxonomist. Contrary to popular opinion, Linnaeus did not originate our present system of scientific nomenclature, but it was formalized and universally applied by him. Instead of giving animals common names which might be used for different species in

FIGURE 458. Antonj van Leeuwenhoek (1632–1723), the Dutch microscopist who discovered Protozoa. (Courtesy of Bausch & Lomb Optical Co., Rochester, New York.)

FIGURE 459. Carolus Linnaeus (1707–1778), the Swedish biologist who made one of the great contributions to natural sciences by his studies in taxonomy.

FIGURE 460. Georges Cuvier (1769–1832), the French comparative anatomist and "father of paleontology."

different localities, he applied the binomial nomenclature, still in use, which gives for each species a concise description in Latin. He succeeded in listing 4378 different species of animals and plants. His greatest work, entitled *Systema Naturae*, was published in 1735 and passed through 12 editions, of which the tenth (1758) has been accepted as the basis for zoological nomenclature. Linnaeus believed in special creation and hence made very little progress in explaining the kinship of the different groups of animals which he named. The work of Linnaeus stimulated other naturalists to discover and name new species of animals. At first this was the only end in view, but at the present time taxonomists are mainly interested in the evolution of animals in general and especially in that of the groups which they are studying.

Cuvier and Lamarck were both at work in France at this time. **Georges Cuvier** (1769–1832) (Fig. 460) is largely responsible for establishing the science of comparative anatomy. He emphasized particularly the relation between structure and function and undertook to determine the characteristics of an animal from a very small part. For example, he said, "Give me a tooth and I will construct the whole animal." His studies involved fossils as well as living animals, and he is sometimes called the father of vertebrate paleontology.

Jean Lamarck (1744–1829) (Fig. 461) was also a paleontologist, devoting himself to the fossil remains of invertebrates, but he is best known as a student of organic evolution. Lamarck believed that environmental influences are the principal cause of evolutionary change; this concept became known as the theory of the inheritance of acquired traits.

Johannes Müller (1801–1858) of Germany, at about this time, was founding the science of comparative physiology by studying the functions of invertebrates as well as those of vertebrates, using in his work physics and chemistry, along with the methods of biology.

FIGURE 461. Jean Baptiste Lamarck (1744–1829), the French biologist who developed a theory of organic evolution based largely on the inheritance of acquired traits. Although there is no good evidence of the inheritance of acquired characters, yet nearly every generation sees a revival of it in one form or another.

Karl Ernst von Baer (1792–1876), a Russian zoologist, developed the science of comparative embryology. His investigations on the cleavage of the egg, the germ layers, and the differentiation of tissues led to the formulation of the germ-layer theory and the recapitulation theory.

Charles Darwin (1809–1882) (Fig. 462) inaugurated a new era in zoology by publication in 1859 of a book entitled *The Origin of Species by Means of Natural Selection.* Natural selection as a factor in organic evolution has already been noted. Darwin spent 20 years accumulating facts which seemed to substantiate his theory and then gave to the world a book that was overwhelming in its effects. Advances in our knowledge, especially in the field of genetics, have necessitated modifications of Darwin's ideas, but no other publication ever exerted as great an influence on biology as did his epoch-making book. Belief was prevalent at

FIGURE 462. Charles Darwin (1809–1882), the English zoologist who wrote *The Origin of Species by Means of Natural Selection.* This photograph was taken at the age of 72. He is wearing the black hat and cloak used for walks in his garden at Down House, the quiet country place near London where he lived most of his adult life. Down House is now a national memorial under the auspices of the British Association. (Courtesy of Underwood and Underwood.)

that time in the inheritance of certain types of variations that are now known not to be passed on to offspring. The modern view of how organic evolution has taken place we owe to the geneticists.

Gregor Mendel (1822–1884) (Fig. 463) initiated modern methods of studying genetics. He was a monk in an Augustinian monastery in what was then Brünn, Austria, but is now Brno, Czechoslovakia. His experiments were carried on in the cloister garden (Fig. 407). He worked principally with garden peas, from which he derived the first scientific expression of the laws of heredity. His results, which were published in 1866,

FIGURE 463. Gregor Johann Mendel (1822–1884), who discovered the fundamental laws of heredity. As a background for the portrait, Mr. Flatter, the artist, has used a scene near Brno, Czechoslovakia.

were ignored until 1900, when three independent investigators whose researches had led them to the same conclusions that Mendel had reached read his paper "Experiments in Plant Hybridization" and announced its importance to the world. Thus, although Mendel discovered the laws of heredity to which his name is now attached, modern genetics really dates from the year 1900.

Louis Pasteur (1822–1895) (Fig. 464) was a French chemist, a contemporary of Mendel, who is best known for his discoveries in the field of microbiology. By proving that only living microorganisms (yeast and bacteria) can cause fermentation, he was able to suggest a method of preventing this process by heating substances to a temperature high enough to kill these germs. This method of killing germs is now known as pasteurization. Pasteur, in 1865, saved the silk industry of France by discovering how eggs containing parasites could be distinguished from good eggs by means of a

FIGURE 464. Louis Pasteur (1822–1895), the French chemist who proved that fermentation and putrefaction resulted from microbes, and thus put an end to the controversy regarding the possibility of spontaneous generation. (Courtesy of Fisher Scientific Company.)

microscope. Diseased eggs could thus be destroyed and silkworms raised from good eggs only. This discovery has saved the world billions of dollars.

Hugo De Vries (1848–1935) (Fig. 465) was a Dutch botanist who, after 20 years of work, published a book on *The Mutation Theory*. This theory was based largely on the results of experiments with the evening primrose *Oenothera lamarckiana*. Among his plants he observed variations that bred true, which he called mutations, and other variations which were not inherited. Most of the changes observed by De Vries in the evening primrose were not gene mutations, some represented chromosomal aberrations, others polyploidy, and a considerable number were the result of unusual types of re-

FIGURE 465. Hugo De Vries (1848–1935), a Dutch botanist who formulated a mutation theory. (From Walter.)

FIGURE 466. Thomas Hunt Morgan (1866–1945), an American biologist who reported the first gene mutation (white eye) in *Drosophila*. (Picture taken in 1932. Courtesy of I.M. Morgan.)

combination. Although there may be a difference of opinion regarding De Vries' contribution to our understanding of mutations, nevertheless, he will always be remembered as the first person to publish on the rediscovery of Mendel's laws.

Thomas Hunt Morgan (1866–1945) (Fig. 466) was an American biologist, who, next to Mendel, is the most important name in the history of genetics. He published more than 200 scientific papers and 8 books. Although much of his work was in the field of experimental embryology, he is best known for his studies in genetics. He used the fruit fly, *Drosophila melanogaster*, as an experimental organism. His contributions to the mechanism of heredity won for him the Nobel prize (1933), which carries more distinction than any other scientific honor conferred by man.

H.J. Muller (1890–   ) (Fig. 467) is another American Nobel prize winner whose scientific recognition came from genetic investigations. He started his studies on the location of genes in chromosomes with Morgan. Later he turned his attention chiefly to the study of the nature and causes of mutations in the genes and chromosomes. He worked out quantitative methods of attacking these problems. He showed that

FIGURE 467. H.J. Muller (1890–   ), a Nobel prize-winning American who was first to show that mutations could be artificially induced by means of radiation. (Courtesy of H.J. Muller.)

mutations in individual genes are usually very rare, and essentially random, but that their frequency is affected by temperature, age, by the stocks used, and by other conditions, as might be expected for chemical reactions. He is famous for his discovery that X rays and related radiations are powerful agents for inducing both gene and chromosomal mutations. These studies in radiogenetics have important social implications for the atomic age.

We have mentioned famous biologists from Greece, Italy, Belgium, England, Holland, Sweden, France, Germany, Russia, Austria, and the United States, no attempt having been made to select men from different countries. As zoological knowledge increased, the subject became subdivided into the subsciences listed on page 10. The development of each of these subsciences has been studied by students of the history of science, but lack of space prevents us from including the interesting details here.

The field of zoology today is greatly expanding; although all branches of this science will probably always be important, the emphases are changing. In the early history of zoology, most of the studies were concerned with observational and descriptive phases of the science, but now experimental and quantitative methods are more widely used. Although there still remains much to be learned from researches in anatomy and taxonomy, experimental studies in physiologic aspects of zoology are receiving the most generous support from foundations which give financial support to pushing back the frontiers of this science. Zoology is becoming increasingly quantitative; that is, more and more statistical methods are being used in solving its problems. Genetics and ecology are newer branches of biological science, and the end is not in sight. The challenge for the student of zoology increases with the advances in modern technology, which create problems in radiation and outer space biology.

SELECTED COLLATERAL READINGS

Dampier, W.C. A Short History of Science. Macmillan, New York, 1944.

Gabriel, M.L., and Fogel, S. Great Experiments in Biology. Prentice-Hall, Englewood Cliffs, N.J., 1955.

Garrison, F.H. An Introduction to the History of Medicine. Saunders, Philadelphia, 1929.

Hall, T.S. Source Book in Animal Biology. McGraw-Hill, New York, 1950.

Knobloch, I.W. Readings in Biological Science. Appleton-Century-Crofts, New York, 1948.

Locy, W.A. Biology and Its Makers. Holt, New York, 1940.

Nordenskiöld, E. The History of Biology. Tudor, New York, 1946.

Peattie, D.C. Green Laurels. Simon & Schuster, New York, 1936.

Singer, Charles. A History of Biology. Abelard-Schuman, New York, 1950.

Vallery-Radot, Pasteur. Louis Pasteur. Knopf, New York, 1958.

Wightman, W.P.D. The Growth of Scientific Ideas. Yale Univ. Press, New Haven, 1951.

Glossary

This glossary is included as an aid to understanding the meaning of zoological terms; frequent reference to it will prove very helpful. It is strongly recommended that the beginning zoology student make a serious systematic study of this list of words in an effort to gain facility in the use of the vocabulary in this field.

Pronunciation is shown by the division of words into syllables by hyphens and by accent marks, both primary (″) and secondary (′).

The derivations of the terms are included to give a better understanding of their meaning and a greater competence in their use. Abbreviations used for the origins of terms are: L., Latin; Gr., Greek; Sp., Spanish; Fr., French; A.S., Anglo-Saxon; N.L., New Latin; O.F., Old French; M.E., Middle English.

Definitions of terms not included in the glossary can be found in the text; see the index for page numbers.

Ab-do′men (L., belly). The body region that contains the viscera; in mammals, limited to the part of the body extending from the diaphragm to the pelvis.

Ab-duc′tor (L. *abducere*, to lead away). A muscle that draws a part away from the median line or center.

Ab′i-o-gen″e-sis (L. *a*, not; Gr. *bios*, life; *genesis*, origin). An old idea, now discredited, that living things may arise from nonliving objects. Spontaneous generation. *See* Biogenesis.

Ab-o′ral (L. *ab*, from; *oris*, mouth). Opposite the mouth.

Ab-sorp′tion (L. *absorbere*, to suck in). The taking in of fluids or other substances by cells or tissues.

Ac-cre′tion (L. *accrescere*, to increase). The process of growth in which material is added to the outside in nonliving matter.

Ac-e-tab′u-lum (L., vinegar cup). The cup-shaped socket of the hip into which the femur fits.

Ac′e-tyl-cho″line. A substance liberated at or near nerve endings. It may be involved in conduction across synapses and is known to be associated with many parasympathetic nerves.

Ac-quired′ char′ac-ter. A modification of the body that occurs during the life of an individual as a result of environmental conditions.

Ac′ro-meg′′a-ly (Gr. *akron*, extremity; *megas*, great). A disease caused by the oversecretion of the anterior pituitary after the bones have reached full growth. It is characterized by an overgrowth of the mandible, phalangeal cartilages, and other areas.

A-cro′mi-on (Gr. *akros*, summit; *amos*, shoulder). Pertaining to the prolongation of the spine of the scapula, forming the point of the shoulder.

Ad-ap-ta′tion (L. *ad*, to; *aptare*, to fit). Fitness for the environment. Fitness may result from an adaptive structive, physiology, or behavior. The process by which the organism becomes fitted to its environment.

A-dap′tive con-ver′gence (L. *ad*, to; *aptare*, to fit. L. *convergo*, incline). The presence within a series of comparable ecologic niches of only distantly related forms which superficially resemble one another in morphologic and other characters, correlated with very similar or identical environmental conditions.

A-dap′tive ra′di-a′′tion (L. *ad*, to; *aptare*, to fit. L. *radius*, ray). The evolution and spread of a single line of descent of organisms into several ecologic niches, resulting in a series, sometimes of strikingly different forms, each adapted to a particular habitat.

Ad-duc′tor (L. *ad*, to; *ducere*, to lead). A muscle which draws a structure toward the median line.

Ad′i-pose (L. *adipo*, fat). Pertaining to fat.

Ad-re′nal gland (L. *ad*, to; *renes*, kidneys. L. *glans*, acorn). A gland of internal secretion situated on or near the kidney. Actually it is two glands combined—the adrenal medulla and adrenal cortex, producing different hormones.

Ad-re′nal-in. A hormone secreted by the medulla of the adrenal glands.

A-e′ri-al (Gr. *aerios*, from air). Inhabiting or frequenting the air.

Af′fer-ent (L. *afferre*, to bring). Carrying to or toward a certain region. Example: the afferent branchial arteries of the amphioxus and the dogfish shark carry blood to the gills. Opposite of efferent.

Al′bi-nism (L. *albus*, white). A condition in which the normal pigment is lacking, such as in the skin, hair, and eyes. Albinism in the rat and in man is a typical Mendelian recessive character.

Al-bi′no (L. *albus*, white). An individual, such as the white rat, lacking normal pigmentation.

Al-bu′men (L. *albumen*, white of egg). The white portion of the reptile's and bird's egg, surrounding the yolk or zygote, and supplying food for the embryo.

Al-i-men′tary (L. *alimentum*, from *alere*, to nourish). Pertaining to digestion or the digestive tract.

Al-lan′to-is (Gr. *allas*, sausage; *eidos*, form). An extraembryonic membrane arising as an outgrowth of the cloaca in mammals, birds, and reptiles.

Al-lele′ (Gr. *allelon*, of one another). One of a pair, or any one of a series of alternate genes having the same locus in homologous chromosomes; for example, the gene responsible for the development of freckles is an allele of the alternative gene for the absence of freckles.

Al-le′lo-morph. *See* Allele.

Al-ter-na′tion of gen-er-a′tions. The alternate succession of sexual and asexual generations in the life cycle of an organism. *See* Metagenesis.

Al-ve′o-lus (L. *alveus*, pit). A small cavity, such as the tiny air sacs in the mammalian lung; the secreting portion of an alveolar gland or the socket of a tooth.

Am-bu-la′cral grooves (L. *ambulare*, to walk. Dutch *groeve*, groove). Grooves in the starfish's arms containing rows of openings through which the tube feet of the starfish are extended. Also true of other echinoderms.

A-mi′no ac′id (From amine). A simple organic compound containing an amino group (NH₂) and at least one acid group (COOH); proteins are built from amino acids.

Am′i-to′′sis (Gr. *a*, without; *mitos*, thread). Direct nuclear division in which the nucleus constricts and separates into two portions. While the cell is in the interphase stage, no condensed chromosomes, asters, or spindle fibers are formed.

Am'ni-on (Gr. *amnos*, lamb). The innermost membrane which encloses the embryo in reptiles, birds, and mammals.

Am'ni-o''ta (N.L. *amniotes*). A group of vertebrates—reptiles, birds, and mammals—that develop an amnion and an allantois.

A-moe'boid (Gr. *amoebe*, change). Pertaining to cell movements resembling those of the amoeba.

Am''phi-as'ter (Gr. *amphi*, both sides of; *aster*, star). The figures produced in the cytoplasm by the two asters and the spindle in the dividing of a nucleus by mitosis.

Am-phib'i-a (Gr. *amphi*, of both kinds; *bios*, life). A class of vertebrates that hatch as gill-breathing larvae and usually metamorphose into lung-breathing adults. The frog, toad, and salamander are examples of the class.

Am-phib'i-ous (Gr. *amphi*, both; *bios*, life). Pertaining to animals capable of living either in water or on land, such as a toad.

Am'phi-coe''lous (Gr. *amphi*, both; *koilos*, hollow). A structure that is concave at both ends; applied to some vertebrae.

Am-pul'la (L. diminutive of *amphora*, jar). A small bladder-shaped enlargement. Water sacs attached to the tube feet of echinoderms.

Am'y-lop''sin (L. *amyl*, starch; Gr. *trypsin*, to wear down). A pancreatic amylase. An enzyme produced by the pancreas, which acts on carbohydrates.

An-ab'o-lism (Gr. *ana*, up; *bole*, stroke). The constructive phase of metabolism in which the cells build protoplasm from food mateials.

A-nal'o-gous (Gr. *ana*, up; *logos*, ratio, proportion). Parts similar in function, but not necessarily alike in their genetic relationship.

An-am'ni-o''ta (Gr. *a*, not; *amnion*, inner membrane around the fetus). A group of vertebrates having no amnion. It includes cyclostomes, fishes, and amphibia.

An'a-phase (Gr. *ana*, up; *phasis*, appearance, aspect). The stage in mitosis when chromosomes move from the equatorial plate to the opposite ends of the mitotic spindle.

A-nas'to-mo''sis (Gr. *ana*, up, back; *stoma*, mouth). A union or joining together, as of two or more blood vessels, nerves, or other structures.

A-nat'o-my (Gr. *ana*, up; *temnien*, to cut). The study of the structure of animals and plants.

An'i-mal hem'i-sphere (L. *animalis*, from *anima*, life. Gr. *hemi*, half; *sphaira*, sphere). That part of the egg composed of active animal cells.

An'ky-lo''sis (Gr. *ankylos*, crooked). A union or knitting together of two or more bones, or parts of bones.

An-nel'i-da (L. *annulus*, ring; Gr. *eidos*, form). The phylum to which the segmented worms such as the earthworms belong.

An-ten'na (L., a sail yard). A movable sense organ on the head of insects, myriapods, and crustaceans. Insects and myriapods have one pair each, crustaceans often two pairs each.

An-ten'nules (L. diminutive of *antenna*). Many-jointed feelers found on some arthropods and located near the antennae; sometimes called the first antennae.

An-te'ri-or (L., foremost). Pertaining to the front or head end of an animal.

An'trum (L., *antrum*, cavity). A cavity or chamber, referring especially to one within a bone.

A'nus (L., ring). The posterior opening of the digestive tract.

A-or'ta (Gr. *aorte*, the great artery). A large artery which leaves the heart.

Ap'er-ture (L. *aperire*, to uncover). An orifice or opening.

Ap'i-cal (L. *apex*, summit). Referring to the end or outermost part, as of a conical structure.

Ap'o-neu-ro''sis (Gr. *apo*, from; *neuron*, sinew). A broad fibrous sheet of tissue or fascia attaching a muscle.

Ap'o-pyle (Gr. *apo*, away; *pyle*, gate). A pore leading from the chambers into the central cavity (spongocoel) in sponges.

Ap-pend'age (L. *ad*, to; *pendere*, to hang). A portion of the body which projects and has a free end, such as limbs.

Ap'pen-dic''u-lar skel'e-ton (L. *ad*, to; *pendere*, to hang. Gr. *skeletos*, hard). That part of a vertebrate which consists of the limbs and limb girdles.

Ap-pen'dix (L. *ad*, to; *pendere*, to hang). *See* vermiform appendix.

Ap'ter-ous (Gr. *a*, without; *pteron*, wing). Wingless.

A-quat'ic (L. *aquaticus*, living in water). Of or pertaining to water. Living in water.

Aq'ue-duct (L. *aqua*, water; *ducere*, to lead). A canal or channel for conduction of a fluid; used especially for specialized lymph passages in the brain, not for lymphatics in general nor for blood vessels.

A-rach'noid (Gr. *arachnes*, spider; *eidos*, form). The arachnoid membrane; the central of the three meninges covering the vertebrate brain and spinal cord. It is very fine and delicate.

Ar-bo're-al (L. *arbor*, tree). Pertaining to trees, as tree-living.

Ar-chen'ter-on (Gr. *arche*, beginning; *enteron*, gut). The primitive digestive tract of a metazoan embryo, formed during gastrulation.

Ar'ter-y (L. *arteria*, windpipe, artery). A blood vessel which carries blood away from the heart.

Ar'thro-pod (Gr. *arthron*, joint; *pous*, foot). An invertebrate animal with jointed appendages, like crayfish, insects, etc.

Ar-tic'u-la-tion (L. *articulus*, joint). A joint as between two segments or structures.

Ar'ti-fi''cial clas'si-fi-ca''tion (L. *ars, artis*, art; *facio*, make. L. *classis*, division). Classification based on characters of convenience without relation to evolutionary (phylogenetic) significance.

Ar'y-te''noid (Gr. *arytaina*, pitcher). Pertaining to a pair of laryngeal cartilages that lie posterior to the thyroid cartilage.

A-sex'u-al re-pro-duc'tion (L. *a*, not; *sexus*, sex. L. *re*, again; *productio*, production). Reproduction not involving gametes (sperms or eggs).

As-sim'i-la'tion (L. *ad*, to; *similis*, like). The changing of digested foods and other materials into protoplasm.

As'ter (Gr., star). A starlike figure formed during mitosis and composed of the centrosome and the lines radiating from it.

A-sym'me-try (Gr. *a*, without; *syn*, with; *metron*, measure). The condition in which opposite sides of an animal are not alike; without symmetry.

At'a-vism (L. *atavus*, ancestor). Resemblance to a remote ancestor.

At'las (Gr., giant). The first cervical vertebra; the first vertebra upon which the skull rests.

At'oll (Maldiv'ian, *atolu*). A horseshoe or ring-shaped island or islands consisting of a belt of coral reef surrounding a central lagoon.

A'tri-al cav'i-ty (L. *atrium*, central room. L. *cavus*, hollow). A cavity in protochordates and some caudate larvae (e.g., tunicates, amphioxus, frog tadpoles) through which water passes after moving out of the gill slits.

A'tri-o-pore (L. *atrium*, central room; *porus*, channel). The exterior opening from the atrial cavity in the amphioxus.

A'tri-um (L. *atrium*, chamber). A chamber or cavity; the term may refer to the atrium of the heart or to the specialized outer cavity of the amphioxus.

At'ro-phy (Gr. *a*, not; *trephein*, to nourish). A wasting away or withering of the body, or of any of its parts.

Au'di-to-ry (L. *audire*, to hear). Pertaining to the organ or sense of hearing, as the eighth cranial nerve.

Au-to-nom'ic (Gr. *autos*, self; *nomos*, law). independent; self-governing.

Au-to-nom'ic nerv'ous sys'tem (Gr. *autos*, self; *nomos*, law. L. *nervosus*, sinewy, vigorous. Gr. *systema*, a placing together). A system of ganglia and nerves controlling the involuntary actions of the body; the action of the ductless glands, viscera, blood vessels, and all organs containing involuntary muscle, and communicating with the central nervous system by way of the roots of the spinal and cranial nerves.

Au'to-some (Gr. *autos*, self; *soma*, body). Any chromosome except a sex chromosome.

Au-tot'o-my (Gr. *autos*, self; *tome*, cutting). Self-mutilation; the automatic "voluntary" breaking off of a part of the body of an animal.

Ax'i-al gra'di-ent (L. *axis*, axle. L. *gradus*, step). Gradation of the rate of metabolism along the length of a principal axis of an animal.

Ax'i-al skel'e-ton. That part of the vertebrate skeleton which consists of the skull, vertebrae, sternum, and ribs.

Ax'is (L. *axis*, axle). The second cervical vertebra. A line such as the anteroposterior axis of the body, around which parts are symmetrically arranged.

Ax'is cyl'in-der (L., axle. Gr. *kylindros*, from

kylindein, to roll). The rodlike central portion of a medullated nerve fiber.

Ax'o-lotl (Sp. *axolotl,* servant of water). A pedogenic larvae of any of several species of salamander of the genus Ambystoma found in Mexico and the southwestern part of the United States. Originally applied to a Mexican species only; now, by extension, to others.

Ax'on (Gr. *axon,* axle). The fiber of a nerve cell that conducts impulses away from the cell body of which it is a part.

Az'y-gos (Gr. *a,* without; *zygon,* yoke). An unpaired anatomic structure such as the azygos vein of mammals.

Back'bone. The vertebral column, especially if composed of bone.

Back'cross. The mating of a hybrid to either of its parents.

Bar'ri-er (F. *barre,* bar). Any type of obstruction—physical, chemical, or biological—that prevents the migration of animals, or gradual extension of their territories.

Be-hav'ior. The reactions of the whole organism to its environment.

Ben'e-dict's so-lu'tion (After Benedict. L. *solutio,* from *solvere,* to dissolve). An alkaline copper sulfate solution, blue in color. If a few drops of a reducing sugar solution are added after heating the copper solution, the cupric copper is reduced to the cuprous state, and a change to a reddish color is noted. Used as a test for the presence of sugars in solution.

Ben'thos (Gr. *benthos,* depth of the sea). Those organisms living on or in the bottom, either of the ocean or fresh waters, from the edge of water down to the greatest depths.

Bi-lat'er-al sym'me-try (L. *bis,* twice; *latus,* side. Gr. *syn,* with; *metron,* measure). The arrangement of the parts of an organism in such a way that the right and left halves of the body are mirror images of each other.

Bile (L. *bilis,* bile). A fluid which is secreted by the liver in vertebrates.

Bile duct (L. *ducere,* to lead). The duct which transports bile from the gall bladder to the small intestine.

Bi'na-ry fis'sion (L. *bis,* twice. L. *fissus,* cleft). That type of asexual reproduction by means of which an organism divides into two approximately equal parts.

Bi-no'mi-al (L. *bis,* twice; *nomen,* name). Having two names; in nomenclature the first is known as the generic and the second as the specific name.

Bi-o-gen'e-sis (Gr. *bios,* life; *genesis,* birth). The doctrine that living things are produced only from living things—the opposite of abiogenesis.

Bi'o-ge-net''ic law (Gr. *bios,* life; *genesis,* production). The principle that an animal may repeat in its embryonic development some of the corresponding stages of its ancestors; also known as the recapitulation theory.

Bi-ol'o-gy (Gr. *bios,* life; *logos,* discourse). The science of life; it includes botany, zoology, and all the fields of study associated with life.

Bi'o-lu''mi-nes''cence (Gr. *bios,* life; L. *lumen,* light). The production of light as the result of chemical reactions in living organisms.

Bi-ra'di-al sym'metry (L. *bis,* having two; *radius,* ray). The condition in which an animal has radially arranged parts that lie half on one side and half on the other side of a median longitudinal plane; example, the Ctenophora.

Bi-ra'mous ap-pend'age (L. *bis,* having two; *ramus,* branch). A two-branched structure.

Blast (Gr. *blasteo,* to sprout). A combining form inferring formation or development.

Blas'to-coel (Gr. *blastos,* bud; *koilos,* hollow). The cavity present within the blastula.

Blas'to-mere (Gr. *blastos,* bud; *meros,* part). A cleavage cell; any one of the cells in an embryo from the first cleavage division to the beginning of gastrulation.

Blas'to-pore (Gr. *blastos,* bud; *poros,* passage). The porelike opening from the archenteron or gastrula cavity to the exterior.

Blas'tu-la (Gr. *blastos,* bud). An early developmental stage of an embryo, usually a hollow ball of cells.

Bow'man's cap'sule (After Sir Wm. Bowman, English physician. L. *capsula,* little box). The cup-shaped end of a kidney tubule that forms around a glomerulus.

Bra'chi-al (L. *brachium,* arm). Belonging or pertaining to the upper part of the forelimb of a vertebrate.

Bran'chi-a (Gr. *branchia,* gills). Gills.

Bran'chi-os''te-gite (Gr. *branchia*, gills; *tege*, roof). The portion of the exoskeleton that covers the gills in higher crustaceans (e.g., crayfish).

Bron'chus (Gr. *bronchos*, windpipe). Either one of the two main branches of the trachea of a lung-breathing vertebrate.

Buc'cal (L. *bucca*, cheek or mouth cavity). Pertaining to the mouth or oral cavity.

Bud (Gr. *beutie*, bag). The developing lateral branch of an organism such as the hydra; term usually used for a young organism produced by budding.

Bud'ding. The production of offspring by the development of a lateral branch from a part of the body.

Bul'bus ar-te'ri-o''sus (L. *bulbus*, akin to. Gr. *arterio*, artery). The enlarged bulblike base of the ventral aorta found chiefly in the bony fishes.

Bul'la (L. *bulla*, water bubble). A hollow bony growth such as the tympanic bulla.

Bur'sa (L. *bursa*, purse). A pouch or saclike structure such as the bursa of a joint.

Cal-ca're-ous (L. *calcarius*, limestone, limy). Chalky; composed of or containing calcium carbonate ($CaCo_3$) or other carbonates.

Cal-cif'er-ous glands (L. *calx*, lime; *ferre*, to carry). Structures that lie at the sides of the esophagus of some annelids (e.g., earthworms).

Cap'il-la-ry (L. *capillaris*, from *capillus*, hair). One of the many minute branches of blood vessels that carry blood directly to the tissues of the body in many animals.

Car'bo-hy''drate (L. *carbo*, coal; Gr. *hydor*, water). An organic compound, such as sugar or starch, composed of carbon, hydrogen, and oxygen, the last two in the same proportion as in water (H_2O).

Car'di-ac (Gr. *kardia*, heart). Pertaining to the heart.

Car-niv'o-rous (L. *caro*, flesh; *vorare*, to devour). Eating or living on other animals.

Ca-rot'id (Gr. *karos*, heavy sleep; from the belief that the carotid arteries cause drowsiness). The principal artery leading to the head.

Car'pals (L. *carpus*, wrist). The bones of the wrist.

Caste (L. *castus*, pure). Any one of the types belonging to any single species of social insects.

Ca-tab'o-lism or ka-tab'o-lism (Gr. *kata*, down; *ballein*, to throw). The breaking down or destructive phase of metabolism; the metabolic processes in which chemical breakdown occurs, for example, respiration.

Cau'dal (L. *cauda*, tail). Pertaining to the tail or the posterior part of the body.

Ce'cum (L. *caecus*, blind gut). A blind pouch of the intestine in vertebrates, or similar pouches elsewhere.

Cell (L. *cella*, compartment). A small mass or unit of protoplasm surrounded by a cell membrane and containing one or more nuclei.

Cel'lu-lar (L. *cellula*, little cell). Pertaining to or consisting of cells.

Cen'tral nerv'ous sys'tem. The brain and the cord, including the dorsal root ganglion. Abbreviated C.N.S.

Cen-tro-mere' (kinetochore) (Gr. *kentron*, center; Gr. *meros*, part). A point where the spindle fiber is attached; this is a constricted region of the chromosome and is not colored by the usual chromosomal stains.

Cen'tro-some (Gr. *kentron* center; *soma*, body). A small differentiated area of a cell containing the centriole.

Cen'trum (L., center). The ventral body portion of a vertebra from which spring the spinous and transverse processes.

Ce-phal'ic (Gr. *kephale*, head). Pertaining to or situated near the head.

Ceph'a-li-za''tion. The tendency toward the centralization of important parts, as the sense organs, in the head or in the head region.

Ceph'a-lo-tho''rax (Gr. *kephale*, head; *thorax*, breast). The body division formed by the fusion of the head and thorax in some arthropods.

Cer'e-bel'lum (L. diminutive of *cerebrum*, brain). The division second from the most posterior part of the brain; it is associated with muscular coordination in the higher vertebrates.

Cer'e-bral aq'ue-duct (L. *cerebrum*, brain. L. *aquaductus*, from *aqua*, water; *ductus*, canal). The canal between the third and fourth ventricles of a vertebrate brain.

Cer′e-brum (L., *cerebrum*, brain). The large, lobed, anterior part of the brain, which in man makes possible thought, memory, and the like.

Cer′vi-cal (L. *cervix*, neck). Pertaining to the neck region.

Cer′vix (L. *cervix*, a neck). A necklike structure, as the uterine cervix of a typical mammal.

Char′ac-ter (Gr. from *charassein*, to engrave). A distinguishing structure or function; any trait of an organism.

Che-lic′er-a (Gr. *chele*, claw; *keras*, horn). The anterior pair of appendages in spiders and related forms.

Che′li-ped (Gr. *chele*, claw; L. *pes*, foot). A crustacean appendage having a pincerlike claw distally, such as the first and second walking legs of a crayfish.

Che-mot′ro-pism (Gr. *chemos*, juice; *trope*, turning). The behavior response of an organism to chemical stimulation.

Chi-as′ma (Gr. *chiazein*, to mark with a cross). Usually pertaining to the optic chiasma, the region in whch the optic nerves from the retina of the eye cross in vertebrates.

Chi′tin (Gr. *chiton*, a kind of garment, tunic). A complex organic substance occurring in the exoskeleton of arthropods and some other animals.

Chlo′ro-phyl (Gr. *chloros*, green; *phyelon*, leaf). Green pigments in plants, and possibly certain animals, that are essential for photosynthesis.

Chlo′ro-plast (Gr. *chloros*, green; *plastos*, molded). A chromatophore containing chlorophyl.

Cho′a-no-cyte (Gr. *choane*, funnel; *kytos*, hollow). Flagellated collar cells found in sponges.

Chon′dri-o-some (Gr. *chondrion*; Gr. *soma*, body). *See* Mitochondria.

Chon′dro-cra″ni-um (Gr. *chondros*, grain; *kranion*, skull). A cartilaginous skull, as found in sharks.

Chor′date (Gr. *chord*, string). Pertaining to the phylum Chordata. Animals having (1) a notochord present some time in their life history, (2) a dorsally located tubular nervous system, and (3) gill slits present at some time in their life history.

Chro′ma-tid (Gr. *chroma*, color). Either one of the two identical halves into which a chromosome appears to split longitudinally in cell division; actually each chromosome duplicates another copy next to itself.

Chro′ma-tin (Gr. *chroma*, color; L. *affinis*, affinity for). The stainable protoplasmic substance in the nucleus of a cell which gives rise to the conspicuous chromosomes during mitosis.

Chro″ma-to-phore′ (Gr. *chroma*, color; *pherein*, to bear). A specialized pigment-bearing body or cell, such as that found in the frog's skin, and responsible for color markings on many animals.

Chro-mo-nem′a (Gr. *chroma*, color; Gr. *nema*, thread). A slender thread of chromatin, distinguishable within the chromosome during mitosis and, in some cases, in the nucleus between periods of division. Plural, chromonemata.

Chro′mo-some (Gr. *chroma*, color; *soma*, body). Deeply staining body visible under the microscope in the cell nucleus. Chromosomes consist essentially of genes (determiners of heredity) arranged in linear order.

Cil′i-a (L. *cilium*, eyelid). Microscopic, hairlike, protoplasmic processes projecting from the free surface of certain cells and capable of vibration.

Cir′ri (L. *cirrus*, curl, ringlet, lock). Small, slender projections or appendages appearing almost like tentacles except for their position.

Cis-ter′na Mag′na (L. *cisterna*, box. L. *magna*, great). The cavity dorsal to the coelom of vertebrates in which the kidneys are located.

Class (L. *classis*, collection). A main subdivision of a phylum.

Clav′i-cle (L. *clavis*, key). The collarbone in man or its homologue in other vertebrates.

Cleav′age (A.S. *cleofan*, to cut). The series of early divisions of an egg into many cells.

Cleav′age cav′i-ty (A.S. *cleofan*, to cut. L. *cavus*, hollow). A blastocoel.

Cli-tel′lum (L. *clitellae*, packsaddle). A thickened glandular portion of the body of an earthworm or other annelid, used in the formation of the cocoon.

Clo-a′ca (L. *cloaca*, a sewer). The common passageway or cavity at the posterior end of the body into which the intestine, kidneys, and genital organs discharge their products. This is found in fishes, amphibians, reptiles, and birds and may also appear in embryonic stages of mammals. Also found in some invertebrates, as in many insects.

Clone (Gr. *klon*, twig). The offspring produced by asexual reproduction of a single animal.

Cni'do-blast (Gr. *knide*, nettle; *blastos*, bud). A type of cell in which the nematocyst is found.

Cni'do-cil (Gr. *knide*, nettle; L. *cilium*, eyelid). A hairlike process projecting from the outer margin of the cnidoblast.

Co-coon' (Fr. *cocon*, shell). A silken protective case about a mass of eggs, a larva, a pupa, or an adult animal.

Coe'lom (Gr. *koilis*, hollow). A body cavity lined with tissue of mesodermal origin.

Coe'no-sarc (Gr. *koinos*, common; *sarx*, flesh). The inner, cellular part of a hydroid as distinguished from the outer surrounding perisarc.

Co-en'zyme (L. *cum*, with; Gr. *en zume*, leaven). A substance associated with and activating an enzyme.

Cold'-blood'ed. Poikilothermic; without ability to regulate the body temperature by physiologic means; commonly said of fish, reptiles, and amphibians whose temperatures approximate that of the environment.

Col'loid (Gr. *kolla*, glue; *eidos*, form). A state of matter in which particles larger than single molecules are distributed throughout a medium such as a liquid, gas, or solid and which is called the dispersion medium.

Co'lon (Gr. *kolon*, colon). The anterior portion of the large intestine of a vertebrate.

Col'o-ny (L. *colonia* from *colere*, to cultivate). A group of individuals, unicellular or multicellular, of the same species, which have developed from a common parent and remain organically attached or held together; also used for insect societies. Opposite of solitary.

Com-men'sal-ism (L. *com*, together; *mensa*, table). An association of individuals of two different species in which at least one is benefited, and the other is neither benefited nor harmed.

Com'mis-sure (L. *cum*, together; *mittere*, to send). A group of connective nerve fibers uniting two like structures in the two sides of the brain or spinal cord; or similar cords connecting nerve centers elsewhere.

Com-mu'ni-ty (L. *communitas*, from *communis*, common). A more or less complex group of plants or animals that occupy a particular area.

Con'ju-ga''tion (L. *cum*, together; *jungere*, to join, marry). A method of reproduction in which two unicellular animals unite, exchange nuclear material, and then divide, as in the paramecium.

Con'junc-ti''va (L. *cum*, together; *jungere*, to join). A continuation of the mucous membrane over the cornea of the eye, connecting the cornea with the outer covering of the eyelid.

Con-trac'tile vac'u-ole (L. *cum*, together; *trahere*, to draw. L. *vacuus*, empty). A structure within the cytoplasm of certain protozoan cells in which liquids collect before they are periodically expelled to the outside.

Co'nus ar-te'ri-o''sus (L., cone. Gr. *arterio*, artery). The expanded cone-shaped structure of the right ventricle which empties into the aorta.

Con-ver'gence (L. *convergere*, to turn). Morphologic similarity in distantly related forms.

Cop'u-la''tion (L. *copulare*, to couple). Sexual union of two individuals involving the transference of sperms from the male to the female body.

Cor'a-coid (Gr. *korax*, crow; *eidos*, form). One of the bones of the pectoral girdle of many vertebrates, especially land forms in vertebrates.

Co'ri-um (L. *corium*, leather). The inner dermal portion of the skin.

Cor'ne-a (L. *cornu*, horn). The outer, very transparent, layer of the eye.

Cor'tex (L. *cortex*, bark). Outer portion of a structure.

Cos'tal car'ti-lage (L. *costa*, rib; *cartilago*, cartilage). The cartilages that attach the ribs to the sternum in a vertebrate.

Cox-op'o-dite (L. *coxa*, hip; Gr. *pous*, foot). That part of an arthropod appendage which lies next to the body.

Cra'ni-um (Gr. *kranion*, head). That part of the vertebrate skull which encloses the brain; the brain case.

Crop (A.S. *crop* or *cropp*, top bunch). An expanded portion of the anterior part of a digestive tract specialized for storage.

Cross–fer'ti-li-za''tion. The fertilization of an egg produced by one individual, with a sperm produced by another individual. Opposite of self-fertilization.

Cross'ing o'ver. The process in which homologous chromosomes break and exchange corresponding segments.

Cu-ta'ne-ous (L. *cutis*, skin). Pertaining to the skin.

Cu'ti-cle (L. *cutis*, skin). A thin, noncellular, outermost covering of an organism.

Cy-clo'sis (Gr. *kyklosis*, whirling round). The rotary streaming movement of the protoplasm in certain cells.

Cyst (Gr. *kystis*, a bladder). An organism enclosed in a thickened resistant wall; a sac or bladderlike structure.

Cy-tol'o-gy (Gr. *kytos*, hollow; *logos*, discourse). The science which deals with the structure of cells.

Cy'to-phar''ynx (Gr. *kytos*, hollow; *pharynx*, gullet). The pharynx or gullet of a protozoan such as Paramecium.

Cy'to-plasm (Gr. *kytos*, hollow; *plasma*, something molded). The protoplasm of a cell exclusive of the nucleus.

Dac'tyl (Gr. *daktylos*, finger). Referring to the finger or toe.

Dar'win-ism. Darwin's theory that species have originated by natural selection.

Daugh'ter cells. The two cells that have been formed by the division of one cell.

Def-e-ca'tion (L. *de*, from; *faecis*, dregs). The passage of waste material from the digestive tract of an animal.

Den'drite (Gr. *dendron*, tree). A fiber of a nerve cell that conducts impulses toward the nerve cell body.

Den'ta-ry (L. *dens*, tooth). The upper bone of the lower jaw of a vertebrate.

Der'mal (Gr. *derma*, skin). Pertaining to the skin, especially the inner connective tissue layers of the vertebrate skin.

Der'mis (Gr. *derma*, skin). The inner layer of the skin, lying below the epidermis. The term is synonymous with corium.

Di-al'y-sis (L. *dialysis*, separation). The separation of crystalloids and colloids in solution by means of their unequal diffusion through certain natural or artificial membranes.

Di'a-phragm (Gr. *diaphragma*, midriff). A sheetlike muscle forming a partition between the thoracic and abdominal cavities in mammals. A dividing membrane.

Di-en-ceph'a-lon (Gr. *dia*, between; *engkephalon*, brain). A region of the vertebrate brain just posterior to the cerebrum in the adult. In the embryo, the second of two divisions of the prosencephalon.

Dif'fer-en'ti-a''tion (L. *differre*, to carry apart). The process whereby cells and tissues become specialized for specific functions during the process of development and growth.

Dif-fu'sion (L. *diffundere*, to pour). The movement of molecules from a region of high concentration to one of lower concentration brought about as a consequence of their kinetic energy.

Di-ges'tion (L. *digestio*, digestion). The conversion of complex, unabsorbable food material into soluble forms that may be absorbed.

Dig'it (L. *digitus*, finger). A finger or toe.

Dig''i-ti-grade' (L. *digitus*, finger, toe; *gradi*, to walk). Walking on the toes.

Di-hy'brid (Gr. *dis*, twice; L. *hibrida*, mixed offspring). The progeny or offspring of parents that differ in 2 traits (characters); an individual which is hybrid (heterozygous) with respect to 2 pairs of genes.

Di-mor'phism (Gr. *dis*, twice; *morphe*, shape). Difference in size, structure, form, color, etc., between 2 types of individuals of the same species.

Di-oe'cious (Gr. *dis*, twice; *oikos*, house). Having the male and female reproductive organs in separate individuals.

Dip'lo-blas'tic (Gr. *diploos*, double; *blastos*, bud). Derived from 2 embryonic germ layers, ectoderm and endoderm.

Dip'loid (Gr. *diploos*, double). Referring to the number of chromosomes in somatic cells; double the number of chromosomes that occur in the mature egg or sperm.

Dis-sim'i-la''tion. The disintegration of protoplasm principally by oxidation.

Dis'tal (L. *dis*, apart; *stare*, to stand). Away from the point of attachment; for example, the hand is the distal part of the arm. Opposite of proximal.

Di-ur'nal (L. *dies*, day). Pertaining to the time of daylight. It is opposed to nocturnal, which pertains to the time of night.

Di'ver-tic'u-lum (L. *de*, away; *vertere*, to turn). A saclike projection of a tubular organ.

Dom'i-nant trait (char'ac-ter) (L. *dominus*, master). A trait which appears as the result of either a single or a double "dose" of a particular gene, as contrasted with the recessive trait, which develops only when both members of a pair of allelic genes are alike. We also speak of dominant and recessive genes.

Dor'sal (L. *dorsum*, back). Pertaining to the back; opposed to ventral in a bilaterally symmetrical animal.

Duct (L. *ducere*, to lead). A tube other than a lympathic or blood vessel, through which a liquid or other product of metabolism is carried.

Duct'less gland. Any gland that secretes a substance (hormone) directly into the blood or lymph stream, or both, instead of into a duct; an endocrine gland.

Du'o-de''num (L. *duodeni*, 12 each). The first part of the small intestine posterior to the stomach. It is so named because its length is approximately 12 fingers' breadth.

Du'ra ma'ter (L. *dura*, hard; L. *mater*, mother). The outermost membrane covering the brain and the spinal cord.

Ec'dy-sis (Gr. *ek*, out; *dyein*, to enter). Molting; the shedding of the outer cuticular covering (skin) of an arthropod.

E-col'o-gy (Gr. *oikos*, house; *logos*, discourse). The science of the interrelationships of organisms in and to their environment.

Ec'to-com-men''sal (Gr. *ektos*, outside; L. *com*, together; *mensa*, table). Pertaining to an organism that lives on the external surface of another organism, the host, without either benefiting or injuring it.

Ec'to-derm (Gr. *ektos*, outside; *derma*, skin). The outer layer of cells in the gastrula. This layer gives rise to the epidermis, sense organs, and nervous system.

Ec'to-par''a-site (Gr. *ektos*, outside; *para*, beside; *sitos*, food). A parasite that lives on the outside of the body of its host.

Ec'to-plasm (Gr. *ektos*, outside; *plasma*, something molded). The layer of cytoplasm nearest the surface of a cell; the protoplasm of the ectosarc.

Ec'to-sarc (Gr. *ektos*, outside; *sarx*, flesh). The structure in a protozoan composed of ectoplasm.

Ef-fect'or (L. *effectus*, to effect). Any part of the body, such as a muscle or gland, transforming motor impulses into motor action.

Ef'fer-ent (L. *efferre*, to carry out). Conveying outward or away from a structure. Opposite of afferent.

Egg (Probably L. *avis*, bird). The nonmotile gamete developed by the female.

E-jac''u-la-to'ry duct (L. *e*, out; *jactare*, to throw). The duct conveying semen to the urethra; especially in mammals.

E-lec'tro-en-ceph''a-lo-gram' (Gr. *elektron*; Gr. *egkephalos*, brain; Gr. *gramma*, letter). A graphic record of the variations in the electric potential of a brain.

E-lec'tron (Gr.). A particle of matter within an atom, having little mass and a negative charge.

E-lec'tron mi'cro-graph (Gr. *elektron*. Gr. *micros*, small; Gr. *graphein*, to write). An enlarged photograph of an object taken by attaching a camera to an electron microscope.

E-lec'tron mi'cro-scope (Gr. *elektron*. Gr. *micros*, small; Gr. *scopein*, to examine). An optical instrument in which a beam of electrons focused by means of a magnetic field (magnetic lens) is used to produce an enlarged image of a minute object on a fluorescent screen or photographic plate.

Em'bry-o (Gr. *embryon*, from *en*, in; *bryein*, to swell). A young animal that is passing through its developmental stages, usually within the egg membranes or within the maternal uterus.

Em'bry-og''e-ny (Gr. *embryon*, embryo; *genesis*, origin). The development of an organism.

Em'bry-ol''o-gy (Gr. *embryon*, embryo; *logos*, discourse). The science which deals with the development of an organism.

Em'bry-o-nal (Gr. *embryon*, embryo). Pertaining to an embryo.

En-am'el (O.F. *esmaillier*, to coat with enamel). The dense white covering of the crown of a tooth; the hardest substance produced in the animal body.

En-cyst' (Gr. *en*, in; *kystis*, bladder). To become enclosed in a sac (cyst).

En-cyst'ment (Gr. *en*, in; *kystis*, bladder). The process whereby an animal becomes enclosed in an impermeable envelope.

En'do-crine (Gr. *endon*, within; *krinein*, to separate). Pertaining to the ductless glands.

En'do-derm (Gr. *endon*, within; *derma*, skin). The innermost layer of the early embryo which gives rise to the lining of the digestive tract. Also called entoderm.

En'do-par"a-site (Gr. *endon*, within; *para*, beside; *sitos*, food). A parasite living within the body of its host.

En'do-plasm (Gr. *endon*, within; *plasma*, something molded). Within a cell, the cytoplasm that is surrounded by ectoplasm.

En-dop'o-dite (Gr. *endon*, within; *pous*, foot). The principal internal (medial) branch of a biramous appendage of a crustacean.

En'do-sarc (Gr. *endon*, within; *sarx*, flesh). The structure formed by the inner mass of protoplasm in a single-celled animal.

En'do-skel"e-ton (Gr. *endon*, within; *skeletos*, hard). A supporting structure on the inside of an animal, whether it be cartilaginous, bony, or of other material.

En'do-some (Gr. *endon*, within; *soma*, body). The central mass, consisting largely of chromatin material, in the nucleus of certain Protozoa.

En'do-style (Gr. *endon*, within; *stylos*, pillar). The ciliated groove in the ventral surface of the pharynx in the amphioxus and some other protochordates.

En'do-the"li-um (Gr. *endon*, within; *thele*, nipple). A cellular membrane that lines the blood vessels, heart, and lymphatic vessels of vertebrates.

En'er-gy (Gr. *energein*, to be active). The exertion of or the capacity for any particular kind of work; ability to do work.

En-ter'ic (Gr. *enteron*, gut). An adjective form of enteron.

En'ter-on (Gr. *enteron*, gut). The digestive tract, especially that part derived from endoderm; zoologists often restrict use of the term to intestine.

En'to-derm (Gr. *endon*, within; *derma*, skin). See Endoderm.

En'to-mol"o-gy (Gr. *entomon*, insect; *logos*, discourse). The study of insects.

En-vi'ron-ment (Fr. *environ*, about, thereabouts). The place where a species of animals is found in nature and the conditions that are present. The total of physical, chemical, and biological conditions surrounding an organism.

En'zyme (Gr. *en*, in; *zyme*, leaven). A substance produced by living cells that causes specific chemical changes such as hydrolysis, oxidation, or reduction, but does not itself undergo significant change. It is a positive catalyst, that is, it speeds up chemical reactions. Pepsin and trypsin are enzymes which help to split proteins into smaller molecules. The human body probably contains thousands of different enzymes.

Ep-ib'o-ly (Gr. *epi*, upon; *ballein*, to throw). The posterior growth of a fold of the blastoderm over the surface of an embryo in the process of forming the enteron during gastrulation.

Ep'i-cra"ni-um (Gr. *epi*, upon; *kranion*, skull). The largest sclerite of the head in the grasshopper and related forms.

Ep-i-der'mis (Gr. *epi*, upon; *derma*, skin). The outer cellular layer or layers covering the external surface of a metazoan; it secretes the cuticle on some animals.

Ep-iph'y-sis (Gr. *epi*, upon; *phyein*, to grow). The end of a long bone; also the pineal body.

E-pip'o-dite (Gr. *epi*, upon; *pous*, foot). A long slender structure, fastened to the protopodite of the walking leg of a crustacean.

Ep'i-the"li-um (Gr. *epi*, upon; *thele*, nipple). Usually a sheet of cells covering either external or internal surfaces of the body.

E'qua-to"ri-al plate (L. *aequator*, one who equalizes). The platelike arrangement of chromosomes in the plane of the equator of the spindle during mitotic cell division.

E-rep'sin (L. *eripere*, to set free). An enzyme mixture produced by the intestinal mucosa, consisting of various peptidases which split peptones and proteoses into simpler products; it has no effect on intact protein molecules.

E-soph'a-gus (Gr. *oisophagos*, gullet). The gullet; the part of the digestive tract extending from the pharynx to the stomach. Also a part of the digestive tract of certain invertebrates, though a pharynx and/or stomach may not be present.

Es'ti-va"tion (L. *aestivus*, pertaining to summer). A dormant condition adopted by certain animals during summer. Compare with Hibernation.

Eth'moid (Gr. *ethmos*, sieve; *eidos*, shape). A small bone forming the upper wall of the nasal passageway.

Eu-gen'ics (Gr. *eu*, well; *genos*, birth). The application of the knowledge of heredity to the improvement of the human species.

Eu-sta'chi-an tube (After Eustachi, Italian physician. L. *tuba*, pipe). The tube leading from the middle ear to the pharynx in higher vertebrates.

Eu-then'ics (Gr. *euthenein*, to thrive). The science of improving the human species by providing the best possible environment.

E-vag'i-na"tion (L. *e*, out; *vagina*, sheath). An outpocketing from any surface by growth, especially a cavity.

E-vis'cer-ate (L. *ex*, out; *viscera*, entrails). To remove the internal organs.

Ev'o-lu"tion, or-gan'ic (L. *evolvere*, to unroll. Gr. *organon*, instrument, tool). The process by which organisms have changed through time, both structurally and functionally; hence, descent with change has made possible the change of organisms from simple to complex forms.

Ex-cre'tion (L. *ex*, out; *cernere*, to sift). The discharge of metabolic wastes; also the substance discharged.

Ex-op'o-dite (Gr. *exo*, outside; *pous*, foot). The external branch of a typical biramous crustacean appendage.

Ex'o-skel"e-ton (Gr. *exo*, outside; *skeletos*, hard). A supporting structure on the outside of the body of an animal. The skeleton of an invertebrate is usually an exoskeleton.

Ex'pi-ra"tion (L. *ex*, out; *spirare*, to breathe). The expulsion of water or air from the lungs in a vertebrate.

Ex-ten'sor (L. *ex*, out; *tendere*, to stretch). Any muscle that straightens out or extends a part of the body such as a foot. The opposite of flexor.

Ex-ter'nal res'pi-ra"tion. Consists of 2 phases: (1) breathing, which brings air and blood together in the lungs, and (2) the transportation of oxygen and carbon dioxide between the lungs and cells.

Fac'et (L. *facies*, face). The external surface of an individual ommatidium.

Fam'i-ly (L. *familia*, from *famulus*, servant). The principal subdivision of an order.

Fas'ci-a (L., band). A band of connective tissue that covers and supports or binds parts together.

Fau'na (L. *faunus*, a god of the woods). A term referring to animal life of a given period or region.

Fe'ces (L. *faeces*, dregs). The indigestible, unabsorbed residue of digestion.

Fe'mur (L. *femur*, thigh). The thighbone; adjective form is femoral.

Fer'ti-li-za"tion (L. *fertilis*, from *ferre*, to bear). The union of a mature ovum and a mature sperm to form a zygote.

Fe'tus (L., a bringing forth). The advanced stages of a mammalian embryo.

Fi-brin'o-gen (L. *fibra*, band; Gr. *gignesthai*, to produce). A protein substance in the blood that is changed to fibrin during clotting.

Fis'sion (L. *fissus*, cleft). An asexual method of reproduction by division into two or more parts approximately equal in size.

Fis'sure (L. *fissus*, cleft). A furrow, cleft, or slit.

Fla-gel'lum (L. *flagellum*, whip). A long whiplike cytoplasmic process of a cell or a single-celled animal, capable of vibration.

Flex'or (L. *flexus*, bent). A muscle whose function is to bend or flex a joint, thereby decreasing the angle between the two component parts.

Fol'li-cle (L. *folliculus*, small sac). A cellular sac or covering.

Fo-ra'men (L. *foramen*, an opening). A natural opening in a bone or membrane through which blood vessels and/or nerves usually run.

Fo-ra'men of Mun-ro' (L. from *forare*, to bore, pierce. After Alexander Munro). A passageway between the lateral ventricles and third ventricle of the brain.

Fos'sa (L. *fossa*, ditch). A pit or depression in a bone.

Fos'sil (L. *fossilis*, from *fodere*, to dig). The remains or other indications of prehistoric forms of life.

Free'-liv'ing. Not parasitic or attached. Compare with Parasite and Sessile.

Fron'to-pa-ri"e-tal (L. *frons*, forehead; *paries*, wall). One of the long flat bones forming the roof of the cranium, as in the frog.

Func'tion (L. *fungi*, to perform). The action of any part of a plant or animal.

Gam'ete (Gr. *gametes*, spouse). A mature reproductive or germ cell, either ovum (egg), sperm, or other type of reproductive cell.

Gam'-e-to-gen"e-sis (Gr. *gametes*, spouse;

genesis, birth). The process of development of gametes.

Gan'gli-on (Gr. *ganglion*, enlargement). A group or mass of nerve cell bodies, usually located outside the central nervous system in vertebrates; in invertebrates, ganglia occur within the central nervous system.

Gas'tric (Gr. *gaster*, belly). Pertaining to the stomach, as the gastric glands.

Gas'troc-ne"mi-us (Gr. *gaster*, belly; *kneme*, tibia). The large muscle on the posterior side of the lower leg of a vertebrate.

Gas'tro-vas"cu-lar (Gr. *gaster*, belly; L. *vasculum*, vessel). Serving the functions of both digestion and circulation.

Gas'tru-la (Gr. *gaster*, belly). A stage in development in which the embryo usually consists of two germ layers (ectoderm and endoderm) with a cavity surrounded by endoderm.

Gas'tru-la"tion (Gr. *gaster*, belly). Process by which a gastrula is formed; the invagination of the blastula.

Gene (Gr. *genesthai*, to be produced). A unit of heredity which is transmitted in the chromosome and which by interaction with the internal and external environment controls the development of a trait (character); the hereditary determiners.

Ge-net'ics (Gr. *gignesthai*, to be born). *See* Heredity.

Gen'i-tal (L. *gignere*, to beget). Pertaining to the reproductive organs of either sex.

Gen'o-type (Gr. *genesthai*, to be produced; *typos*, impression). The entire genetic make-up of an individual which shows how it will breed. It tells the kind of genes an individual has. Compare with Phenotype.

Ge'nus (L. *genere*, to beget). The taxonomic subdivision of a family. A genus is usually composed of several species. Genus names are Latinized, capitalized; and, when printed, italicized.

Ge-ot'ro-pism (Gr. *ge*, earth; *repein*, to turn). The response in behavior of an organism to gravity.

Germ cell (L. *germen*, germ. L. *cella*, compartment). Gametes, or cells which give rise to gametes.

Germ lay'er (L. *germen*, germ). One of the primary cell layers in an embryo; ectoderm, endoderm, or mesoderm. There are no permanent or clear-cut distinctions, as shown by transplantation experiments, yet in the mammal development each tends to produce separate parts.

Germ plasm (L. *germen*, germ. Gr. *plasma*, something molded). The material basis of heredity. Weismann's term for the hereditary substance in the germ cells.

Ges-ta'tion (L. *gerere*, to carry). The period between fertilization and birth of a mammal.

Gill (Gr. *cheilos*, lip). A type of respiratory organ for aquatic organisms.

Gill arches (Gr. *cheilos*, lip. L. *arcus*, bow). The walls adjacent to the gill slits; walls bearing the gills.

Gill slit (pharyngeal cleft) (Gr. *cheilos*, lip. A.S. *slitan*). A series of paired openings in the wall of the pharynx and body of chordates.

Giz'zard (Fr. *giser*, gizzard). A muscular part of the digestive tract, as in earthworms, insects, and birds, used for grinding ingested food.

Gland (L. *glans*, acorn). One or many associated cells that secrete or excrete one or more special substances.

Glo-mer'u-lus (L. *glomare*, to make a ball). A small coiled mass of capillaries contained in the Bowman's capsule of the vertebrate kidney.

Glot'tis (Gr. *glotta*, tongue). The opening from the pharynx into the larynx of a vertebrate with lungs.

Gly'co-gen (Gr. *glykus*, sweet; *gen*, producing). A form of carbohydrate (polysaccharide) food material stored in the liver, muscles, and some other tissues; an "animal starch."

Gob'let cell (L. *cuppa*, cup. L. *cella*, compartment). A modified epithelial cell which secretes mucus.

Go'nad (Gr. *gonos*, reproduction). Reproductive organ, either ovary, testis, or ovotestis, in which gametes are produced.

Go-nan'gi-um (Gr. *gone*, seed; *angeion*, vessel). The reproductive individual of a hydroid colony.

Gon'o-the"ca (Gr. *gone*, seed; *theke*, cup). The firm external covering of a gonangium.

Gre-gar'i-ous (L. *gregarius*, from *grex*, herd). Living in company, as in flocks and herds.

Gul′let (L. *gula*, gullet). Synonym for esophagus.

Gy-nan′dro-morph (Gr. *gyne*, woman; *aner*, man; *morphe*, form). An individual showing a condition where part of an animal may be male and another part female. This should not be confused with hermaphroditism, which is concerned chiefly with the reproductive organs.

Hab′i-tat (L. *habitare*, to dwell). The environment in which an animal lives.

Hap′loid (Gr. *haploos*, single; *eidos*, form). The reduced or halved number of chromosomes typically found in a mature gamete; half the diploid number of chromosomes.

Hav-er′sian ca-nal (After Havers, an English physician. L. *canalis*, water pipe). One of the canals of the bone that permits the passage of blood vessels and nerves.

He′li-ot′ro-pism (Gr. *helios*, sun; *trepein*, to turn). *See* Phototropism.

He′mal (Gr. *haima*, blood). Referring to the blood or blood-vascular system.

He′mo-coel (Gr. *haima*, blood; *koilos*, hollow). A portion of the body cavity functioning as a part of the circulatory system, as in the arthropods.

He′mo-glo″bin (Gr. *haima*, blood; L. *globus*, globe). The pigment in red corpuscles of the vertebrate capable of carrying oxygen; in invertebrates, it is usually in the plasma.

He′mo-phil″i-a (Gr. *haima*, blood; *phil*, to love). An abnormal condition in man in which there is a delayed clotting of the blood. It is an inherited condition.

He-pat′ic (Gr. *hepar*, liver). Pertaining to the liver.

Her-biv′o-rous (L. *herba*, herb; *vorare*, to devour). Feeding chiefly on plants.

Her-ed′i-ty (L. *hereditas*, heirship). The study of the transmission, from parents to offspring, of developmental potentialities (genes) and how they come to expression.

Her-maph′ro-dite (Gr. *Hermes*; *Aphrodite*). An individual possessing both male and female reproductive organs.

Het′er-o-cer″cal (Gr. *heteros*, other; *kerkos*, tail). Pertaining to the type of tail which is asymmetrical internally as well as externally. Examples: the shark and sturgeon tails.

Het′er-on″o-mous (Gr. *heteros*, other; *nomos*, law). The condition in which the metameres of an animal are not similar; metameres specialized in various parts of the body.

Het′er-o-zy″gote (Gr. *heteros*, different; *zeugon*, yolk). An individual having two members of an allelic pair of genes dissimilar; for example Bb, which has unlike genes as a result of mutation and therefore produces gametes of two kinds with respect to such a gene. The unlike genes may be any two of an allelic series. Compare with Homozygote.

Hi′ber-na″tion (L. *hiems*, winter). The passing of the winter in a dormant inactive state.

His′ta-mine. A powerful dilator of the capillaries; it is found in all animal and plant tissues.

His′to-gen″e-sis (Gr. *histos*, tissue; *gignesthai*, to be born). The origin, development, and differentiation of the tissues of an organism.

His-tol′o-gy (Gr. *histos*, tissue; *logos*, study). That branch of anatomy which deals with the miscroscopic structure of tissues and organs.

Hol′o-blas″tic egg (Gr. *holos*, whole; *blastos*, germ). An egg that divides completely into cells during cleavage.

Hol′o-phyt″ic (Gr. *holos*, whole; *phyton*, plant). A type of nutrition found in green plants and in some flagellates, which involves photosynthesis.

Hol′o-zo″ic (Gr. *holos*, whole; *zoion*, animal). A type of nutrition, found in most animals, that involves ingestion and digestion of organic material.

Ho′mo-cer′cal (Gr. *homos*, same; *kerkos*, tail). Pertaining to the type of tail which is externally symmetrical but internally asymmetrical.

Ho-mol′o-gous chro′mo-somes (Gr. *homos*, one and the same. Gr. *chroma*, color; *soma*, body). Chromosomes carrying genes affecting the same traits; one is paternal and the other maternal in origin. They come together in synapsis. Thus the individual is, genetically speaking, double in composition.

Ho-mol′o-gy (Gr. *homos*, same; *logos*, study). Basic similarity; structural likeness of an organ or part of one kind of animal with the comparable unit in another, resulting from descent from a common ancestry. These organs may or may not have the same function.

Ho′mo-zy″gote (Gr. *homos,* same; *zeugon,* yolk). An individual in which the members of a given allelic pair of genes are alike, for example, BB or bb. Compare with Heterozygote.

Hor′mone (Gr. *hormon,* from *hormaein,* to arouse or excite). A chemical regulator or coordinator secreted by cells or a ductless gland and having a specific action on some organ or organs at a distance from the gland. It is carried by the blood or other body fluids.

Host (L. *hostis,* stranger). An organism that provides food, shelter, or other benefits to another organism.

Hu′mer-us (L. *humerus,* shoulder). A bone of the vertebrate upper arm.

Hy′a-line (Gr. *hyalos,* clear). Glassy or semi-transparent. Applied to the clear substance of protoplasm.

Hy′brid (L. *hybrida,* mongrel). An individual resulting from the union of a sperm and egg which differ in one or more genes; a heterozygote.

Hy′dranth (Gr. *hydra,* water serpent; *anthos,* flower). The expanded end of a branch of a hydroid colony that is specialized for vegetative function.

Hy′dro-caul″us (Gr. *hydor,* water; *kaulos,* stalk). The main stalklike stem of a hydroid colony.

Hy′droid (Gr. *hydra,* water serpent; *oid,* like). Hydroid used as an adjective pertains to the Hydrozoa; used as a noun it refers to the polyp form of a hydrozoan, as distinguished from the medusa form.

Hy-drol′y-sis (Gr. *hydor,* water; *lysis,* loosing). A process in which a complex compound is digested into one or more simpler compounds through a reaction with water.

Hy′dro-rhi″za (Gr. *hydor,* water; *rhiza,* root). The basal portion of a hydroid colony, often branched and rootlike; used for attachment to substratum.

Hy′dro-the″ca (Gr. *hydor,* water; *theke,* cup). The transparent membrane that extends from the perisarc and surrounds the main part of a hydranth.

Hy′oid (Gr. *hyoides,* Y-shaped). A group of bones and cartilages at or near the base of the tongue.

Hy′per-ton″ic (Gr. *huper,* beyond; *tonikos,* strength). In terms of a living cell, the concentration of water molecules is greater inside the cell than on the outside; therefore more water molecules pass out of the cell than into it. This results in the cell's shrinking.

Hy-poph′y-sis (Gr. *hupo,* under; *physis,* growth). The pituitary gland in the invertebrate. *See* Pituitary *and* Infundibulum.

Hy′po-stome (Gr. *hupo,* under; *stoma,* mouth). The region surrounding the mouth in coelenterates.

Hy-poth′e-sis (Gr., proposal). A tentative solution or explanation of a problem which has not yet been proved to be either true or false.

Hy′po-ton″ic (Gr. *hupo,* under; *tonikos,* strength). In terms of a living cell, the concentration of water molecules is greater on the outside of the cell than inside; therefore more water molecules pass into than out of the cell. This results in the cell swelling.

I-den′ti-cal twins. Two individuals developed from a single fertilized egg and, therefore, having identical sets of genes. Also called monozygotic or one-egg twins.

Il′e-um (L., grain). The posterior and longest part of the small intestine of a mammal.

In″breed′ing (L. *in,* in; M.E. *breden*). The crossing or mating of closely related individuals, such as first cousins, or brother and sister.

In-fun-dib′u-lum (L. *infundibulum,* funnel). A stalklike down-pushing of the diencephalon of the brain, which, along with the embryonic hypophysis, will give rise to the pituitary gland of the adult.

In-gest′ (L. *ingestus,* from *ingerere,* to put in). To take any substance from the outside, especially food, into the digestive tract of an animal.

In-ser′tion (L. *insertus,* from *inserere,* to connect, insert). The place of attachment of a muscle to a movable part, in contrast to the origin which is the point of attachment to a relatively immovable part.

In′su-lin (L. *insula,* island). Hormone secreted by the islets of Langerhans of the pancreas.

In-teg′u-ment (L. *integumentum,* covering). The outer covering, especially the skin, of a vertebrate.

In'ter-cel''lu-lar (L. *inter*, between; *cellula*, cells). Between cells.

In-ter'nal se-cre'tion. A hormone, the product of an endocrine gland.

In''ter-phase' cell (L. *inter*, among, between; Gr. *phasis*, to make to appear. L. *cella*, compartment). A cell that is not undergoing mitotic division; a metabolic cell; the stage between two mitoses.

In-tes'tine (L. *intestinus*, internal). Part of the digestive tract posterior to the stomach. In animals without a stomach, the intestine is usually the digestive tract posterior to the ingestive region.

In'tra-cel''lu-lar (L. *intra*, within; *cellula*, cells). Within cells.

In'tus-sus-cep''tion (L. *intus*, within; *suscipere*, to receive). Growth of living things accomplished by adding new materials within the protoplasm.

In-vag'i-nate (L. *in*, in; *vagina*, sheath). To infold; the folding or inpushing of a layer of cells into a cavity, as of a blastula to form a gastrula.

In-ver'te-brate (L. *in*, not; *vertebra*, joint). An animal without a vertebrae (backbone). Also used as an adjective, from protozoans to vertebrates.

In'vo-lu''tion (L. *in*, in; *volvere*, to roll). The process of rolling or turning in of cells over a rim.

Ir'ri-ta-bil''i-ty (L. *irrito*, excite). The ability to respond to stimuli, one of the fundamental characteristics of protoplasm.

I'so-ton''ic (Gr. *isos*, equal; *tonikos*, strength). In terms of a living cell, concentration of water molecules is the same inside and outside the cell; therefore, the water molecules pass in and out of the cell in equal numbers. This results in no change in cell size.

Je-ju'num (L. *jejunus*, empty). That part of the intestine extending from the duodenum to the ileum in a vertebrate.

Jug'u-lar (L. *jugulum*, collarbone). Pertaining to the throat, as jugular vein.

Ka-tab'o-lism. *See* Catabolism.

Kid'ney. The chief organ for the excretion of liquid nitrogenous wastes in vertebrates; also often loosely applied to analogous organs in certain other animals.

La'bi-al (L. *labium*, lip). Pertaining to the lips.

La'bi-um (L., lip). A lip, specifically the lower lip of an insect's mouth-part structures.

La'brum (L., lip). Upper lip of the insect's mouth. Dorsal to the mouth opening.

Lac'ri-mal (L. *lacrima*, tear). Pertaining to tears.

Lac'te-al (L. *lac*, milk). Pertains to milk; often refers to the lymph vessels of the small intestine of a vertebrate.

La-cu'na (L. *lacuna*, cavity). A small cavity or space, particularly in cartilage or bone, that in life contains a cartilage or bone cell.

La-mel'la (L., small plate). A thin leaflike layer.

Lar'va (L. *larva*, ghost). An immature, free-living stage in the life cycle of various animals, which reach the adult form by undergoing a metamorphosis.

Lar'ynx (Gr. *larynx*, larynx). The organ situated between the trachea and the base of the tongue, into which the glottis opens and which contains the vocal folds. A larynx is typically found in all lunged vertebrates above fishes, except birds.

Lat'er-al (L. *latus*, side). The side of the body. At each side of the median line.

Le'thal gene (L. *lethum*, death. Gr. *genesthai*, to be produced). A gene that is capable of bringing about death. Lethal genes may be either dominant or recessive and kill the organism at any stage of its development.

Leu'co-cyte (Gr. *leucos*, white; *kytos*, cell). A white blood cell or corpuscle.

Lig'a-ment (L. *ligamentum*, bandage). A tough, fibrous band of tissue connecting bones or supporting viscera.

Lin'gual (L. *lingua*, tongue). Pertaining to the tongue, as lingual artery.

Link'age (M.E. *linke*). A tendency for certain traits (characters) to stick together in heredity because the genes for such traits are located on the same chromosome.

Li'pase (Gr. *lipos*, fat). A fat-splitting enzyme.

Lip'oid (Gr. *lipos*, fat). Of fatty nature.

Lum'bar (L. *lumbus*, loin). Pertaining to that region usually known as the small of the back; the region just posterior to the ribs of vertebrates.

Lu'men (L., cavity). Internal cavity within a body or structure, such as the lumen of the intestine, a gland duct, or a blood vessel.

Lu′mi-nes″cence (L. *lumen*, light). The production of light as a result of chemical reactions in cells.

Lymph (L. *lympha*, clear spring water). A clear fluid, containing white blood corpuscles, found in the lymph vessels of the body. Practically, blood without red corpuscles.

Lym-phat′ic sys′tem (L. *lympha*, spring water. Gr. *systema*, system). A system of vessels and nodes in vertebrates which lead from the tissue spaces to large veins entering the heart; a part of the circulatory system.

Mac′ro-mere (Gr. *makros*, large; *meros*, part). The relatively large, yolk-laden cells that are present during the cleavage stages of certain animals.

Mad′re-po-rite (Fr. *madre*, mother; Gr. *poros*, light). The strainerlike cover of the opening to the water-vascular system in echinoderms.

Mag′got (M.E. *mathek*). A wormlike legless larva of a fly (Diptera).

Ma-la′ri-a (L. *mal*, bad; *aria*, air). Any of several fevers, each produced by a specific sporozoan parasite which invades the red corpuscles of various mammals and birds. Formerly thought due to bad air.

Mal-pigh′ian body (After Malpighi, of Pisa; A.S. *bodig*). Structure in the vertebrate kidney composed of Bowman's capsule and the glomerulus. Also called renal corpuscle.

Man′di-ble (L. *mandere*, to chew). A jaw; the lower jaw in vertebrates; either jaw of an arthropod.

Man′tle (L. *mantellum*, cloak). A fold of the body wall that encloses the soft structures of an animal such as a mollusk and which secretes the shell.

Ma-nu′bri-um (L. *manus*, hand). A structure projecting from the middle of the subumbrellar surface of the medusa and bearing the mouth at its free end.

Ma-rine′ (L. *marinus*, from *mare*, the sea). Of or pertaining to the ocean, sea, or other bodies of salt water.

Mas′ti-ca″tion (L. *masticare*, to chew). The act of chewing food with the teeth or other mouth parts, as in many insects.

Ma-ter′nal (L. *maternus*, of a mother). Pertaining to a mother.

Ma′trix (L. *mater*, mother). In animal histology, an intercellular substance. The noncellular substance of connective tissue as in bone and cartilage.

Mat′u-ra″tion (L. *maturus*, ripe). The last stages in the development of gametes, characterized by two divisions, in which the number of chromosomes is reduced by 50 per cent to the haploid number.

Max-il′la (L. *maxilla*, jaw). One of the several mouth-part structures of the crayfish and other arthropods; in the vertebrates, the large bone of the upper jaw.

Max-il′li-ped (L. *maxilla*, jaw; *pes*, foot). One of the first three pairs of thoracic appendages in the Crustacea.

Me′di-an (L. *medius*, middle). Refers to the midline or near the middle of the body.

Me-dul′la (L. *medulla*, marrow). The inner region of a gland or other structure in animals.

Me-dul′la ob-lon-ga′ta (L., oblong medulla). The most posterior of the principal divisions of the vertebrate brain.

Med′ul-la-ry plate, groove, and tube (L. *medullaris*, narrow). Synonymous with neural plate, groove, or tube. Three successive stages in the embryonic development of the vertebrate central nervous system.

Med′ul-lat-ed. Used principally for certain nerve fibers covered with a myelin sheath.

Mei-o′sis (Gr., to make smaller). *See* Maturation.

Mem′brane (L. *membrana*, membrane). A thin, pliable sheet of cells or material secreted by cells.

Me-nin′ges (Gr. *meninx*, membrane). The three membranes (dura mater, arachnoid, and pia mater) covering the brain and spinal cord.

Men′to-meck-e″li-an (L. *mentum*, chin; after J.F. Meckel, a German anatomist). Refers to the anterior bones or cartilages of the vertebrate lower jaw.

Mes′en-chyme (Gr. *mesos*, middle; *engchein*, to pour in). A loose embryonic connective tissue derived chiefly from mesoderm, although some of its cells may have an ectodermal or endodermal origin.

Mes′en-ter-y (Gr. *mesos*, middle; *enteron*, intestine). A thin double-walled sheet of peritoneum that supports organs in the abdominal cavity of vertebrates; also one of the partitions in the body cavity of anthozoan coelenterates.

Mes'o-derm (Gr. *mesos*, middle; *derma*, skin). The middle layer of embryonic cells, between the ectoderm and endoderm.

Mes'o-gle"a (Gr. *mesos*, middle; *gloia*, glue). Noncellular jellylike substance lying between the epidermis and gastrodermis in coelenterates such as the hydra; also other jellylike layers as in the sponge.

Mes'o-neph"ric duct (Gr. *mesos*, middle; *nephros*, kidney). Duct leading from the mesonephric type of kidney to the cloaca.

Mes'o-neph"ros (Gr. *mesos*, middle; *nephros*, kidney). A type of vertebrate kidney. It is present in the embryos of most vertebrates, but is replaced by another type in reptiles, birds, and mammals before birth. It is the functional kidney in the adult vertebrate from cyclostomes to amphibians, inclusive.

Me-tab'o-lism (Gr. *meta*, beyond; *ballein*, to throw). The sum total of the reactions, mainly chemical, that occur within the protoplasm of an organism.

Met'a-car"pals (Gr. *meta*, after; L. *carpus*, the wrist). Proximal bones of the hand.

Met'a-gen"e-sis (Gr. *meta*, over; *genesis*, origin). The alternation of a sexual with an asexual generation in reproduction in the life cycle of a coelenterate such as *Obelia*. Same as alternation of generations.

Met'a-mere (Gr. *meta*, over; *meros*, part). One of a series of homologous segments in a body; a somite.

Me-tam'er-ism (Gr. *meta*, beyond; Gr. *meros*, part). The condition where the body of an animal is made up of a succession of homologous parts (metameres).

Met'a-mor"pho-sis (Gr. *meta*, over; *morphe*, form). A marked structural change or transformation during development; for example, as from the larva to the adult.

Met'a-phase (Gr. *meta*, after; *phasis*, appearance). The stage of mitosis during which the chromosomes are lined up in the equatorial plane of the spindle.

Met'a-pleu"ral folds (Gr. *meta*, after; *pleura*, side). Two folds on the anterior, ventral surface of the amphioxus, extending posteriorly from the mouth to the atriopore.

Met'a-tar"sals (Gr. *meta*, after; L. *tarsus*, ankle). Proximal bones of the foot.

Met'a-zo"a (Gr. *meta*, after; *zoion*, animal). All multicellular animals in which there is a differentiation of the soma (body cells); usually includes all animals but Protozoa.

Mi'cron (Gr. *mikros*, small). The $\frac{1}{1000}$ part of a millimeter.

Mi-gra'tion (L. *migratio*, removal from one place of abode to another). Movement of a part of a population of a species (usually in groups) from one region to another.

Mil'li-li"ter (L. *mille*, one thousand; G. *litra*, pound). The $\frac{1}{1000}$ part of a liter; for all practical purposes, equivalent to a cubic centimeter. Abbreviated ml.

Mit'o-chon"dri-a (Gr. *mitos*, thread; *chondros*, grain). Small, spherical or rodlike, cytoplasmic structures, associated with important metabolic reactions in a cell.

Mi-to'sis (Gr. *mitos*, thread). Cell division during which chromosomes appear to become doubled longitudinally, the halves of each one passing into separate daughter cells. Mitosis is sometimes considered, in a restricted sense, as only nuclear division.

Molt (M.E. *mouten*, from L. *mutare*, to change). To cast off the exoskeleton. To shed portions of the skin, feathers, or hair.

Mo-noe'cious. *See* Hermaphrodite.

Mon'o-hy"brid (Gr. *monos*, single; L. *hybrida*, mongrel). A hybrid with respect to only one pair of allelic genes as Aa or Bb.

Mon'o-ploid. *See* Haploid.

Mor-phol'o-gy (Gr. *morphe*, form; *logos*, discourse). The study which deals with the form and structure of organisms.

Mu'cous (L. *mucus*, slime). Pertaining to mucus.

Mu'cous mem'brane (L. *mucus*, slime. L. *membrana*, membrane). Consists of an epithelium with some subepithelial connective tissue, which lines cavities that communicate with the exterior. In some cases, as in the digestive tract, the mucosa includes the muscularis mucosae.

Mu'cus (L. *mucus*, slime). A viscous secretion containing mucin; a product of the mucous glands.

Mus"cu-la'ris mu-co'sae (L. *musculus*, muscle. L. *mucus*, slime). Thin layer of smooth muscle between the tunica propria and the submucosa in the wall of the esophagus, stomach, and intestine.

Mu-ta'tion (L. *mutare*, to change). A change in a gene in a gamete which results in a new hereditary variation (trait). Broadly used to include all kinds of hereditary variations resulting from gross chromosome changes. Mutations may also occur in somatic cells, but these are not hereditary unless the individual reproduces asexually.

Mu'tu-al-ism (L. *mutuus*, exchange). An association of two species which is beneficial to both of them.

My'e-lin (Gr. *myelos*, marrow). The fatlike substance surrounding the axis cylinder of a medullated nerve fiber.

My'o-fi''bril (Gr. *mys*, muscle; L. *fibrilla*, a small fiber). One of the numerous longitudinal small fibrils contained within the protoplasm of the muscle cell or fiber.

My'o-neme (Gr. *mys*, muscle; *nema*, thread). A type of contractile fibril in certain Protozoa.

Nai'ad (L. *naias*, water nymph). An aquatic gill-breathing nymph.

Na'res (L. *naris*, nostril). The openings of the air passages, both external and internal, in the head of a vertebrate.

Na'sal (L. *nasus*, nose). Pertaining to the nose or nostrils.

Nat'u-ral par'the-no-gen''e-sis (L. *natura*, nature. Gr. *parthenos*, virgin; *genesis*, origin). Development of an egg without fertilization during the normal life cycle of an animal, as in aphids.

Nat'u-ral se-lec'tion. The "selection" in nature of those individuals or species best fitted to survive in a particular environment; the elimination of the "unfit."

Nem'a-to-cyst (Gr. *nema*, thread; *kystis*, bladder). One of the stinging capsules found in coelenterates; each is produced by a single cell, a cnidoblast.

Ne-phrid'i-o-pore (Gr. *nephros*, kidney; *poros*, passage). The external opening of an excretory tubule or nephridium.

Ne-phrid'i-um (Gr. *nephros*, kidney). A tubular excretory structure characteristic of many invertebrates, such as the annelids.

Neph'ro-stome (Gr. *nephros*, kidney; *stoma*, mouth). The ciliated funnel-shaped opening at the inner end of a nephridium through which the liquid wastes enter the tubule.

Neu'ral (Gr. *neuron*, nerve). Pertaining to the nervous system.

Neu'ral ca-nal' (Gr. *neuron*, nerve; L. *canalis*, canal). A canal through the vertebrae; the canal formed by the neural arches.

Neu'ral plate, groove, and **tube** (Gr. *neuron*, nerve). Three successive phases in the development of the central nervous system in vertebrates.

Neu'ral spine (Gr. *neuron*, nerve. L. *spina*, spine). The dorsal projection of a vertebra.

Neu'ri-lem''ma (Gr. *neuron*, nerve; *lemma*, covering). The outermost sheath of a nerve fiber; also spelled *neurolemma*.

Neu'ro-coele (Gr. *neuron*, nerve; *koilos*, hollow). The cavity in a chordate nerve cord.

Neu'ron or **neu'rone** (Gr. *neuron*, nerve). A nerve cell, including the cell body and all of its processes.

Niche (**ecologic**) (O.F. *nichiere*, to nestle). The constellation of environmental factors into which a species fits or which is required by a species.

Node of Ran'vi-er (L. *nodus*, knot. After Louis Ranvier, French histologist). The place on a nerve fiber where the medullary sheath is constricted.

No'to-chord (Gr. *notos*, back; *chorde*, string). Characteristic cylindrical rod of supporting cells in the chordates, found dorsal to the digestive tract and ventral to the nerve cord; either surrounded or supplanted by the vertebrae in most vertebrates.

Nu-cle'ol-us (L. diminutive of *nucleus*, kernel). A spherical, well-defined body found within the nucleus of many kinds of cells.

Nu'cle-us (L., kernel). It is a specialized protoplasmic body within the cell which contains chromosomes.

Nu-tri'tion (L. *nutrimentum*, nourishment). The sum of the processes concerned in the growth, maintenance, and repair of the living body as a whole, or of its constituent parts.

Ob-jec'tive (L. *objectivus*, from *objicere*, to place before). The lens or combination of lenses of a microscope nearest the object under observation.

Oc-cip'i-tal (L. *occiput*, back of the head). Pertaining to the base of the skull of a vertebrate.

O-cel′lus (L., little eye). A simple type of eye as in many invertebrates, especially in insects or other arthropods.

Oc′u-lar (L. *oculus*, eye). Eyepiece of the microscope; pertaining to the eye.

Ol-fac′to-ry (L. *olfacere*, to smell). Pertaining to the sense of smell.

Om-ma-tid′i-um (Gr. *omna*, eye). One of the elongated rodlike units of a compound eye of an arthropod.

Om-niv′o-rous (L. *omnis*, all; *vorare*, to devour). Eating all kinds of food, both plants and animals.

On-tog′e-ny (Gr. *onto*, being; *genos*, birth). The entire developmental history of the individual organism.

O′o-cyte (Gr. *oon*, egg; *kytos*, cell). The egg mother cell from which are produced, by the first maturation division, the secondary oocyte and the first polar body.

O′o-gen″e-sis (Gr. *oon*, egg; *genesis*, origin). The process of formation of ova.

O′o-gon″i-um (Gr. *oon*, egg; *gonos*, offspring). In animals, the primordial egg cell prior to the process of maturation (meiosis); it is the cell from which primary oocytes are produced.

O-per′cu-lum (L., lid). The structure covering the gills of fishes and tadpoles; also the plate serving to cover the opening of some snail shells.

Oph-thal′mic (L. *ophthalmia*, eye). Pertaining to the eye.

Op′tic (Gr. *optikos*, sight). Pertaining to the eye or to sight.

Op′tic lobes (Gr. *optikos*, pertaining to sight. L. *lobus*). Thickenings on the dorsal surface of the midbrain (mesencephalon).

Op′tic nerves (Gr. *optikos*, pertaining to sight. L. *nervus*, nerve). Nerves from the eye to the brain.

O′ral (L. *os*, mouth). Pertaining to the mouth.

O′ral groove. A groove having ciliated ridges, which starts at the anterior end and runs posteriorly to the cell mouth (cytostome) in some ciliated protozoans, such as the paramecium.

Or′bit (L. *orbis*, circle). The region of the skull of the vertebrate surrounding the eye.

Or′gan (Gr. *organon*, instrument). Any part of an animal performing a definite function, a group of cells or tissues that are associated in the body to perform one or more functions.

Or′gan-elle″ (Gr. *dim*, from *organon*). A specialized part within a single-celled animal, differentiated to perform a certain function, and comparable to an organ of a metazoan. Compare with Organ.

Or′gan′ic com′pound (Gr. *organon*, implement. L. *componere*, to put together). A molecule containing the element carbon. A few simple carbon compounds such as carbon dioxide are considered by some as inorganic.

Or′gan-ism (Gr. *organon*, instrument). Any living individual, either plant or animal.

Or′ga-nog″e-ny (Gr. *organon*, an instrument, implement; *genesis*, origin). The process of the formation of specialized tissues and organ systems during embryonic development.

Or′i-gin (L. *orior*, rise, become visible). End of a muscle which remains relatively fixed during contraction of the muscle.

Or′tho-gen″e-sis (Gr. *orthos*, straight; *genesis*, descent). A term usually applied to a tendency to evolve consistently in the same direction, or to the concept of "predetermined" evolution toward a definite goal.

Os′cu-lum (L., little mouth). The relatively large external opening of the central cavity (spongocoel) through which water leaves a sponge.

Os-mo′sis (Gr. *osmos*, pushing). In a narrow biologic sense it may be defined as diffusion of a solvent through a semipermeable membrane. In biologic processes the solvent is almost universally water.

Os′se-ous (L. *osseus*, bony). Pertaining to the bone.

Os′te-ol″o-gy (Gr. *osteon*, bone; *logos*, study). Study of bones.

Os′ti-um (L., door). A small mouthlike opening such as the anterior end of the oviduct in the frog and other vertebrates; in general, an opening in both invertebrates and vertebrates, usually guarded by a valve or circular muscle.

O′to-lith (Gr. *ous*, ear; *lithos*, stone). A limy particle in the inner ear of vertebrates or in the auditory organ of some invertebrates.

O′va-ry (L. *ovarium*, ovary). The female gonad in which the eggs (ova) multiply and develop.

O'vi-duct (L. *ovum*, egg; *ducere*, to lead). A tube which conveys the eggs from the ovary to the uterus or to the exterior.

O-vip'a-rous (L. *ovum*, egg; *parare*, to produce). Producing eggs which hatch outside the body of the mother; egg-laying animals.

O'vi-pos'i-tor (L. *ovum*, egg; *ponere*, to place). An organ of female insects which aids in the depositing of eggs.

O'vo-vi-vip'a-rous (L. *ovum*, egg; *vivus*, alive; *parere*, to bear). Producing eggs that hatch within the parent's body but which are not nourished by the mother's blood stream through a placenta.

O-vu-la'tion (L. *ovum*, egg). The release of eggs from the ovary.

O'vum (L., egg). An egg; a nonmotile female gamete.

Ox'i-da''tion (Gr. *oxys*, acid). The chemical change in which a molecule loses one or more electrons; sometimes involves combining with oxygen.

Pal'a-tine (L. *palatium*, from Palatium, one of the 7 hills of Rome). Bone which serves as an anterior brace of the upper jaw in the skull of the frog and other vertebrates.

Pa'le-on-tol''o-gy (Gr. *palaios*, old; *ons*, being; *logos*, discourse). The science that deals with the ancient life of the earth as revealed by fossils, impressions, and other remains found in the strata of the earth's surface layers.

Palp (L. *palpare*, to feel). A projecting part or process, sensory in function, often near the mouth.

Pal'pus (L. *palpo*, touch). Used mostly for a palp which is a process of an appendage, as in insects.

Pan'cre-as (Gr. *pan*, all; *kreas*, flesh). A digestive gland which discharges into the intestine; it produces digestive enzymes and insulin.

Pa-pil'la (L., nipple). Any small nipple-shaped elevations.

Par'a-po''di-um (Gr. *para*, beside; *pous*, foot). Flattened, movable, paired appendages on the body segments of many polychaete annelids.

Par'a-site (Gr. *para*, beside; *sitos*, food; or *parasitos*, eating beside another). An organism that lives during the whole or a phase of its life upon or within another organism (host) and from which it derives nourishment.

Par'a-sphe''noid (Gr. *para*, beyond; *sphenoid*, wedge, form). Bone forming the floor of the cranium of a vertebrate.

Par'a-thy''roid (Gr. *para*, near; *thyreoeides*, shield-shaped). One of several (usually 4) small ductless glands, closely associated with the thyroid gland of the vertebrates.

Pa-ren'chy-ma (Gr. *para*, beside; *enchyma*, infusion). A type of loose, spongy, connective tissue found in some of the invertebrates; in vertebrates, the specific tissue component of an organ, such as hepatic cells in the liver.

Pa-ri'e-tal (L. *parietis*, wall). Pertaining to the outer wall of the coelom.

Pa-ri'e-tal bone (L. *parietis*, a wall. A.S. *ban*, bone). One of a pair of bones located just posterior to the frontal bones.

Par'the-no-gen''e-sis (Gr. *parthenos*, virgin; *genesis*, origin. The production of offspring from unfertilized eggs. This is unisexual reproduction. See Natural parthenogenesis.

Par'the-no-go-nid''i-um (Gr. *parthenos*, virgin; *gonos*, offspring). A cell that produces a miniature colony through asexual methods of multiplication in such forms as the volvox.

Pa-ter'nal (L. *paternus*, from *pater*, father). Pertaining to the father.

Path'o-gen''ic (Gr. *pathos*, disease; *genesis*, production). Disease-producing.

Pa-thol'o-gy (Gr. *pathos*, disease; *logos*, study). The study of abnormal (diseased) structures and abnormal functioning of life processes.

Pec'to-ral gir'dle (L. plural of *pectus*, breast. A.S. *gyrdel*, to encircle). Group of bones and cartilage connecting the forelimb to the axial skeleton in vertebrates.

Ped'al (L. *pes*, foot). Pertaining to the feet.

Ped'i-cel-la'ri-a (L. *pediculus*, small foot). Small pincer or scissorlike processes on the surface of certain echinoderms, such as the starfishes.

Ped'i-cle (L. *pediculus*, little foot). The narrow waist between the cephalothorax and the abdomen in spiders.

Ped'i-palp (L. *pes*, foot; *palpare*, to feel). Either of the second pair of appendages in Arachnida. They are often sensory and sometimes are used in seizing prey, as in scorpions.

Pe'do-gen''e-sis (Gr. *pais*, child; *genesis*, origin). Reproduction by larvae.

Pe-lag'ic (L. *pelagicus*, from *pelagus*, sea). Of or inhabiting the open water, away from shore, as in the ocean.

Pel'li-cle (L. *pellicula*, small skin). The thin protective layer on the surface of some protozoans, for example, the paramecium.

Pel'vic gir'dle (L. *pelvis*, a basin). The group of bones to which the bones of the hindlimb are attached, connecting the hindlimb to the axial skeleton in the vertebrates.

Pe'nis (L.) The male organ of copulation for conveying sperms to the genital tract of the female.

Pen'ta-dac''tyl (Gr. *pente*, five; *daktylos*, finger). Having 5 fingers, toes, or digits.

Pep'sin (Gr. *pepsis*, a cooking, digesting). An enzyme concerned with protein digestion in animals.

Per-ei'o-pods (Gr. *peraioun*, to convey; *pous*, foot). The walking legs of a crayfish or related crustacean.

Per'i-car''di-um (Gr. *peri*, around; *cardia*, heart). The closed membranous sac surrounding the heart. The part in contact with the heart is the visceral pericardium; the other, the parietal pericardium.

Per'i-os''te-um (Gr. *peri*, around; *osteon*, bone). Connective tissue sheath that covers the surface of a bone.

Pe-riph'er-al (Gr. *periphereia*, from *peri*, around; *pherein*, to bear, carry). Of, belonging to, or situated at the surface.

Per'i-sarc (Gr. *peri*, around; *sarx*, flesh). The outer transparent membrane that encloses the inner coenosarc of a hydroid.

Per'i-stal''sis (Gr. *peri*, around; *stalsis*, constriction). A type of smooth muscle contraction in which a wave of contraction follows a wave of relaxation, passing along a hollow organ, especially the digestive tract.

Per'i-stome (Gr. *peri*, around; *stoma*, mouth). The region around the mouth of a radially symmetrical animal, such as the hydra.

Per'i-to-ne''um (Gr. *peri*, around; *tenein*, to stretch). The thin membrane (mesoderm) that lines the coelom and covers the viscera in many animals, especially the vertebrates.

Phag'o-cyte (Gr. *phagein*, to eat; *kytos*, cell). A type of white blood cell that engulfs and digests bacteria and other foreign materials.

Pha-lan'ges (Gr. *phalanx*, long line of battle). Bones of the digits. Singular, phalanx.

Pha-ryn'ge-al cleft (Gr. *pharynx*, gullet. A.S. *cleofian*, to split). Slit in the wall of the pharynx; same as gill slit, gill cleft, or branchial slit.

Phar'ynx (Gr. *pharynx*, gullet). That anterior portion of the digestive tract between the mouth cavity and the esophagus, often muscular; and the gill region of many aquatic vertebrates; sometimes with teeth in invertebrates.

Phe'no-type (Gr. *phaino*, show; *typto*, strike). The expressed traits of an individual, as contrasted with its genetic constitution or genotype. The sum total of the realized characteristics of an individual; in other words, the structural and physiologic traits of an individual. Sometimes incorrectly defined as external appearance of an individual which would exclude physiologic traits such as blood groups. Compare with Genotype.

Pho'to-syn''the-sis (Gr. *phos*, light; *synthesis*, putting together). The formation of glucose from carbon dioxide and water by chlorophyl in the presence of light.

Pho-tot'ro-pism (Gr. *phos*, light; Gr. *trepein*, to turn). The behavior response of an animal to light stimuli.

Phy-log'e-ny (Gr. *phylon*, race, branch; *geny*, become). Ancestral or evolutionary history of a species or higher group.

Phy'lum (Gr. *phylon*, tribe). Any one of the main taxonomic divisions into which the animal kingdom is divided.

Phys'i-ol''o-gy (Gr. *physis*, nature; *logos*, study). The science dealing with the functions in organisms.

Pi'a ma'ter (L., tender mother). The thin, innermost, membranous covering of the brain and spinal cord.

Pig'ment (L. *pingere*, to paint). Coloring matter.

Pin'e-al (L. *pinea*, pine cone). A structure located on the roof of the brain of vertebrate animals; phylogenetically associated with a median eye.

Pi-tu''i-tary bod'y (L. *pituita*, phlegm. A.S. *bodig*). An endocrine gland located on the ventral surface of the brain and composed of anterior, posterior, and intermediate lobes.

Pla-cen'ta (L. *placenta*, flat cake). The organ for attaching the fetus of mammals to the uterine wall; it serves in fetal nourishment, respiration, and excretion.

Plan'ti-grade (L. *planta*, sole; *gradi*, to step). Walking with the whole sole of the foot; bearing on the ground as does the bear or man.

Plan'u-la (L. *planus*, flat). The ciliated, free-swimming, larval form of most coelenterates.

Plas'ma (Gr., something molded). The liquid part of the blood or lymph.

Plas'ma mem'brane (Gr., something molded. L. *membrana,* skin covering). The external membrane formed by the cytoplasm of a cell.

Plas'tid (Gr. *plastides*, to form). A cytoplasmic body found in certain cells, often containing pigment.

Plat'y-hel-min'thes (Gr. *platy*, flat; *helmins*, worm). Phylum which includes the flatworms such as the planaria.

Pleur'al (Gr. *pleura*, side). Pertaining to the cavity, that portion of the coelom, which contains the lungs. The membrane covering the lung and lining the pleural cavity.

Pleur'on (Gr., side). The lateral portion of a typical segment of such an arthropod as the crayfish.

Plex'us (L., interwoven). A network, chiefly of nerves or blood vessels.

Po'lar bod'y (L. *polaris*, axis). A small non-functional cell thrown off during the meiosis (maturation) of the egg cell.

Pol'y-mor'phism (Gr. *polys*, many; *morphe*, form). The occurrence of more than one form in a single species; when only two such forms occur, dimorphism is the term usually applied, hence polymorphism, according to usage, implies more than two such different forms.

Pol'yp (Gr. *polypous*, many-footed). The form of a coelenterate having the shape of an elongated cylinder fastened at the aboral end, with mouth and tentacles at the free oral end.

Pos-te'ri-or (L., latter). The tail, or toward the hind or rear end. Opposite of anterior.

Pre-co'cious (L. *praecox*, ripe before its time). Characterized by early maturity.

Pre-da'ceous (L. *praedo*, prey). Capturing living animals for food.

Pre-max-il'lae (L. *prae*, before; *maxilla*, jaw). A pair of anterior bones of the upper jaw in vertebrates.

Pri-mor'di-al (L. *primordium*, beginning). First in order of time; the primitive form.

Prin'ci-ple (L. *principium*, beginning). A scientific theory, fact, or law of wide application.

Pro-bos'cis (Gr. *proboskis*, trunk). A tubular extension of the nose, lips, or pharynx. The extended beaklike mouth parts of insects.

Pro-neph'ros (Gr. *pro*, before; *nephros*, kidney). The first kidney embryologically formed in the vertebrate.

Pro-nu'cle-us (Gr. *pro*, before; L. *nucleus*, kernel). One of the two nuclear bodies of a fertilized egg, the male pronucleus and the female pronucleus, the fusion of which results in the cleavage nucleus.

Pro'phase (Gr. *pro*, before; *phasis*, appearance). Any one of the first stages of mitosis during which the chromosomes become distinctly visible.

Pros'o-pyle (Gr. *proso*, forward; *pyle*, opening). One of the surface pores opening into a chamber of a sponge.

Pros'tate gland (Gr. *prostates*, one who stands before; L. *glans*, acorn). A gland surrounding the neck of the bladder and urethra in the male mammal.

Pro-sto'mi-um (Gr. *pro*, before; *stoma*, mouth). The anterior portion of the first segment of the annelids such as the earthworm, overhanging the mouth region.

Pro'te-in (Gr. *protos*, first). An organic compound always containing nitrogen, carbon, oxygen, and hydrogen, and often other elements. Each is made up of amino acids and is an essential part of protoplasm.

Pro'to-plasm (Gr. *protos*, first; *plasma*, something molded). The living substance of which all organisms are composed; it is a complex physicochemical colloidal solution and constitutes the physical basis of life.

Pro-top'o-dite (Gr. *protos*, first; *pous*, foot). The basal portion, usually composed of two segments of a biramous appendage, of a crustacean, such as the crayfish.

Pro-to-zo''a (Gr. *protos*, first; *zoion*, animal). The phylum of animals, usually unicellular, but when multicellular, showing no specialization of somatic cells.

Prox'i-mal (L. *proximus*, next). Nearer the point of attachment of an organ; for example, the shoulder is at the proximal end of the arm. Opposite of distal.

Pseu'do-coel (Gr. *pseudo*, false; *koilia*, body cavity). A body cavity, such as that of the ascaris, not completely lined with a membrane derived from mesoderm.

Pseu'do-po''di-a (Gr. *pseudo*, false; *pous*, foot). The blunt temporary protoplasmic projections which are pushed out from an amoeba or amoebalike cell in feeding and locomotor activities.

Pty'a-lin (Gr. *ptyalon*, spittle). An enzyme of the saliva in some vertebrates which acts on starch.

Pul'mo-nar-y (L. *pulmo*, lung). Pertaining to the lung.

Py-lor'ic (Gr. *pylorus*, gate). Pertaining to the pylorus.

Py-lor'ic cae'ca (Gr. *pylorus*, gate; L. *caecus*, blind gut). Digestive glands.

Py-lor'ic valve (Gr. *pylorus*, gate; L. *valva*, folding door). Valve at the posterior end of the stomach.

Py-re'noid (Gr. *pyren*, fruit; *eidos*, form). In some chloroplasts, a center for the formation of a starchlike substance called paramylum.

Pyr'i-for'mis (L. *pirum*, a pear; *ferire*, to strike, hew). A muscle arising from the urostyle in the frog.

Quad-ra'to-ju''gal (L. *quadratus*, square; *jugum*, yoke). Posterior bone of the upper jaw in some vertebrates.

Quad'ru-ped (L. *quattuor*, four; *pes*, foot). Four-footed animal.

Queen. The reproductive female of social insects as bees and ants.

Ra'di-al ca-nal' (L. *radius*, ray. L. *canalis*, channel). A canal radiating from the disk of starfishes and related animals. Also certain canals in jellyfishes.

Ra'di-al sym'me-try (L. *radius*, canal. Gr. *symmetria*, symmetry). The condition in which similar parts are arranged about a common center like the spokes of a wheel.

Ra'di-o-ge-net''ics (L. *radius*, ray; Gr. *gignesthai*, to be born). The study of the effects of radiation upon heredity.

Ra'di-o-ul'na (L. *radius*, ray; *ulna*, elbow). The fused radius and ulna bones as in frogs and toads.

Ra'di-us (L., ray). The bone of the lower arm, located on the thumb side of vertebrates.

Ra'mus (L., branch). A branch or branching part.

Re'ca-pit-u-la''tion the'o-ry (L. *re*, again; *caput*, head. Gr. *theoria*, a beholding). The theory that the individual in its development passes through the ancestral history of the race. Ontogeny repeats phylogeny.

Re-cep'tor (L. *receptor*, receiver). A sensory end organ.

Re-ces'sive trait (char'ac-ter) (L. *recessus*, to withdraw. L. *tractus*, a drawing. Gr. from *charassein*, to engrave). A trait which appears only when both members of an allelic pair of genes are alike, that is, in the homozygous condition. Compare with Dominant trait. The term recessive is also applied to genes.

Rec'tum (L. *rectus*, straight). The terminal portion of the large intestine in vertebrates; posterior intestinal region in some higher invertebrates.

Re'di-a (Redi, the Italian scientist). One of several types of larvae found in the life cycle of most trematodes.

Re-duc'tion di-vi'sion (L. *reducere*, to lead back. *Diviso*, from *dividere*, to divide). The maturation division in which the homologous pairs of chromosomes are separated to form daughter cells; in this division the paternal and maternal chromosomes of a given homologous pair are separated so that they go to different daughter cells.

Re'flex act (L. *reflexus*, bent back; *actum*, deed). A relatively simple, automatic response to a stimulus which is independent of the higher nerve centers of the brain.

Re-gen'er-a''tion (L. *re*, again; *generare*, to beget). Replacement by growth of a part of the body that has been lost.

Re'nal (L. *renes*, kidneys). Pertaining to the kidney.

Ren'nin (A.S. *gerinnan*, to curdle, coagulate). A stomach enzyme which acts on casein, a protein of milk. It causes milk to curdle.

Re'pro-duc''tion (L. *re*, again; *pro*, forth; *ducere*, to lead). The production by an organism of others of its kind.

Res'pi-ra"tion (L. *re*, again; *spirare*, to breathe). The actual use of oxygen by the cell; this is usually termed cellular or internal respiration. Compare with External respiration.

Re-sponse' (L. *re*, again; *spondere*, to promise). Reaction to a stimulus either internal or external.

Rest'ing cell. *See* Interphase cell.

Ret'i-na (L. *rete*, net). The light-sensitive layer of an eye.

Rhab'dites (Gr. *rhabdos*, rod). Rodlike bodies in the epidermis of certain flatworms, as in the planaria.

Rhab'dom (Gr. *rhabdos*, rod). A rodlike structure formed of the inner surfaces of adjacent sensory cells in the ommatidium of a compound arthropod eye.

Rhab'do-mere (Gr. *rhabdos*, rod; Gr. *meros*, part). The receptive area of a retinal cell that is one of the component parts of the rhabdom.

Rh fac'tor. A kind of antigen found in some red blood corpuscles. An antigen first found in the red blood cells of the rhesus monkey, hence the name Rh positive and Rh negative, denoting presence or absence of this factor.

Ri'bo-fla'vin. Constituent of the vitamin B complex, important in cell metabolism.

Ros'trum (L. *rostrum*, beak). The anteriorly projecting beak, as in the crayfish.

Ro'ta-tor (L. *rota*, wheel). The type of voluntary muscle which brings about the rotary motion of one part of an organism on another.

Ru'gae (L., wrinkles). Ridges or folds as in the lining of the vertebrate stomach.

Ru'mi-nant (L. *rumen*, throat). A cud-chewing mammal as the cow.

Sap'ro-zo"ic (Gr. *sapros*, rotten; *zoion*, living being). Pertaining to an animal which lives upon decaying organic matter.

Sar'co-lem"ma (Gr. *sarx*, flesh; *lemma*, covering). A thin membrane surrounding a skeletal or striated muscle cell.

Sar'co-plasm (Gr. *sarx*, flesh; *plasma*, liquid). The protoplasmic substance of skeletal muscle cells.

Scap'u-la (L., shoulder blade). Shoulder blade in a vertebrate.

Sci'en-tif"ic meth'od (L. *scientia*, knowledge; Gr. *metahodos*, road, way). The scientific method involves, primarily, the formulation of ideas (hypotheses) on the basis of a relatively small amount of knowledge, then testing the correctness of the ideas by securing more facts by observation, arranging the facts observed in some orderly manner to determine relationships, and then drawing logical conclusions.

Sci'en-tif"ic name (L. *scientia*, knowledge. Gr. *onoma*, name). The binomial or trinomial designation of an animal.

Scle'rite (Gr. *skleros*, hard). A hardened body wall plate bounded by sutures, as in the arthropods.

Sco'lex (Gr. *skolex*, worm). The small knoblike "head" at the anterior end of a tapeworm.

Se-ba'ceous glands (L. *sebum*, tallow, grease. L. *glans*, acorn). Small skin glands, usually found in connection with the hair follicles of the mammals. They produce an oily secretion which lubricates the skin and hair.

Se'bum (L. *sebum*, tallow). The fatty secretion of the sebaceous glands.

Sec'ond-ary sex'u-al char'ac-ters. Characters other than the sex glands (gonads) and related organs in which males and females of a species differ.

Se-cre'tion (L. *secretio*, from *secernere*, to separate). The production by the protoplasm of a substance of use to the organism; also the substance produced.

Seg'ment (L. *segmentum*, piece cut off). One part of a metameric animal.

Self'-fer-ti-li-za'tion. Fertilizing an egg by a sperm from the same individual.

Se'men (L. *serere*, to sow). Fluid which carries the sperms in the males of most animals.

Sem'i-cir"cu-lar ca-nals' (L. *semi*, half; *circulus*, circle). Canals in the vertebrate ear, associated with the sense of equilibrium.

Sem'i-nal (L. *semen*, seed). Pertaining to spermotozoa.

Sem'i-nal re-cep'ta-cles (L. *semen*, seed. L. *recipere*, to receive). Saclike organs in several types of animals, which receive and store sperms after their release. They are considered a part of the female genital system.

Sem'in-al ves'i-cles (L. *semen*, seed. L. *vesica*, bladder). Saclike organs in several types of animals in which the seminal fluid is stored before being discharged. They are considered a part of the male genital system.

Sem'i-nif"er-ous tu'bule (L. *semen*, seed; *ferro*, to carry. L. *tubulus*, small tube). A tube to conduct seminal fluid.

Sen'so-ry cell (L. *sensus*, sense. L. *cella*, compartment). A cell that is very sensitive to stimuli; a receptor.

Sep'tum (L. *septum*, partition). A partition that separates two cavities or two structures.

Ser'i-al ho-mol'o-gy (L. *series*, join. Gr. *homos*, same; *logos*, discourse). Occurrence of homologous structures in different segments of the same individual; homology repeated in a series.

Se-rol'o-gy (L. *serum*, liquid). The study of serums and their action.

Se'rous (L. *serum*, liquid). Pertaining to, producing, or resembling serum.

Se'rous coat (L. *serum*, liquid. O.F. *cote*, coat). The peritoneal covering of the visceral organs.

Ses'sile (L. *sedere*, to sit). Attached; not free moving; sedentary.

Se'tae (L. *seta*, bristle). Bristles such as those embedded in the body wall of the earthworm.

Sex chro'mo-somes (L. *sexus*, sex. Gr. *chroma*, color; *soma*, body). The X, Y chromosomes especially concerned with the determination of sex. See X, Y chromosomes.

Sex'u-al di-mor'phism (L. *sexualis*, of sex. L. *dis*, indicating separation; Gr. *morphe*, form). Phenomenon of the two sexes of a given species differing in secondary sexual characters. Many common animals, including mankind, are sexually dimorphic.

Sex'u-al re'pro-duc"tion (L. *sexualis*, of sex. L. *re*, again; *pro*, forth; *ducere*, to lead). Reproduction involving a gamete or gametes (sex cell or sex cells).

shaft (A.S. *sceaft*, dart). The slender, middle portion of a long bone.

Si'nus (L., cavity). A thin-walled cavity.

Si'nus-oid (L. *sinus*, fold; Gr. *eidos*, form). Large, irregular, tortuous, blood spaces which are comparable to capillaries in that their walls form an endothelial tube, but they differ from capillaries in that their lumina are of greater size.

So'ma (Gr., body). The entire body, exclusive of the reproductive cells.

So'mite. One of the serial segments or metameres of a metameric animal.

Spe'cies (L., appearance). Groups of actually or potentially interbreeding natural populations that resemble one another closely and which are reproductively isolated from other such groups.

Sperm (Gr., seed). A mature male reproductive cell or gamete.

Sper'ma-ry (Gr. *sperma*, seed). The male reproductive gland.

Sper'ma-tid (Gr. *sperma*, seed). A male germ cell immediately before assuming the form of a sperm.

Sper'ma-to-gen"e-sis (Gr. *sperma*, seed; *genesis*, origin). The process of formation of spermatozoa.

Sphinc'ter (Gr. *sphinggein*, to bind tightly). A ring of smooth muscle surrounding a tube or opening, which, by its contraction, closes the lumen.

Spic'ule (L. *spiculum*, a little point). One of the many solid structures that comprise the skeletal framework of a sponge.

Spi'nal col'umn (L. *spina*, thorn. L. *columna*, column). A series of vertebrae in the vertebrates, which encloses the spinal cord.

Spi'nal cord (L. *spina*, thorn. Gr. *corde*, string). Part of the central nervous system extending the length of the spinal column and continuing anteriorly into the brain of vertebrates.

Spin'dle (A.S. *spinnan*, to spin). A structure formed in the cytoplasm during mitosis and appearing to be made up of fibers arranged in the form of a spindle.

Spin'ner-et (A.S. *spinnan*). Structures present on the abdomen of spiders; fingerlike organs, having tiny spinning tubes at their bases, from which a fluid issues which hardens as it comes in contact with air to form silk threads.

Spi'ra-cle (L. *spiraculum*, air hole). In insects, an external opening of the tracheal or respiratory system; in the cartilaginous fishes, the modified first gill slit. Also in tadpoles, the atriopore.

Splanch'nic (Gr. *splanchnon*, entrail). Pertaining to the viscera.

Spleen (Gr. *splen*, spleen). A large organ, characteristic of most vertebrates, lying near the stomach and known to destroy red blood corpuscles in mammals.

Spore (Gr. *spora*, seed). A special reproductive body of one of the lower organisms. It is usually protected by a resistant covering and is capable of developing independently into a new individual.

Spor'u-la"tion (Gr. *spora*, seed). Process of forming spores; reproduction by multiple fission.

Squa-mo'sal (L. *squamosus*, scaly). T-shaped bone of the skull of a vertebrate, bracing the posterior end of the jaws.

Stat'o-cyst (Gr. *statos*, stationary; *kystis*, sac). Organ of equilibrium in animals such as the crayfish.

Stat'o-lith (Gr. *statos*, standing; *lithos*, stone). A solid body within a statocyst.

Ste-ap'sin (Gr. *stear*, tallow; *pepsis*, digest). An enzyme of the pancreas that acts on fats.

Ster'num (L., breastbone). Bone or bones of the ventral side of the thorax of a vertebrate; breastbone.

Stig'ma (Gr., pricked mark). A sensitive pigment or eye spot in certain Protozoa.

Stim'u-lus (L. *stimulare*, to incite). A change in the external or internal environment of an animal that brings about a response.

Stra'ti-fied (L. *stratum*, covering). Arranged in layers, one above the other.

Stra'tum com-pac'tum (L. *stratum*, covering. L. *cum*, with; *pangere*, to fasten). Inner layer of the corium or dermis of the skin.

Stra'tum cor'ne-um (L., covering. L. *corneus*, horny). Outer layers of cells in the epidermis of the skin of a vertebrate.

Stra'tum ger'mi-na-ti"vum (L., covering. L. *germinare*, to sprout). Mitotic layer of cells in the epidermis of the skin of a vertebrate.

Stra'tum spon-gi-o'sum (L., covering. Gr. *spongos*, sponge). Outer layer of connective tissue in the dermis (corium) of a vertebrate.

Stri'at-ed (L. *stria*, channel). Cross striped, as one of the principal types of muscle cells.

Sub-cla'vi-an (L. *sub*, under; *clavis*, clavicle). Under the collarbone (clavicle); it refers to a particular muscle, blood vessel, or other structure in this region.

Sub-cu-ta'ne-ous (L. *sub*, under; *cutis*, skin). Just beneath the skin, as subcutaneous connective tissue.

Sul'cus (L. *sulcus*, furrow). A fissure or groove.

Su'ture (L. *sutura* from *suere*, *sutum*, to sew). Line of fusion between 2 bones.

Swim'mer-et (A.S. *swima*, swoon). An ab-

dominal appendage that functions as a swimming organ.

Sym'bi-o"sis (Gr. *syn*, together; *bios*, life). Living together of two different species of organisms. Symbiosis is best used as an inclusive term to cover mutualism, commensalism, and parasitism.

Sym'me-try (Gr. *syn*, together; *meton*, measure). The state of being symmetrical; an organ is said to possess symmetry if it can be divided by a line or plane into two parts which are essentially similar.

Syn'apse (Gr. *syn*, together; *hapto*, unite). The region of communication between neurons; the point at which an impulse passes from an axon of one neuron to a dendrite of another.

Syn-ap'sis (Gr. *synapsis*, contact). The temporary union of homologous chromosomes (maternal and paternal) previous to the first maturation division.

Syn-cyt'i-um (Gr. *syn*, togther; *kytos*, cell). An undivided mass of cytoplasm containing many nuclei. It is a product of nuclear division without cell division.

Sys'tem (Gr. *syn*, together; *histanai*, to place). A group of organs concerned with the same general function, as circulation or digestion.

Sys-tem'ic arch (Gr. *systema*, placing together. L. *arcus*, bow). Any large artery of a vertebrate, carrying blood from the heart to the dorsal aorta.

Tac'tile (L. *tangere*, to touch). Pertaining to the sense of touch.

Tar'sals (Gr. *tarsos*, flat of the foot). Bones of the ankle.

Tar'sus (Gr. *tarsos*, flat of the foot). The distal end of the leg of an insect; it consists of one or more segments, the most distal bearing claws. An ankle bone of vertebrates.

Tax-on'o-my (Gr. *taxis*, arrangement; *nomos*, law). The science that deals with the classification of organisms.

Tel'e-ol"o-gy (Gr. *telos*, end; *logis*, study). An unscientific method of thinking. The use of purpose in which a result is treated as a cause in the explanation of natural phenomenon.

Tel'o-phase (Gr. *telos*, end; *phasis*, aspect). Any of the final phases of mitosis in which the cell divides and the daughter nuclei are formed.

Tel'son (Gr., a boundary). A terminal extension of the last abdominal appendage of a crustacean such as the crayfish.

Ten'don (L. *tendere*, to stretch). The tough, cordlike connective tissue extension at the end of a muscle which attaches it to other structures.

Ten'ta-cle (L. *tentare*, to touch, feel). A flexible, armlike extension from the body of many nonchordates, such as the hydra; used in grasping and movement.

Ter'gum (L., the back). The dorsal portion of the exoskeleton of any body segment in the arthropods, such as the grasshopper.

Ter-res'tri-al (L. *terra*, earth). Living on the ground.

Tes'tis (L. *testis*). Male reproductive gland (gonad), in which sperms are formed.

Tet'rad (Gr. *tetra*, four). A group of 4 chromatids which appears during maturation, the product of a pair of homologous chromosomes.

The'o-ry (Gr. *theoria*, a beholding, speculation). A possible explanation of natural phenomenon for which there is some evidence but not enough for proof.

Ther'mo-tax"is (Gr. *therme*, heat; *taxis*, response). The behavior response of an organism to heat or cold.

Ther-mot'ro-pism (Gr. *therme*, heat; *trope*, turning). The behavior response of an organism to heat.

Thig-mot'ro-pism (Gr. *thigma*, touch; *trope*, turning). The behavior response of an organism to contact.

Tho-rac'ic (Gr. *thorax*, chest). Pertaining to the thorax or chest.

Tho'rax (Gr., chest). The major division of an animal just posterior to the neck, or head, if no neck is present.

Thy'mus (Gr. *thymos*, thymus). A two-lobed organ located just below the thyroid of mammals.

Thy'roid (Gr. *thyreos*, shield; *eidos*, form). An endocrine gland in the neck of vertebrates, which exerts an influence on growth and metabolism.

Thy-rox'ine. The hormone secreted by the thyroid gland.

Tib'i-a L. *tibia*, pipe). The larger medial bone of the vertebrate lower leg; the part between the femur and tarsus in insects.

Tis'sue (L. *texere*, to weave). A group of cells of similar structure, with intercellular substances, if any, which perform a specialized function.

Tis'sue flu'id. The extracellular fluid which constitutes the environment of the body cells.

Tox'in (Gr. *toxicon*, poison). A poisonous product of animal or plant origin.

Tra'che-a (Gr. *tracheia*, windpipe). The windpipe of vertebrates; an air tube in breathing arthropods.

Trait (L. *tractus*, a drawing). A term loosely used by geneticists as a synonym of "character."

Trans-verse' proc'ess (L. *trans*, across; *vertere*, to turn. L. *procedere*, to go before). One of the lateral projections of a vertebra.

Trich'o-cysts (Gr. *trichos*, hair; *kystis*, bladder). One of the definite bodies lying in the ectoplasm and producing hairlike fibers in such animals as the paramecium.

Tri-gem'i-nus (L. *trigeminus*, born three together). Fifth cranial nerve.

Trip'lo-blas"tic (Gr. *triplax*, triple; *blastos*, bud). Derived from the 3 primary germ layers—ectoderm, mesoderm, and endoderm. The embryonic tissue is not always in the form of a layer, but sometimes consists of groups of cells.

Tro-chan'ter (Gr. *trechein*, to run). The second segment of the insect leg between the coxa and the femur.

Tro'pho-zo"ite (Gr. *trophe*, from *trophein*, nourishment; *zoion*, living being, animal). An endozoic protozoan in the phase of its life cycle where its principal activity is nutrition and growth.

Tro'pism (Gr. *trope*, turning). The automatic response of an animal to a particular stimulus.

Tube feet (L. *tuba*, pipe. A.S. *fet*, feet). Tubular organs of locomotion found in the ambulacral grooves of starfishes and some other echinoderms.

Tym-pan'ic mem'brane (Gr. *tympanon*, eardrum. L. *membrana*, skin covering). The eardrum.

Typh'lo-sole (Gr. *typhlos*, blind; *solen*, channel). A median dorsal internal fold in the intestine of several types of animals, including the earthworms.

Ul′na (L. *ulna*, elbow). The bone of the little-finger side of the forearm in the vertebrates from amphibians to man, inclusive.

Um-bil′i-cal cord (L. *umbilicus*, navel. Gr. *corde*, string). The cordlike connection between the embryo or fetus of a mammal and the placenta, composed mainly of blood vessels and connective tissue.

Un′gu-late (L. *ungula*, hoof). Having hoofs.

Un′gu-li-grade′ (L. *ungula*, hoof; *gradi*, to walk). Walking or adapted for walking on hoofs.

U-re′a (Gr. *ouron*, urine). The main nitrogenous metabolic waste of most mammals.

U-re′ter (Gr. *oureter*, ureter). The tube that carries urine away from the kidney to the urinary bladder or the cloaca.

U-re′thra (Gr. *oureter*, ureter). The duct that carries urine from the bladder to the outside in mammals.

U′rine (L. *urina*, urine). The liquid waste excreted by the kidneys.

U′rin-if″er-ous tu′bule (L. *urina*, urine; *ferre*, to bear. L. *tubulus*, any small tube). One of the excretory tubules within the kidney of higher animals, consisting of a coiled tube and a capsule.

U′ro-gen″i-tal (U′ri-no-gen″i-tal sys′tem) (Gr. *ouron*, urine; *gignesthai*, to produce. Gr. *systema*, system). The organs of both the urinary and the reproductive systems taken collectively.

U′ro-style (Gr. *oura*, tail; *style*, pillar). The terminal, rodlike bone of the frog spinal column.

U′ter-us (L., *womb*). The enlarged portion of an oviduct in which at least part of the development of an animal takes place. Technically, the term uterus is applicable only to animals in which the embryo becomes attached to the wall of the organ.

Vac′u-ole (L. *vacuum*, empty). A small structure consisting of a cavity in the cytoplasm filled with a liquid and/or other products.

Va-gi′na (L., sheath). The posterior part of the female reproductive tract. It often receives the copulatory organ of the male in mating.

Va′gus (L., wandering). Tenth cranial nerve in vertebrates.

Va′ri-a″tion (L. *variare*, to change). Difference in structure or function shown by individuals of the same species.

Va-ri′e-ty (L. *varietas*, difference). In taxonomy, a division of a species; a group of individuals within a single interbreeding population that differs in some minor respect from the rest of the species.

Vas de′fer-ens (L., vessel. L., carrying down). A duct which carries sperms away from the testis.

Va′sa ef′fer-en′ti-a (L., vessels. L. *efferens*, bringing out). Small ducts carrying sperms from the testes to the kidney in the frog and to the ductus epididymis or to other similar tubules in higher animals.

Vas′cu-lar (L. *vasculum*, little vessel). Pertaining to vessels in animals; they usually carry blood or lymph.

Va′so-mo′tor nerves (L. *vas*, vessel; from *movere*, *motum*, to move). Nerves which control the contraction and expansion of blood vessels.

Veg′e-tal hem′i-sphere (L. *vegetare*, to enliven. Gr. *hemi*, half; Gr. *sphaira*, ball). The part of the egg where the rate of metabolism is lower than that of the animal pole opposite; usually contains yolk material.

Vein (L. *vena*, vein). A blood vessel that carries blood toward the heart.

Ven′tral (L. *venter*, belly). Pertaining to the belly; away from the back. Opposite of dorsal.

Ven′tri-cle (L. *ventriculus*, little belly). Any of the small chambers in the anatomy of animals, specifically in the heart, a chamber from which blood is distributed; in the brain, any of the several larger subdivisions of the central space.

Ver′mi-form ap-pen′dix (L. *vermis*, worm; *forma*, form. L. *ad*, to; *pendo*, hang). A slender, tubular pouch projecting from the cecum of the large intestine of some mammals.

Ver′te-bral col′umn (L. *vertere*, to turn. L. *columna*, column). The series of vertebrae in a vertebrate animal. Backbone.

Ver′te-brate (L. *vertebratus*, jointed). Animals having a vertebral column.

Ves-tig′i-al (L. *vestigium*, footstep). A degenerate structure that was better developed or functional at one time.

Vil′lus (L. *villus*, hair). A minute, fingerlike

projection; especially those on the intestinal lining of vertebrates which increase the absorptive surface.

Vis'cer-a (L., internal organs). Organs enclosed within the great cavities of the body, especially the abdomen.

Vi'ta-min (L. *vita*, life; E. *amine*, a chemical radical). Any of a number of unrelated organic substances that are essential for normal growth and function. Vitamins are necessary only in minute quantities.

Vit're-ous (L. *vitrum*, glass). Glassy in appearance.

Vi-vip'a-rous (L. *vivus*, alive; *parere*, to bear). Giving birth to living young that develop from eggs within the body of the mother and are nourished from her blood stream, as with most mammals.

Warm'-blood'ed. Animals—birds and mammals—whose body temperature remains rather constant, regardless of external temperature.

White blood cor'pus-cle. A colorless blood cell (leucocyte).

Wolffian ducts (After the German anatomist Wolff. L. *ductus*, to lead). The mesonephric ducts.

X, Y chro'mo-somes. Chromosomes concerned especially with the determination of sex. In some animals the females have two X chromosomes, and the males one X, accompanied by its unmatched mate, the Y chromosome. Certain others, moths for example, have XX males and XY females; a few animals are known without a chromosome, hence having XO males and XX females.

Y chro'mo-some. *See* X, Y chromosomes.

Zo'o-ge-og"ra-phy (Gr. *zoion*, animal; *ge*, earth; *graphein*, to write). The branch of zoology dealing with the geographic distribution of animals.

Zo'oid (Gr. *goiozides*, like an animal). (1) one of the members of a hydroid or siphonophore colony. Often in a restricted sense, a particular kind of individual, as hydranth or gonangium. (2) A subordinate individual formed by transverse fission in such forms as the planaria.

Zo-ol'o-gy (Gr. *zoion*, animal, living being; *logos*, study). The science of animal life. Coordinate with botany as a division of biology.

Zyg'a-poph"y-sis (Gr. *zygon*, yoke; N.L. *apophysis*, offshoot). One of the four projections, two anterior and two posterior, extending from the neural arch of a vertebra. Those of the posterior pair articulate with the anterior of the vertebra next behind.

Zy'gote (Gr. *zygotos*, united). The cell which results from the fertilization of one gamete by another. The product of the union of two gametes of any type, not necessarily an egg and sperm.

INDEX

All numbers in this index refer to pages; those in bold face type contain figures or illustrations of the entries. Scientific names of genera and species are in italics. The index omits many references to common structures such as the brain of the earthworm, but there is an entry for the earthworm, and in that section of the text the brain will be found.